# STATISTICS

THE EXPLORATION AND ANALYSIS OF DATA

CUSTOM EDITION FOR LOYOLA UNIVERSITY MARYLAND

ROXY PECK I JAY L. DEVORE

 CENGAGE
Learning™

Australia • Brazil • Japan • Korea • Mexico • Singapore • Spain • United Kingdom • United States

# CENGAGE
## Learning™

**STATISTICS, THE EXPLORATION AND ANALYSIS OF DATA, CUSTOM EDITION FOR LOYOLA UNIVERSITY MARYLAND**

Executive Editors:
 Maureen Staudt
 Michael Stranz

Senior Project Development Manager:
 Linda deStefano

Marketing Specialist:
 Courtney Sheldon

Senior Production/Manufacturing Manager:
 Donna M. Brown

PreMedia Manager:
 Joel Brennecke

Sr. Rights Acquisition Account Manager:
 Todd Osborne

Cover Image:
Getty Images*

STATISTICS: THE EXPLORATION AND ANALYSIS OF DATA
ROXY PECK | JAY L. DEVORE

For product information and technology assistance, contact us at
**Cengage Learning Customer & Sales Support, 1-800-354-9706**

For permission to use material from this text or product,
submit all requests online at **cengage.com/permissions**
Further permissions questions can be emailed to
**permissionrequest@cengage.com**

This book contains select works from existing Cengage Learning resources and was produced by Cengage Learning Custom Solutions for collegiate use. As such, those adopting and/or contributing to this work are responsible for editorial content accuracy, continuity and completeness.

**Compilation © 2010 Cengage Learning.**

ISBN-13: 978-1-111-46492-9

ISBN-10: 1-111-46492-8

**Cengage Learning**
5191 Natorp Boulevard
Mason, Ohio 45040
USA

Cengage Learning is a leading provider of customized learning solutions with office locations around the globe, including Singapore, the United Kingdom, Australia, Mexico, Brazil, and Japan. Locate your local office at:
**international.cengage.com/region**

Cengage Learning products are represented in Canada by Nelson Education, Ltd. For your lifelong learning solutions, visit **www.cengage.com/custom**
Visit our corporate website at **www.cengage.com**.

# BRIEF CONTENTS

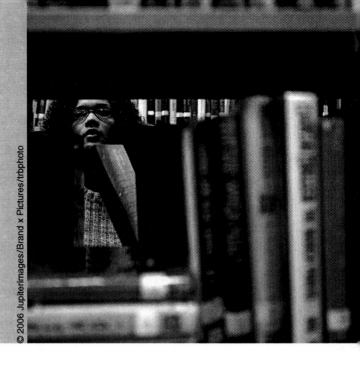

Chapter 1

# The Role of Statistics and the Data Analysis Process

We encounter data and conclusions based on data every day. **Statistics** is the scientific discipline that provides methods to help us make sense of data. Some people are suspicious of conclusions based on statistical analyses. Extreme skeptics, usually speaking out of ignorance, characterize the discipline as a subcategory of lying—something used for deception rather than for positive ends. However, we believe that statistical methods, used intelligently, offer a set of powerful tools for gaining insight into the world around us. Statistical methods are used in business, medicine, agriculture, social sciences, natural sciences, and applied sciences, such as engineering. The widespread use of statistical analyses in diverse fields has led to increased recognition that statistical literacy—a familiarity with the goals and methods of statistics—should be a basic component of a well-rounded educational program.

The field of statistics teaches us how to make intelligent judgments and informed decisions in the presence of uncertainty and variation. In this chapter, we consider the nature and role of variability in statistical settings, introduce some basic terminology, and look at some simple graphical displays for summarizing data.

## 1.1  Three Reasons to Study Statistics

Because statistical methods are used to organize, summarize, and draw conclusions from data, a familiarity with statistical techniques and statistical literacy is vital in today's society. Everyone needs to have a basic understanding of statistics, and many college majors require at least one course in statistics. There are three important reasons why statistical literacy is important: (1) to be informed, (2) to understand issues and be able to make sound decisions based on data, and (3) to be able to evaluate decisions that affect your life. Let's explore each reason in detail.

## ■ The First Reason: Being Informed ........................................................................

How do we decide whether claims based on numerical information are reasonable? We are bombarded daily with numerical information in news, in advertisements, and even in conversation. For example, here are a few of the items employing statistical methods that were part of just two weeks' news.

- The increasing popularity of online shopping has many consumers using Internet access at work to browse and shop online. In fact, the Monday after Thanksgiving has been nicknamed "Cyber Monday" because of the large increase in online purchases that occurs on that day. Data from a large-scale survey conducted in early November, 2005, by a market research firm was used to compute estimates of the percent of men and women who shop online while at work. The resulting estimates probably won't make most employers happy—42% of the men and 32% of the women in the sample were shopping online at work! (*Detroit Free Press* and *San Luis Obispo Tribune*, November 26, 2005)

- A story in the *New York Times* titled "Students Ace State Tests, but Earn D's From U.S." investigated discrepancies between state and federal standardized test results. When researchers compared state test results to the most recent results on the National Assessment of Educational Progress (NAEP), they found that large differences were common. For example, one state reported 89% of fourth graders were proficient in reading based on the state test, while only 18% of fourth graders in that state were considered proficient in reading on the federal test! An explanation of these large discrepancies and potential consequences was discussed. (*New York Times*, November 26, 2005)

- Can dogs help patients with heart failure by reducing stress and anxiety? One of the first scientific studies of the effect of therapeutic dogs found that a measure of anxiety decreased by 24% for heart patients visited by a volunteer and dog, but only by 10% for patients visited by just the volunteer. Decreases were also noted in measures of stress and heart and lung pressure, leading researchers to conclude that the use of therapeutic dogs is beneficial in the treatment of heart patients. (*San Luis Obispo Tribune*, November 16, 2005)

- Late in 2005, those eligible for Medicare had to decide which, if any, of the many complex new prescription medication plans was right for them. To assist with this decision, a program called PlanFinder that compares available options was made available online. But are seniors online? Based on a survey conducted by the *Los Angeles Times*, it was estimated that the percentage of senior citizens that go online is only between 23% and 30%, causing concern over whether providing only an online comparison is an effective way to assist seniors with this important decision. (*Los Angeles Times*, November 27, 2005)

- Are kids ruder today than in the past? An article titled "Kids Gone Wild" summarized data from a survey conducted by the Associated Press. Nearly 70% of those who participated in the survey said that people were ruder now than 20 years ago, with kids being the biggest offenders. As evidence that this is a serious problem, the author of the article also referenced a 2004 study conducted by Public Agenda, a public opinion research group. That study indicated that more than one third of teachers had either seriously considered leaving teaching or knew a colleague who left because of intolerable student behavior. (*New York Times*, November 27, 2005)

* When people take a vacation, do they really leave work behind? Data from a poll conducted by Travelocity led to the following estimates: Approximately 40% of travelers check work email while on vacation, about 33% take cell phones on vacation in order to stay connected with work, and about 25% bring a laptop computer on vacation. The travel industry is paying attention—hotels, resorts, and even cruise ships are now making it easier for "vacationers" to stay connected to work. (*San Luis Obispo Tribune*, December 1, 2005)

* How common is domestic violence? Based on interviews with 24,000 women in 10 different countries, a study conducted by the World Health Organization found that the percentage of women who have been abused by a partner varied widely— from 15% of women in Japan to 71% of women in Ethiopia. Even though the domestic violence rate differed dramatically from country to country, in all of the countries studied women who were victims of domestic violence were about twice as likely as other women to be in poor health, even long after the violence had stopped. (*San Francisco Chronicle*, November 25, 2005)

* Does it matter how long children are bottle-fed? Based on a study of 2121 children between the ages of 1 and 4, researchers at the Medical College of Wisconsin concluded that there was an association between iron deficiency and the length of time that a child is bottle-fed. They found that children who were bottle-fed between the ages of 2 and 4 were three times more likely to be iron deficient than those who stopped by the time they were 1 year old. (*Milwaukee Journal Sentinel* and *San Luis Obispo Tribune*, November 26, 2005)

* Parental involvement in schools is often regarded as an important factor in student achievement. However, data from a study of low-income public schools in California led researchers to conclude that other factors, such as prioritizing student achievement, encouraging teacher collaboration and professional development, and using assessment data to improve instruction, had a much greater impact on the schools' Academic Performance Index. (*Washington Post* and *San Francisco Chronicle*, November 26, 2005)

To be an informed consumer of reports such as those described above, you must be able to do the following:

1. Extract information from tables, charts, and graphs.
2. Follow numerical arguments.
3. Understand the basics of how data should be gathered, summarized, and analyzed to draw statistical conclusions.

Your statistics course will help prepare you to perform these tasks.

## ■ The Second Reason: Making Informed Judgments

Throughout your personal and professional life, you will need to understand statistical information and make informed decisions using this information. To make these decisions, you must be able to do the following:

1. Decide whether existing information is adequate or whether additional information is required.
2. If necessary, collect more information in a reasonable and thoughtful way.
3. Summarize the available data in a useful and informative manner.

4. Analyze the available data.
5. Draw conclusions, make decisions, and assess the risk of an incorrect decision.

People informally use these steps to make everyday decisions. Should you go out for a sport that involves the risk of injury? Will your college club do better by trying to raise funds with a benefit concert or with a direct appeal for donations? If you choose a particular major, what are your chances of finding a job when you graduate? How should you select a graduate program based on guidebook ratings that include information on percentage of applicants accepted, time to obtain a degree, and so on? The study of statistics formalizes the process of making decisions based on data and provides the tools for accomplishing the steps listed.

### ■ The Third Reason: Evaluating Decisions That Affect Your Life .....................

While you will need to make informed decisions based on data, it is also the case that other people will use statistical methods to make decisions that affect you as an individual. An understanding of statistical techniques will allow you to question and evaluate decisions that affect your well-being. Some examples are:

* Many companies now require drug screening as a condition of employment. With these screening tests there is a risk of a false-positive reading (incorrectly indicating drug use) or a false-negative reading (failure to detect drug use). What are the consequences of a false result? Given the consequences, is the risk of a false result acceptable?
* Medical researchers use statistical methods to make recommendations regarding the choice between surgical and nonsurgical treatment of such diseases as coronary heart disease and cancer. How do they weigh the risks and benefits to reach such a recommendation?
* University financial aid offices survey students on the cost of going to school and collect data on family income, savings, and expenses. The resulting data are used to set criteria for deciding who receives financial aid. Are the estimates they use accurate?
* Insurance companies use statistical techniques to set auto insurance rates, although some states restrict the use of these techniques. Data suggest that young drivers have more accidents than older ones. Should laws or regulations limit how much more young drivers pay for insurance? What about the common practice of charging higher rates for people who live in urban areas?

An understanding of elementary statistical methods can help you to evaluate whether important decisions such as the ones just mentioned are being made in a reasonable way.

We hope that this textbook will help you to understand the logic behind statistical reasoning, prepare you to apply statistical methods appropriately, and enable you to recognize when statistical arguments are faulty.

## 1.2 The Nature and Role of Variability

Statistics is a science whose focus is on collecting, analyzing, and drawing conclusions from data. If we lived in a world where all measurements were identical for every individual, all three of these tasks would be simple. Imagine a population consisting of all students at a particular university. Suppose that *every* student took the same number of units, spent exactly the same amount of money on textbooks this semester, and favored increasing student fees to support expanding library services. For this population, there is *no* variability in the number of units, amount spent on books, or student opinion on the fee increase. A researcher studying a sample from this population to draw conclusions about these three variables would have a particularly easy task. It would not matter how many students the researcher included in the sample or how the sampled students were selected. In fact, the researcher could collect information on number of units, amount spent on books, and opinion on the fee increase by just stopping the next student who happened to walk by the library. Because there is no variability in the population, this one individual would provide complete and accurate information about the population, and the researcher could draw conclusions based on the sample with no risk of error.

The situation just described is obviously unrealistic. Populations with no variability are exceedingly rare, and they are of little statistical interest because they present no challenge! In fact, variability is almost universal. It is variability that makes life (and the life of a statistician, in particular) interesting. We need to understand variability to be able to collect, analyze, and draw conclusions from data in a sensible way. One of the primary uses of descriptive statistical methods is to increase our understanding of the nature of variability in a population.

Examples 1.1 and 1.2 illustrate how an understanding of variability is necessary to draw conclusions based on data.

## Example 1.1    If the Shoe Fits

The graphs in Figure 1.1 are examples of a type of graph called a histogram. (The construction and interpretation of such graphs is discussed in Chapter 3.) Figure 1.1(a) shows the distribution of the heights of female basketball players who played at a particular university between 1990 and 1998. The height of each bar in the

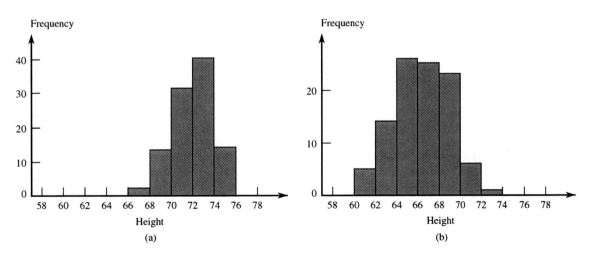

**Figure 1.1** Histograms of heights (in inches) of female athletes: (a) basketball players; (b) gymnasts.

graph indicates how many players' heights were in the corresponding interval. For example, 40 basketball players had heights between 72 in. and 74 in., whereas only 2 players had heights between 66 in. and 68 in. Figure 1.1(b) shows the distribution of heights for members of the women's gymnastics team over the same period. Both histograms are based on the heights of 100 women.

The first histogram shows that the heights of female basketball players varied, with most heights falling between 68 in. and 76 in. In the second histogram we see that the heights of female gymnasts also varied, with most heights in the range of 60 in. to 72 in. It is also clear that there is more variation in the heights of the gymnasts than in the heights of the basketball players, because the gymnast histogram spreads out more about its center than does the basketball histogram.

Now suppose that a tall woman (5 ft 11 in.) tells you she is looking for her sister who is practicing with her team at the gym. Would you direct her to where the basketball team is practicing or to where the gymnastics team is practicing? What reasoning would you use to decide? If you found a pair of size 6 shoes left in the locker room, would you first try to return them by checking with members of the basketball team or the gymnastics team?

You probably answered that you would send the woman looking for her sister to the basketball practice and that you would try to return the shoes to a gymnastics team member. To reach these conclusions, you informally used statistical reasoning that combined your own knowledge of the relationship between heights of siblings and between shoe size and height with the information about the distributions of heights presented in Figure 1.1. You might have reasoned that heights of siblings tend to be similar and that a height as great as 5 ft 11 in., although not impossible, would be unusual for a gymnast. On the other hand, a height as tall as 5 ft 11 in. would be a common occurrence for a basketball player. Similarly, you might have reasoned that tall people tend to have bigger feet and that short people tend to have smaller feet. The shoes found were a small size, so it is more likely that they belong to a gymnast than to a basketball player, because small heights and small feet are usual for gymnasts and unusual for basketball players.

∎

----

# Example 1.2   Monitoring Water Quality

© David Chasey/Getty Images

As part of its regular water quality monitoring efforts, an environmental control board selects five water specimens from a particular well each day. The concentration of contaminants in parts per million (ppm) is measured for each of the five specimens, and then the average of the five measurements is calculated. The histogram in Figure 1.2 summarizes the average contamination values for 200 days.

Now suppose that a chemical spill has occurred at a manufacturing plant 1 mile from the well. It is not known whether a spill of this nature would contaminate groundwater in the area of the spill and, if so, whether a spill this distance from the well would affect the quality of well water.

One month after the spill, five water specimens are collected from the well, and the average contamination is 15.5 ppm. Considering the variation before the spill, would you take this as convincing evidence that the well water was affected by the spill? What if the calculated average was 17.4 ppm? 22.0 ppm? How is your reasoning related to the graph in Figure 1.2?

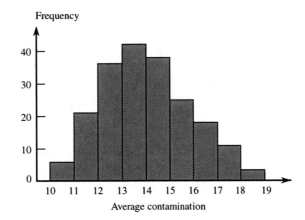

Frequency

**Figure 1.2** Frequency of contaminant concentration (in parts per million) in well water.

Average contamination

Before the spill, the average contaminant concentration varied from day to day. An average of 15.5 ppm would not have been an unusual value, so seeing an average of 15.5 ppm after the spill isn't necessarily an indication that contamination has increased. On the other hand, an average as large as 17.4 ppm is less common, and an average as large as 22.0 ppm is not at all typical of the prespill values. In this case, we would probably conclude that the well contamination level has increased.

■

In these two examples, reaching a conclusion required an understanding of variability. Understanding variability allows us to distinguish between usual and unusual values. The ability to recognize unusual values in the presence of variability is the key to most statistical procedures and is also what enables us to quantify the chance of being incorrect when a conclusion is based on sample data. These concepts will be developed further in subsequent chapters.

## 1.3 Statistics and the Data Analysis Process

Data and conclusions based on data appear regularly in a variety of settings: newspapers, television and radio advertisements, magazines, and professional publications. In business, industry, and government, informed decisions are often data driven. Statistical methods, used appropriately, allow us to draw reliable conclusions based on data.

Once data have been collected or once an appropriate data source has been identified, the next step in the data analysis process usually involves organizing and summarizing the information. Tables, graphs, and numerical summaries allow increased understanding and provide an effective way to present data. Methods for organizing and summarizing data make up the branch of statistics called **descriptive statistics**.

After the data have been summarized, we often wish to draw conclusions or make decisions based on the data. This usually involves generalizing from a small group of individuals or objects that we have studied to a much larger group.

For example, the admissions director at a large university might be interested in learning why some applicants who were accepted for the fall 2006 term failed to enroll at the university. The population of interest to the director consists of all accepted applicants who did not enroll in the fall 2006 term. Because this population is large and it may be difficult to contact all the individuals, the director might decide to collect data from only 300 selected students. These 300 students constitute a sample.

> **DEFINITION**
>
> The entire collection of individuals or objects about which information is desired is called the **population** of interest. A **sample** is a subset of the population, selected for study in some prescribed manner.

The second major branch of statistics, **inferential statistics**, involves generalizing from a sample to the population from which it was selected. When we generalize in this way, we run the risk of an incorrect conclusion, because a conclusion about the population is based on incomplete information. An important aspect in the development of inferential techniques involves quantifying the chance of an incorrect conclusion.

> **DEFINITION**
>
> **Descriptive statistics** is the branch of statistics that includes methods for organizing and summarizing data. **Inferential statistics** is the branch of statistics that involves generalizing from a sample to the population from which it was selected and assessing the reliability of such generalizations.

## ■ The Data Analysis Process

Statistics involves the collection and analysis of data. Both tasks are critical. Raw data without analysis are of little value, and even a sophisticated analysis cannot extract meaningful information from data that were not collected in a sensible way.

■ **Planning and Conducting a Statistical Study**  Scientific studies are undertaken to answer questions about our world. Is a new flu vaccine effective in preventing illness? Is the use of bicycle helmets on the rise? Are injuries that result from bicycle accidents less severe for riders who wear helmets than for those who do not? How many credit cards do college students have? Do engineering students pay more for textbooks than do psychology students? Data collection and analysis allow researchers to answer such questions.

The data analysis process can be viewed as a sequence of steps that lead from planning to data collection to informed conclusions based on the resulting data. The process can be organized into the following six steps:

1. **Understanding the nature of the problem.** Effective data analysis requires an understanding of the research problem. We must know the goal of the research and what questions we hope to answer. It is important to have a clear direction before gathering data to lessen the chance of being unable to answer the questions of interest using the data collected.
2. **Deciding what to measure and how to measure it.** The next step in the process is deciding what information is needed to answer the questions of interest. In some

cases, the choice is obvious (e.g., in a study of the relationship between the weight of a Division I football player and position played, you would need to collect data on player weight and position), but in other cases the choice of information is not as straightforward (e.g., in a study of the relationship between preferred learning style and intelligence, how would you define learning style and measure it and what measure of intelligence would you use?). It is important to carefully define the variables to be studied and to develop appropriate methods for determining their values.

3. **Data collection.** The data collection step is crucial. The researcher must first decide whether an existing data source is adequate or whether new data must be collected. Even if a decision is made to use existing data, it is important to understand how the data were collected and for what purpose, so that any resulting limitations are also fully understood and judged to be acceptable. If new data are to be collected, a careful plan must be developed, because the type of analysis that is appropriate and the subsequent conclusions that can be drawn depend on how the data are collected.

4. **Data summarization and preliminary analysis.** After the data are collected, the next step usually involves a preliminary analysis that includes summarizing the data graphically and numerically. This initial analysis provides insight into important characteristics of the data and can provide guidance in selecting appropriate methods for further analysis.

5. **Formal data analysis.** The data analysis step requires the researcher to select and apply the appropriate inferential statistical methods. Much of this textbook is devoted to methods that can be used to carry out this step.

6. **Interpretation of results.** Several questions should be addressed in this final step—for example, What conclusions can be drawn from the analysis? How do the results of the analysis inform us about the stated research problem or question? and How can our results guide future research? The interpretation step often leads to the formulation of new research questions, which, in turn, leads back to the first step. In this way, good data analysis is often an iterative process.

Example 1.3 illustrates the steps in the data analysis process.

........................................................................................................................

# Example 1.3    A Proposed New Treatment for Alzheimer's Disease

The article "Brain Shunt Tested to Treat Alzheimer's" (*San Francisco Chronicle,* October 23, 2002) summarizes the findings of a study that appeared in the journal *Neurology.* Doctors at Stanford Medical Center were interested in determining whether a new surgical approach to treating Alzheimer's disease results in improved memory functioning. The surgical procedure involves implanting a thin tube, called a shunt, which is designed to drain toxins from the fluid-filled space that cushions the brain. Eleven patients had shunts implanted and were followed for a year, receiving quarterly tests of memory function. Another sample of Alzheimer's patients was used as a comparison group. Those in the comparison group received the standard care for Alzheimer's disease. After analyzing the data from this study, the investigators concluded that the "results suggested the treated patients essentially held their own in the cognitive tests while the patients in the control group steadily declined. However, the study was too small to produce conclusive statistical evidence." Based on these results, a much larger 18-month study was planned. That study was to include 256 patients at 25 medical centers around the country.

This study illustrates the nature of the data analysis process. A clearly defined research question and an appropriate choice of how to measure the variable of interest (the cognitive tests used to measure memory function) preceded the data collection. Assuming that a reasonable method was used to collect the data (we will see how this can be evaluated in Chapter 2) and that appropriate methods of analysis were employed, the investigators reached the conclusion that the surgical procedure showed promise. However, they recognized the limitations of the study, especially those resulting from the small number of patients in the group that received surgical treatment, which in turn led to the design of a larger, more sophisticated study. As is often the case, the data analysis cycle led to further research, and the process began anew.

■

■ **Evaluating a Research Study**   The six data analysis steps can also be used as a guide for evaluating published research studies. The following questions should be addressed as part of a study evaluation:

- What were the researchers trying to learn? What questions motivated their research?
- Was relevant information collected? Were the right things measured?
- Were the data collected in a sensible way?
- Were the data summarized in an appropriate way?
- Was an appropriate method of analysis used, given the type of data and how the data were collected?
- Are the conclusions drawn by the researchers supported by the data analysis?

Example 1.4 illustrates how these questions can guide an evaluation of a research study.

.....................................................................................................................................

# Example 1.4   Spray Away the Flu

The newspaper article "Spray Away Flu" (*Omaha World-Herald*, June 8, 1998) reported on a study of the effectiveness of a new flu vaccine that is administered by nasal spray rather than by injection. The article states that the "researchers gave the spray to 1070 healthy children, 15 months to 6 years old, before the flu season two winters ago. One percent developed confirmed influenza, compared with 18 percent of the 532 children who received a placebo. And only one vaccinated child developed an ear infection after coming down with influenza. . . . Typically 30 percent to 40 percent of children with influenza later develop an ear infection." The researchers concluded that the nasal flu vaccine was effective in reducing the incidence of flu and also in reducing the number of children with flu who subsequently develop ear infections.

   The researchers here were trying to find out whether the nasal flu vaccine was effective in reducing the number of flu cases and in reducing the number of ear infections in children who did get the flu. They recorded whether a child received the nasal vaccine or a placebo. (A placebo is a treatment that is identical in appearance to the treatment of interest but contains no active ingredients.) Whether or not the child developed the flu and a subsequent ear infection was also noted. These are appropriate determinations to make in order to answer the research question of interest. We typically cannot tell much about the data collection process from a newspaper article. As we will see in Section 2.3, to fully evaluate this study, we would also want to know how the participating children were selected, how it was determined that a particular child received the vaccine or the placebo, and how the subsequent diagnoses of flu and ear infection were made.

We will also have to delay discussion of the data analysis and the appropriateness of the conclusions because we do not yet have the necessary tools to evaluate these aspects of the study.

■

Many other interesting examples of statistical studies can be found in *Statistics: A Guide to the Unknown* and in *Forty Studies That Changed Psychology: Exploration into the History of Psychological Research* (the complete references for these two books can be found in the back of the book).

■ Exercises 1.1–1.9 ...............................................................................................................

**1.1** Give a brief definition of the terms *descriptive statistics* and *inferential statistics*.

**1.2** Give a brief definition of the terms *population* and *sample*.

**1.3** Data from a poll conducted by Travelocity led to the following estimates: Approximately 40% of travelers check work email while on vacation, about 33% take cell phones on vacation in order to stay connected with work, and about 25% bring a laptop computer on vacation (*San Luis Obispo Tribune*, December 1, 2005). Are the given percentages population values or were they computed from a sample?

**1.4** Based on a study of 2121 children between the ages of one and four, researchers at the Medical College of Wisconsin concluded that there was an association between iron deficiency and the length of time that a child is bottle-fed (*Milwaukee Journal Sentinel*, November 26, 2005). Describe the sample and the population of interest for this study.

**1.5** The student senate at a university with 15,000 students is interested in the proportion of students who favor a change in the grading system to allow for plus and minus grades (e.g., B+, B, B−, rather than just B). Two hundred students are interviewed to determine their attitude toward this proposed change. What is the population of interest? What group of students constitutes the sample in this problem?

**1.6** The supervisors of a rural county are interested in the proportion of property owners who support the construction of a sewer system. Because it is too costly to contact all 7000 property owners, a survey of 500 owners (selected at random) is undertaken. Describe the population and sample for this problem.

**1.7** ▼ Representatives of the insurance industry wished to investigate the monetary loss resulting from earthquake damage to single-family dwellings in Northridge, California, in January 1994. From the set of all single-family homes in Northridge, 100 homes were selected for inspection. Describe the population and sample for this problem.

**1.8** A consumer group conducts crash tests of new model cars. To determine the severity of damage to 2006 Mazda 6s resulting from a 10-mph crash into a concrete wall, the research group tests six cars of this type and assesses the amount of damage. Describe the population and sample for this problem.

**1.9** A building contractor has a chance to buy an odd lot of 5000 used bricks at an auction. She is interested in determining the proportion of bricks in the lot that are cracked and therefore unusable for her current project, but she does not have enough time to inspect all 5000 bricks. Instead, she checks 100 bricks to determine whether each is cracked. Describe the population and sample for this problem.

**Bold** exercises answered in back　　●　Data set available online but not required　　▼　Video solution available

## 1.4  Types of Data and Some Simple Graphical Displays

Every discipline has its own particular way of using common words, and statistics is no exception. You will recognize some of the terminology from previous math and science courses, but much of the language of statistics will be new to you.

### ■ Describing Data

The individuals or objects in any particular population typically possess many characteristics that might be studied. Consider a group of students currently enrolled in a statistics course. One characteristic of the students in the population is the brand of calculator owned (Casio, Hewlett-Packard, Sharp, Texas Instruments, and so on). Another characteristic is the number of textbooks purchased that semester, and yet another is the distance from the university to each student's permanent residence. A **variable** is any characteristic whose value may change from one individual or object to another. For example, *calculator brand* is a variable, and so are *number of textbooks purchased* and *distance to the university*. **Data** result from making observations either on a single variable or simultaneously on two or more variables.

A univariate data set consists of observations on a single variable made on individuals in a sample or population. There are two types of univariate data sets: categorical and numerical. In the previous example, *calculator brand* is a categorical variable, because each student's response to the query, "What brand of calculator do you own?" is a category. The collection of responses from all these students forms a categorical data set. The other two attributes, *number of textbooks purchased* and *distance to the university*, are both numerical in nature. Determining the value of such a numerical variable (by counting or measuring) for each student results in a numerical data set.

> **D E F I N I T I O N**
>
> A data set consisting of observations on a single attribute is a **univariate data set**. A univariate data set is **categorical** (or **qualitative**) if the individual observations are categorical responses. A univariate data set is **numerical** (or **quantitative**) if each observation is a number.

## Example 1.5    Airline Safety Violations

© PhotoLink/Getty Images

The Federal Aviation Administration (FAA) monitors airlines and can take administrative actions for safety violations. Information about the fines assessed by the FAA appeared in the article "Just How Safe Is That Jet?" (*USA Today*, March 13, 2000). Violations that could lead to a fine were categorized as Security (S), Maintenance (M), Flight Operations (F), Hazardous Materials (H), or Other (O). Data for the variable *type of violation* for 20 administrative actions are given in the following list (these data are a subset of the data described in the article, but they are consistent with summary values given in the paper; for a description of the full data set, see Exercise 1.24):

```
S   S   M   H   M   O   S   M   S   S
F   S   O   M   S   M   S   M   S   M
```

Because *type of violation* is a categorical (nonnumerical) response, this is a categorical data set.

■

In Example 1.5, the data set consisted of observations on a single variable (*type of violation*), so this is univariate data. In some studies, attention focuses simultaneously on two different attributes. For example, both height (in inches) and weight (in pounds) might be recorded for each individual in a group. The resulting data set consists of pairs of numbers, such as (68, 146). This is called a **bivariate data set**. **Multivariate data** result from obtaining a category or value for each of two or more attributes (so bivariate data are a special case of multivariate data). For example, multivariate data would result from determining height, weight, pulse rate, and systolic blood pressure for each individual in a group. Example 1.6 illustrates a bivariate data set.

..................................................................................................................................

## Example 1.6    Revisiting Airline Safety Violations

● The same article referenced in Example 1.5 ("Just How Safe Is That Jet?" *USA Today*, March 13, 2000) gave data on both the number of violations and the average fine per violation for the period 1985–1998 for 10 major airlines. The resulting bivariate data are given in the following table:

| Airline | Number of Violations | Average Fine per Violation ($) |
|---------|----------------------|--------------------------------|
| Alaska | 258 | 5038.760 |
| America West | 257 | 3112.840 |
| American | 1745 | 2693.410 |
| Continental | 973 | 5755.396 |
| Delta | 1280 | 3828.125 |
| Northwest | 1097 | 2643.573 |
| Southwest | 535 | 3925.234 |
| TWA | 642 | 2803.738 |
| United | 1110 | 2612.613 |
| US Airways | 891 | 3479.237 |

Each of the two variables considered here is numerical (rather than categorical).

■

## ■ Two Types of Numerical Data ........................................................................

There are two different types of numerical data: *discrete* and *continuous*. Visualize a number line (Figure 1.3) for locating values of the numerical variable being studied. Each possible number (2, 3.125, 8.12976, etc.) corresponds to exactly one point on the number line. Now suppose that the variable of interest is the number of cylinders of an automobile engine. The possible values of 4, 6, and 8 are identified in Figure 1.4(a) by

● Data set available online

**Figure 1.3** A number line.

**Figure 1.4** Possible values of a variable: (a) number of cylinders; (b) quarter-mile time.

the dots at the points marked 4, 6, and 8. These possible values are isolated from one another on the line; around any possible value, we can place an interval that is small enough that no other possible value is included in the interval. On the other hand, the line segment in Figure 1.4(b) identifies a plausible set of possible values for the time it takes a car to travel one-quarter mile. Here the possible values make up an entire interval on the number line, and no possible value is isolated from the other possible values.

■

### DEFINITION

A numerical variable results in **discrete** data if the possible values of the variable correspond to isolated points on the number line. A numerical variable results in **continuous** data if the set of possible values forms an entire interval on the number line.

Discrete data usually arise when each observation is determined by counting (e.g., the number of classes for which a student is registered or the number of petals on a certain type of flower).

........................................................................................................

## Example 1.7 Calls to a Drug Abuse Hotline

● The number of telephone calls per day to a drug abuse hotline is recorded for 12 days. The resulting data set is

    3    0    4    3    1    0    6    2    0    0    1    2

Possible values for the variable *number of calls* are 0, 1, 2, 3, . . . ; these are isolated points on the number line, so we have a sample consisting of discrete numerical data.

■

The observations on the variable *number of violations* in Example 1.6 are also an example of discrete numerical data. However, in the same example, the variable *average fine per violation* could be 3000, 3000.1, 3000.125, 3000.12476, or any other value in an entire interval, so the observations on this variable provide an example of continuous data. Other examples of continuous data result from determining task completion times, body temperatures, and package weights.

● Data set available online

In general, data are continuous when observations involve making measurements, as opposed to counting. In practice, measuring instruments do not have infinite accuracy, so possible measured values, strictly speaking, do not form a continuum on the number line. However, any number in the continuum *could* be a value of the variable. The distinction between discrete and continuous data will be important in our discussion of probability models.

## ■ Frequency Distributions and Bar Charts for Categorical Data .................

An appropriate graphical or tabular display of data can be an effective way to summarize and communicate information. When the data set is categorical, a common way to present the data is in the form of a table, called a *frequency distribution.*

A **frequency distribution for categorical data** is a table that displays the possible categories along with the associated frequencies and/or relative frequencies. The **frequency** for a particular category is the number of times the category appears in the data set. The **relative frequency** for a particular category is the fraction or proportion of the observations resulting in the category. It is calculated as

$$\text{relative frequency} = \frac{\text{frequency}}{\text{number of observations in the data set}}$$

If the table includes relative frequencies, it is sometimes referred to as a **relative frequency distribution.**

## Example 1.8    Motorcycle Helmets—Can You See Those Ears?

In 2003, the U.S. Department of Transportation established standards for motorcycle helmets. To ensure a certain degree of safety, helmets should reach the bottom of the motorcyclist's ears. The report "Motorcycle Helmet Use in 2005—Overall Results" (National Highway Traffic Safety Administration, August 2005) summarized data collected in June of 2005 by observing 1700 motorcyclists nationwide at selected roadway locations. Each time a motorcyclist passed by, the observer noted whether the rider was wearing no helmet, a noncompliant helmet, or a compliant helmet. Using the coding

$$N = \text{no helmet}$$
$$NH = \text{noncompliant helmet}$$
$$CH = \text{compliant helmet}$$

a few of the observations were

    CH    N    CH    NH    N    CH    CH    CH    N    N

There were also 1690 additional observations, which we didn't reproduce here!
In total, there were 731 riders who wore no helmet, 153 who wore a noncompliant helmet, and 816 who wore a compliant helmet.

The corresponding frequency distribution is given in Table 1.1.

**Table 1.1**   Frequency Distribution for Helmet Use

| Helmet Use Category | Frequency | Relative Frequency |
|---|---|---|
| No helmet | 731 | .430 ◄— *731/1700* |
| Noncompliant helmet | 153 | .090 ◄— *153/1700* |
| Compliant helmet | 816 | .480 |
| | 1700 | 1.00 |

*Total number of observations*

*Should total 1, but in some cases may be slightly off due to rounding*

From the frequency distribution, we can see that a large number of riders (43%) were not wearing a helmet, but most of those who wore a helmet were wearing one that met the Department of Transportation safety standard.

■

A frequency distribution gives a tabular display of a data set. It is also common to display categorical data graphically. A bar chart is one of the most widely used types of graphical displays for categorical data.

## ■ Bar Charts

A **bar chart** is a graph of the frequency distribution of categorical data. Each category in the frequency distribution is represented by a bar or rectangle, and the picture is constructed in such a way that the *area* of each bar is proportional to the corresponding frequency or relative frequency.

### Bar Charts

**When to Use**   Categorical data.

**How to Construct**

1. Draw a horizontal line, and write the category names or labels below the line at regularly spaced intervals.
2. Draw a vertical line, and label the scale using either frequency or relative frequency.
3. Place a rectangular bar above each category label. The height is determined by the category's frequency or relative frequency, and all bars should have the same width. With the same width, both the height and the area of the bar are proportional to frequency and relative frequency.

**What to Look For**

- Frequently and infrequently occurring categories.

■

## Example 1.9   Revisiting Motorcycle Helmets

Example 1.8 used data on helmet use from a sample of 1700 motorcyclists to construct a frequency distribution (Table 1.1). Figure 1.5 shows the bar chart corresponding to this frequency distribution.

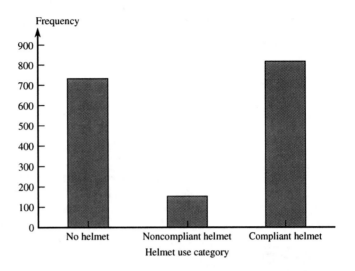

**Figure 1.5**  Bar chart of helmet use.

The bar chart provides a visual representation of the information in the frequency distribution. From the bar chart, it is easy to see that the compliant helmet use category occurred most often in the data set. The bar for complaint helmets is about five times as tall (and therefore has five times the area) as the bar for noncompliant helmets because approximately five times as many motorcyclists wore compliant helmets than wore noncompliant helmets.

■

### ■ Dotplots for Numerical Data

A dotplot is a simple way to display numerical data when the data set is reasonably small. Each observation is represented by a dot above the location corresponding to its value on a horizontal measurement scale. When a value occurs more than once, there is a dot for each occurrence and these dots are stacked vertically.

### Dotplots

**When to Use**   Small numerical data sets.

**How to Construct**

1. Draw a horizontal line and mark it with an appropriate measurement scale.

*(continued)*

2. Locate each value in the data set along the measurement scale, and represent it by a dot. If there are two or more observations with the same value, stack the dots vertically.

**What to Look For**   Dotplots convey information about:

- A representative or typical value in the data set.
- The extent to which the data values spread out.
- The nature of the distribution of values along the number line.
- The presence of unusual values in the data set.

# Example 1.10   Graduation Rates for NCAA Division I Schools in California and Texas

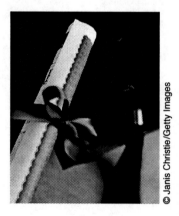

© Janis Christie/Getty Images

● *The Chronicle of Higher Education* (Almanac Issue, August 31, 2001) reported graduation rates for NCAA Division I schools. The rates reported are the percentages of full-time freshmen in fall 1993 who had earned a bachelor's degree by August 1999. Data from the two largest states (California, with 20 Division I schools; and Texas, with 19 Division I schools) are as follows:

| California: | 64 | 41 | 44 | 31 | 37 | 73 | 72 | 68 | 35 | 37 |
|---|---|---|---|---|---|---|---|---|---|---|
|  | 81 | 90 | 82 | 74 | 79 | 67 | 66 | 66 | 70 | 63 |
| Texas: | 67 | 21 | 32 | 88 | 35 | 71 | 39 | 35 | 71 | 63 |
|  | 12 | 46 | 35 | 39 | 28 | 65 | 25 | 24 | 22 |  |

MINITAB, a computer software package for statistical analysis, was used to construct a dotplot of the 39 graduation rates. This dotplot is given in Figure 1.6. From the dotplot, we can see that graduation rates varied a great deal from school to school and that the graduation rates seem to form two distinguishable groups of about the same size—one group with higher graduation rates and one with lower graduation rates.

**Figure 1.6** MINITAB dotplot of graduation rates.

Figure 1.7 shows separate dotplots for the California and Texas schools. The dotplots are drawn using the same scale to facilitate comparisons. From the two plots, we can see that, although both states have a high group and a low group, there are only six schools in the low group for California and only six schools in the high group for Texas.

♪♪ Step-by-step technology instructions available online          ● Data set available online

**Figure 1.7** MINITAB dotplot of graduation rates for California and Texas.

■

## Exercises 1.10–1.26 ..............................................................

**1.10** Classify each of the following attributes as either categorical or numerical. For those that are numerical, determine whether they are discrete or continuous.
a. Number of students in a class of 35 who turn in a term paper before the due date
b. Gender of the next baby born at a particular hospital
c. Amount of fluid (in ounces) dispensed by a machine used to fill bottles with soda pop
d. Thickness of the gelatin coating of a vitamin E capsule
e. Birth order classification (only child, firstborn, middle child, lastborn) of a math major

**1.11** Classify each of the following attributes as either categorical or numerical. For those that are numerical, determine whether they are discrete or continuous.
**a.** Brand of computer purchased by a customer
**b.** State of birth for someone born in the United States
**c.** Price of a textbook
**d.** Concentration of a contaminant (micrograms per cubic centimeter) in a water sample
**e.** Zip code (Think carefully about this one.)
**f.** Actual weight of coffee in a 1-lb can

**1.12** For the following numerical attributes, state whether each is discrete or continuous.
a. The number of insufficient-funds checks received by a grocery store during a given month
b. The amount by which a 1-lb package of ground beef decreases in weight (because of moisture loss) before purchase
c. The number of New York Yankees during a given year who will not play for the Yankees the next year
d. The number of students in a class of 35 who have purchased a used copy of the textbook

**1.13** For the following numerical attributes, state whether each is discrete or continuous.
**a.** The length of a 1-year-old rattlesnake
**b.** The altitude of a location in California selected randomly by throwing a dart at a map of the state

c. The distance from the left edge at which a 12-in. plastic ruler snaps when bent sufficiently to break
**d.** The price per gallon paid by the next customer to buy gas at a particular station

**1.14** For each of the following situations, give a set of possible data values that might arise from making the observations described.
a. The manufacturer for each of the next 10 automobiles to pass through a given intersection is noted.
b. The grade point average for each of the 15 seniors in a statistics class is determined.
c. The number of gas pumps in use at each of 20 gas stations at a particular time is determined.
d. The actual net weight of each of 12 bags of fertilizer having a labeled weight of 50 lb is determined.
e. Fifteen different radio stations are monitored during a 1-hr period, and the amount of time devoted to commercials is determined for each.

**1.15** In a survey of 100 people who had recently purchased motorcycles, data on the following variables was recorded:

Gender of purchaser
Brand of motorcycle purchased
Number of previous motorcycles owned by purchaser
Telephone area code of purchaser
Weight of motorcycle as equipped at purchase

**a.** Which of these variables are categorical?
**b.** Which of these variables are discrete numerical?
**c.** Which type of graphical display would be an appropriate choice for summarizing the gender data, a bar chart or a dotplot?
**d.** Which type of graphical display would be an appropriate choice for summarizing the weight data, a bar chart or a dotplot?

**1.16** ● *Spider-Man* and *Star Wars: Episode II* were the top moneymakers among the summer 2002 movie releases.

**Bold** exercises answered in back     ● Data set available online but not required     ▼ Video solution available

Box office totals for the top summer films in 2002 are given in the following table (*USA Today*, September 3, 2002):

| Film | Box Office (millions of dollars) |
| --- | --- |
| *Spider-Man* | 403.7 |
| *Star Wars: Episode II* | 300.1 |
| *Austin Powers in Goldmember* | 203.5 |
| *Signs* | 195.1 |
| *Men in Black II* | 189.7 |
| *Scooby-Doo* | 151.6 |
| *Lilo & Stitch* | 141.8 |
| *Minority Report* | 130.1 |
| *Mr. Deeds* | 124.0 |
| *XXX* | 123.9 |
| *The Sum of All Fears* | 118.5 |
| *The Bourne Identity* | 118.1 |
| *Road to Perdition* | 99.1 |
| *My Big Fat Greek Wedding* | 82.3 |
| *Spirit: Stallion of the Cimarron* | 73.2 |
| *Spy Kids 2: Island of Lost Dreams* | 69.1 |
| *Divine Secrets of the Ya-Ya Sisterhood* | 68.8 |
| *Insomnia* | 67.0 |
| *Stuart Little 2* | 61.9 |
| *Unfaithful* | 52.8 |

Use a dotplot to display these data. Write a few sentences commenting on the notable features of the dotplot.

**1.17** ● The article "Fraud, Identity Theft Afflict Consumers" (*San Luis Obispo Tribune*, February 2, 2005) included the accompanying breakdown of identity theft complaints by type.

| Type of Complaint | Percent of All Complaints |
| --- | --- |
| Credit card fraud | 28% |
| Phone or utilities fraud | 19% |
| Bank fraud | 18% |
| Employment fraud | 13% |
| Other | 22% |

Construct a bar chart for these data and write a sentence or two commenting on the most common types of identity theft complaints.

**1.18** The U.S. Department of Education reported that 14% of adults were classified as being below a basic literacy level, 29% were classified as being at a basic literacy level, 44% were classified as being at an intermediate literacy level, and 13% were classified as being at a proficient level (*2003 National Assessment of Adult Literacy*).
a. Is the variable *literacy level* categorical or numerical?
b. Would it be appropriate to display the given information using a dotplot? Explain why or why not.
c. Construct a bar chart to display the given data on literacy level.

**1.19** ● ▼ The Computer Assisted Assessment Center at the University of Luton published a report titled "Technical Review of Plagiarism Detection Software." The authors of this report asked faculty at academic institutions about the extent to which they agreed with the statement "Plagiarism is a significant problem in academic institutions." The responses are summarized in the accompanying table. Construct a bar chart for these data.

| Response | Frequency |
| --- | --- |
| Strongly disagree | 5 |
| Disagree | 48 |
| Not sure | 90 |
| Agree | 140 |
| Strongly agree | 39 |

**1.20** ● A 2005 AP-IPSOS poll found that 21% of American adults surveyed said their child was heavier than doctors recommend. The reasons given as the most important contributing factor to the child's weight problem is summarized in the accompanying table.

| | |
| --- | --- |
| Lack of exercise | 38% |
| Easy access to junk food | 23% |
| Genetics | 12% |
| Eating unhealthy food | 9% |
| Medical condition | 8% |
| Overeating | 7% |

a. Construct a bar chart for the data on the most important contributing factor.
b. Do you think that it would be reasonable to combine some of these contributing factors into a single category? If so, which categories would you combine and why?

**1.21** ● ▼ *USA Today* compared the average graduation rates for male football and basketball scholarship players at top-ranked universities. The graduation rates were expressed as a difference between the graduation rate for scholarship athletes and the university's overall graduation rate for men. A positive number means that the athletes had a graduation rate higher than the overall graduation rate (+2 means 2% higher) and a negative number means the athletes had a lower graduation rate than the overall graduation rate (−2 means 2% lower). Using the same scale, construct a dotplot of the graduation rate differences for football players and a dotplot for the graduation rate differences for basketball players. Comment on the similarities and differences in the two plots.

| Football | | Basketball | |
|---|---|---|---|
| **School** | **Difference from overall graduation rate** | **School** | **Difference from overall graduation rate** |
| Nebraska | +8 | Butler | +29 |
| Kansas State | +6 | Kansas | +20 |
| Arizona State | 0 | Dayton | +12 |
| Penn State | −2 | Stanford | +9 |
| Georgia | −2 | Xavier | −1 |
| Purdue | −4 | Marquette | −8 |
| Iowa | −4 | Michigan State | −10 |
| Florida State | −9 | Creighton | −17 |
| Southern Cal | −10 | Florida | −23 |
| Miami | −11 | Duke | −25 |
| LSU | −12 | Texas | −26 |
| Notre Dame | −13 | Arizona | −27 |
| Ohio State | −13 | Illinois | −29 |
| Tennessee | −13 | Wisconsin | −29 |
| Virginia | −14 | Notre Dame | −30 |
| N.C. State | −14 | Syracuse | −32 |
| Oklahoma | −14 | Maryland | −33 |
| Auburn | −19 | Connecticut | −38 |
| Virginia Tech | −20 | Wake Forest | −39 |
| Colorado | −21 | | |
| Wisconsin | −21 | | |
| Florida | −24 | | |
| Pittsburgh | −24 | | |
| Texas | −26 | | |
| Michigan | −35 | | |

**1.22** ● The article "So Close, Yet So Far: Predictors of Attrition in College Seniors" (*Journal of College Student Development* [1998]: 343–348) examined the reasons that

college seniors leave their college programs before graduating. Forty-two college seniors at a large public university who dropped out before graduation were interviewed and asked the main reason for discontinuing enrollment at the university. Data consistent with that given in the article are summarized in the following frequency distribution:

| Reason for Leaving the University | Frequency |
|---|---|
| Academic problems | 7 |
| Poor advising or teaching | 3 |
| Needed a break | 2 |
| Economic reasons | 11 |
| Family responsibilities | 4 |
| To attend another school | 9 |
| Personal problems | 3 |
| Other | 3 |

Summarize the given data on reason for leaving the university using a bar chart and write a few sentences commenting on the most common reasons for leaving.

**1.23** ● Water quality ratings of 36 Southern California beaches were given in the article "How Safe Is the Surf?" (*Los Angeles Times*, October 26, 2002). The ratings, which ranged from A to F and which reflect the risk of getting sick from swimming at a particular beach, are given in the following list:

| A+ | A+ | A+ | F | A+ | A+ |
|---|---|---|---|---|---|
| A | B | A | C | C | A− |
| A | F | B | A+ | C | A |
| D | F | A+ | D | A+ | A |
| D | A | A | D | A+ | A+ |
| A | A | C | F− | B | A+ |

**a.** Summarize the given ratings by constructing a relative frequency distribution and a bar chart. Comment on the interesting features of your bar chart.
**b.** Would it be appropriate to construct a dotplot for these data? Why or why not?

**1.24** ● The article "Just How Safe Is That Jet?" (*USA Today*, March 13, 2000) gave the following relative frequency distribution that summarized data on the type of violation for fines imposed on airlines by the Federal Aviation Administration:

| Type of Violation | Relative Frequency |
| --- | --- |
| Security | .43 |
| Maintenance | .39 |
| Flight operations | .06 |
| Hazardous materials | .03 |
| Other | .09 |

Use this information to construct a bar chart for type of violation, and then write a sentence or two commenting on the relative occurrence of the various types of violation.

1.25 ▼ The article "Americans Drowsy on the Job and the Road" (Associated Press, March 28, 2001) summarized data from the 2001 Sleep in America poll. Each individual in a sample of 1004 adults was asked questions about his or her sleep habits. The article states that "40 percent of those surveyed say they get sleepy on the job and their work suffers at least a few days each month, while 22 percent said the problems occur a few days each week. And 7 percent say sleepiness on the job is a daily occurrence." Assuming that everyone else reported that sleepiness on the job was not a problem, summarize the given information by constructing a relative frequency bar chart.

1.26 "Ozzie and Harriet Don't Live Here Anymore" (*San Luis Obispo Tribune*, February 26, 2002) is the title of an article that looked at the changing makeup of America's suburbs. The article states that nonfamily households (e.g., homes headed by a single professional or an elderly widow) now outnumber married couples with children in suburbs of the nation's largest metropolitan areas. The article goes on to state:

> In the nation's 102 largest metropolitan areas, "nonfamilies" comprised 29 percent of households in 2000, up from 27 percent in 1990. While the number of married-with-children homes grew too, the share did not keep pace. It declined from 28 percent to 27 percent. Married couples without children at home live in another 29 percent of suburban households. The remaining 15 percent are single-parent homes.

Use the given information on type of household in 2000 to construct a frequency distribution and a bar chart. (Be careful to extract the 2000 percentages from the given information).

**Bold** exercises answered in back    ● Data set available online but not required    ▼ Video solution available

## Activity 1.1    Head Sizes: Understanding Variability

**Materials needed:** Each team will need a measuring tape.

For this activity, you will work in teams of 6 to 10 people.

1. Designate a team leader for your team by choosing the person on your team who celebrated his or her last birthday most recently.

2. The team leader should measure and record the head size (measured as the circumference at the widest part of the forehead) of each of the other members of his or her team.

3. Record the head sizes for the individuals on your team as measured by the team leader.

4. Next, each individual on the team should measure the head size of the team leader. Do not share your measurement with the other team members until all team members have measured the team leader's head size.

5. After all team members have measured the team leader's head, record the different team leader head size measurements obtained by the individuals on your team.

6. Using the data from Step 3, construct a dotplot of the team leader's measurements of team head sizes. Then, using the same scale, construct a separate dotplot of the different measurements of the team leader's head size (from Step 5).

Now use the available information to answer the following questions:

7. Do you think the team leader's head size changed in between measurements? If not, explain why the measurements of the team leader's head size are not all the same.

8. Which data set was more variable—head size measurements of the different individuals on your team or the different measurements of the team leader's head size? Explain the basis for your choice.

9. Consider the following scheme (you don't actually have to carry this out): Suppose that a group of 10 people measured head sizes by first assigning each person in the group a number between 1 and 10. Then person 1 measured person 2's head size, person 2 measured person 3's head size, and so on, with person 10 finally measuring person 1's head size. Do you think that the resulting head size measurements would be more variable, less variable, or show about the same amount of variability as a set of 10 measurements resulting from a single individual measuring the head size of all 10 people in the group? Explain.

# A c t i v i t y  **1.2**    Estimating Sizes

1. Construct an activity sheet that consists of a table that has 6 columns and 10 rows. Label the columns of the table with the following six headings: (1) Shape, (2) Estimated Size, (3) Actual Size, (4) Difference (Est. − Actual), (5) Absolute Difference, and (6) Squared Difference. Enter the numbers from 1 to 10 in the "Shape" column.

2. Next you will be visually estimating the sizes of the shapes in Figure 1.8. Size will be described as the number of squares of this size

that would fit in the shape. For example, the shape

**Figure 1.8**  Shapes for Activity 1.2.

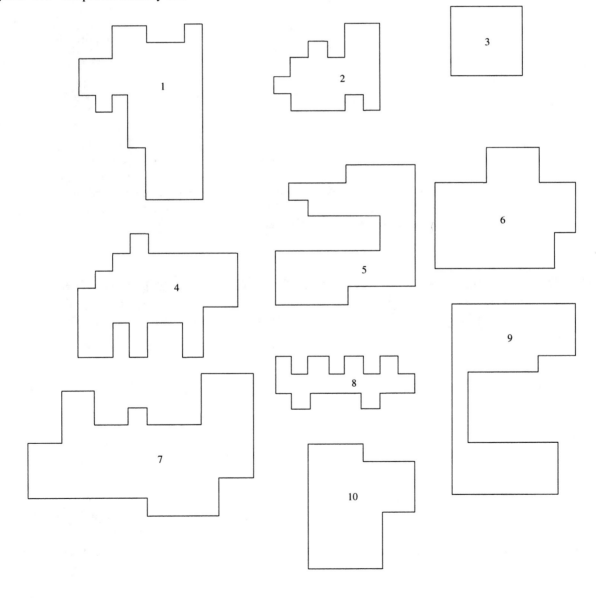

would be size 3, as illustrated by

You should now quickly *visually* estimate the sizes of the shapes in Figure 1.8. *Do not* draw on the figure—these are to be quick visual estimates. Record your estimates in the "Estimated Size" column of the activity sheet.

3. Your instructor will provide the actual sizes for the 10 shapes, which should be entered into the "Actual Size" column of the activity sheet. Now complete the "Difference" column by subtracting the actual value from your estimate for each of the 10 shapes.

4. What would cause a difference to be negative? positive?

5. Would the sum of the differences tell you if the estimates and actual values were in close agreement? Does a sum of 0 for the differences indicate that all the estimates were equal to the actual value? Explain.

6. Compare your estimates with those of another person in the class by comparing the sum of the absolute values of the differences between estimates and corresponding actual values. Who was better at estimating shape sizes? How can you tell?

7. Use the last column of the activity sheet to record the squared differences (e.g., if the difference for shape 1 was $-3$, the squared difference would be $(-3)^2 = 9$). Explain why the sum of the squared differences can also be used to assess how accurate your shape estimates were.

8. For this step, work with three or four other students from your class. For each of the 10 shapes, form a new size estimate by computing the average of the size estimates for that shape made by the individuals in your group. Is this new set of estimates more accurate than your own individual estimates were? How can you tell?

9. Does your answer from Step 8 surprise you? Explain why or why not.

## Activity 1.3    A Meaningful Paragraph

Write a meaningful paragraph that includes the following six terms: **sample, population, descriptive statistics, bar chart, numerical variable,** and **dotplot.**

A "meaningful paragraph" is a coherent piece of writing in an appropriate context that uses all of the listed words. The paragraph should show that you understand the meaning of the terms and their relationship to one another. A sequence of sentences that just define the terms is *not* a meaningful paragraph. When choosing a context, think carefully about the terms you need to use. Choosing a good context will make writing a meaningful paragraph easier.

# Summary of Key Concepts and Formulas

| Term or Formula | Comment |
| --- | --- |
| Descriptive statistics | Numerical, graphical, and tabular methods for organizing and summarizing data. |
| Population | The entire collection of individuals or measurements about which information is desired. |
| Sample | A part of the population selected for study. |
| Categorical data | Individual observations are categorical responses (nonnumerical). |
| Numerical data | Individual observations are numerical (quantitative) in nature. |
| Discrete numerical data | Possible values are isolated points along the number line. |
| Continuous numerical data | Possible values form an entire interval along the number line. |

| Term or Formula | Comment |
|---|---|
| Bivariate and multivariate data | Each observation consists of two (bivariate) or more (multivariate) responses or values. |
| Frequency distribution for categorical data | A table that displays frequencies, and sometimes relative frequencies, for each of the possible values of a categorical variable. |
| Bar chart | A graph of a frequency distribution for a categorical data set. Each category is represented by a bar, and the area of the bar is proportional to the corresponding frequency or relative frequency. |
| Dotplot | A picture of numerical data in which each observation is represented by a dot on or above a horizontal measurement scale. |

# Chapter Review Exercises 1.27–1.31

**Thomson**NOW  Know exactly what to study! Take a pre-test and receive your Personalized Learning Plan.

**1.27** ● Each year, *U.S. News and World Report* publishes a ranking of U.S. business schools. The following data give the acceptance rates (percentage of applicants admitted) for the best 25 programs in the most recent survey:

16.3 12.0 25.1 20.3 31.9 20.7 30.1 19.5 36.2
46.9 25.8 36.7 33.8 24.2 21.5 35.1 37.6 23.9
17.0 38.4 31.2 43.8 28.9 31.4 48.9

Construct a dotplot, and comment on the interesting features of the plot.

**1.28** ● Many adolescent boys aspire to be professional athletes. The paper "Why Adolescent Boys Dream of Becoming Professional Athletes" (*Psychological Reports* [1999]: 1075–1085) examined some of the reasons. Each boy in a sample of teenage boys was asked the following question: "Previous studies have shown that more teenage boys say that they are considering becoming professional athletes than any other occupation. In your opinion, why do these boys want to become professional athletes?" The resulting data are shown in the following table:

| Response | Frequency |
|---|---|
| Fame and celebrity | 94 |
| Money | 56 |
| Attract women | 29 |

| Response | Frequency |
|---|---|
| Like sports | 27 |
| Easy life | 24 |
| Don't need an education | 19 |
| Other | 19 |

Construct a bar chart to display these data.

**1.29** ● The paper "Profile of Sport / Leisure Injuries Treated at Emergency Rooms of Urban Hospitals" (*Canadian Journal of Sports Science* [1991]: 99–102) classified noncontact sports injuries by sport, resulting in the following table:

| Sport | Number of Sport Injuries |
|---|---|
| Touch football | 38 |
| Soccer | 24 |
| Basketball | 19 |
| Baseball/softball | 11 |
| Jogging/running | 11 |
| Bicycling | 11 |
| Volleyball | 17 |
| Other | 47 |

**Bold** exercises answered in back    ● Data set available online but not required    ▼ Video solution available

Calculate relative frequencies and draw the corresponding bar chart.

**1.30** ● Nonresponse is a common problem facing researchers who rely on mail questionnaires. In the paper "Reasons for Nonresponse on the Physicians' Practice Survey" (*1980 Proceedings of the Section on Social Statistics* [1980]: 202), 811 doctors who did not respond to the AMA Survey of Physicians were contacted about the reason for their nonparticipation. The results are summarized in the accompanying relative frequency distribution. Draw the corresponding bar chart.

| Reason | Relative Frequency |
|---|---|
| 1. No time to participate | .264 |
| 2. Not interested | .300 |
| 3. Don't like surveys in general | .145 |
| 4. Don't like this particular survey | .025 |
| 5. Hostility toward the government | .054 |
| 6. Desire to protect privacy | .056 |
| 7. Other reason for refusal | .053 |
| 8. No reason given | .103 |

**1.31** ● The article "Can We Really Walk Straight?" (*American Journal of Physical Anthropology* [1992]: 19–27) reported on an experiment in which each of 20 healthy men was asked to walk as straight as possible to a target 60 m away at normal speed. Consider the following observations on cadence (number of strides per second):

0.95  0.85  0.92  1.95  0.93  1.86  1.00
0.92  0.85  0.81  0.78  0.93  0.93  1.05
0.93  1.06  1.06  0.96  0.81  0.96

Construct a dotplot for the cadence data. Do any data values stand out as being unusual?

**Bold** exercises answered in back      ● Data set available online but not required      ▼ Video solution available

# Chapter 2

# Collecting Data Sensibly

A primary goal of statistical studies is to collect data that can then be used to make informed decisions. It should come as no surprise that the correctness of such decisions depends on the quality of the information on which they are based. The data collection step is critical to obtaining reliable information; both the type of analysis that is appropriate and the conclusions that can be drawn depend on how the data are collected. In this chapter, we first consider two types of statistical studies and then focus on two widely used methods of data collection: sampling and experimentation.

## 2.1 Statistical Studies: Observation and Experimentation

Two articles with the following headlines appeared in *USA Today*:

"Prayer Can Lower Blood Pressure" (August 11, 1998)
"Wired Homes Watch 15% Less Television" (August 13, 1998)

In each of these articles, a conclusion is drawn from data. In the study on prayer and blood pressure, 2391 people, 65 years or older, were followed for six years. The article states that people who attended a religious service once a week and prayed or studied the Bible at least once a day were less likely to have high blood pressure. The researcher then concluded that "attending religious services lowers blood pressure."

The second article reported on a study of 5000 families, some of whom had online Internet services. The researcher concluded that TV use was lower in homes that were wired for the Internet, compared to nonwired homes. The researcher who conducted the study cautioned that the study does not answer the question of whether higher family income could be another factor in lower TV usage.

Are these conclusions reasonable? As we will see, the answer in each case depends in a critical way on how the data were collected.

## ▪ Observation and Experimentation ............................................................

Data collection is an important step in the data analysis process. When we set out to collect information, it is important to keep in mind the questions we hope to answer on the basis of the resulting data. Sometimes we are interested in answering questions about characteristics of a single existing population or in comparing two or more well-defined populations. To accomplish this, we select a sample from each population under consideration and use the sample information to gain insight into characteristics of the population(s).

For example, an ecologist might be interested in estimating the average shell thickness of bald eagle eggs. A social scientist studying a rural community may want to determine whether gender and attitude toward abortion are related. These are examples of studies that are *observational* in nature. In these studies, we want to observe characteristics of members of an existing population or of several populations, and then use the resulting information to draw conclusions. In an observational study, it is important to obtain a sample that is representative of the corresponding population.

Sometimes the questions we are trying to answer deal with the effect of certain explanatory variables on some response and cannot be answered using data from an observational study. Such questions are often of the form, What happens when . . . ? or, What is the effect of . . . ? For example, an educator may wonder what would happen to test scores if the required lab time for a chemistry course were increased from 3 hr to 6 hr per week. To answer such questions, the researcher conducts an experiment to collect relevant data. The value of some response variable (test score in the chemistry example) is recorded under different experimental conditions (3-hr lab and 6-hr lab). In an experiment, the researcher manipulates one or more variables, called **factors**, to create the experimental conditions.

### Observational Study

A study is an **observational study** if the investigator observes characteristics of a subset of the members of one or more existing populations. The goal of an observational study is usually to draw conclusions about the corresponding population or about differences between two or more populations.

### Experiment

A study is an **experiment** if the investigator observes how a response variable behaves when the researcher manipulates one or more explanatory variables, sometimes also called factors. The usual goal of an experiment is to determine the effect of the manipulated factors on the response variable. In a well-designed experiment, the composition of the groups that will be exposed to different experimental conditions is determined by random assignment.

The type of conclusion that can be drawn from a research study depends on the study design. Both observational studies and experiments can be used to compare groups, but in an experiment the researcher controls who is in which group, whereas this is not the case in an observational study. This seemingly small difference is critical when it comes to the interpretation of results from the study.

A well-designed experiment can result in data that provide evidence for a cause-and-effect relationship. This is an important difference between an observational study and an experiment. In an observational study, it is impossible to draw cause-and-effect conclusions because we cannot rule out the possibility that the observed effect is due to some variable other than the factor being studied. Such variables are called confounding variables.

A **confounding variable** is one that is related to both group membership and the response variable of interest in a research study. ■

Consider the role of confounding variables in the following three studies:

- The article "Panel Can't Determine the Value of Daily Vitamins" (*San Luis Obispo Tribune*, July 1, 2003) summarized the conclusions of a government advisory panel that investigated the benefits of vitamin use. The panel looked at a large number of studies on vitamin use and concluded that the results were "inadequate or conflicting." A major concern was that many of the studies were observational in nature and the panel worried that people who take vitamins might be healthier just because they tend to take better care of themselves in general. This potential confounding variable prevented the panel from concluding that taking vitamins is the cause of observed better health among those who take vitamins.
- Studies have shown that people over age 65 who get a flu shot are less likely than those who do not get a flu shot to die from a flu-related illness during the following year. However, recent research has shown that people over age 65 who get a flu shot are also less likely than those who don't to die from *any* cause during the following year (*International Journal of Epidemiology*, December 21, 2005). This has lead to the speculation that those over age 65 who get flu shots are healthier as a group than those who do not get flu shots. If this is the case, observational studies that compare two groups—those who get flu shots and those who do not—may overestimate the effectiveness of the flu vaccine because general health differs in the two groups and so general health would be a possible confounding variable in such studies.
- The article "Heartfelt Thanks to Fido" (*San Luis Obispo Tribune*, July 5, 2003) summarized a study that appeared in the *American Journal of Cardiology* (March 15, 2003). In this study researchers measured heart rate variability (a measure of the heart's ability to handle stress) in patients who had recovered from a heart attack. They found that heart rate variability was higher (which is good and means the heart can handle stress better) for those who owned a dog than for those who did not. Should someone who suffers a heart attack immediately go out and get a dog? Well, maybe not yet. The American Heart Association recommends additional studies to determine if the improved heart rate variability is attributable to dog ownership or due to the fact that dog owners get more exercise. If in fact dog owners do tend to get more exercise than nonowners, level of exercise is a confounding variable that would prevent us from concluding that owning a dog is the cause of improved heart rate variability.

Each of the three studies described above illustrates why potential confounding variables make it unreasonable to draw a cause-and-effect conclusion from an observational study.

Returning to the studies reported in the *USA Today* articles described at the beginning of this section, notice that both are observational studies. In the TV viewing example, the researcher merely observed the TV viewing behavior of individuals in two groups (wired and nonwired) but did not control which individuals were in which group. A possible confounding variable here is family income. Although it may be reasonable to conclude that the wired and nonwired groups differ with respect to TV viewing, it is not reasonable to conclude that the lower TV use in wired homes is caused by the fact that they have Internet service. In the prayer example, two groups were compared (those who attend a religious service at least once a week and those who do not), but the researcher did not manipulate this factor to observe the effect on blood pressure by assigning people at random to service-attending or nonservice-attending groups. As a result, cause-and-effect conclusions such as "prayer can lower blood pressure" are not reasonable based on the observed data. It is possible that some other variable, such as lifestyle, is related to both religious service attendance and blood pressure. In this case, lifestyle is an example of a potential confounding variable.

## ▪ Drawing Conclusions from Statistical Studies ...............................................

In this section, two different types of conclusions have been described. One type involves generalizing from what we have seen in a sample to some larger population, and the other involves reaching a cause-and-effect conclusion about the effect of an explanatory variable on a response. When is it reasonable to draw such conclusions? The answer depends on the way that the data were collected. Table 2.1 summarizes the types of conclusions that can be made with different study designs.

**Table 2.1**   Drawing Conclusions from Statistical Studies

| Study Description | Reasonable to Generalize Conclusions about Group Characteristics to the Population? | Reasonable to Draw Cause-and-Effect Conclusion? |
|---|---|---|
| Observational study with sample selected at random from population of interest | Yes | No |
| Observational study based on convenience or voluntary response sample (poorly designed sampling plan) | No | No |
| Experiment with groups formed by random assignment of individuals or objects to experimental conditions | | |
| Individuals or objects used in study are volunteers or not randomly selected from some population of interest | No | Yes |
| Individuals or objects used in study are randomly selected from some population of interest | Yes | Yes |
| Experiment with groups not formed by random assignment to experimental conditions (poorly designed experiment) | No | No |

As you can see from Table 2.1, it is important to think carefully about the objectives of a statistical study before planning how the data will be collected. Both observational studies and experiments must be carefully designed if the resulting data are to be useful. The common sampling procedures used in observational studies are considered in Section 2.2. In Sections 2.3 and 2.4, we consider experimentation and explore what constitutes good practice in the design of simple experiments.

■ **Exercises 2.1–2.9** ...........................................................................................................

**2.1** ▼ The article "Television's Value to Kids: It's All in How They Use It" (*Seattle Times*, July 6, 2005) described a study in which researchers analyzed standardized test results and television viewing habits of 1700 children. They found that children who averaged more than two hours of television viewing per day when they were younger than 3 tended to score lower on measures of reading ability and short term memory.
**a.** Is the study described an observational study or an experiment?
**b.** Is it reasonable to conclude that watching two or more hours of television is the cause of lower reading scores? Explain.

**2.2** "Fruit Juice May Be Fueling Pudgy Preschoolers, Study Says" is the title of an article that appeared in the *San Luis Obispo Tribune* (February 27, 2005). This article describes a study that found that for 3- and 4-year-olds, drinking something sweet once or twice a day doubled the risk of being seriously overweight one year later. The authors of the study state

> Total energy may be a confounder if consumption of sweet drinks is a marker for other dietary factors associated with overweight . . . (*Pediatrics*, November 2005)

Give an example of a dietary factor that might be one of the potentially confounding variables the study authors are worried about.

**2.3** The article "Americans are 'Getting the Wrong Idea' on Alcohol and Health" (Associated Press, April 19, 2005) reported that observational studies in recent years that have concluded that moderate drinking is associated with a reduction in the risk of heart disease may be misleading. The article refers to a study conducted by the Centers for Disease Control and Prevention that showed that moderate drinkers, as a group, tended to be better educated, wealthier, and more active than nondrinkers. Explain why the existence of these potentially confounding factors prevent drawing the conclusion that moderate drinking is the cause of reduced risk of heart disease.

**2.4** An article titled "Guard Your Kids Against Allergies: Get Them a Pet" (*San Luis Obispo Tribune*, August 28, 2002) described a study that led researchers to conclude that "babies raised with two or more animals were about half as likely to have allergies by the time they turned six."
a. Do you think this study was an observational study or an experiment? Explain.
b. Describe a potential confounding variable that illustrates why it is unreasonable to conclude that being raised with two or more animals is the cause of the observed lower allergy rate.

**2.5** Researchers at the Hospital for Sick Children in Toronto compared babies born to mothers with diabetes to babies born to mothers without diabetes ("Conditioning and Hyperanalgesia in Newborns Exposed to Repeated Heel Lances," *Journal of the American Medical Association* [2002]: 857–861). Babies born to mothers with diabetes have their heels pricked numerous times during the first 36 hours of life in order to obtain blood samples to monitor blood sugar level. The researchers noted that the babies born to diabetic mothers were more likely to grimace or cry when having blood drawn than the babies born to mothers without diabetes. This led the researchers to conclude that babies who experience pain early in life become highly sensitive to pain. Comment on the appropriateness of this conclusion.

**Bold** exercises answered in back     ◉ Data set available online but not required     ▼ Video solution available

**2.6** Based on a survey conducted on the DietSmart.com web site, investigators concluded that women who regularly watched *Oprah* were only one-seventh as likely to crave fattening foods as those who watched other daytime talk shows (*San Luis Obispo Tribune*, October 14, 2000).
a. Is it reasonable to conclude that watching *Oprah* causes a decrease in cravings for fattening foods? Explain.
b. Is it reasonable to generalize the results of this survey to all women in the United States? To all women who watch daytime talk shows? Explain why or why not.

**2.7** ▼ A survey of affluent Americans (those with incomes of $75,000 or more) indicated that 57% would rather have more time than more money (*USA Today*, January 29, 2003).
**a.** What condition on how the data were collected would make the generalization from the sample to the population of affluent Americans reasonable?
**b.** Would it be reasonable to generalize from the sample to say that 57% of all Americans would rather have more time than more money? Explain.

**2.8** Does living in the South cause high blood pressure? Data from a group of 6278 whites and blacks questioned in the Third National Health and Nutritional Examination Survey between 1988 and 1994 (see CNN.com web site article of January 6, 2000, titled "High Blood Pressure Greater Risk in U.S. South, Study Says") indicates that a greater percentage of Southerners have high blood pressure than do people in any other region of the United States. This difference in rate of high blood pressure was found in every ethnic group, gender, and age category studied. List at least two possible reasons we cannot conclude that living in the South causes high blood pressure.

**2.9** Does eating broccoli reduce the risk of prostate cancer? According to an observational study from the Fred Hutchinson Cancer Research Center (see CNN.com web site article titled "Broccoli, Not Pizza Sauce, Cuts Cancer Risk, Study Finds," January 5, 2000), men who ate more cruciferous vegetables (broccoli, cauliflower, brussels sprouts, and cabbage) had a lower risk of prostate cancer. This study made separate comparisons for men who ate different levels of vegetables. According to one of the investigators, "at any given level of total vegetable consumption, as the percent of cruciferous vegetables increased, the prostate cancer risk decreased." Based on this study, is it reasonable to conclude that eating cruciferous vegetables causes a reduction in prostate cancer risk? Explain.

**Bold** exercises answered in back ● Data set available online but not required ▼ Video solution available

## 2.2 Sampling

Many studies are conducted in order to generalize from a sample to the corresponding population. As a result, it is important that the sample be representative of the population. To be reasonably sure of this, the researcher must carefully consider the way in which the sample is selected. It is sometimes tempting to take the easy way out and gather data in a haphazard way; but if a sample is chosen on the basis of convenience alone, it becomes impossible to interpret the resulting data with confidence. For example, it might be easy to use the students in your statistics class as a sample of students at your university. However, not all majors include a statistics course in their curriculum, and most students take statistics in their sophomore or junior year. The difficulty is that it is not clear whether or how these factors (and others that we might not be aware of) affect inferences based on information from such a sample.

There is no way to tell just by looking at a sample whether it is representative of the population from which it was drawn. Our only assurance comes from the method used to select the sample.

There are many reasons for selecting a sample rather than obtaining information from an entire population (a **census**). Sometimes the process of measuring the characteristics of interest is destructive, as with measuring the lifetime of flashlight batteries or the sugar content of oranges, and it would be foolish to study the entire population. But the most common reason for selecting a sample is limited resources; restrictions on available time or money usually prohibit observation of an entire population.

## ■ Bias in Sampling

Bias in sampling is the tendency for samples to differ from the corresponding population in some systematic way. Bias can result from the way in which the sample is selected or from the way in which information is obtained once the sample has been chosen. The most common types of bias encountered in sampling situations are selection bias, measurement or response bias, and nonresponse bias.

**Selection bias** (sometimes also called undercoverage) is introduced when the way the sample is selected systematically excludes some part of the population of interest. For example, a researcher may wish to generalize from the results of a study to the population consisting of all residents of a particular city, but the method of selecting individuals may exclude the homeless or those without telephones. If those who are excluded from the sampling process differ in some systematic way from those who are included, the sample is virtually guaranteed to be unrepresentative of the population. If this difference between the included and the excluded occurs on a variable that is important to the study, conclusions based on the sample data may not be valid for the population of interest. Selection bias also occurs if only volunteers or self-selected individuals are used in a study, because self-selected individuals (e.g., those who choose to participate in a call-in telephone poll) may well differ from those who choose not to participate.

**Measurement or response bias** occurs when the method of observation tends to produce values that systematically differ from the true value in some way. This might happen if an improperly calibrated scale is used to weigh items or if questions on a survey are worded in a way that tends to influence the response. For example, a Gallup survey sponsored by the American Paper Institute (*Wall Street Journal*, May 17, 1994) included the following question: "It is estimated that disposable diapers account for less than 2 percent of the trash in today's landfills. In contrast, beverage containers, third-class mail and yard waste are estimated to account for about 21 percent of trash in landfills. Given this, in your opinion, would it be fair to tax or ban disposable diapers?" It is likely that the wording of this question prompted people to respond in a particular way.

Other things that might contribute to response bias are the appearance or behavior of the person asking the question, the group or organization conducting the study, and the tendency for people not to be completely honest when asked about illegal behavior or unpopular beliefs.

Although the terms *measurement bias* and *response bias* are often used interchangeably, the term *measurement bias* is usually used to describe systematic deviation from the true value as a result of a faulty measurement instrument (as with the improperly calibrated scale).

**Nonresponse bias** occurs when responses are not obtained from all individuals selected for inclusion in the sample. As with selection bias, nonresponse bias can distort results if those who respond differ in important ways from those who do not respond. Although some level of nonresponse is unavoidable in most surveys, the biasing effect on the resulting sample is lowest when the response rate is high. To minimize nonresponse bias, it is critical that a serious effort be made to follow up with individuals who do not respond to an initial request for information.

The nonresponse rate for surveys or opinion polls varies dramatically, depending on how the data are collected. Surveys are commonly conducted by mail, by phone, and by personal interview. Mail surveys are inexpensive but often have high nonresponse rates. Telephone surveys can also be inexpensive and can be implemented quickly, but they work well only for short surveys and they can also have high nonresponse rates. Personal interviews are generally expensive but tend to have better response rates. Some of the many challenges of conducting surveys are discussed in Section 2.5.

## Types of Bias

### Selection Bias

Tendency for samples to differ from the corresponding population as a result of systematic exclusion of some part of the population.

### Measurement or Response Bias

Tendency for samples to differ from the corresponding population because the method of observation tends to produce values that differ from the true value.

### Nonresponse Bias

Tendency for samples to differ from the corresponding population because data are not obtained from all individuals selected for inclusion in the sample.

*It is important to note that bias is introduced by the way in which a sample is selected or by the way in which the data are collected from the sample. Increasing the size of the sample, although possibly desirable for other reasons, does nothing to reduce bias if the method of selecting the sample is flawed or if the nonresponse rate remains high.* A good discussion of the types of bias appears in the sampling book by Lohr listed in the references in the back of the book.

## ■ Random Sampling

Most of the inferential methods introduced in this text are based on the idea of random selection. The most straightforward sampling method is called simple random sampling. A **simple random sample** is a sample chosen using a method that ensures that each different possible sample of the desired size has an equal chance of being the one chosen. For example, suppose that we want a simple random sample of 10 employees chosen from all those who work at a large design firm. For the sample to be a simple random sample, each of the many different subsets of 10 employees must be equally likely to be the one selected. A sample taken from only full-time employees would not be a simple random sample of *all* employees, because someone who works part-time has no chance of being selected. Although a simple random sample may, by chance, include only full-time employees, it must be selected in such a way that each possible sample, and therefore *every* employee, has the same chance of inclusion in the sample. *It is the selection process, not the final sample, which determines whether the sample is a simple random sample.*

The letter *n* is used to denote sample size; it is the number of individuals or objects in the sample. For the design firm scenario of the previous paragraph, $n = 10$.

---

**D E F I N I T I O N**

A **simple random sample of size *n*** is a sample that is selected from a population in a way that ensures that every different possible sample of the desired size has the same chance of being selected.

---

The definition of a simple random sample implies that every individual member of the population has an equal chance of being selected. *However, the fact that every individual has an equal chance of selection, by itself, is not enough to guarantee that the sample is a simple random sample.* For example, suppose that a class is made up of 100 students, 60 of whom are female. A researcher decides to select 6 of the female students by writing all 60 names on slips of paper, mixing the slips, and then picking 6. She then selects 4 male students from the class using a similar procedure. Even though every student in the class has an equal chance of being included in the sample (6 of 60 females are selected and 4 of 40 males are chosen), the resulting sample is *not* a simple random sample because not all different possible samples of 10 students from the class have the same chance of selection. Many possible samples of 10 students—for example, a sample of 7 females and 3 males or a sample of all females—have no chance of being selected. The sample selection method described here is not necessarily a bad choice (in fact, it is an example of stratified sampling, to be discussed in more detail shortly), but it does not produce a simple random sample; this must be considered when a method is chosen for analyzing data resulting from such a sampling method.

■ **Selecting a Simple Random Sample**   A number of different methods can be used to select a simple random sample. One way is to put the name or number of each member of the population on different but identical slips of paper. The process of thoroughly mixing the slips and then selecting *n* slips one by one yields a random sample of size *n*. This method is easy to understand, but it has obvious drawbacks. The mixing must be adequate, and producing the necessary slips of paper can be extremely tedious, even for populations of moderate size.

A commonly used method for selecting a random sample is to first create a list, called a **sampling frame**, of the objects or individuals in the population. Each item on the list can then be identified by a number, and a table of random digits or a random number generator can be used to select the sample. A random number generator is a procedure that produces a sequence of numbers that satisfies properties associated with the notion of randomness. Most statistics software packages include a random number generator, as do many calculators. A small table of random digits can be found in Appendix Table 1.

When selecting a random sample, researchers can choose to do the sampling with or without replacement. **Sampling with replacement** means that after each successive item is selected for the sample, the item is "replaced" back into the population and may therefore be selected again at a later stage. In practice, sampling with replacement is rarely used. Instead, the more common method is to not allow the same item to be included in the sample more than once. After being included in the sample, an individual or object would not be considered for further selection. Sampling in this manner is called **sampling without replacement**.

### Sampling without Replacement

Once an individual from the population is selected for inclusion in the sample, it may not be selected again in the sampling process. A sample selected without replacement includes $n$ distinct individuals from the population.

### Sampling with Replacement

After an individual from the population is selected for inclusion in the sample and the corresponding data are recorded, the individual is placed back in the population and can be selected again in the sampling process. A sample selected with replacement might include any particular individual from the population more than once.

**Although these two forms of sampling are different, when the sample size $n$ is small relative to the population size, as is often the case, there is little practical difference between them. In practice, the two can be viewed as equivalent if the sample size is at most 5% of the population size.** (A less conservative approach that allows the sample size to be up to 10% of the population size is used in some texts.)

........................................................................................................................................

# Example 2.1   Selecting a Random Sample of Glass Soda Bottles

Breaking strength is an important characteristic of glass soda bottles. Suppose that we want to measure the breaking strength of each bottle in a random sample of size $n = 3$ selected from four crates containing a total of 100 bottles (the population). Each crate contains five rows of five bottles each. We can identify each bottle with a number from 1 to 100 by numbering across the rows, starting with the top row of crate 1, as pictured:

Using a random number generator from a calculator or statistical software package, we could generate three random numbers between 1 and 100 to determine which bottles would be included in our sample. This might result in bottles 15 (row 3 column 5 of crate 1), 89 (row 3 column 4 of crate 4), and 60 (row 2 column 5 of crate 3) being selected.

The goal of random sampling is to produce a sample that is likely to be representative of the population. Although random sampling does not *guarantee* that the sample will be representative, probability-based methods can be used to assess the risk of an unrepresentative sample. It is the ability to quantify this risk that allows us to generalize with confidence from a random sample to the corresponding population.

!! Step-by-step technology instructions available online

## ■ A Note Concerning Sample Size

It is a common misconception that if the size of a sample is relatively small compared to the population size, the sample can't possibly accurately reflect the population. Critics of polls often make statements such as, "There are 14.6 million registered voters in California. How can a sample of 1000 registered voters possibly reflect public opinion when only about 1 in every 14,000 people is included in the sample?" These critics do not understand the power of random selection!

Consider a population consisting of 5000 applicants to a state university, and suppose that we are interested in math SAT scores for this population. A dotplot of the values in this population is shown in Figure 2.1(a). Figure 2.1(b) shows dotplots of the math SAT scores for individuals in five different random samples from the population, ranging in sample size from $n = 50$ to $n = 1000$. Notice that the samples tend to reflect the distribution of scores in the population. If we were interested in using the sample to estimate the population average or to say something about the variability in SAT scores, even the smallest of the samples ($n = 50$) pictured would provide reliable information. Although it is possible to obtain a simple random sample that does not do a reasonable job of representing the population, this is likely only when the sample size is very small, and unless the population itself is small, this risk does not depend on what fraction of the population is sampled. The random selection process allows us to be confident that

**Figure 2.1** (a) Dotplot of math SAT scores for the entire population. (b) Dotplots of math SAT scores for random samples of sizes 50, 100, 250, 500, and 1000.

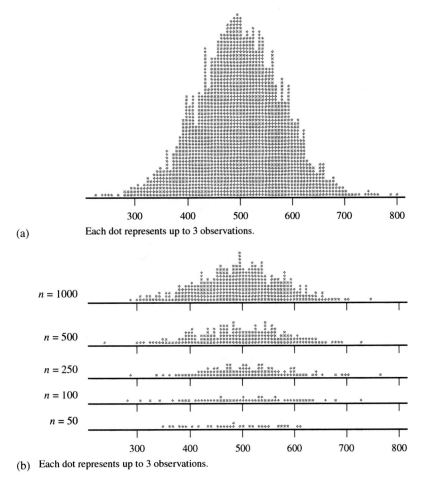

(a)    Each dot represents up to 3 observations.

(b)  Each dot represents up to 3 observations.

the resulting sample adequately reflects the population, even when the sample consists of only a small fraction of the population.

# ■ Other Sampling Methods

Simple random sampling provides researchers with a sampling method that is objective and free of selection bias. In some settings, however, alternative sampling methods may be less costly, easier to implement, or more accurate.

■ **Stratified Random Sampling**    When the entire population can be divided into a set of nonoverlapping subgroups, a method known as **stratified sampling** often proves easier to implement and more cost-effective than simple random sampling. In stratified random sampling, separate simple random samples are independently selected from each subgroup. For example, to estimate the average cost of malpractice insurance, a researcher might find it convenient to view the population of all doctors practicing in a particular metropolitan area as being made up of four subpopulations: (1) surgeons, (2) internists and family practitioners, (3) obstetricians, and (4) a group that includes all other areas of specialization. Rather than taking a random simple sample from the population of all doctors, the researcher could take four separate simple random samples—one from the group of surgeons, another from the internists and family practitioners, and so on. These four samples would provide information about the four subgroups as well as information about the overall population of doctors.

When the population is divided in this way, the subgroups are called **strata** and each individual subgroup is called a stratum (the singular of strata). Stratified sampling entails selecting a separate simple random sample from each stratum. Stratified sampling can be used instead of simple random sampling if it is important to obtain information about characteristics of the individual strata as well as of the entire population, although a stratified sample is not required to do this—subgroup estimates can also be obtained by using an appropriate subset of data from a simple random sample.

The real advantage of stratified sampling is that it often allows us to make more accurate inferences about a population than does simple random sampling. In general, it is much easier to produce relatively accurate estimates of characteristics of a homogeneous group than of a heterogeneous group. For example, even with a small sample, it is possible to obtain an accurate estimate of the average grade point average (GPA) of students graduating with high honors from a university. The individual GPAs of these students are all quite similar (a homogeneous group), and even a sample of three or four individuals from this subpopulation should be representative. On the other hand, producing a reasonably accurate estimate of the average GPA of *all* seniors at the university, a much more diverse group of GPAs, is a more difficult task. Thus, if a varied population can be divided into strata, with each stratum being much more homogeneous than the population with respect to the characteristic of interest, then a stratified random sample can produce more accurate estimates of population characteristics than a simple random sample of the same size.

■ **Cluster Sampling**    Sometimes it is easier to select groups of individuals from a population than it is to select individuals themselves. **Cluster sampling** involves dividing the population of interest into nonoverlapping subgroups, called **clusters**. Clusters are then selected at random, and all individuals in the selected clusters are included in the sample. For example, suppose that a large urban high school has 600 senior students, all of whom are enrolled in a first period homeroom. There are 24 senior homerooms, each with approximately 25 students. If school administrators wanted to select a sample of roughly 75 seniors to participate in an evaluation of the college and career placement advising available to students, they might find it much easier to select three of the senior homerooms at random and then include all the students in the selected homerooms in the sample. In this way, an evaluation survey could be administered to all students in the selected homerooms at the same time—certainly easier logistically than randomly selecting 75 students and then administering the survey to the individual seniors.

Because whole clusters are selected, the ideal situation occurs when each cluster mirrors the characteristics of the population. When this is the case, a small number of clusters results in a sample that is representative of the population. If it is not reasonable to think that the variability present in the population is reflected in each cluster, as is often the case when the cluster sizes are small, then it becomes important to ensure that a large number of clusters are included in the sample.

Be careful not to confuse clustering and stratification. Even though both of these sampling strategies involve dividing the population into subgroups, both the way in which the subgroups are sampled and the optimal strategy for creating the subgroups are different. In stratified sampling, we sample from every stratum, whereas in cluster sampling, we include only selected whole clusters in the sample. Because of this difference, to increase the chance of obtaining a sample that is representative of the population, we want to create homogeneous (similar) groups for strata and heterogeneous (reflecting the variability in the population) groups for clusters.

■ **Systematic Sampling**  **Systematic sampling** is a procedure that can be used when it is possible to view the population of interest as consisting of a list or some other sequential arrangement. A value $k$ is specified (e.g., $k = 50$ or $k = 200$). Then one of the first $k$ individuals is selected at random, after which every $k$th individual in the sequence is included in the sample. A sample selected in this way is called a **1 in $k$ systematic sample**.

For example, a sample of faculty members at a university might be selected from the faculty phone directory. One of the first $k = 20$ faculty members listed could be selected at random, and then every 20th faculty member after that on the list would also be included in the sample. This would result in a 1 in 20 systematic sample.

The value of $k$ for a 1 in $k$ systematic sample is generally chosen to achieve a desired sample size. For example, in the faculty directory scenario just described, if there were 900 faculty members at the university, the 1 in 20 systematic sample described would result in a sample size of 45. If a sample size of 100 was desired, a 1 in 9 systematic sample could be used.

As long as there are no repeating patterns in the population list, systematic sampling works reasonably well. However, if there are such patterns, systematic sampling can result in an unrepresentative sample.

■ **Convenience Sampling: Don't Go There!**  It is often tempting to resort to "convenience" sampling—that is, using an easily available or convenient group to form a sample. This is a recipe for disaster! Results from such samples are rarely informative, and it is a mistake to try to generalize from a convenience sample to any larger population.

One common form of convenience sampling is sometimes called **voluntary response sampling**. Such samples rely entirely on individuals who volunteer to be a part of the sample, often by responding to an advertisement, calling a publicized telephone number to register an opinion, or logging on to an Internet site to complete a survey. It is extremely unlikely that individuals participating in such voluntary response surveys are representative of any larger population of interest.

## ■ Exercises 2.10–2.30 ..............................................................................

**2.10** As part of a curriculum review, the psychology department would like to select a simple random sample of 20 of last year's 140 graduates to obtain information on how graduates perceived the value of the curriculum. Describe two different methods that might be used to select the sample.

**2.11** A petition with 500 signatures is submitted to a university's student council. The council president would like to determine the proportion of those who signed the petition who are actually registered students at the university. There is not enough time to check all 500 names with the registrar, so the council president decides to select a simple random sample of 30 signatures. Describe how this might be done.

**2.12** During the previous calendar year, a county's small claims court processed 870 cases. Describe how a simple random sample of size $n = 50$ might be selected from the case files to obtain information regarding the average award in such cases.

**2.13** The financial aid officers of a university wish to estimate the average amount of money that students spend on textbooks each term. For each of the following proposed stratification schemes, discuss whether it would be worthwhile to stratify the university students in this manner.
**a.** Strata corresponding to class standing (freshman, sophomore, junior, senior, graduate student)
**b.** Strata corresponding to field of study, using the following categories: engineering, architecture, business, other
**c.** Strata corresponding to the first letter of the last name: A–E, F–K, etc.

**2.14** Suppose that a group of 1000 orange trees is laid out in 40 rows of 25 trees each. To determine the sugar content of fruit from a sample of 30 trees, researcher A suggests randomly selecting five rows and then randomly selecting six trees from each sampled row. Researcher B suggests numbering each tree on a map of the trees from 1 to 1000 and using random numbers to select 30 of the trees. Which selection method is preferred? Explain.

**2.15** ▼ For each of the situations described, state whether the sampling procedure is simple random sampling, stratified random sampling, cluster sampling, systematic sampling, or convenience sampling.
**a.** All freshmen at a university are enrolled in 1 of 30 sections of a seminar course. To select a sample of freshmen at this university, a researcher selects 4 sections of the seminar course at random from the 30 sections and all students in the 4 selected sections are included in the sample.
**b.** To obtain a sample of students, faculty, and staff at a university, a researcher randomly selects 50 faculty members from a list of faculty, 100 students from a list of students, and 30 staff members from a list of staff.
**c.** A university researcher obtains a sample of students at his university by using the 85 students enrolled in his Psychology 101 class.
**d.** To obtain a sample of the seniors at a particular high school, a researcher writes the name of each senior on a slip of paper, places the slips in a box and mixes them, and then selects 10 slips. The students whose names are on the selected slips of paper are included in the sample.
**e.** To obtain a sample of those attending a basketball game, a researcher selects the 24th person through the door. Then, every 50th person after that is also included in the sample.

**2.16** Of the 6500 students enrolled at a community college, 3000 are part time and the other 3500 are full time. The college can provide a list of students that is sorted so that all full-time students are listed first, followed by the part-time students.
a. Select a stratified random sample that uses full-time and part-time students as the two strata and that includes 10 students from each stratum. Describe the procedure you used to select the sample, and identify the students included in your sample by placement on the sorted list.
b. Does every student at this community college have the same chance of being selected for inclusion in the sample? Explain.

**2.17** Briefly explain why it is advisable to avoid the use of convenience samples.

**2.18** Sometimes samples are composed entirely of volunteer responders. Give a brief description of the dangers of using voluntary response samples.

**2.19** A sample of pages from this book is to be obtained, and the number of words on each selected page will be determined. For the purposes of this exercise, equations are not counted as words and a number is counted as a word only if it is spelled out—that is, *ten* is counted as a word, but *10* is not.

**a.** Describe a sampling procedure that would result in a simple random sample of pages from this book.

**b.** Describe a sampling procedure that would result in a stratified random sample. Explain why you chose the specific strata used in your sampling plan.

**c.** Describe a sampling procedure that would result in a systematic sample.

**d.** Describe a sampling procedure that would result in a cluster sample.

e. Using the process you gave in Part (a), select a simple random sample of at least 20 pages, and record the number of words on each of the selected pages. Construct a dotplot of the resulting sample values, and write a sentence or two commenting on what it reveals about the number of words on a page.

f. Using the process you gave in Part (b), select a stratified random sample that includes a total of at least 20 selected pages, and record the number of words on each of the selected pages. Construct a dotplot of the resulting sample values, and write a sentence or two commenting on what it reveals about the number of words on a page.

2.20 In 2000, the chairman of a California ballot initiative campaign to add "none of the above" to the list of ballot options in all candidate races was quite critical of a Field poll that showed his measure trailing by 10 percentage points. The poll was based on a random sample of 1000 registered voters in California. He is quoted by the Associated Press (January 30, 2000) as saying, "Field's sample in that poll equates to one out of 17,505 voters," and he added that this was so dishonest that Field should get out of the polling business! If you worked on the Field poll, how would you respond to this criticism?

**2.21** A pollster for the Public Policy Institute of California explains how the Institute selects a sample of California adults ("It's About Quality, Not Quantity," *San Luis Obispo Tribune*, January 21, 2000):

> That is done by using computer-generated random residential telephone numbers with all California prefixes, and when there are no answers, calling back repeatedly to the original numbers selected to avoid a bias against hard-to-reach people. Once a call is completed, a second random selection is made by asking for the adult in the household who had the most recent birthday. It is as important to randomize who you speak to in the household as it is to randomize the household you select. If you didn't, you'd primarily get women and older people.

Comment on this approach to selecting a sample. How does the sampling procedure attempt to minimize certain types of bias? Are there sources of bias that may still be a concern?

2.22 The report "Undergraduate Students and Credit Cards in 2004: An Analysis of Usage Rates and Trends" (Nellie Mae, May 2005) estimated that 21% of undergraduates with credit cards pay them off each month and that the average outstanding balance on undergraduates' credit cards is $2169. These estimates were based on an online survey that was sent to 1260 students. Responses were received from 132 of these students. Is it reasonable to generalize the reported estimates to the population of all undergraduate students? Address at least two possible sources of bias in your answer.

**2.23** A newspaper headline stated that at a recent budget workshop, nearly three dozen people supported a sales tax increase to help deal with the city's financial deficit (*San Luis Obispo Tribune*, January 22, 2005). This conclusion was based on data from a survey acknowledged to be unscientific, in which 34 out of the 43 people who chose to attend the budget workshop recommended raising the sales tax. Briefly discuss why the survey was described as "unscientific" and how this might limit the conclusions that can be drawn from the survey data.

2.24 Suppose that you were asked to help design a survey of adult city residents in order to estimate the proportion that would support a sales tax increase. The plan is to use a stratified random sample, and three stratification schemes have been proposed.

Scheme 1: Stratify adult residents into four strata based on the first letter of their last name (A–G, H–N, O–T, U–Z)

Scheme 2: Stratify adult residents into three strata: college students, nonstudents who work full time, nonstudents who do not work full time.

Scheme 3: Stratify adult residents into five strata by randomly assigning residents into one of the five strata.

Which of the three stratification schemes would be best in this situation? Explain.

**2.25** The article "High Levels of Mercury Are Found in Californians" (*Los Angeles Times*, February 9, 2006) describes a study in which hair samples were tested for mercury. The hair samples were obtained from more than 6000 people who voluntarily sent hair samples to researchers at Greenpeace and The Sierra Club. The researchers found that nearly one-third of those tested had mercury levels that exceeded the concentration thought to be safe. Is it reasonable to generalize these results to the larger population of U.S. adults? Explain why or why not.

2.26 "More than half of California's doctors say they are so frustrated with managed care they will quit, retire early, or leave the state within three years." This conclusion from an article titled "Doctors Feeling Pessimistic, Study Finds" (*San Luis Obispo Tribune*, July 15, 2001) was based on a mail survey conducted by the California Medical Association. Surveys were mailed to 19,000 California doctors, and 2000 completed surveys were returned. Describe any concerns you have regarding the conclusion drawn.

2.27 ▼ Whether or not to continue a Mardi Gras Parade through downtown San Luis Obispo, CA, is a hotly debated topic. The parade is popular with students and many residents, but some celebrations have led to complaints and a call to eliminate the parade. The local newspaper conducted online and telephone surveys of its readers and was surprised by the results. The survey web site received more than 400 responses, with more than 60% favoring continuing the parade, while the telephone response line received more than 120 calls, with more than 90% favoring banning the parade (*San Luis Obispo Tribune*, March 3, 2004). What factors may have contributed to these very different results?

2.28 Based on a survey of 4113 U.S. adults, researchers at Stanford University concluded that Internet use leads to increased social isolation. The survey was conducted by an Internet-based polling company that selected its samples from a pool of 35,000 potential respondents, all of whom had been given free Internet access and WebTV hardware in exchange for agreeing to regularly participate in surveys conducted by the polling company. Two criticisms of this study were expressed in an article that appeared in the *San Luis Obispo Tribune* (February 28, 2000). The first criticism was that increased social isolation was measured by asking respondents if they were talking less to family and friends on the phone. The second criticism was that the sample was selected only from a group that was induced to participate by the offer of free Internet service, yet the results were generalized to all U.S. adults. For each criticism, indicate what type of bias is being described and why it might make you question the conclusion drawn by the researchers.

2.29 The article "I'd Like to Buy a Vowel, Drivers Say" (*USA Today*, August 7, 2001) speculates that young people prefer automobile names that consist of just numbers and/or letters that do not form a word (such as Hyundai's XG300, Mazda's 626, and BMW's 325i). The article goes on to state that Hyundai had planned to identify the car now marketed as the XG300 with the name Concerto, until they determined that consumers hated it and that they thought XG300 sounded more "technical" and deserving of a higher price. Do the students at your school feel the same way? Describe how you would go about selecting a sample to answer this question.

2.30 The article "Gene's Role in Cancer May Be Overstated" (*San Luis Obispo Tribune*, August 21, 2002) states that "early studies that evaluated breast cancer risk among gene mutation carriers selected women in families where sisters, mothers, and grandmothers all had breast cancer. This created a statistical bias that skewed risk estimates for women in the general population." Is the bias described here selection bias, measurement bias, or nonresponse bias? Explain.

**Bold** exercises answered in back     ● Data set available online but not required     ▼ Video solution available

## 2.3    Simple Comparative Experiments

Sometimes the questions we are trying to answer deal with the effect of certain explanatory variables on some response. Such questions are often of the form, What happens when . . . ? or What is the effect of . . . ? For example, an industrial engineer may be considering two different workstation designs and might want to know whether the choice of design affects work performance. A medical researcher may want to determine how a proposed treatment for a disease compares to a standard treatment.

To address these types of questions, the researcher conducts an experiment to collect the relevant information. Experiments must be carefully planned to obtain information that will give unambiguous answers to questions of interest.

> **DEFINITION**
>
> An **experiment** is a planned intervention undertaken to observe the effects of one or more explanatory variables, often called **factors**, on a response variable. The fundamental purpose of the intervention is to increase understanding of the nature of the relationships between the explanatory and response variables. Any particular combination of values for the explanatory variables is called an **experimental condition** or **treatment**.
>
> The **design** of an experiment is the overall plan for conducting an experiment.

Suppose that we are interested in determining how student performance on a first-semester calculus exam is affected by room temperature. There are four sections of calculus being offered in the fall semester. We might design an experiment in this way: Set the room temperature (in degrees Fahrenheit) to 65° in two of the rooms and to 75° in the other two rooms on test day, and then compare the exam scores for the 65° group and the 75° group. Suppose that the average exam score for the students in the 65° group was noticeably higher than the average for the 75° group. Could we conclude that the increased temperature resulted in a lower average score? Based on the information given, the answer is no because many other factors might be related to exam score. Were the sections at different times of the day? Did they have the same instructor? Different textbooks? Did the sections differ with respect to the abilities of the students? Any of these other factors could provide a plausible explanation (having nothing to do with room temperature) for why the average test score was different for the two groups. It is not possible to separate the effect of temperature from the effects of these other factors. As a consequence, simply setting the room temperatures as described makes for a poorly designed experiment. *A well-designed experiment requires more than just manipulating the explanatory variables; the design must also eliminate rival explanations or the experimental results will not be conclusive.*

The goal is to design an experiment that will allow us to determine the effects of the relevant factors on the chosen response variable. To do this, we must take into consideration other extraneous factors that, although not of interest in the current study, might also affect the response variable.

> **DEFINITION**
>
> An **extraneous factor** is one that is not of interest in the current study but is thought to affect the response variable.

A well-designed experiment copes with the potential effects of extraneous factors by using random assignment to experimental conditions and sometimes also by incorporating direct control and/or blocking into the design of the experiment. Each of these strategies—random assignment, direct control, and blocking—is described in the paragraphs that follow.

A researcher can **directly control** some extraneous factors. In the calculus test example, the textbook used is an extraneous factor because part of the differences in test results might be attributed to this factor. We could control this factor directly, by requiring that all sections use the same textbook. Then any observed differences between temperature groups could not be explained by the use of different textbooks. The extraneous factor *time of day* might also be directly controlled in this way by having all sections meet at the same time.

The effects of some extraneous factors can be filtered out by a process known as **blocking**. Extraneous factors that are addressed through blocking are called *blocking factors*. Blocking creates groups (called blocks) that are similar with respect to blocking factors; then all treatments are tried in each block. In our example, we might use *instructor* as a blocking factor. If two instructors are each teaching two sections of calculus, we would make sure that for each instructor, one section was part of the 65° group and the other section was part of the 75° group. With this design, if we see a difference in exam scores for the two temperature groups, the factor *instructor* can be ruled out as a possible explanation, because both instructors' students were present in each temperature group. (Had we controlled the instructor variable by choosing to have only one instructor, that would be an example of direct control.) If one instructor taught both 65° sections and the other taught both 75° sections, we would be unable to distinguish the effect of temperature from the effect of the instructor. In this situation, the two factors (temperature and instructor) are said to be **confounded**.

Two factors are **confounded** if their effects on the response variable cannot be distinguished from one another.

If an extraneous factor is confounded with the factors defining the treatments (experimental conditions), it is not possible to draw an unambiguous conclusion about the effect of the treatment on the response. Both direct control and blocking are effective in ensuring that the controlled factors and blocking factors are not confounded with the factors that define the treatments.

We can directly control some extraneous factors by holding them constant, and we can use blocking to create groups that are similar to essentially filter out the effect of others. But what about factors, such as student ability in our calculus test example, which cannot be controlled by the experimenter and which would be difficult to use as blocking factors? These extraneous factors are handled by the use of random assignment to experimental groups—a process called **randomization**. Randomization ensures that our experiment does not systematically favor one experimental condition over any other and attempts to create experimental groups that are as much alike as possible. For example, if the students requesting calculus could be assigned to one of the four available sections using a random mechanism, we would expect the resulting groups to be similar with respect to student ability as well as with respect to other extraneous factors that we are not directly controlling or using as a basis for blocking. Note that randomization in an experiment is different from random selection of subjects. The ideal situation would be to have both random selection of subjects and random assignment of subjects to experimental conditions as this would allow conclusions from the experiment to be generalized to a larger population. For many experiments the random selection of subjects is not possible. As long as subjects are assigned at random to experimental conditions it is still possible to assess treatment effects.

To get a sense of how random assignment tends to create similar groups, suppose that 50 college freshmen are available to participate as subjects in an experiment to investigate whether completing an online review of course material before an exam improves exam performance. The 50 subjects vary quite a bit with respect to achievement, which is reflected in their math and verbal SAT scores, as shown in Figure 2.2.

**Figure 2.2** Dotplots of math and verbal SAT scores for 50 freshmen.

If these 50 students are to be assigned to the two experimental groups (one that will complete the online review and one that will not), we want to make sure that the assignment of students to groups does not favor one group over the other by tending to assign the higher achieving students to one group and the lower achieving students to the other.

Creating groups of students with similar achievement levels in a way that considers both verbal and math SAT scores simultaneously would be difficult, so we rely on random assignment. Figure 2.3(a) shows the math SAT scores of the students assigned to each of the two experimental groups (one shown in orange and one shown in blue) for each of three different random assignments of students to groups. Figure 2.3(b) shows the verbal SAT scores for the two experimental groups for each of the same three random assignments. Notice that each of the three random assignments produced groups that are similar with respect to *both* verbal and math SAT scores. So, if any of these three assignments were used and the two groups differed on exam performance, we could rule out differences in math or verbal SAT scores as possible competing explanations for the difference.

**Figure 2.3** Dotplots for three different random assignments to two groups, one shown in orange and one shown in blue: (a) math SAT score; (b) verbal SAT score.

Not only will random assignment tend to create groups that are similar with respect to verbal and math SAT scores, but it will also tend to even out the groups with respect to other extraneous variables. *As long as the number of subjects is not too small, we can rely on the random assignment to produce comparable experimental groups. This is the reason that randomization is a part of all well-designed experiments.*

Not all experiments require the use of human subjects. For example, a researcher interested in comparing three different gasoline additives with respect to gasoline mileage might conduct an experiment using a single car with an empty tank. One gallon of gas with one of the additives will be put in the tank, and the car will be driven along a standard route at a constant speed until it runs out of gas. The total distance traveled on the gallon of gas could then be recorded. This could be repeated a number of times—10, for example—with each additive.

The experiment just described can be viewed as consisting of a sequence of trials. Because a number of extraneous factors (such as variations in environmental conditions like wind speed or humidity and small variations in the condition of the car) might have an effect on gas mileage, it would not be a good idea to use additive 1 for the first 10 trials, additive 2 for the next 10 trials, and so on. A better approach would be to randomly assign additive 1 to 10 of the 30 planned trials, and then randomly assign additive 2 to 10 of the remaining 20 trials. The resulting plan for carrying out the experiment might look as follows:

| Trial | 1 | 2 | 3 | 4 | 5 | 6 | 7 | . . . | 30 |
|---|---|---|---|---|---|---|---|---|---|
| **Additive** | 2 | 2 | 3 | 3 | 2 | 1 | 2 | . . . | 1 |

When an experiment can be viewed as a sequence of trials, randomization involves the random assignment of treatments to trials. *Remember that random assignment— either of subjects to treatments or of treatments to trials—is a critical component of a good experiment.* Randomization can be effective only if the number of subjects or observations in each treatment or experimental condition is large enough for each experimental group to reliably reflect variability in the population. For example, if there were only eight students requesting calculus, it is unlikely that we would get equivalent groups for comparison, even with random assignment to the four sections.

**Replication** is the design strategy of making multiple observations for each experimental condition. Together, replication and randomization allow the researcher to be reasonably confident of comparable experimental groups.

## Key Concepts in Experimental Design

### Randomization

Random assignment (of subjects to treatments or of treatments to trials) to ensure that the experiment does not systematically favor one experimental condition (treatment) over another.

### Blocking

Using extraneous factors to create groups (blocks) that are similar. All experimental conditions (treatments) are then tried in each block.

### Direct Control

Holding extraneous factors constant so that their effects are not confounded with those of the experimental conditions (treatments).

### Replication

Ensuring that there is an adequate number of observations for each experimental condition.

To illustrate the design of a simple experiment, consider the dilemma of Anna, a waitress in a local restaurant. She would like to increase the amount of her tips, and her strategy is simple: She will write "Thank you" on the back of some of the checks before giving them to the patrons and on others she will write nothing. She plans to calculate the percentage of the tip as her measure of success (for instance, a 15% tip is common). She will compare the average percentage of the tip calculated from checks with and without the handwritten "Thank you." If writing "Thank you" does not produce higher tips, she may try a different strategy.

Anna is untrained in the art of planning experiments, but already she has taken some commonsense steps in the right direction to answer her question—Will writing "Thank you" produce the desired outcome of higher tips? Anna has defined a manageable problem, and collecting the appropriate data is feasible. It should be easy to gather data as a normal part of her work. Anna wonders whether writing "Thank you" on the customers' bills will have an effect on the amount of her tip. In the language of experimentation, we would refer to the writing of "Thank you" and the not writing of "Thank you" as **treatments** (the two experimental conditions to be compared in the experiment). The two treatments together are the possible values of the **explanatory variable**. The tipping percentage is the **response variable**. The idea behind this terminology is that the outcome of the experiment (the tipping percentage) is a *response* to the treatments *writing "Thank you"* or *not writing "Thank you."* Anna's experiment may be thought of as an attempt to explain the variability in the response variable in terms of its presumed cause, the variability in the explanatory variable. That is, as she manipulates the explanatory variable, she expects the response by her customers to vary. Anna has a good start, but now she must consider the four fundamental design principles.

**Replication**. Anna cannot run a successful experiment by gathering tipping information on only one person for each treatment. There is no reason to believe that any single tipping incident is representative of what would happen in other incidents, and therefore it would be impossible to evaluate the two treatments with only two subjects. To interpret the effects of a particular treatment, she must **replicate** each treatment in the experiment.

**Direct Control and Randomization**. There are a number of extraneous variables that might have an effect on the size of tip. Some restaurant patrons will be seated near the window with a nice view; some will have to wait for a table, whereas others may be seated immediately; and some may be on a fixed income and cannot afford a large tip. Some of these variables can be directly controlled. For example, Anna may choose to use only window tables in her experiment, thus eliminating table location as a potential confounding variable. Other variables, such as length of wait and customer income, cannot be easily controlled. As a result, it is important that Anna use randomization to decide which of the window tables will be in the "Thank you" group and which will be in the no "Thank you" group. She might do this by flipping a coin as she prepares the check for each window table. If the coin lands with the head side up, she could write "Thank you" on the bill, omitting the "Thank you" when a tail is observed.

**Blocking**. Suppose that Anna works on both Thursdays and Fridays. Because day of the week might affect tipping behavior, Anna should block one day of the week and make sure that observations for both treatments are made on each of the two days.

## ■ Evaluating an Experimental Design

The key concepts of experimental design provide a framework for evaluating an experimental design, as illustrated in the following examples.

## Example 2.2   Revenge Is Sweet

The article "The Neural Basis of Altruistic Punishment" (*Science*, August 27, 2004) described a study that examined motivation for revenge. Subjects in the study were all healthy, right-handed men. Subjects played a game with another player in which they could both earn money by trusting each other or one player could double-cross the other player and keep all of the money. In some cases the double cross was required by the rules of the game in certain circumstances, while in other cases the double cross was the result of a deliberate choice. The victim of a double cross was then given the opportunity to retaliate by imposing a fine, but sometimes the victim had to spend some of his own money in order to impose the fine. This study was an experiment with four experimental conditions or treatments:

1. double cross not deliberate (double cross dictated by the rules of the game) and no cost to the victim to retaliate
2. double cross deliberate and no cost to the victim to retaliate
3. double cross not deliberate and a cost to the victim to retaliate
4. double cross deliberate and a cost to the victim to retaliate

All subjects chose revenge (imposed a fine on the double-crosser) when the double cross was deliberate and retaliation was free, and 86% of the subjects chose revenge when the double cross was deliberate, even if it cost them money. Only 21% imposed a fine if the double cross was dictated by the rules of the game and was not deliberate.

Assuming that the researchers randomly assigned the subjects to the four experimental conditions, this study is an experiment that incorporated randomization, direct control (controlled sex, health, and handedness by using only healthy, right-handed males as subjects), and replication (many subjects assigned to each experimental condition).

■

## Example 2.3   Subliminal Messages

The article "The Most Powerful Manipulative Messages Are Hiding in Plain Sight" (*Chronicle of Higher Education*, January 29, 1999) reported the results of an interesting experiment on priming—the effect of subliminal messages on how we behave. In the experiment, subjects completed a language test in which they were asked to construct a sentence using each word in a list of words. One group of subjects received a list of words related to politeness, and a second group was given a list of words related to rudeness. Subjects were told to complete the language test and then come into the hall and find the researcher so that he could explain the next part of the test. When each subject came into the hall, he or she found the researcher engaged in conversation. The researcher wanted to see whether the subject would interrupt the conversation. The researcher found that 63% of those primed with words related to rudeness interrupted the conversation, whereas only 17% of those primed with words related to politeness interrupted.

If we assume that the researcher randomly assigned the subjects to the two groups, then this study is an experiment that compares two treatments (primed with words related to rudeness and primed with words related to politeness). The response variable, *politeness*, has the values *interrupted conversation* and *did not interrupt conversation*. The experiment uses replication (many subjects in each treatment group) and randomization to control for extraneous variables that might affect the response.

■

Many experiments compare a group that receives a particular treatment to a **control group** that receives no treatment.

..................................................................................

# Example 2.4    Chilling Newborns? Then You Need a Control Group . . .

Researchers for the National Institute of Child Health and Human Development studied 208 infants whose brains were temporarily deprived of oxygen as a result of complications at birth (*The New England Journal of Medicine*, October 13, 2005). These babies were subjects in an experiment to determine if reducing body temperature for three days after birth improved their chances of surviving without brain damage. The experiment was summarized in a paper that stated "infants were randomly assigned to usual care (control group) or whole-body cooling." Including a control group in the experiment provided a basis for comparison of death and disability rates for the proposed cooling treatment and those for usual care. Some extraneous factors that might also affect death and disability rates, such as the duration of oxygen deprivation, could not be directly controlled, so to ensure that the experiment didn't unintentionally favor one experimental condition over the other, random assignment of the infants to the two groups was critical. Because this was a well-designed experiment, the researchers were able to use the resulting data and statistical methods that you will see in Chapter 11 to conclude that cooling did reduce the risk of death and disability for infants deprived of oxygen at birth.

■

Before proceeding with an experiment, you should be able to give a satisfactory answer to each of the following 10 questions.

1. What is the research question that data from the experiment will be used to answer?
2. What is the response variable?
3. How will the values of the response variable be determined?
4. What are the factors (explanatory variables) for the experiment?
5. For each factor, how many different values are there, and what are these values?
6. What are the treatments for the experiment?
7. What extraneous variables might influence the response?
8. How does the design incorporate random assignment of subjects to treatments (or treatments to subjects) or random assignment of treatments to trials?
9. For each extraneous variable listed in Question 7, how does the design protect against its potential influence on the response through blocking, direct control, or randomization?
10. Will you be able to answer the research question using the data collected in this experiment?

■ Exercises 2.31–2.39 ...........................................................

**2.31** ▼ Based on observing more than 400 drivers in the Atlanta area, two investigators at Georgia State University concluded that people exiting parking spaces did so more slowly when a driver in another car was waiting for the space than when no one was waiting ("Territorial Defense in Parking Lots: Retaliation Against Waiting Drivers," *Journal of Applied Social Psychology* [1997]:

821–834). Describe how you might design an experiment to determine whether this phenomenon is true for your city. What is the response variable? What are some extraneous factors and how does your design control for them?

**2.32** The head of the quality control department at a printing company would like to carry out an experiment to

**Bold** exercises answered in back    ● Data set available online but not required    ▼ Video solution available

determine which of three different glues results in the greatest binding strength. Although they are not of interest in the current investigation, other factors thought to affect binding strength are the number of pages in the book and whether the book is being bound as a paperback or a hardback.

a. What is the response variable in this experiment?

b. What factor will determine the experimental conditions?

c. What two extraneous factors are mentioned in the problem description? Are there other extraneous factors that should be considered?

**2.33** A 1993 study showed that college students temporarily gained up to 9 IQ points after listening to a Mozart piano sonata. This conclusion, dubbed the Mozart effect, has since been criticized by a number of researchers who have been unable to confirm the result in similar studies. Suppose that you wanted to see whether there is a Mozart effect for students at your school.

a. Describe how you might design an experiment for this purpose.

b. Does your experimental design include direct control of any extraneous variables? Explain.

c. Does your experimental design use blocking? Explain why you did or did not include blocking in your design.

d. What role does randomization play in your design?

2.34 The following is from an article titled "After the Workout, Got Chocolate Milk?" that appeared in the *Chicago Tribune* (January 18, 2005):

> Researchers at Indiana University at Bloomington have found that chocolate milk effectively helps athletes recover from an intense workout. They had nine cyclists bike, rest four hours, then bike again, three separate times. After each workout, the cyclists downed chocolate milk or energy drinks Gatorade or Endurox (two to three glasses per hour); then, in the second workout of each set, they cycled to exhaustion. When they drank chocolate milk, the amount of time they could cycle until they were exhausted was similar to when they drank Gatorade and longer than when they drank Endurox.

The article isn't explicit about this, but in order for this to have been a well-designed experiment, it must have incorporated randomization. Briefly explain where the researcher would have needed to randomize in order for the conclusion of the experiment to be valid.

**2.35** The report "Comparative Study of Two Computer Mouse Designs" (Cornell Human Factors Laboratory Technical Report RP7992) included the following description of the subjects used in an experiment:

> Twenty-four Cornell University students and staff (12 males and 12 females) volunteered to participate in the study. Three groups of 4 men and 4 women were selected by their stature to represent the 5th percentile (female 152.1 ± 0.3 cm, male 164.1 ± 0.4 cm), 50th percentile (female 162.4 ± 0.1 cm, male 174.1 ± 0.7 cm), and 95th percentile (female 171.9 ± 0.2 cm, male 185.7 ± 0.6 cm) ranges . . . All subjects reported using their right hand to operate a computer mouse.

This experimental design incorporated direct control and blocking.

a. Are the potential effects of the extraneous variable stature (height) addressed by blocking or direct control?

b. Whether the right or left hand is used to operate the mouse was considered to be an extraneous variable. Are the potential effects of this variable addressed by blocking or direct control?

2.36 The Institute of Psychiatry at Kings College London found that dealing with "infomania" has a temporary, but significant derogatory effect on IQ. (*Discover*, November 2005). In this experiment, researchers divided volunteers into two groups. Each subject took an IQ test. One group had to check email and respond to instant messages while taking the test while the second group took the test without any distraction. The distracted group had an average score that was 10 points lower than the average for the control group. Explain why it is important that the researchers created the two experimental groups in this study by using random assignment.

**2.37** An article from the Associated Press (May 14, 2002) led with the headline "Academic Success Lowers Pregnancy Risk." The article described an evaluation of a program that involved about 350 students at 18 Seattle schools in high crime areas. Some students took part in a program beginning in elementary school in which teachers showed children how to control their impulses, recognize the feelings of others, and get what they want without aggressive behavior. Others did not participate in the program. The study concluded that the program was effective because by the time young women in the program reached age 21, the pregnancy rate among them was 38%, compared to 56% for the women in the experiment who did not take part in the program. Explain why this conclusion is valid only if the women in the experiment were randomly assigned to one of the two experimental groups.

2.38 A study in Florida is examining whether health literacy classes and using simple medical instructions that include pictures and avoid big words and technical terms can keep Medicaid patients healthier (*San Luis Obispo Tribune*, October 16, 2002). Twenty-seven community health centers are participating in the study. For 2 years, half of the centers will administer standard care. The other centers will have patients attend classes and will provide special health materials that are easy to understand. Explain why it is important for the researchers to assign the 27 centers to the two groups (standard care and classes with simple health literature) at random.

2.39 Is status related to a student's understanding of science? The article "From Here to Equity: The Influence of Status on Student Access to and Understanding of Science" (*Culture and Comparative Studies* [1999]: 577–602) described a study on the effect of group discussions on learning biology concepts. An analysis of the relationship between status and "rate of talk" (the number of on-task speech acts per minute) during group work included gender as a blocking variable. Do you think that gender is a useful blocking variable? Explain.

**Bold** exercises answered in back    ● Data set available online but not required    ▼ Video solution available

## 2.4 More on Experimental Design

The previous section covered basic principles for designing simple comparative experiments—control, blocking, randomization, and replication. The goal of an experimental design is to provide a method of data collection that (1) minimizes extraneous sources of variability in the response so that any differences in response for various experimental conditions can be more easily assessed and (2) creates experimental groups that are similar with respect to extraneous variables that cannot be controlled either directly or through blocking.

In this section, we look at some additional considerations that you may need to think about when planning an experiment.

### ■ Use of a Control Group

If the purpose of an experiment is to determine whether some treatment has an effect, it is important to include an experimental group that does not receive the treatment. Such a group is called a **control group**. The use of a control group allows the experimenter to assess how the response variable behaves when the treatment is not used. This provides a baseline against which the treatment groups can be compared to determine whether the treatment had an effect.

## Example 2.5   Comparing Gasoline Additives

© Royalty Free/Getty Images

Suppose that an engineer wants to know whether a gasoline additive increases fuel efficiency (miles per gallon). Such an experiment might use a single car (to eliminate car-to-car variability) and a sequence of trials in which 1 gallon of gas is put in an empty tank, the car is driven around a racetrack at a constant speed, and the distance traveled on the gallon of gas is recorded.

To determine whether the additive increases gas mileage, it would be necessary to include a control group of trials where distance traveled was measured when gasoline without the additive was used. The trials would be assigned *at random* to one of the two experimental conditions (additive or no additive).

Even though this experiment consists of a sequence of trials all with the same car, random assignment of trials to experimental conditions is still important because there will always be uncontrolled variability. For example, temperature or other environmental conditions might change over the sequence of trials, the physical condition of the car might change slightly from one trial to another, and so on. Random assignment of experimental conditions to trials will tend to even out the effects of these uncontrollable factors.

■

Although we usually think of a control group as one that receives no treatment, in experiments designed to compare a new treatment to an existing standard treatment, the term *control group* is sometimes also used to describe the group that receives the current standard treatment.

Not all experiments require the use of a control group. For example, many experiments are designed to compare two or more conditions—an experiment to compare density for three different formulations of bar soap or an experiment to determine how oven temperature affects the cooking time of a particular type of cake. However, sometimes a control group is included even when the ultimate goal is to compare two or more different treatments. An experiment with two treatments and no control group might allow us to determine whether there is a difference between the two treatments and even to assess the magnitude of the difference if one exists, but it would not allow us to assess the individual effect of either treatment. For example, without a control group, we might be able to say that there is no difference in the increase in mileage for two different gasoline additives, but we wouldn't be able to tell if this was because both additives increased gas mileage by a similar amount or because neither additive had any effect on gas mileage.

## ■ Use of a Placebo

In experiments that use human subjects, use of a control group may not be enough to determine whether a treatment really does have an effect. People sometimes respond merely to the power of suggestion! For example, suppose a study designed to determine whether a particular herbal supplement is effective in promoting weight loss uses an experimental group that takes the herbal supplement and a control group that takes nothing. It is possible that those who take the herbal supplement and believe that they are taking something that will help them to lose weight may be more motivated and may unconsciously change their eating behavior or activity level, resulting in weight loss.

Although there is debate about the degree to which people respond, many studies have shown that people sometimes respond to treatments with no active ingredients and that they often report that such "treatments" relieve pain or reduce symptoms. So, if an experiment is to enable researchers to determine whether a treatment really has an effect, comparing a treatment group to a control group may not be enough. To address the problem, many experiments use what is called a placebo.

A **placebo** is something that is identical (in appearance, taste, feel, etc.) to the treatment received by the treatment group, except that it contains no active ingredients.

■

For example, in the herbal supplement experiment, rather than using a control group that received *no* treatment, the researchers might want to include a placebo group. Individuals in the placebo group would take a pill that looked just like the herbal supplement but did not contain the herb or any other active ingredient. As long as the subjects did not know whether they were taking the herb or the placebo, the placebo group would provide a better basis for comparison and would allow the researchers to determine whether the herbal supplement had any real effect over and above the "placebo effect."

## ■ Single-Blind and Double-Blind Experiments ........................................

Because people often have their own personal beliefs about the effectiveness of various treatments, it is desirable to conduct experiments in such a way that subjects do not know what treatment they are receiving. For example, in an experiment comparing four different doses of a medication for relief of headache pain, someone who knows that he is receiving the medication at its highest dose may be subconsciously influenced to report a greater degree of headache pain reduction. By ensuring that subjects are not aware of which treatment they receive, we can prevent the subjects' personal perception from influencing the response.

An experiment in which subjects do not know what treatment they have received is described as **single-blind**. Of course, not all experiments can be made single-blind. For example, in an experiment to compare the effect of two different types of exercise on blood pressure, it is not possible for participants to be unaware of whether they are in the swimming group or the jogging group! However, when it is possible, "blinding" the subjects in an experiment is generally a good strategy.

In some experiments, someone other than the subject is responsible for measuring the response. To ensure that the person measuring the response does not let personal beliefs influence the way in which the response is recorded, the researchers should make sure that the measurer does not know which treatment was given to any particular individual. For example, in a medical experiment to determine whether a new vaccine reduces the risk of getting the flu, doctors must decide whether a particular individual who is not feeling well actually has the flu or some other unrelated illness. If the doctor knew that a participant with flu-like symptoms had received the new flu vaccine, she might be less likely to determine that the participant had the flu and more likely to interpret the symptoms as being the result of some other illness.

There are two ways in which blinding might occur in an experiment. One involves blinding the participants, and the other involves blinding the individuals who measure the response. If participants do not know which treatment was received *and* those measuring the response do not know which treatment was given to which participant, the experiment is described as **double-blind**. If only one of the two types of blinding is present, the experiment is single-blind.

A **double-blind** experiment is one in which neither the subjects nor the individuals who measure the response know which treatment was received.

A **single-blind** experiment is one in which the subjects do not know which treatment was received but the individuals measuring the response do know which treatment was received, or one in which the subjects do know which treatment was received but the individuals measuring the response do not know which treatment was received.

## ■ Experimental Units and Replication ........................................

An **experimental unit** is the smallest unit to which a treatment is applied. In the language of experimental design, treatments are assigned at random to experimental units, and replication means that each treatment is applied to more than one experimental unit.

Replication is necessary for randomization to be an effective way to create similar experimental groups and to get a sense of the variability in the values of the response for individuals that receive the same treatment. As we will see in Chapters 9–15, this enables us to use statistical methods to decide whether differences in the responses in different treatment groups can be attributed to the treatment received or whether they can be explained by chance variation (the natural variability seen in the responses to a single treatment).

Be careful when designing an experiment to ensure that there is replication. For example, suppose that children in two third-grade classes are available to participate in an experiment to compare two different methods for teaching arithmetic. It might at first seem reasonable to select one class at random to use one method and then assign the other method to the remaining class. But what are the experimental units here? If treatments are randomly assigned to classes, classes are the experimental units. Because only one class is assigned to each treatment, this is an experiment with no replication, even though there are many children in each class. We would *not* be able to determine whether there was a difference between the two methods based on data from this experiment, because we would have only one observation per treatment.

One last note on replication: Don't confuse replication in an experimental design with replicating an experiment. Replicating an experiment means conducting a new experiment using the same experimental design as a previous experiment; it is a way of confirming conclusions based on a previous experiment, but it does not eliminate the need for replication in each of the individual experiments themselves.

## ■ Using Volunteers as Subjects in an Experiment ...............................................

Although the use of volunteers in a study that involves collecting data through sampling is never a good idea, it is a common practice to use volunteers as subjects in an experiment. Even though the use of volunteers limits the researcher's ability to generalize to a larger population, random assignment of the volunteers to treatments should result in comparable groups, and so treatment effects can still be assessed.

## ■ Exercises 2.40–2.50 ....................................................................................................

**2.40** Explain why some studies include both a control group and a placebo treatment. What additional comparisons are possible if both a control group and a placebo group are included?

**2.41** Explain why blinding is a reasonable strategy in many experiments.

**2.42** Give an example of an experiment for each of the following:
a. Single-blind experiment with the subjects blinded
b. Single-blind experiment with the individuals measuring the response blinded
c. Double-blind experiment
d. An experiment that is not possible to blind

**2.43** ▼ Swedish researchers concluded that viewing and discussing art soothes the soul and helps relieve medical conditions such as high blood pressure and constipation (AFP International News Agency, October 14, 2005). This conclusion was based on a study in which 20 elderly women gathered once a week to discuss different works of art. The study also included a control group of 20 elderly women who met once a week to discuss their hobbies and interests. At the end of 4 months, the art discussion group was found to have a more positive attitude, to have lower blood pressure, and to use fewer laxatives than the control group.
a. Why would it be important to determine if the researchers assigned the women participating in the study at random to one of the two groups?

**b.** Explain why you think that the researchers included a control group in this study.

2.44  A novel alternative medical treatment for heart attacks seeds the damaged heart muscle with cells from the patient's thigh muscle ("Doctors Mend Damaged Hearts with Cells from Muscles," *San Luis Obispo Tribune*, November 18, 2002). Doctor Dib from the Arizona Heart Institute evaluated the approach on 16 patients with severe heart failure. The article states that "ordinarily, the heart pushes out more than half its blood with each beat. Dib's patients had such severe heart failure that their hearts pumped just 23 percent. After bypass surgery and cell injections, this improved to 36 percent, although it was impossible to say how much, if any, of the new strength resulted from the extra cells."
a. Explain why it is not reasonable to generalize to the population of all heart attack victims based on the data from these 16 patients.
b. Explain why it is not possible to say whether any of the observed improvement was due to the cell injections, based on the results of this study.
c. Describe a design for an experiment that would allow researchers to determine whether bypass surgery plus cell injections was more effective than bypass surgery alone.

2.45  ▼ The article "Doctor Dogs Diagnose Cancer by Sniffing It Out" (*Knight Ridder Newspapers*, January 9, 2006) reports the results of an experiment described in the journal *Integrative Cancer Therapies*. In this experiment, dogs were trained to distinguish between people with breast and lung cancer and people without cancer by sniffing exhaled breath. Dogs were trained to lay down if they detected cancer in a breath sample. After training, dogs' ability to detect cancer was tested using breath samples from people whose breath had not been used in training the dogs. The paper states "The researchers blinded both the dog handlers and the experimental observers to the identity of the breath samples." Explain why this blinding is an important aspect of the design of this experiment.

2.46  An experiment to evaluate whether vitamins can help prevent recurrence of blocked arteries in patients who have had surgery to clear blocked arteries was described in the article "Vitamins Found to Help Prevent Blocked Arteries" (Associated Press, September 1, 2002). The study involved 205 patients who were given either a treatment consisting of a combination of folic acid, vitamin B12, and vitamin B6 or a placebo for 6 months.

a. Explain why a placebo group was used in this experiment.
b. Explain why it would be important for the researchers to have assigned the 205 subjects to the two groups (vitamin and placebo) at random.
c. Do you think it is appropriate to generalize the results of this experiment to the population of all patients who have undergone surgery to clear blocked arteries? Explain.

2.47  Pismo Beach, California, has an annual clam festival that includes a clam chowder contest. Judges rate clam chowders from local restaurants, and the judging is done in such a way that the judges are not aware of which chowder is from which restaurant. One year, much to the dismay of the seafood restaurants on the waterfront, Denny's chowder was declared the winner! (When asked what the ingredients were, the cook at Denny's said he wasn't sure—he just had to add the right amount of nondairy creamer to the soup stock that he got from Denny's distribution center!)
**a.** Do you think that Denny's chowder would have won the contest if the judging had not been "blind"? Explain.
**b.** Although this was not an experiment, your answer to Part (a) helps to explain why those measuring the response in an experiment are often blinded. Using your answer in Part (a), explain why experiments are often blinded in this way.

2.48  The *San Luis Obispo Tribune* (May 7, 2002) reported that "a new analysis has found that in the majority of trials conducted by drug companies in recent decades, sugar pills have done as well as—or better than—antidepressants." What effect is being described here? What does this imply about the design of experiments with a goal of evaluating the effectiveness of a new medication?

2.49  Researchers at the University of Pennsylvania suggest that a nasal spray derived from pheromones (chemicals emitted by animals when they are trying to attract a mate) may be beneficial in relieving symptoms of premenstrual syndrome (PMS) (*Los Angeles Times*, January 17, 2003).
**a.** Describe how you might design an experiment using 100 female volunteers who suffer from PMS to determine whether the nasal spray reduces PMS symptoms.
**b.** Does your design from Part (a) include a placebo treatment? Why or why not?
**c.** Does your design from Part (a) involve blinding? Is it single-blind or double-blind? Explain.

2.50 The article "A Debate in the Dentist's Chair" (*San Luis Obispo Tribune*, January 28, 2000) described an ongoing debate over whether newer resin fillings are a better alternative to the more traditional silver amalgam fillings. Because amalgam fillings contain mercury, there is concern that they could be mildly toxic and prove to be a health risk to those with some types of immune and kidney disorders. One experiment described in the article used sheep as subjects and reported that sheep treated with amalgam fillings had impaired kidney function.

a. In the experiment, a control group of sheep that received no fillings was used but there was no placebo group. Explain why it is not necessary to have a placebo group in this experiment.

b. The experiment compared only an amalgam filling treatment group to a control group. What would be the benefit of also including a resin filling treatment group in the experiment?

c. Why do you think the experimenters used sheep rather than human subjects?

**Bold** exercises answered in back　　● Data set available online but not required　　▼ Video solution available

## 2.5 More on Observational Studies: Designing Surveys (Optional)

Designing an observational study to compare two populations on the basis of some easily measured characteristic is relatively straightforward, with attention focusing on choosing a reasonable method of sample selection. However, many observational studies attempt to measure personal opinion or attitudes using responses to a survey. In such studies, both the sampling method and the design of the survey itself are critical to obtaining reliable information.

It would seem at first glance that a survey must be a simple method for acquiring information. However, it turns out that designing and administering a survey is not as easy as it might seem. Great care must be taken in order to obtain good information from a survey.

### ■ Survey Basics

A **survey** is a voluntary encounter between strangers in which an interviewer seeks information from a respondent by engaging in a special type of conversation. This conversation might take place in person, over the telephone, or even in the form of a written questionnaire, and it is quite different from usual social conversations. Both the interviewer and the respondent have certain roles and responsibilities. The interviewer gets to decide what is relevant to the conversation and may ask questions—possibly personal or even embarrassing questions. The respondent, in turn, may refuse to participate in the conversation and may refuse to answer any particular question. But having agreed to participate in the survey, the respondent is responsible for answering the questions truthfully. Let's consider the situation of the respondent.

### ■ The Respondent's Tasks

Our understanding of the survey process has been improved in the past two decades by contributions from the field of psychology, but there is still much uncertainty about how people respond to survey questions. Survey researchers and psychologists generally agree that the respondent is confronted with a sequence of tasks when asked a question: comprehension of the question, retrieval of information from memory, and reporting the response.

■ **Task 1: Comprehension**   Comprehension is the single most important task facing the respondent, and fortunately it is the characteristic of a survey question that is most easily controlled by the question writer. Comprehensible directions and questions are characterized by (1) a vocabulary appropriate to the population of interest, (2) simple sentence structure, and (3) little or no ambiguity. Vocabulary is often a problem. As a rule, it is best to use the simplest possible word that can be used without sacrificing clear meaning.

Simple sentence structure also makes it easier for the respondent to understand the question. A famous example of difficult syntax occurred in 1993 when the Roper organization created a survey related to the Holocaust. One question in this survey was

"Does it seem possible or does it seem impossible to you that the Nazi extermination of the Jews never happened?"

The question has a complicated structure and a double negative—"impossible . . . never happened"—that could lead respondents to give an answer opposite to what they actually believed. The question was rewritten and given a year later in an otherwise unchanged survey:

"Does it seem possible to you that the Nazi extermination of the Jews never happened, or do you feel certain that it happened?"

This question wording is much clearer, and in fact the respondents' answers were quite different, as shown in the following table (the "unsure" and "no opinion" percentages have been omitted):

| Original Roper Poll | | Revised Roper Poll | |
|---|---|---|---|
| Impossible | 65% | Certain it happened | 91% |
| Possible | 12% | Possible it never happened | 1% |

It is also important to filter out ambiguity in questions. Even the most innocent and seemingly clear questions can have a number of possible interpretations. For example, suppose that you are asked, "When did you move to Cedar Rapids?" This would seem to be an unambiguous question, but some possible answers might be (1) "In 1971," (2) "When I was 23," and (3) "In the summer." The respondent must decide which of these three answers, if any, is the appropriate response. It may be possible to lessen the ambiguity with more precise questions:

1. In what year did you move to Cedar Rapids?
2. How old were you when you moved to Cedar Rapids?
3. In what season of the year did you move to Cedar Rapids?

One way to find out whether or not a question is ambiguous is to field-test the question and to ask the respondents if they were unsure how to answer a question.

Ambiguity can arise from the placement of questions as well as from their phrasing. Here is an example of ambiguity uncovered when the order of two questions differed in two versions of a survey on happiness. The questions were

1. Taken altogether, how would you say things are these days: Would you say that you are very happy, pretty happy, or not too happy?

2. Taking things altogether, how would you describe your marriage: Would you say that your marriage is very happy, pretty happy, or not too happy?

The proportions of responses to the general happiness question differed for the different question orders, as follows:

Response to General Happiness Question

|  | General Asked First | General Asked Second |
|---|---|---|
| Very happy | 52.4% | 38.1% |
| Pretty happy | 44.2% | 52.8% |
| Not too happy | 3.4% | 9.1% |

If the goal in this survey was to estimate the proportion of the population that is generally happy, these numbers are quite troubling—they cannot both be right! What seems to have happened is that Question 1 was interpreted differently depending on whether it was asked first or second. When the general happiness question was asked after the marital happiness question, the respondents apparently interpreted it to be asking about their happiness in all aspects of their lives *except* their marriage. This was a reasonable interpretation, given that they had just been asked about their marital happiness, but it is a different interpretation than when the general happiness question was asked first. The troubling lesson here is that even carefully worded questions can have different interpretations in the context of the rest of the survey.

■ **Task 2: Retrieval from Memory**   Retrieving relevant information from memory to answer the question is not always an easy task, and it is not a problem limited to questions of fact. For example, consider this seemingly elementary "factual" question:

How many times in the past 5 years did you visit your dentist's office?

a.  0 times
b.  1–5 times
c.  6–10 times
d.  11–15 times
e.  more than 15 times

It is unlikely that many people will remember with clarity every single visit to the dentist in the past 5 years. But generally, people will respond to such a question with answers consistent with the memories and facts they are able to reconstruct given the time they have to respond to the question. An individual may, for example, have a sense that he usually makes about two trips a year to the dentist's office, so he may extrapolate the typical year and get 10 times in 5 years. Then there may be three particularly memorable visits, say, for a root canal in the middle of winter. Thus, the best recollection is now 13, and the respondent will choose Answer (d), 11–15 times. Perhaps not exactly correct, but the best that can be reported under the circumstances.

What are the implications of this relatively fuzzy memory for those who construct surveys about facts? First, the investigator should understand that most factual answers are going to be approximations of the truth. Second, events closer to the time of a survey are easier to recall.

Attitude and opinion questions can also be affected in significant ways by the respondent's memory of recently asked questions. One recent study contained a survey question asking respondents their opinion about how much they followed politics. When that question was preceded by a factual question asking whether they knew the name of the congressional representative from their district, the percentage who reported they follow politics "now and then" or "hardly ever" jumped from 21% to 39%! Respondents apparently concluded that, because they didn't know the answer to the previous knowledge question, they must not follow politics as much as they might have thought otherwise. In a survey that asks for an opinion about the degree to which the respondent believes drilling for oil should be permitted in national parks, the response might be different if the question is preceded by questions about the high price of gasoline than if the question is preceded by questions about the environment and ecology.

▪ **Task 3: Reporting the Response**    The task of formulating and reporting a response can be influenced by the social aspects of the survey conversation. In general, if a respondent agrees to take a survey, he or she will be motivated to answer truthfully. Therefore, if the questions aren't too difficult (taxing the respondent's knowledge or memory) and if there aren't too many questions (taxing the respondent's patience and stamina), the answers to questions will be reasonably accurate. However, it is also true that the respondents often wish to present themselves in a favorable light. This desire leads to what is known as a social desirability bias. Sometimes this bias is a response to the particular wording in a question. In 1941, the following questions were analyzed in two different forms of a survey (emphasis added):

1. Do you think the United States should *forbid* public speeches against democracy?
2. Do you think the United States should *allow* public speeches against democracy?

It would seem logical that these questions are opposites and that the proportion who would not allow public speeches against democracy should be equal to the proportion who would forbid public speeches against democracy. But only 45% of those respondents offering an opinion on Question 1 thought the United States should "forbid," whereas 75% of the respondents offering an opinion on Question 2 thought the United States should "not allow" public speeches against democracy. Most likely, respondents reacted negatively to the word *forbid*, as forbidding something sounds much harsher than not allowing it.

Some survey questions may be sensitive or threatening, such as questions about sex, drugs, or potentially illegal behavior. In this situation a respondent not only will want to present a positive image but also will certainly think twice about admitting illegal behavior! In such cases the respondent may shade the actual truth or may even lie about particular activities and behaviors. In addition, the tendency toward positive presentation is not limited to obviously sensitive questions. For example, consider the question about general happiness previously described. Several investigators have reported higher happiness scores in face-to-face interviews than in responses to a mailed questionnaire. Presumably, a happy face presents a more positive image of the respondent to the interviewer. On the other hand, if the interviewer was a clearly unhappy person, a respondent might shade answers to the less happy side of the scale, perhaps thinking that it is inappropriate to report happiness in such a situation.

It is clear that constructing surveys and writing survey questions can be a daunting task. Keep in mind the following three things:

1. Questions should be understandable by the individuals in the population being surveyed. Vocabulary should be at an appropriate level, and sentence structure should be simple.

2. Questions should, as much as possible, recognize that human memory is fickle. Questions that are specific will aid the respondent by providing better memory cues. The limitations of memory should be kept in mind when interpreting the respondent's answers.

3. As much as possible, questions should not create opportunities for the respondent to feel threatened or embarrassed. In such cases respondents may introduce a social desirability bias, the degree of which is unknown to the interviewer. This can compromise conclusions drawn from the survey data.

Constructing good surveys is a difficult task, and we have given only a brief introduction to this topic. For a more comprehensive treatment, we recommend the book by Sudman and Bradburn listed in the references in the back of the book.

## ■ Exercises 2.51–2.56 ....................................................................

2.51 A tropical forest survey conducted by Conservation International included the following statements in the material that accompanied the survey:

"A massive change is burning its way through the earth's environment."

"The band of tropical forests that encircle the earth is being cut and burned to the ground at an alarming rate."

"Never in history has mankind inflicted such sweeping changes on our planet as the clearing of rain forest taking place right now!"

The survey that followed included the questions given in Parts (a)–(d). For each of these questions, identify a word or phrase that might affect the response and possibly bias the results of any analysis of the responses.
a. "Did you know that the world's tropical forests are being destroyed at the rate of 80 acres per minute?"
b. "Considering what you know about vanishing tropical forests, how would you rate the problem?"
c. "Do you think we have an obligation to prevent the man-made extinction of animal and plant species?"
d. "Based on what you know now, do you think there is a link between the destruction of tropical forests and changes in the earth's atmosphere?"

2.52 Fast-paced lifestyles, where students balance the requirements of school, after-school activities, and jobs, are thought by some to lead to reduced sleep. Suppose that you are assigned the task of designing a survey that will provide answers to the accompanying questions. Write a set of survey questions that might be used. In some cases, you may need to write more than one question to adequately address a particular issue. For example, responses might be different for weekends and school nights. You may also have to

define some terms to make the questions comprehensible to the target audience, which is adolescents.

Topics to be addressed:
How much sleep do the respondents get? Is this enough sleep?
Does sleepiness interfere with schoolwork?
If they could change the starting and ending times of the school day, what would they suggest?
(Sorry, they cannot reduce the total time spent in school during the day!)

2.53 Asthma is a chronic lung condition characterized by difficulty in breathing. Some studies have suggested that asthma may be related to childhood exposure to some animals, especially dogs and cats, during the first year of life ("Exposure to Dogs and Cats in the First Year of Life and Risk of Allergic Sensitization at 6 to 7 Years of Age," *Journal of the American Medical Association* [2002]: 963–972). Some environmental factors that trigger an asthmatic response are (1) cold air, (2) dust, (3) strong fumes, and (4) inhaled irritants.
a. Write a set of questions that could be used in a survey to be given to parents of young children suffering from asthma. The survey should include questions about the presence of pets in the first year of the child's life as well as questions about the presence of pets today. Also, the survey should include questions that address the four mentioned household environmental factors.
b. It is generally thought that low-income persons, who tend to be less well educated, have homes in environments where the four environmental factors are present. Mindful of the importance of comprehension, can you improve the questions in Part (a) by making your vocabulary simpler or by changing the wording of the questions?

c. One problem with the pet-related questions is the reliance on memory. That is, parents may not actually remember when they got their pets. How might you check the parents' memories about these pets?

2.54 In national surveys, parents consistently point to school safety as an important concern. One source of violence in junior high schools is fighting ("Self-Reported Characterization of Seventh-Grade Student Fights," *Journal of Adolescent Health* [1998]: 103–109). To construct a knowledge base about student fights, a school administrator wants to give two surveys to students after fights are broken up. One of the surveys is to be given to the participants, and the other is to be given to students who witnessed the fight. The type of information desired includes (1) the cause of the fight, (2) whether or not the fight was a continuation of a previous fight, (3) whether drugs or alcohol was a factor, (4) whether or not the fight was gang related, and (5) the role of bystanders.
a. Write a set of questions that could be used in the two surveys. Each question should include a set of possible responses. For each question, indicate whether it would be used on both surveys or just on one of the two.
b. How might the tendency toward positive self-presentation affect the responses of the fighter to the survey questions you wrote for Part (a)?
c. How might the tendency toward positive self-presentation affect the responses of a bystander to the survey questions you wrote for Part (a)?

2.55 Doctors are concerned about young women drinking large amounts of soda and about their decreased consump-tion of milk in recent years ("Teenaged Girls, Carbonated Beverage Consumption, and Bone Fractures," *Archives of Pediatric and Adolescent Medicine* [2000]: 610–613). In parts (a)–(d), construct two questions that might be included in a survey of teenage girls. Each question should include possible responses from which the respondent can select. (Note: The questions as written are vague. Your task is to clarify the questions for use in a survey, not just to change the syntax!)
a. How much "cola" beverage does the respondent consume?
b. How much milk (and milk products) is consumed by the respondent?
c. How physically active is the respondent?
d. What is the respondent's history of bone fractures?

2.56 A recent survey attempted to address psychosocial factors thought to be of importance in preventive health care for adolescents ("The Adolescent Health Review: A Brief Multidimensional Screening Instrument," *Journal of Adolescent Health* [2001]: 131–139). For each risk area in the following list, construct a question that would be comprehensible to students in grades 9–12 and that would provide information about the risk factor. Make your questions multiple-choice, and provide possible responses.
a. Lack of exercise
b. Poor nutrition
c. Emotional distress
d. Sexual activity
e. Cigarette smoking
f. Alcohol use

---

**Bold** exercises answered in back     ● Data set available online but not required     ▼ Video solution available

---

## 2.6 Interpreting and Communicating the Results of Statistical Analyses

Statistical studies are conducted to allow investigators to answer questions about characteristics of some population of interest or about the effect of some treatment. Such questions are answered on the basis of data, and how the data are obtained determines the quality of information available and the type of conclusions that can be drawn. As a consequence, when describing a study you have conducted (or when evaluating a published study), you must consider how the data were collected.

The description of the data collection process should make it clear whether the study is an observational study or an experiment. For observational studies, some of the issues that should be addressed are:

1. What is the population of interest? What is the sampled population? Are these two populations the same? If the sampled population is only a subset of the population

of interest, **undercoverage** limits our ability to generalize to the population of interest. For example, if the population of interest is all students at a particular university, but the sample is selected from only those students who choose to list their phone number in the campus directory, undercoverage may be a problem. We would need to think carefully about whether it is reasonable to consider the sample as representative of the population of all students at the university. **Overcoverage** results when the sampled population is actually larger than the population of interest. This would be the case if we were interested in the population of all high schools that offer Advanced Placement (AP) Statistics but sampled from a list of all schools that offered an AP class in any subject. Both undercoverage and overcoverage can be problematic.

2. How were the individuals or objects in the sample actually selected? A description of the sampling method helps the reader to make judgments about whether the sample can reasonably be viewed as representative of the population of interest.

3. What are potential sources of bias, and is it likely that any of these will have a substantial effect on the observed results? When describing an observational study, you should acknowledge that you are aware of potential sources of bias and explain any steps that were taken to minimize their effect. For example, in a mail survey, nonresponse can be a problem, but the sampling plan may seek to minimize its effect by offering incentives for participation and by following up one or more times with those who do not respond to the first request. A common misperception is that increasing the sample size is a way to reduce bias in observational studies, but this is not the case. For example, if measurement bias is present, as in the case of a scale that is not correctly calibrated and tends to weigh too high, taking 1000 measurements rather than 100 measurements cannot correct for the fact that the measured weights will be too large. Similarly, a larger sample size cannot compensate for response bias introduced by a poorly worded question.

For experiments, some of the issues that should be addressed are:

1. What is the role of randomization? All good experiments use random assignment as a means of coping with the effects of potentially confounding variables that cannot easily be directly controlled. When describing an experimental design, you should be clear about how random assignment (subjects to treatments, treatments to subjects, or treatments to trials) was incorporated into the design.

2. Were any extraneous variables directly controlled by holding them at fixed values throughout the experiment? If so, which ones and at which values?

3. Was blocking used? If so, how were the blocks created? If an experiment uses blocking to create groups of homogeneous experimental units, you should describe the criteria used to create the blocks and their rationale. For example, you might say something like "Subjects were divided into two blocks—those who exercise regularly and those who do not exercise regularly—because it was believed that exercise status might affect the responses to the diets."

Because each treatment appears at least once in each block, the block size must be at least as large as the number of treatments. Ideally, the block sizes should be equal to the number of treatments, because this presumably would allow the experimenter to create small groups of extremely homogeneous experimental units. For example, in an experiment to compare two methods for teaching calculus to first-year college students, we may want to block on previous mathematics knowledge by using math SAT scores. If 100 students are available as subjects for this experiment, rather than creating two large groups (above-average math SAT score and below-average math SAT score), we might want to create 50 blocks of two students each, the first consisting of the two students with the highest math SAT scores, the second containing the two students with the next highest scores, and so on. We would then select one student in each block at random and assign that student to teaching method 1. The other student in the block would be assigned to teaching method 2.

## ■ A Word to the Wise: Cautions and Limitations ...............................................

It is a big mistake to begin collecting data before thinking carefully about research objectives and developing a research plan, and doing so may result in data that do not enable the researcher to answer key questions of interest or to generalize conclusions based on the data to the desired populations of interest.

Clearly defining the objectives at the outset enables the investigator to determine whether an experiment or an observational study is the best way to proceed. Watch out for the following *inappropriate* actions:

1. Drawing a cause-and-effect conclusion from an observational study. Don't do this, and don't believe it when others do it!
2. Generalizing results of an experiment that uses volunteers as subjects to a larger population without a convincing argument that the group of volunteers can reasonably be considered a representative sample from the population.
3. Generalizing conclusions based on data from a sample to some population of interest. This is sometimes a sensible thing to do, but on other occasions it is not reasonable. Generalizing from a sample to a population is justified only when there is reason to believe that the sample is likely to be representative of the population. This would be the case if the sample was a random sample from the population and there were no major potential sources of bias. If the sample was not selected at random or if potential sources of bias were present, these issues would have to be addressed before a judgment could be made regarding the appropriateness of generalizing the study results.

   For example, the Associated Press (January 25, 2003) reported on the high cost of housing in California. The median home price was given for each of the 10 counties in California with the highest home prices. Although these 10 counties are a sample of the counties in California, they were not randomly selected and (because they are the 10 counties with the highest home prices) it would not be reasonable to generalize to all California counties based on data from this sample.
4. Generalizing conclusions based on an observational study that used voluntary response or convenience sampling to a larger population. This is almost never reasonable.

## A c t i v i t y   **2.1**   Designing a Sampling Plan

**Background:** In this activity, you will work with a partner to develop a sampling plan.

Suppose that you would like to select a sample of 50 students at your school to learn something about how many hours per week, on average, students at your school spend engaged in a particular activity (such as studying, surfing the Internet, or watching TV).

1. Discuss with your partner whether you think it would be easy or difficult to obtain a simple random sample of students at your school and to obtain the desired information from all the students selected for the sample. Write a summary of your discussion.
2. With your partner, decide how you might go about selecting a sample of 50 students from your school

that reasonably could be considered representative of the population of interest even if it may not be a simple random sample. Write a brief description of your sampling plan, and point out the aspects of your plan that you think make it reasonable to argue that it will be representative.

3. Explain your plan to another pair of students. Ask them to critique your plan. Write a brief summary of the comments you received. Now reverse roles, and provide a critique of the plan devised by the other pair.

4. Based on the feedback you received in Step 3, would you modify your original sampling plan? If not, explain why this is not necessary. If so, describe how the plan would be modified.

## A c t i v i t y  **2.2**    An Experiment to Test for the Stroop Effect

**Background:** In 1935, John Stroop published the results of his research into how people respond when presented with conflicting signals. Stroop noted that most people are able to read words quickly and that they cannot easily ignore them and focus on other attributes of a printed word, such as text color. For example, consider the following list of words:

> **green   blue   red   blue   yellow   red**

It is easy to quickly read this list of words. It is also easy to read the words even if the words are printed in color, and even if the text color is different from the color of the word. For example, people can read the words in the list

> **green   blue   red   blue   yellow   red**

as quickly as they can read the list that isn't printed in color.

However, Stroop found that if people are asked to name the text colors of the words in the list (red, yellow, blue, green, red, green), it takes them longer. Psychologists believe that this is because the reader has to inhibit a natural response (reading the word) and produce a different response (naming the color of the text).

If Stroop is correct, people should be able to name colors more quickly if they do not have to inhibit the word response, as would be the case if they were shown the following:

1. Design an experiment to compare times to identify colors when they appear as text to times to identify colors when there is no need to inhibit a word response. Indicate how randomization is incorporated into your design. What is your response variable? How will you measure it? How many subjects will you use in your experiment, and how will they be chosen?

2. When you are satisfied with your experimental design, carry out the experiment. You will need to construct your list of colored words and a corresponding list of colored bars to use in the experiment. You will also need to think about how you will implement your randomization scheme.

3. Summarize the resulting data in a brief report that explains whether your findings are consistent with the Stroop effect.

## A c t i v i t y  **2.3**    McDonald's and the Next 100 Billion Burgers

**Background:** The article "Potential Effects of the Next 100 Billion Hamburgers Sold by McDonald's" (*American Journal of Preventative Medicine* [2005]:379–381) estimated that 992.25 million pounds of saturated fat would be consumed as McDonald's sells its next 100 billion hamburgers. This estimate was based on the assumption that the average weight of a burger sold would be 2.4 oz. This is the average of the weight of a regular hamburger

(1.6 oz.) and a Big Mac (3.2 oz.). The authors took this approach because

> "McDonald's does not publish sales and profits of individual items. Thus, it is not possible to estimate how many of McDonald's first 100 billion beef burgers sold were 1.6 oz hamburgers, 3.2 oz. Big Macs (introduced in 1968), 4.0 oz. Quarter Pounders (introduced in 1973), or other sandwiches."

This activity can be completed as an individual or as a team. Your instructor will specify which approach (individual or team) you should use.

1. The authors of the article believe that the use of 2.4 oz. as the average size of a burger sold at McDonald's is "conservative," which would result in the estimate of 992.25 million pounds of saturated fat being lower than the actual amount that would be consumed. Explain why the authors' belief might be justified.

2. Do you think it would be possible to collect data that could lead to a value for the average burger size that would be better than 2.4 oz.? If so, explain how you would recommend collecting such data. If not, explain why you think it is not possible.

## A c t i v i t y  **2.4**    Video Games and Pain Management

**Background:** Video games have been used for pain management by doctors and therapists who believe that the attention required to play a video game can distract the player and thereby decrease the sensation of pain. The paper "Video Games and Health" (*British Medical Journal* [2005]:122–123) states:

> "However, there has been no long term follow-up and no robust randomized controlled trials of such interventions. Whether patients eventually tire of such games is also unclear. Furthermore, it is not known whether any distracting effect depends simply on concentrating on an interactive task or whether the content of games is also an important factor as there have been no controlled trials comparing video games with other distracters. Further research should examine factors within games such as novelty, users' preferences, and relative levels of challenge and should compare video games with other potentially distracting activities."

1. Working with a partner, select one of the areas of potential research suggested in the passage from the paper and formulate a specific question that could be addressed by performing an experiment.

2. Propose an experiment that would provide data to address the question from Step 1. Be specific about how subjects might be selected, what the experimental conditions (treatments) would be, and what response would be measured.

3. At the end of Section 2.3 there are 10 questions that can be used to evaluate an experimental design. Answer these 10 questions for the design proposed in Step 2.

4. After evaluating your proposed design, are there any changes you would like to make to your design? Explain.

# Summary of Key Concepts and Formulas

| Term or Formula | Comment |
| --- | --- |
| Observational study | A study that observes characteristics of an existing population. |
| Simple random sample | A sample selected in a way that gives every different sample of size $n$ an equal chance of being selected. |
| Stratified sampling | Dividing a population into subgroups (strata) and then taking a separate random sample from each stratum. |
| Cluster sampling | Dividing a population into subgroups (clusters) and forming a sample by randomly selecting clusters and including all individuals or objects in the selected clusters in the sample. |
| 1 in $k$ systematic sampling | A sample selected from an ordered arrangement of a population by choosing a starting point at random from the first $k$ individuals on the list and then selecting every $k$th individual thereafter. |

| Term or Formula | Comment |
|---|---|
| Confounding variable | A variable that is related both to group membership and to the response variable. |
| Measurement or response bias | The tendency for samples to differ from the population because the method of observation tends to produce values that differ from the true value. |
| Selection bias | The tendency for samples to differ from the population because of systematic exclusion of some part of the population. |
| Nonresponse bias | The tendency for samples to differ from the population because measurements are not obtained from all individuals selected for inclusion in the sample. |
| Experiment | A procedure for investigating the effect of *experimental conditions* (which are manipulated by the experimenter) on a *response variable*. |
| Treatments | The experimental conditions imposed by the experimenter. |
| Extraneous factor | A variable that is not of interest in the current study but is thought to affect the response variable. |
| Direct control | Holding extraneous factors constant so that their effects are not confounded with those of the experimental conditions. |
| Blocking | Using extraneous factors to create experimental groups that are similar with respect to those factors, thereby filtering out their effect. |
| Randomization | Random assignment of experimental units to treatments or of treatments to trials. |
| Replication | A strategy for ensuring that there is an adequate number of observations on each experimental treatment. |
| Placebo treatment | A treatment that resembles the other treatments in an experiment in all apparent ways but that has no active ingredients. |
| Control group | A group that receives no treatment or one that receives a placebo treatment. |
| Single-blind experiment | An experiment in which the subjects do not know which treatment they received but the individuals measuring the response do know which treatment was received, or an experiment in which the subjects do know which treatment they received but the individuals measuring the response do not know which treatment was received. |
| Double-blind experiment | An experiment in which neither the subjects nor the individuals who measure the response know which treatment was received. |

# Chapter Review Exercises 2.57–2.70

**2.57** The article "Tots' TV-Watching May Spur Attention Problems" (*San Luis Obispo Tribune*, April 5, 2004) describes a study that appeared in the journal *Pediatrics*. In this study, researchers looked at records of 2500 children who were participating in a long-term health study. They found that 10% of these children had attention disorders at age 7 and that hours of television watched at age 1 and age 3 was associated with an increased risk of having an attention disorder at age 7.
**a.** Is the study described an observational study or an experiment?
**b.** Give an example of a potentially confounding variable that would make it unwise to draw the conclusion that hours of television watched at a young age is the cause of the increased risk of attention disorder.

**2.58** A study of more than 50,000 U.S. nurses found that those who drank just one soda or fruit punch a day tended to gain much more weight and had an 80% increased risk in developing diabetes compared to those who drank less than one a month. (*The Washington Post*, August 25, 2004). "The message is clear. . . . Anyone who cares about their health or the health of their family would not consume these beverages" said Walter Willett of the Harvard School of Public Health who helped conduct the study. The sugar and beverage industries said that the study was fundamentally flawed. "These allegations are inflammatory. Women who drink a lot of soda may simply have generally unhealthy lifestyles" said Richard Adamson of the American Beverage Association.
a. Do you think that the study described was an observational study or an experiment?
b. Is it reasonable to conclude that drinking soda or fruit punch causes the observed increased risk of diabetes? Why or why not?

**2.59** "Crime Finds the Never Married" is the conclusion drawn in an article from *USA Today* (June 29, 2001). This conclusion is based on data from the Justice Department's National Crime Victimization Survey, which estimated the number of violent crimes per 1000 people, 12 years of age or older, to be 51 for the never married, 42 for the divorced or separated, 13 for married individuals, and 8 for the widowed. Does being single cause an increased risk of violent crime? Describe a potential confounding variable

that illustrates why it is unreasonable to conclude that a change in marital status causes a change in crime risk.

2.60 The paper "Prospective Randomized Trial of Low Saturated Fat, Low Cholesterol Diet During the First Three Years of Life" (*Circulation* [1996]: 1386–1393) describes an experiment in which "1062 infants were randomized to either the intervention or control group at 7 months of age. The families of the 540 intervention group children were counseled to reduce the child's intake of saturated fat and cholesterol but to ensure adequate energy intake. The control children consumed an unrestricted diet."
a. The researchers concluded that the blood cholesterol level was lower for children in the intervention group. Is it reasonable to conclude that the parental counseling and subsequent reduction in dietary fat and cholesterol are the cause of the reduction in blood cholesterol level? Explain why or why not.
b. Is it reasonable to generalize the results of this experiment to all children? Explain.

**2.61** The article "Workers Grow More Dissatisfied" in the *San Luis Obispo Tribune* (August 22, 2002) states that "a survey of 5000 people found that while most Americans continue to find their jobs interesting, and are even satisfied with their commutes, a bare majority like their jobs." This statement was based on the fact that only 51 percent of those responding to a mail survey indicated that they were satisfied with their jobs. Describe any potential sources of bias that might limit the researcher's ability to draw conclusions about working Americans based on the data collected in this survey.

2.62 According to the article "Effect of Preparation Methods on Total Fat Content, Moisture Content, and Sensory Characteristics of Breaded Chicken Nuggets and Beef Steak Fingers" (*Family and Consumer Sciences Research Journal* [1999]: 18–27), sensory tests were conducted using 40 college student volunteers at Texas Women's University. Give three reasons, apart from the relatively small sample size, why this sample may not be ideal as the basis for generalizing to the population of all college students.

**2.63** Do ethnic group and gender influence the type of care that a heart patient receives? The following passage is from the article "Heart Care Reflects Race and Sex, Not

Symptoms" (*USA Today*, February 25, 1999, reprinted with permission):

> Previous research suggested blacks and women were less likely than whites and men to get cardiac catheterization or coronary bypass surgery for chest pain or a heart attack. Scientists blamed differences in illness severity, insurance coverage, patient preference, and health care access. The researchers eliminated those differences by videotaping actors— two black men, two black women, two white men, and two white women—describing chest pain from identical scripts. They wore identical gowns, used identical gestures, and were taped from the same position. Researchers asked 720 primary care doctors at meetings of the American College of Physicians or the American Academy of Family Physicians to watch a tape and recommend care. The doctors thought the study focused on clinical decision-making.

Evaluate this experimental design. Do you think this is a good design or a poor design, and why? If you were designing such a study, what, if anything, would you propose to do differently?

**2.64** Does alcohol consumption cause increased cravings for cigarettes? Research at Purdue University suggests this is so (see CNN.com web site article "Researchers Find Link Between Cigarette Cravings and Alcohol," dated June 13, 1997). In an experiment, 60 heavy smokers and moderate drinkers were divided into two groups. One group drank vodka tonics and the other group drank virgin tonics (tonic water alone), but all subjects were told they were drinking vodka tonics. The researchers then measured the level of nicotine cravings (by monitoring heart rate, skin conductance, etc.). Those who had consumed the vodka tonics had 35% more cravings than those who did not. Assuming that the assignment of subjects to the treatment (vodka) and control groups was made at random, do you think there are any confounding factors that would make conclusions based on this experiment questionable?

**2.65** An article in the *San Luis Obispo Tribune* (September 7, 1999) described an experiment designed to investigate the effect of creatine supplements on the development of muscle fibers. The article states that the researchers "looked at 19 men, all about 25 years of age and similar in weight, lean body mass, and capacity to lift weights. Ten were given creatine—25 grams a day for the first week, followed by 5 grams a day for the rest of the study. The rest were given a fake preparation. No one was told what he was getting. All the men worked out under the

guidance of the same trainer. The response variable measured was gain in fat-free mass (in percent)."
**a.** What extraneous variables are identified in the given statement, and what strategy did the researchers use to deal with them?
**b.** Do you think it was important that the men participating in the experiment were not told whether they were receiving creatine or the placebo? Explain.
**c.** This experiment was not conducted in a double-blind manner. Do you think it would have been a good idea to make this a double-blind experiment? Explain.

**2.66** The article "Heavy Drinking and Problems among Wine Drinkers" (*Journal of Studies on Alcohol* [1999]: 467–471) investigates whether wine drinkers tend to drink less excessively than those who drink beer and spirits. A sample of Canadians, stratified by province of residence and other socioeconomic factors, was selected.
a. Why might stratification by province be a good thing?
b. List two socioeconomic factors that would be appropriate to use for stratification. Explain how each factor would relate to the consumption of alcohol in general and of wine in particular.

**2.67** Researchers at the University of Houston decided to test the hypothesis that restaurant servers who squat to the level of their customers would receive a larger tip ("Effect of Server Posture on Restaurant Tipping," *Journal of Applied Social Psychology* [1993]: 678–685). In the experiment, the waiter would flip a coin to determine whether he would stand or squat next to the table. The waiter would record the amount of the bill and of the tip and whether he stood or squatted.
**a.** Describe the treatments and the response variable.
**b.** Discuss possible extraneous factors and how they could be controlled.
**c.** Discuss whether blocking would be necessary.
**d.** Identify possible confounding variables.
**e.** Discuss the role of randomization in this experiment.

**2.68** You have been asked to determine on what types of grasslands two species of birds, northern harriers and short-eared owls, build nests. The types of grasslands to be used include undisturbed native grasses, managed native grasses, undisturbed nonnative grasses, and managed nonnative grasses. You are allowed a plot of land 500 m square to study. Explain how you would determine where to plant the four types of grasses. What role would randomization play in this determination? Identify any confounding variables. Would this study be considered an observational study or an experiment? (Based on the article

"Response of Northern Harriers and Short-Eared Owls to Grassland Management in Illinois," *Journal of Wildlife Management* [1999]: 517–523.)

**2.69** A manufacturer of clay roofing tiles would like to investigate the effect of clay type on the proportion of tiles that crack in the kiln during firing. Two different types of clay are to be considered. One hundred tiles can be placed in the kiln at any one time. Firing temperature varies slightly at different locations in the kiln, and firing temperature may also affect cracking. Discuss the design of an experiment to collect information that could be used to decide between the two clay types. How does your proposed design deal with the extraneous factor *temperature*?

2.70 A mortgage lender routinely places advertisements in a local newspaper. The advertisements are of three different types: one focusing on low interest rates, one featuring low fees for first-time buyers, and one appealing to people who may want to refinance their homes. The lender would like to determine which advertisement format is most successful in attracting customers to call for more information. Describe an experiment that would provide the information needed to make this determination. Be sure to consider extraneous factors, such as the day of the week that the advertisement appears in the paper, the section of the paper in which the advertisement appears, or daily fluctuations in the interest rate. What role does randomization play in your design?

Mentor¨
Do you need a live tutor for homework problems?

**Thomson** NOW
Are you ready? Take your exam-prep post-test now.

**Bold** exercises answered in back     ● Data set available online but not required     ▼ Video solution available

# Chapter 3

# Graphical Methods for Describing Data

© John Terence Turner/Taxi/Getty Images

Most college students (and their parents) are concerned about the cost of a college education. *The Chronicle of Higher Education* (August, 2005) reported the average tuition and fees for 4-year public institutions in each of the 50 U.S. states for the 2003–2004 academic year. Average tuition and fees (in dollars) are given for each state:

| | | | | | | | | | |
|---|---|---|---|---|---|---|---|---|---|
| 3977 | 3423 | 3586 | 4010 | 3785 | 3447 | 5761 | 6176 | 2773 | 3239 |
| 3239 | 3323 | 5653 | 5384 | 4991 | 3686 | 3868 | 3208 | 5011 | 6230 |
| 6080 | 6015 | 5754 | 3754 | 5367 | 4155 | 4238 | 2724 | 7623 | 7266 |
| 3161 | 4885 | 3251 | 3855 | 6561 | 3200 | 4677 | 7633 | 5387 | 7482 |
| 4441 | 4043 | 3579 | 2902 | 8260 | 5069 | 4630 | 3172 | 4675 | 3090 |

Several questions could be posed about these data. What is a typical value of average tuition and fees for the 50 states? Are observations concentrated near the typical value, or does average tuition and fees differ quite a bit from state to state? Do states with low tuition and fees or states with high tuition and fees predominate, or are there roughly equal numbers of the two types? Are there any states whose average tuition and fees are somehow unusual compared to the rest? What proportion of the states have average tuition and fees exceeding $4000? exceeding $6000?

Questions such as these are most easily answered if the data can be organized in a sensible manner. In this chapter, we introduce some techniques for organizing and describing data using tables and graphs.

## 3.1 Displaying Categorical Data: Comparative Bar Charts and Pie Charts

■ **Comparative Bar Charts** ...............................................................

In Chapter 1 we saw that categorical data could be summarized in a frequency distribution and displayed graphically using a bar chart. Bar charts can also be used to give a visual comparison of two or more groups. This is accomplished by constructing two or more bar charts that use the same set of horizontal and vertical axes, as illustrated in Example 3.1.

## Example 3.1    Perceived Risk of Smoking

The article "Most Smokers Wish They Could Quit" (*Gallup Poll Analyses,* November 21, 2002) noted that smokers and nonsmokers perceive the risks of smoking differently. The accompanying relative frequency table summarizes responses regarding the perceived harm of smoking for each of three groups: a sample of 241 smokers, a sample of 261 former smokers, and a sample of 502 nonsmokers.

| Perceived Risk of Smoking | Frequency | | | Relative Frequency | | |
|---|---|---|---|---|---|---|
| | Smokers | Former Smokers | Nonsmokers | Smokers | Former Smokers | Nonsmokers |
| Very harmful | 145 | 204 | 432 | .60 | .78 $\frac{432}{502}$ → | .86 |
| Somewhat harmful | 72 | 42 | 50 | .30 | .16 | .10 |
| Not too harmful | 17 | 10 | 15 | .07 $\frac{5}{261}$ | .04 | .03 |
| Not harmful at all | 7 | 5 | 5 | .03 → | .02 | .01 |

*When constructing a comparative bar graph we use the relative frequency rather than the frequency to construct the scale on the vertical axis so that we can make meaningful comparisons even if the sample sizes are not the same.* The comparative bar chart for these data is shown in Figure 3.1. It is easy to see the differences among the three groups. The proportion believing that smoking is very harmful is noticeably smaller for smokers than for either former smokers or nonsmokers, and the proportion of former smokers who believe smoking is very harmful is smaller than the proportion for nonsmokers.

To see why it is important to use relative frequencies rather than frequencies to compare groups of different sizes, consider the *incorrect* bar chart constructed using the frequencies rather than the relative frequencies (Figure 3.2). The incorrect bar chart conveys a very different and misleading impression of the differences among the three groups.

*!* Step-by-step technology instructions available online.

**Figure 3.1** Comparative bar chart of perceived harm of smoking.

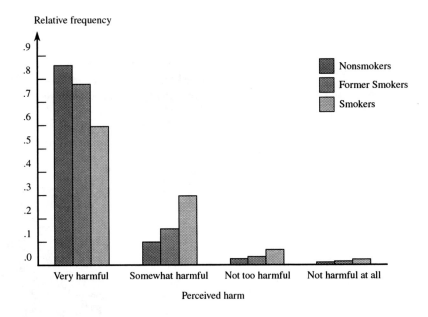

**Figure 3.2** An *incorrect* comparative bar chart for the data of Example 3.1.

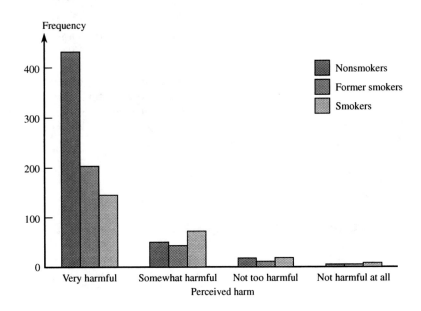

■

■ Pie Charts ....................................................................................................

A categorical data set can also be summarized using a pie chart. In a pie chart, a circle is used to represent the whole data set, with "slices" of the pie representing the possible categories. The size of the slice for a particular category is proportional to the corresponding frequency or relative frequency. Pie charts are most effective for summarizing data sets when there are not too many different categories.

# Example 3.2    Life Insurance for Cartoon Characters??

The article "Fred Flintstone, Check Your Policy" (*The Washington Post,* October 2, 2005) summarized the results of a survey of 1014 adults conducted by the Life and Health Insurance Foundation for Education. Each person surveyed was asked to select which of five fictional characters, Spider-Man, Batman, Fred Flintstone, Harry Potter, and Marge Simpson, he or she thought had the greatest need for life insurance. The resulting data are summarized in the pie chart of Figure 3.3.

**Figure 3.3**  Pie chart of data on which fictional character most needs life insurance.

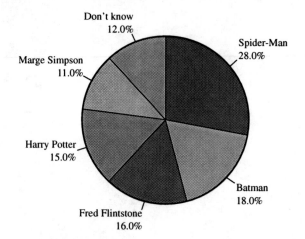

The survey results were quite different from an insurance expert's assessment. His opinion was that Fred Flintstone, a married father with a young child, was by far the one with the greatest need for life insurance. Spider-Man, unmarried with an elderly aunt, would need life insurance only if his aunt relied on him to supplement her income. Batman, a wealthy bachelor with no dependents, doesn't need life insurance in spite of his dangerous job!

---

## Pie Chart for Categorical Data

**When to Use**    Categorical data with a relatively small number of possible categories. Pie charts are most useful for illustrating proportions of the whole data set for various categories.

**How to Construct**

1. Draw a circle to represent the entire data set.
2. For each category, calculate the "slice" size. Because there are 360 degrees in a circle

    slice size = 360 (category relative frequency)

3. Draw a slice of appropriate size for each category. This can be tricky, so most pie charts are generated using a graphing calculator or a statistical software package.

**What to Look For**

▪ Categories that form large and small proportions of the data set.

# Example 3.3    Birds That Fish

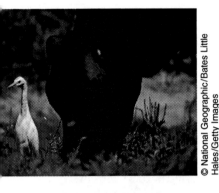

Night herons and cattle egrets are species of birds that feed on aquatic prey in shallow water. These birds wade through shallow water, stalking submerged prey and then striking rapidly and downward through the water in an attempt to catch the prey. The article "Cattle Egrets Are Less Able to Cope with Light Refraction Than Are Other Herons" (*Animal Behaviour* [1999]: 687–694) gave data on outcome when 240 cattle egrets attempted to capture submerged prey. The data are summarized in the following frequency distribution:

| Outcome | Frequency | Relative Frequency |
|---------|-----------|--------------------|
| Prey caught on first attempt | 103 | .43 |
| Prey caught on second attempt | 41 | .17 |
| Prey caught on third attempt | 2 | .01 |
| Prey not caught | 94 | .39 |

155 degrees, to represent first attempt category

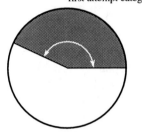

To draw a pie chart by hand, we would first compute the slice size for each category. For the first attempt category, the slice size would be

$$\text{slice size} = (.43)(360) = 154.8 \text{ degrees}$$

We would then draw a circle and use a protractor to mark off a slice corresponding to about 155°, as illustrated here in the figure shown in the margin. Continuing to add slices in this way leads to a completed pie chart.

It is much easier to use a statistical software package to create pie charts than to construct them by hand. A pie chart for the cattle egret data, created with the statistical software package MINITAB is shown in Figure 3.4(a). Figure 3.4(b) shows a pie chart constructed using similar data for 180 night herons. Although some differences

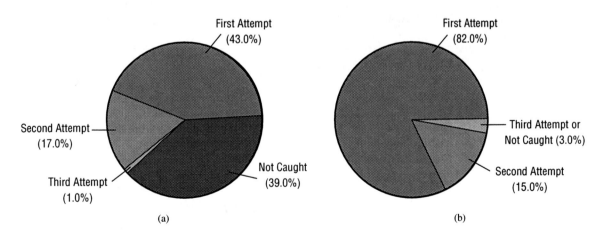

**Figure 3.4**   Pie charts for Example 3.3: (a) cattle egret data; (b) night heron data.

*Step-by-step technology instructions available online.*

**Figure 3.5** Comparative bar chart for the egret and heron data.

between night herons and cattle egrets can be seen by comparing the pie charts in Figures 3.4(a) and 3.4(b), it is difficult to actually compare category proportions using pie charts. A comparative bar chart (Figure 3.5) makes this type of comparison easier.

▪

## ▪ A Different Type of "Pie" Chart: Segmented Bar Charts ..............................

A pie chart can be difficult to construct by hand, and the circular shape sometimes makes it difficult to compare areas for different categories, particularly when the relative frequencies for categories are similar. The **segmented bar chart** (also sometimes called a stacked bar chart) avoids these difficulties by using a rectangular bar rather than a circle to represent the entire data set. The bar is divided into segments, with different segments representing different categories. As with pie charts, the area of the segment for a particular category is proportional to the relative frequency for that category. Example 3.4 illustrates the construction of a segmented bar graph.

## Example 3.4    Gun Permit Denials

Between 1998 and 2004, more than 53 million background checks for gun purchases were conducted. One reason for denial of a gun permit is having a criminal history, and during this period approximately 748,000 permits were denied for this reason. The accompanying table categorizes these denials by type of criminal history (*San Francisco Chronicle,* November 2005).

| Criminal History | Relative Frequency |
|---|---|
| Felony offense | .59 |
| Domestic violence | .15 |
| Drug-related offense | .07 |
| Other | .19 |

To construct a segmented bar graph for these data, first draw a bar of any fixed width and length, and then add a scale that ranges from 0 to 1, as shown.

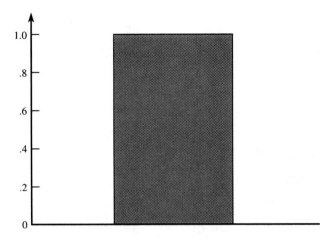

Then divide the bar into four segments, corresponding to the four possible categories in this example. The first segment, corresponding to felony offense, ranges from 0 to .59. The second segment, corresponding to domestic violence, ranges from .59 to .74 (for a length of .15, the relative frequency for this category), and so on. The segmented bar can be displayed either vertically or horizontally, as shown in Figure 3.6.

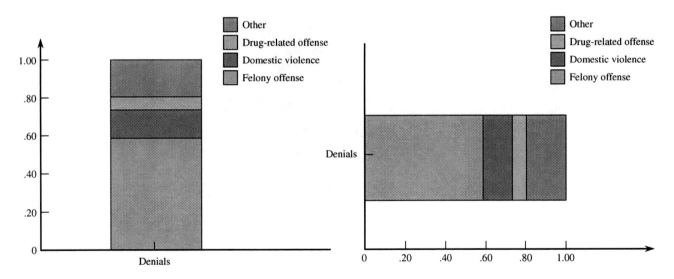

**Figure 3.6**   Segmented bar graphs for the gun permit data of Example 3.4.

■

## ■ Other Uses of Bar Charts and Pie Charts ...................................................

As we have seen in previous examples, bar charts and pie charts can be used to summarize categorical data sets. However, they are occasionally used for other purposes, as illustrated in Examples 3.5 and 3.6.

# Example 3.5    Grape Production

● The 1998 Grape Crush Report for San Luis Obispo and Santa Barbara counties in California gave the following information on grape production for each of seven different types of grapes (*San Luis Obispo Tribune,* February 12, 1999):

| Type of Grape | Tons Produced |
|---|---|
| Cabernet Sauvignon | 21,656 |
| Chardonnay | 39,582 |
| Chenin Blanc | 1,601 |
| Merlot | 11,210 |
| Pinot Noir | 2,856 |
| Sauvignon Blanc | 5,868 |
| Zinfandel | 7,330 |
| **Total** | **90,103** |

Although this table is not a frequency distribution, it is common to represent information of this type graphically using a pie chart, as shown in Figure 3.7. The pie represents the total grape production, and the slices show the proportion of the total production for each of the seven types of grapes.

**Figure 3.7**   Pie chart for grape production data.

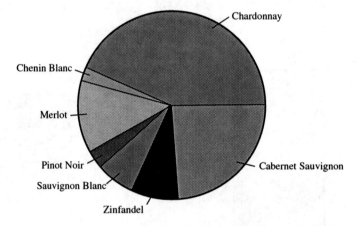

# Example 3.6    Identity Theft

The article "Fraud, Identity Theft Afflict Consumers" (*San Luis Obispo Tribune,* February 2, 2005) gave the following identity theft rates for three states.

● Data set available online

| State | Identity Theft (Cases per 100,000 Population) |
|---|---|
| California | 122.1 |
| Arizona | 142.5 |
| Oregon | 87.8 |

Even though this table is not a frequency distribution, this type of information is often represented graphically in the form of a bar chart, as illustrated in Figure 3.8.

**Figure 3.8** Bar chart for the identity theft rate data of Example 3.6.

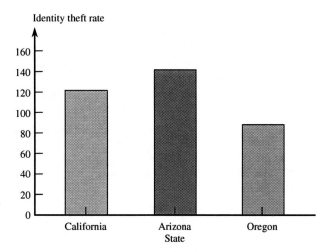

The article also gave Internet fraud rates for the same three states, again reported in cases per 100,000 population. Figure 3.9 is a comparative bar chart of the Internet fraud rates and identity theft rates for the three states.

**Figure 3.9** Bar chart comparing Internet fraud and identity theft rates.

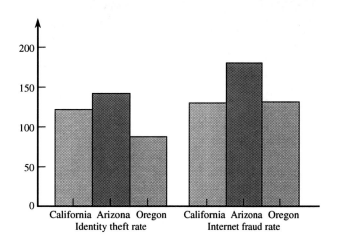

■

## Exercises 3.1–3.14

**3.1** ▼ *The Chronicle of Higher Education* (August 31, 2001) published data collected in a survey of a large number of students who were college freshmen in the fall of 2001. Of those surveyed, 70.6% reported that they were attending their first-choice college, 20.8% their second-choice college, 5.5% their third-choice college, and 3.1% their fourth- or higher-choice college. Use a pie chart to display this information.

**3.2** The article "Rinse Out Your Mouth" (Associated Press, March 29, 2006) summarized results from a survey of 1001 adults on the use of profanity. When asked "How many times do you use swear words in conversations?" 46% responded a few or more times per week, 32% responded a few times a month or less, and 21% responded never. Use the given information to construct a segmented bar chart.

**3.3** Data from the U.S Census Bureau was used to construct the accompanying pie chart that reflects changes of residence between 1995 and 2000. Construct a bar graph for these data. Which graph is a more effective display of the data? Explain.

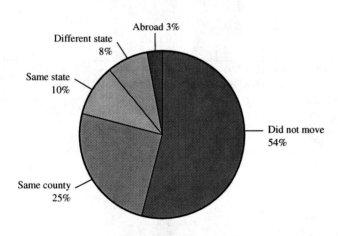

**3.4** The California Healthy Kids Survey in 1999 and 2001 asked 7th, 9th, and 11th graders in San Luis Obispo County whether they smoked tobacco. In 1999, 6% of 7th graders, 17% of 9th graders, and 23% of 11th graders admitted smoking tobacco while in 2001 the corresponding figures were 3%, 13%, and 22%. Create a comparative bar chart showing bars for 7th graders together, bars for 9th

graders together, and bars for 11th graders together. Comment on any interesting features of the chart.

**3.5** The Institute for Highway Safety tracks which cars are most likely to be stolen by looking at theft claims per 1000 insured vehicles. For cars manufactured between 2001 and 2003, the top five were as follows:

| Type of Vehicle | Claims per 1000 Vehicles |
|---|---|
| '02–'03 Cadillac Escalade EXT (luxury pickup) | 20.2 |
| '02–'03 Nissan Maxima (midsize 4-door car) | 17.0 |
| '02–'03 Cadillac Escalade (luxury SUV) | 10.2 |
| Dodge Stratus/Chrysler Sebring (midsize 4-door car) | 8.3 |
| Dodge Intrepid (large 4-door car) | 7.9 |

Use this information to construct a pie chart.

**3.6** The article "The Need to Be Plugged In" (Associated Press, December 22, 2005) described the results of a survey of 1006 adults who were asked about various technologies, including personal computers, cell phones, and DVD players. The accompanying table summarizes the responses to questions about how essential these technologies were.

| | Relative Frequency | | |
|---|---|---|---|
| Response | Personal Computer | Cell Phone | DVD Player |
| Cannot imagine living without | .46 | .41 | .19 |
| Would miss but could do without | .28 | .25 | .35 |
| Could definitely live without | .26 | .34 | .46 |

Construct a comparative bar chart that shows the distribution of responses for the three different technologies.

**3.7** Students in California are required to pass an exit exam in order to graduate from high school. The pass rate for San Luis Obispo High School has been rising, as have the rates for San Luis Obispo County and the state of California (*San Luis Obispo Tribune,* August 17, 2004). The percentage of students that passed the test was as follows:

| Year | District | Pass Rate |
|------|----------|-----------|
| 2002 | San Luis Obispo High School | 66% |
| 2003 | | 72% |
| 2004 | | 93% |
| 2002 | San Luis Obispo County | 62% |
| 2003 | | 57% |
| 2004 | | 85% |
| 2002 | State of California | 32% |
| 2003 | | 43% |
| 2004 | | 74% |

a. Construct a comparative bar chart that allows the change in the pass rate for each group to be compared.
**b.** Is the change the same for each group? Comment on any difference observed.

3.8 A poll conducted by the Associated Press–Ipsos on public attitudes found that most Americans are convinced that political corruption is a major problem (*San Luis Obispo Tribune,* December 9, 2005). In the poll, 1002 adults were surveyed. Two of the questions and the summarized responses to these questions follow:

How widespread do you think corruption is in public service in America?

| | |
|---|---|
| Hardly anyone | 1% |
| A small number | 20% |
| A moderate number | 39% |
| A lot of people | 28% |
| Almost everyone | 10% |
| Not sure | 2% |

In general, which elected officials would you say are more ethical?

| | |
|---|---|
| Democrats | 36% |
| Republicans | 33% |
| Both equally | 10% |
| Neither | 15% |
| Not sure | 6% |

a. For each question, construct a pie chart summarizing the data.
b. For each question construct a segmented bar chart displaying the data.
c. Which type of graph (pie chart or segmented bar graph) does a better job of presenting the data? Explain.

**3.9 ▼** Poor fitness in adolescents and adults increases the risk of cardiovascular disease. In a study of 3110 adolescents and 2205 adults (*Journal of the American Medical Association,* December 21, 2005), researchers found 33.6% of adolescents and 13.9% of adults were unfit; the percentage was similar in adolescent males (32.9%) and females (34.4%), but was higher in adult females (16.2%) than in adult males (11.8%).
a. Summarize this information using a comparative bar graph that shows differences between males and females within the two different age groups.
**b.** Comment on the interesting features of your graphical display.

3.10 A survey of 1001 adults taken by Associated Press–Ipsos asked "How accurate are the weather forecasts in your area?" (*San Luis Obispo Tribune,* June 15, 2005). The responses are summarized in the table below.

| | |
|---|---|
| Extremely | 4% |
| Very | 27% |
| Somewhat | 53% |
| Not too | 11% |
| Not at all | 4% |
| Not sure | 1% |

a. Construct a pie chart to summarize this data.
b. Construct a bar chart to summarize this data.
c. Which of these charts—a pie chart or a bar chart best summarizes the important information? Explain.

3.11 The article "Online Shopping Grows, But Department, Discount Stores Still Most Popular with Holiday Shoppers" (*Gallup Poll Analyses,* December 2, 2002) included the data in the accompanying table. The data are based on two telephone surveys, one conducted in November 2000 and one in November 2002. Respondents were asked if they were very likely, somewhat likely, not too likely, or not at all likely to do Christmas shopping online.

|  | **Relative Frequency** | |
| **Response** | **2000** | **2002** |
| Very likely | .09 | .15 |
| Somewhat likely | .12 | .14 |
| Not too likely | .14 | .12 |
| Not at all likely | .65 | .59 |

**a.** Construct a comparative bar chart. What aspects of the chart justify the claim in the title of the article that "online shopping grows?"

**b.** Respondents were also asked about the likelihood of doing Christmas shopping from mail order catalogues. Use the data in the accompanying table to construct a comparative bar chart. Are the changes in responses from 2000 to 2002 similar to what was observed for online shopping? Explain.

|  | **Relative Frequency** | |
| **Response** | **2000** | **2002** |
| Very likely | .12 | .13 |
| Somewhat likely | .22 | .17 |
| Not too likely | .20 | .16 |
| Not at all likely | .46 | .54 |

3.12 The article "So Close, Yet So Far: Predictors of Attrition in College Seniors" (*Journal of College Student Development* [1998]: 343–348) examined the reasons that college seniors leave their college programs before graduating. Forty-two college seniors at a large public university who dropped out before graduation were interviewed and asked the main reason for discontinuing enrollment at the university. Data consistent with that given in the article are summarized in the following frequency distribution:

| Reason for Leaving the University | Frequency |
| --- | --- |
| Academic problems | 7 |
| Poor advising or teaching | 3 |
| Needed a break | 2 |
| Economic reasons | 11 |
| Family responsibilities | 4 |
| To attend another school | 9 |
| Personal problems | 3 |
| Other | 3 |

**a.** Would a bar chart or a pie chart be a better choice for summarizing this data set? Explain.

**b.** Based on your answer to Part (a), construct an appropriate graphical summary of the given data.

**c.** Write a few sentences describing the interesting features of your graphical display.

**3.13** In a discussion of roadside hazards, the web site highwaysafety.com included a pie chart like the one shown:

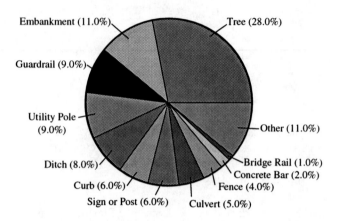

**a.** Do you think this is an effective use of a pie chart? Why or why not?

**b.** Construct a bar chart to show the distribution of deaths by object struck. Is this display more effective than the pie chart in summarizing this data set? Explain.

3.14 The article "Death in Roadwork Zones at Record High" (*San Luis Obispo Tribune,* July 25, 2001) included a bar chart similar to this one:

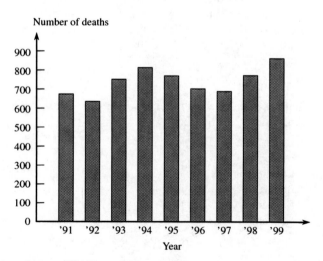

a. Comment on the trend over time in the number of people killed in highway work zones.

b. Would a pie chart have also been an effective way to summarize these data? Explain why or why not.

**Bold** exercises answered in back   ● Data set available online but not required   ▼ Video solution available

## 3.2   Displaying Numerical Data: Stem-and-Leaf Displays

A stem-and-leaf display is an effective and compact way to summarize univariate numerical data. Each number in the data set is broken into two pieces, a stem and a leaf. The **stem** is the first part of the number and consists of the beginning digit(s). The **leaf** is the last part of the number and consists of the final digit(s). For example, the number 213 might be split into a stem of 2 and a leaf of 13 or a stem of 21 and a leaf of 3. The resulting stems and leaves are then used to construct the display.

## Example 3.7   Should Doctors Get Auto Insurance Discounts?

● Many auto insurance companies give job-related discounts of between 5 and 15%. The article "Auto-Rate Discounts Seem to Defy Data" (*San Luis Obispo Tribune*, June 19, 2004) included the accompanying data on the number of automobile accidents per year for every 1000 people in 40 occupations.

| Occupation | Accidents per 1000 | Occupation | Accidents per 1000 |
|---|---|---|---|
| Student | 152 | Banking-finance | 89 |
| Physician | 109 | Customer service | 88 |
| Lawyer | 106 | Manager | 88 |
| Architect | 105 | Medical support | 87 |
| Real estate broker | 102 | Computer-related | 87 |
| Enlisted military | 99 | Dentist | 86 |
| Social worker | 98 | Pharmacist | 85 |
| Manual laborer | 96 | Proprietor | 84 |
| Analyst | 95 | Teacher, professor | 84 |
| Engineer | 94 | Accountant | 84 |
| Consultant | 94 | Law enforcement | 79 |
| Sales | 93 | Physical therapist | 78 |
| Military officer | 91 | Veterinarian | 78 |
| Nurse | 90 | Clerical, secretary | 77 |
| School administrator | 90 | Clergy | 76 |
| Skilled labor | 90 | Homemaker | 76 |
| Librarian | 90 | Politician | 76 |
| Creative arts | 90 | Pilot | 75 |
| Executive | 89 | Firefighter | 67 |
| Insurance agent | 89 | Farmer | 43 |

*♪♪* Step-by-step technology instructions available online   ● Data set available online

**Figure 3.10** Stem-and-leaf display for accident rate per 1000 for forty occupations

```
 4 | 3
 5 |
 6 | 7
 7 | 56667889
 8 | 44567788999
 9 | 000013445689
10 | 2569
11 |
12 |
13 |
14 |                            Stem:  Tens
15 | 2                          Leaf:  Ones
```

Figure 3.10 shows a stem-and-leaf display for the accident rate data.

The numbers in the vertical column on the left of the display are the **stems**. Each number to the right of the vertical line is a **leaf** corresponding to one of the observations in the data set. The legend

Stem: Tens
Leaf: Ones

tells us that the observation that had a stem of 4 and a leaf of 3 corresponds to an occupation with an accident rate of 43 per 1000 (as opposed to 4.3 or 0.43). Similarly, the observation with the stem of 10 and leaf of 2 corresponds to 102 accidents per 1000 (the leaf of 2 is the ones digit) and the observation with the stem of 15 and leaf of 2 corresponds to 152 accidents per 1000.

The display in Figure 3.10 suggests that a typical or representative value is in the stem 8 or 9 row, perhaps around 90. The observations are mostly concentrated in the 75 to 109 range, but there are a couple of values that stand out on the low end (43 and 67) and one observation (152) that is far removed from the rest of the data on the high end.

From the point of view of an auto insurance company it might make sense to offer discounts to occupations with low accident rates—maybe farmers (43 auto accidents per 1000 farmers) or firefighters (67 accidents per 1000 firefighters) or even some of the occupations with accident rates in the 70s. The "discounts seem to defy data" in the title of the article refers to the fact that some insurers provide discounts to doctors and engineers, but not to homemakers, politicians, and other occupations with lower accident rates. Two possible explanations were offered for this apparent discrepancy. One is that it is possible that while some occupations have higher accident rates, they also have lower average cost per claim. Accident rates alone may not reflect the actual cost to the insurance company. Another possible explanation is that the insurance companies may offer the discounted auto insurance in order to attract people who would then also purchase other types of insurance such as malpractice or liability insurance.

■

The leaves on each line of the display in Figure 3.10 have been arranged in order from smallest to largest. Most statistical software packages order the leaves this way, but it is not necessary to do so to get an informative display that still shows many of the important characteristics of the data set, such as shape and spread.

Stem-and-leaf displays can be useful to get a sense of a typical value for the data set, as well as a sense of how spread out the values in the data set are. It is also easy to spot data values that are unusually far from the rest of the values in the data set. Such values are called **outliers**. The stem-and-leaf display of the accident rate data (Figure 3.10) shows an outlier on the low end (43) and an outlier on the high end (152).

> **DEFINITION**
>
> An **outlier** is an unusually small or large data value. In Chapter 4 a precise rule for deciding when an observation is an outlier is given.

## Stem-and-Leaf Displays

**When to Use**

Numerical data sets with a small to moderate number of observations (does not work well for very large data sets)

**How to Construct**

1. Select one or more leading digits for the stem values. The trailing digits (or sometimes just the first one of the trailing digits) become the leaves.
2. List possible stem values in a vertical column.
3. Record the leaf for every observation beside the corresponding stem value.
4. Indicate the units for stems and leaves someplace in the display.

**What to Look For**   The display conveys information about

■ a representative or typical value in the data set
■ the extent of spread about a typical value

■ the presence of any gaps in the data
■ the extent of symmetry in the distribution of values
■ the number and location of peaks

........................................................................................................................................

# Example 3.8   Tuition at Public Universities

● The introduction to this chapter gave data on average tuition and fees at public institutions in the year 2004 for the 50 U.S. states. The observations ranged from a low value of 2724 to a high value of 8260. The data are reproduced here:

| | | | | | | | | |
|---|---|---|---|---|---|---|---|---|
| 3977 | 3423 | 3586 | 4010 | 3785 | 3447 | 5761 | 6176 | 2773 | 3239 |
| 3239 | 3323 | 5653 | 5384 | 4991 | 3686 | 3868 | 3208 | 5011 | 6230 |
| 6080 | 6015 | 5754 | 3754 | 5367 | 4155 | 4238 | 2724 | 7623 | 7266 |
| 3161 | 4885 | 3251 | 3855 | 6561 | 3200 | 4677 | 7633 | 5387 | 7482 |
| 4441 | 4043 | 3579 | 2902 | 8260 | 5069 | 4630 | 3172 | 4675 | 3090 |

A natural choice for the stem is the leading (thousands) digit. This would result in a display with 7 stems (2, 3, 4, 5, 6, 7, and 8). Using the first two digits of a number as the stem would result in 56 stems (27, 28, . . . , 82). A stem-and-leaf display with 56 stems would not be an effective summary of the data. *In general, stem-and-leaf displays that use between 5 and 20 stems tend to work well.*

● Data set available online

If we choose the thousands digit as the stem, the remaining three digits (the hundreds, tens, and ones) would form the leaf. For example, for the first few values in the first row of data, we would have

$$3977 \rightarrow \text{stem} = 3, \text{leaf} = 977$$
$$3423 \rightarrow \text{stem} = 3, \text{leaf} = 423$$
$$3586 \rightarrow \text{stem} = 3, \text{leaf} = 586$$

The leaves have been entered in the display of Figure 3.11 in the order they are encountered in the data set. Commas are used to separate the leaves only when each leaf has two or more digits. Figure 3.11 shows that most states had average tuition and fees in the $3000 to $5000 range and that the typical average tuition and fees is around $4000. A few states have average tuition and fees at public four-year institutions that are quite a bit higher than most other states (the four states with the highest values were Vermont, Pennsylvania, New Hampshire, and New Jersey).

```
2 | 773, 724, 902
3 | 977, 423, 586, 785, 447, 239, 239, 323, 686, 868, 208, 754, 161, 251, 855, 200, 579, 172, 090
4 | 010, 991, 155, 238, 885, 677, 441, 043, 630, 675
5 | 761, 653, 384, 011, 754, 367, 387, 069
6 | 176, 230, 080, 015, 561
7 | 623, 266, 633, 482                          Stem: Thousands
8 | 260                                         Leaf: Ones
```

**Figure 3.11** Stem-and-leaf displays of average tuition and fees.

An alternative display (Figure 3.12) results from dropping all but the first digit of the leaf. This is what most statistical computer packages do when generating a display; little information about typical value, spread, or shape is lost in this truncation and the display is simpler and more compact.

**Figure 3.12** Stem-and-leaf display of the average tuition and fees data using truncated leaves.

```
2 | 779
3 | 9457422368271282510
4 | 0912864066
5 | 76307330
6 | 12005
7 | 6264        Stem: Thousands
8 | 2           Leaf: Hundreds
```

## ■ Repeated Stems to Stretch a Display

Sometimes a natural choice of stems gives a display in which too many observations are concentrated on just a few stems. A more informative picture can be obtained by dividing the leaves at any given stem into two groups: those that begin with 0, 1, 2, 3, or 4 (the "low" leaves) and those that begin with 5, 6, 7, 8, or 9 (the "high" leaves). Then each stem value is listed twice when constructing the display, once for the low leaves and once again for the high leaves. It is also possible to repeat a stem more than twice. For example, each stem might be repeated five times, once for each of the leaf groupings {0, 1}, {2, 3}, {4, 5}, {6, 7}, and {8, 9}.

# Example 3.9  Median Ages in 2030

◉ The accompanying data on the Census Bureau's projected median age in 2030 for the 50 U.S. states and Washington D.C. appeared in the article "2030 Forecast: Mostly Gray" (*USA Today,* April 21, 2005). The median age for a state is the age that divides the state's residents so that half are younger than the median age and half are older than the median age.

**Projected Median Age**

| | | | | | | | | | | |
|---|---|---|---|---|---|---|---|---|---|---|
| 41.0 | 32.9 | 39.3 | 29.3 | 37.4 | 35.6 | 41.1 | 43.6 | 33.7 | 45.4 | 35.6 | 38.7 |
| 39.2 | 37.8 | 37.7 | 42.0 | 39.1 | 40.0 | 38.8 | 46.9 | 37.5 | 40.2 | 40.2 | 39.0 |
| 41.1 | 39.6 | 46.0 | 38.4 | 39.4 | 42.1 | 40.8 | 44.8 | 39.9 | 36.8 | 43.2 | 40.2 |
| 37.9 | 39.1 | 42.1 | 40.7 | 41.3 | 41.5 | 38.3 | 34.6 | 30.4 | 43.9 | 37.8 | 38.5 |
| 46.7 | 41.6 | 46.4 | | | | | | | | |

The ages in the data set range from 29.3 to 46.9. Using the first two digits of each data value for the stem results in a large number of stems, while using only the first digit results in a stem-and-leaf display with only three stems.

The stem-and-leaf display using single digit stems and leaves truncated to a single digit is shown in Figure 3.13. A stem-and-leaf display that uses repeated stems is shown in Figure 3.14. Here each stem is listed twice, once for the low leaves (those beginning with 0, 1, 2, 3, 4) and once for the high leaves (those beginning with 5, 6, 7, 8, 9). This display is more informative than the one in Figure 3.13, but is much more compact than a display based on two digit stems.

**Figure 3.13**  Stem-and-leaf display for the projected median age data.

```
2 | 9
3 | 023455677777888889999999
4 | 000000111111222333456666      Stem:  Tens
                                  Leaf:  Ones
```

**Figure 3.14**  Stem-and-leaf display for the projected median age data using repeated stems.

```
2H | 9
3L | 0234
3H | 5567777778888899999999
4L | 0000001111112223334
4H | 56666                         Stem:  Tens
                                   Leaf:  Ones
```

■

## ■ Comparative Stem-and-Leaf Displays

Frequently an analyst wishes to see whether two groups of data differ in some fundamental way. A comparative stem-and-leaf display, in which the leaves for one group extend to the right of the stem values and the leaves for the second group extend to the left, can provide preliminary visual impressions and insights.

◉ Data set available online

# Example 3.10  Progress for Children

● The UNICEF report "Progress for Children" (April, 2005) included the accompanying data on the percentage of primary-school-age children who were enrolled in school for 19 countries in Northern Africa and for 23 countries in Central Africa.

**Northern Africa**

| 54.6 | 34.3 | 48.9 | 77.8 | 59.6 | 88.5 | 97.4 | 92.5 | 83.9 | 96.9 | 88.9 |
|------|------|------|------|------|------|------|------|------|------|------|
| 98.8 | 91.6 | 97.8 | 96.1 | 92.2 | 94.9 | 98.6 | 86.6 |      |      |      |

**Central Africa**

| 58.3 | 34.6 | 35.5 | 45.4 | 38.6 | 63.8 | 53.9 | 61.9 | 69.9 | 43.0 | 85.0 |
|------|------|------|------|------|------|------|------|------|------|------|
| 63.4 | 58.4 | 61.9 | 40.9 | 73.9 | 34.8 | 74.4 | 97.4 | 61.0 | 66.7 | 79.6 |
| 98.9 |      |      |      |      |      |      |      |      |      |      |

We will construct a comparative stem-and-leaf display using the first digit of each observation as the stem and the remaining two digits as the leaf. To keep the display simple the leaves will be truncated to one digit. For example, the observation 54.6 would be processed as

$$54.6 \rightarrow \text{stem} = 5, \text{leaf} = 4 \text{ (truncated from 4.6)}$$

and the observation 34.3 would be processed as

$$34.3 \rightarrow \text{stem} = 3, \text{leaf} = 4 \text{ (truncated from 4.3)}$$

The resulting comparative stem-and-leaf display is shown in Figure 3.15.

**Figure 3.15** Comparative stem-and-leaf display for percentage of children enrolled in primary school.

| Central Africa | | Northern Africa | |
|---:|:---:|:---|:---|
| 4854 | 3 | 4 | |
| 035 | 4 | 8 | |
| 838 | 5 | 49 | |
| 6113913 | 6 | | |
| 943 | 7 | 76 | |
| 5 | 8 | 8386 | Stem:  Tens |
| 87 | 9 | 7268176248 | Leaf:  Ones |

From the comparative stem-and-leaf display you can see that there is quite a bit of variability in the percentage enrolled in school for both Northern and Central African countries and that the shapes of the two data distributions are quite different. The percentage enrolled in school tends to be higher in Northern African countries than in Central African countries, although the smallest value in each of the two data sets is about the same. For Northern African countries the distribution of values has a single peak in the 90s with the number of observations declining as we move toward the stems corresponding to lower percentages enrolled in school. For Central African countries the distribution is more symmetric, with a typical value in the mid 60s.

■

● Data set available online

Exercises 3.15–3.21 ·····································································

**3.15** ● ▼ The National Survey on Drug Use and Health, conducted in 2002 and 2003 by the Office of Applied Studies, led to the following state estimates of the total number of people (ages 12 and older) who had smoked within the last month).

| State | Number of People (in thousands) |
|---|---|
| Alabama | 976 |
| Alaska | 129 |
| Arizona | 1215 |
| Arkansas | 730 |
| California | 5508 |
| Colorado | 985 |
| Connecticut | 678 |
| Delaware | 174 |
| District of Columbia | 125 |
| Florida | 3355 |
| Georgia | 1779 |
| Hawaii | 217 |
| Idaho | 260 |
| Illinois | 2754 |
| Indiana | 1427 |
| Iowa | 647 |
| Kansas | 573 |
| Kentucky | 1178 |
| Louisiana | 1021 |
| Maine | 297 |
| Maryland | 1039 |
| Massachusetts | 1207 |
| Michigan | 2336 |
| Minnesota | 1122 |
| Mississippi | 680 |
| Missouri | 1472 |
| Montana | 212 |
| Nebraska | 367 |
| Nevada | 543 |
| New Hampshire | 281 |
| New Jersey | 1662 |
| New Mexico | 363 |
| New York | 4052 |
| North Carolina | 2010 |
| North Dakota | 145 |
| Ohio | 2865 |
| Oklahoma | 858 |

| State | Number of People (in thousands) |
|---|---|
| Oregon | 735 |
| Pennsylvania | 2858 |
| Rhode Island | 246 |
| South Carolina | 907 |
| South Dakota | 188 |
| Tennessee | 1343 |
| Texas | 4428 |
| Utah | 304 |
| Vermont | 134 |
| Virginia | 1487 |
| Washington | 1172 |
| West Virginia | 452 |
| Wisconsin | 1167 |
| Wyoming | 111 |

**a.** Construct a stem-and-leaf display using hundreds (of thousands) as the stems and truncating the leaves to the tens (of thousands) digit.
**b.** Write a few sentences describing the shape of the distribution and any unusual observations.
**c.** The three largest values were for California, New York, and Texas. Does this indicate that tobacco use is more of a problem in these states than elsewhere? Explain.
**d.** If you wanted to compare states on the basis of the extent of tobacco use, would you use the data in the given table? If yes, explain why this would be reasonable. If no, what would you use instead as the basis for the comparison?

**3.16** ● The Connecticut Agricultural Experiment Station conducted a study of the calorie content of different types of beer. The calorie content (calories per 100 ml) for 26 brands of light beer are (from the web site brewery.org):

29  28  33  31  30  33  30  28  27  41  39  31  29
23  32  31  32  19  40  22  34  31  42  35  29  43

Construct a stem-and-leaf display using stems 1, 2, 3, and 4. Write a sentence or two describing the calorie content of light beers.

**3.17** The stem-and-leaf display of Exercise 3.16 uses only four stems. Construct a stem-and-leaf display for these data using repeated stems 1H, 2L, 2H, . . . , 4L. For example, the first observation, 29, would have a stem of 2 and a leaf of 9. It would be entered into the display for the stem 2H, because it is a "high" 2—that is, it has a leaf that is on the high end (5, 6, 7, 8, 9).

3.18 ● Many states face a shortage of fully credentialed teachers. The percentages of teachers who are fully credentialed for each county in California were published in the *San Luis Obispo Tribune* (July 29, 2001) and are given in the following table:

| County | Percentage Credentialed |
|---|---|
| Alameda | 85.1 |
| Alpine | 100.0 |
| Amador | 97.3 |
| Butte | 98.2 |
| Calaveras | 97.3 |
| Colusa | 92.8 |
| Contra Costa | 87.7 |
| Del Norte | 98.8 |
| El Dorado | 96.7 |
| Fresno | 91.2 |
| Glenn | 95.0 |
| Humbolt | 98.6 |
| Imperial | 79.8 |
| Inyo | 94.4 |
| Kern | 85.1 |
| Kings | 85.0 |
| Lake | 95.0 |
| Lassen | 89.6 |
| Los Angeles | 74.7 |
| Madera | 91.0 |
| Marin | 96.8 |
| Mariposa | 95.5 |
| Mendicino | 97.2 |
| Merced | 87.8 |
| Modoc | 94.6 |
| Mono | 95.9 |
| Monterey | 84.6 |
| Napa | 90.8 |
| Nevada | 93.9 |
| Orange | 91.3 |
| Placer | 97.8 |
| Plumas | 95.0 |
| Riverside | 84.5 |
| Sacramento | 95.3 |

| County | Percentage Credentialed |
|---|---|
| San Benito | 83.5 |
| San Bernardino | 83.1 |
| San Diego | 96.6 |
| San Francisco | 94.4 |
| San Joaquin | 86.3 |
| San Luis Obispo | 98.1 |
| San Mateo | 88.8 |
| Santa Barbara | 95.5 |
| Santa Clara | 84.6 |
| Santa Cruz | 89.6 |
| Shasta | 97.5 |
| Sierra | 88.5 |
| Siskiyou | 97.7 |
| Solano | 87.3 |
| Sonoma | 96.5 |
| Stanislaus | 94.4 |
| Sutter | 89.3 |
| Tehama | 97.3 |
| Trinity | 97.5 |
| Tulare | 87.6 |
| Tuolomne | 98.5 |
| Ventura | 92.1 |
| Yolo | 94.6 |
| Yuba | 91.6 |

a. Construct a stem-and-leaf display for this data set using stems 7, 8, 9, and 10. Truncate the leaves to a single digit. Comment on the interesting features of the display.
b. Construct a stem-and-leaf display using repeated stems. Are there characteristics of the data set that are easier to see in the plot with repeated stems, or is the general shape of the two displays similar?

3.19 ● ▼ A report from Texas Transportation Institute (Texas A&M University System, 2005) titled "Congestion Reduction Strategies" included the accompanying data on extra travel time for peak travel time in hours per year per traveler for different sized urban areas.

| Very Large Urban Areas | Extra Hours per Year per Traveler |
|---|---|
| Los Angeles, CA | 93 |
| San Francisco, CA | 72 |
| Washington DC, VA, MD | 69 |

| Very Large Urban Areas | Extra Hours per Year per Traveler |
|---|---|
| Atlanta, GA | 67 |
| Houston, TX | 63 |
| Dallas, Fort Worth, TX | 60 |
| Chicago, IL-IN | 58 |
| Detroit, MI | 57 |
| Miami, FL | 51 |
| Boston, MA, NH, RI | 51 |
| New York, NY-NJ-CT | 49 |
| Phoenix, AZ | 49 |
| Philadelphia, PA-NJ-DE-MD | 38 |

| Large Urban Areas | Extra Hours per Year per Traveler |
|---|---|
| Riverside, CA | 55 |
| Orlando, FL | 55 |
| San Jose, CA | 53 |
| San Diego, CA | 52 |
| Denver, CO | 51 |
| Baltimore, MD | 50 |
| Seattle, WA | 46 |
| Tampa, FL | 46 |
| Minneapolis, St Paul, MN | 43 |
| Sacramento, CA | 40 |
| Portland, OR, WA | 39 |
| Indianapolis, IN | 38 |
| St Louis, MO-IL | 35 |
| San Antonio, TX | 33 |
| Providence, RI, MA | 33 |
| Las Vegas, NV | 30 |
| Cincinnati, OH-KY-IN | 30 |
| Columbus, OH | 29 |
| Virginia Beach, VA | 26 |
| Milwaukee, WI | 23 |
| New Orleans, LA | 18 |
| Kansas City, MO-KS | 17 |
| Pittsburgh, PA | 14 |
| Buffalo, NY | 13 |
| Oklahoma City, OK | 12 |
| Cleveland, OH | 10 |

**a.** Construct a back-to-back stem-and-leaf plot for annual delay per traveler for each of the two different sizes of urban areas.

**b.** Is the following statement consistent with the display constructed in part (a)? Explain.

The larger the urban areas, the greater the extra travel time during peak period travel.

3.20 ● The article "A Nation Ablaze with Change" (*USA Today,* July 3, 2001) gave the accompanying data on percentage increase in population between 1990 and 2000 for the 50 U.S. states. Also provided in the table is a column that indicates for each state whether the state is in the eastern or western part of the United States (the states are listed in order of population size):

| State | Percentage Change | East/West |
|---|---|---|
| California | 13.8 | W |
| Texas | 22.8 | W |
| New York | 5.5 | E |
| Florida | 23.5 | E |
| Illinois | 8.6 | E |
| Pennsylvania | 3.4 | E |
| Ohio | 4.7 | E |
| Michigan | 6.9 | E |
| New Jersey | 8.9 | E |
| Georgia | 26.4 | E |
| North Carolina | 21.4 | E |
| Virginia | 14.4 | E |
| Massachusetts | 5.5 | E |
| Indiana | 9.7 | E |
| Washington | 21.1 | W |
| Tennessee | 16.7 | E |
| Missouri | 9.3 | E |
| Wisconsin | 9.6 | E |
| Maryland | 10.8 | E |
| Arizona | 40.0 | W |
| Minnesota | 12.4 | E |
| Louisiana | 5.9 | E |
| Alabama | 10.1 | E |
| Colorado | 30.6 | W |
| Kentucky | 9.7 | E |
| South Carolina | 15.1 | E |
| Oklahoma | 9.7 | W |
| Oregon | 20.4 | W |
| Connecticut | 3.6 | E |
| Iowa | 5.4 | E |
| Mississippi | 10.5 | E |
| Kansas | 8.5 | W |

(*continued*)

**Bold** exercises answered in back ● Data set available online but not required ▼ Video solution available

| State | Percentage Change | East/West |
|---|---|---|
| Arkansas | 13.7 | E |
| Utah | 29.6 | W |
| Nevada | 66.3 | W |
| New Mexico | 20.1 | W |
| West Virginia | 0.8 | E |
| Nebraska | 8.4 | W |
| Idaho | 28.5 | W |
| Maine | 3.9 | E |
| New Hampshire | 11.4 | E |
| Hawaii | 9.3 | W |
| Rhode Island | 4.5 | E |
| Montana | 12.9 | W |
| Delaware | 17.6 | E |
| South Dakota | 8.5 | W |
| North Dakota | 0.5 | W |
| Alaska | 14.0 | W |
| Vermont | 8.2 | E |
| Wyoming | 8.9 | W |

a. Construct a stem-and-leaf display for percentage growth for the data set consisting of all 50 states. Hints: Regard the observations as having two digits to the left of the decimal place. That is, think of an observation such as 8.5 as 08.5. It will also be easier to truncate leaves to a single digit; for example, a leaf of 8.5 could be truncated to 8 for purposes of constructing the display.

b. Comment on any interesting features of the data set. Do any of the observations appear to be outliers?

c. Now construct a comparative stem-and-leaf display for the eastern and western states. Write a few sentences comparing the percentage growth distributions for eastern and western states.

**3.21** ● High school dropout rates (percentages) for the period 1997–1999 for the 50 states were given in *The Chronicle of Higher Education* (August 31, 2001) and are shown in the following table:

| State | Rate |
|---|---|
| Alabama | 10 |
| Alaska | 7 |
| Arizona | 17 |
| Arkansas | 12 |
| California | 9 |
| Colorado | 13 |

| State | Rate |
|---|---|
| Connecticut | 9 |
| Delaware | 11 |
| Florida | 12 |
| Georgia | 13 |
| Hawaii | 5 |
| Idaho | 10 |
| Illinois | 9 |
| Indiana | 6 |
| Iowa | 7 |
| Kansas | 7 |
| Kentucky | 11 |
| Louisiana | 11 |
| Maine | 7 |
| Maryland | 7 |
| Massachusetts | 6 |
| Michigan | 9 |
| Minnesota | 6 |
| Mississippi | 10 |
| Missouri | 9 |
| Montana | 8 |
| Nebraska | 8 |
| Nevada | 17 |
| New Hampshire | 7 |
| New Jersey | 6 |
| New Mexico | 13 |
| New York | 9 |
| North Carolina | 11 |
| North Dakota | 5 |
| Ohio | 8 |
| Oklahoma | 9 |
| Oregon | 13 |
| Pennsylvania | 7 |
| Rhode Island | 11 |
| South Carolina | 9 |
| South Dakota | 8 |
| Tennessee | 12 |
| Texas | 12 |
| Utah | 9 |
| Vermont | 6 |
| Virginia | 8 |
| Washington | 8 |
| West Virginia | 8 |
| Wisconsin | 5 |
| Wyoming | 9 |

Note that dropout rates range from a low of 5% to a high of 17%. In constructing a stem-and-leaf display for these data, if we regard each dropout rate as a two-digit number and use the first digit for the stem, then there are only two possible stems, 0 and 1. One solution is to use repeated stems. Consider a scheme that divides the leaf range into five parts: 0 and 1, 2 and 3, 4 and 5, 6 and 7, and 8 and 9. Then, for example, stem 1 could be repeated as

1.   with leaves 0 and 1
1t   with leaves 2 and 3

1f   with leaves 4 and 5
1s   with leaves 6 and 7

If there had been any dropout rates as large as 18 or 19 in the data set, we would also need to include a stem 1* to accommodate the leaves of 8 and 9. Construct a stem-and-leaf display for this data set that uses stems 0f, 0s, 0*, 1., 1t, 1f, and 1s. Comment on the important features of the display.

**Bold** exercises answered in back    ● Data set available online but not required    ▼ Video solution available

## 3.3 Displaying Numerical Data: Frequency Distributions and Histograms

A stem-and-leaf display is not always an effective summary technique; it is unwieldy when the data set contains a large number of observations. Frequency distributions and histograms are displays that are useful for summarizing even a large data set in a compact fashion.

### ■ Frequency Distributions and Histograms for Discrete Numerical Data

Discrete numerical data almost always result from counting. In such cases, each observation is a whole number. As in the case of categorical data, a frequency distribution for discrete numerical data lists each possible value (either individually or grouped into intervals), the associated frequency, and sometimes the corresponding relative frequency. Recall that relative frequency is calculated by dividing the frequency by the total number of observations in the data set.

## Example 3.11  Promiscuous Raccoons!

Alan and Sandy Carey/Getty Images

● The authors of the article "Behavioral Aspects of the Raccoon Mating System: Determinants of Consortship Success" (*Animal Behaviour* [1999]: 593–601) monitored raccoons in southern Texas during three mating seasons in an effort to describe mating behavior. Twenty-nine female raccoons were observed, and the number of male partners during the time the female was accepting partners (generally 1 to 4 days each year) was recorded for each female. The resulting data were as follows:

| 1 | 3 | 2 | 1 | 1 | 4 | 2 | 4 | 1 | 1 | 1 |
|---|---|---|---|---|---|---|---|---|---|---|
| 3 | 1 | 1 | 1 | 1 | 2 | 2 | 1 | 1 | 4 | 1 |
| 1 | 2 | 1 | 1 | 1 | 1 | 3 |   |   |   |   |

The corresponding frequency distribution is given in Table 3.1. From the frequency distribution we can see that 18 of the female raccoons had a single partner. The corresponding relative frequency, $18/29 = .621$, tells us that the proportion of female raccoons in the sample with a single partner was .621, or, equivalently, 62.1% of the

● Data set available online

**Table 3.1** Frequency Distribution for Number of Partners

| Number of Partners | Frequency | Relative Frequency |
|:---:|:---:|:---:|
| 1 | 18 | .621 |
| 2 | 5 | .172 |
| 3 | 3 | .103 |
| 4 | 3 | .103 |
| | 29 | .999 ← Differs from 1 due to rounding |

females had a single partner. Adding the relative frequencies for the values of 1 and 2 gives

$$.621 + .172 = .793$$

indicating that 79.3% of the raccoons had 2 or fewer partners.

■

A histogram for discrete numerical data is a graph of the frequency distribution, and it is similar to the bar chart for categorical data. Each frequency or relative frequency is represented by a rectangle centered over the corresponding value (or range of values) and the area of the rectangle is proportional to the corresponding frequency or relative frequency.

## Histogram for Discrete Numerical Data

**When to Use**

Discrete numerical data. Works well even for large data sets.

**How to Construct**

1. Draw a horizontal scale, and mark the possible values of the variable.
2. Draw a vertical scale, and mark it with either frequency or relative frequency.
3. Above each possible value, draw a rectangle centered at that value (so that the rectangle for 1 is centered at 1, the rectangle for 5 is centered at 5, and so on). The height of each rectangle is determined by the corresponding frequency or relative frequency. Often possible values are consecutive whole numbers, in which case the base width for each rectangle is 1.

**What to Look For**

- Central or typical value
- Extent of spread or variation
- General shape
- Location and number of peaks
- Presence of gaps and outliers

■

# Example 3.12 Revisiting Promiscuous Raccoons

The raccoon data of Example 3.11 were summarized in a frequency distribution. The corresponding histogram is shown in Figure 3.16. Note that each rectangle in the histogram is centered over the corresponding value. When relative frequency instead of frequency is used for the vertical scale, the scale on the vertical axis is different but all essential characteristics of the graph (shape, location, spread) are unchanged.

**Figure 3.16** Histogram and relative frequency histogram of raccoon data.

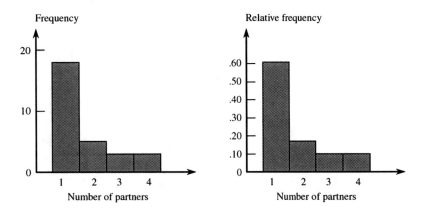

Sometimes a discrete numerical data set contains a large number of possible values and perhaps also has a few large or small values that are far away from most of the data. In this case, rather than forming a frequency distribution with a very long list of possible values, it is common to group the observed values into intervals or ranges. This is illustrated in Example 3.13.

# Example 3.13 Math SAT Score Distribution

Each of the 1,475,623 students who took the math portion of the SAT exam in 2005 received a score between 200 and 800. The score distribution was summarized in a frequency distribution table that appeared in the College Board report titled "2005 College Bound Seniors." A relative frequency distribution is given in Table 3.2 and the corresponding relative frequency histogram is shown in Figure 3.17. Notice that rather than list each possible individual score value between 200 and 800, the scores are grouped into intervals (200 to 249, 250 to 299, etc.). This results in a much more compact table that still communicates the important features of the data set. Also, notice that because the data set is so large, the frequencies are also large numbers. Because of these large frequencies, it is easier to focus on the relative frequencies in our interpretation. From the relative frequency distribution and histogram, we can see that while there is a lot of variability in individual math SAT scores, the majority were in the 400 to 600 range and a typical value for math SAT looks to be something in the low 500s.

Before leaving this example, take a second look at the relative frequency histogram of Figure 3.17. Notice that there is one rectangle for each score interval in the relative frequency distribution. For simplicity we have chosen to treat the very

**Table 3.2**  Relative Frequency Distribution of Math SAT Score

| Score | Frequency | Relative Frequency |
|-------|-----------|--------------------|
| 200–249 | 33,841 | .02 ← $\frac{33,841}{1,475,623}$ |
| 250–299 | 67,117 | .05 |
| 300–349 | 124,032 | .08 |
| 350–399 | 166,446 | .11 |
| 400–449 | 210,449 | .14 |
| 450–499 | 255,904 | .17 |
| 500–549 | 225,335 | .15 |
| 550–599 | 188,780 | .13 |
| 600–649 | 111,350 | .08 |
| 650–699 | 58,762 | .04 |
| 700–749 | 22,270 | .02 |
| 750–800 | 11,337 | .01 |
| **Total** | **1,475,623** | **1.00** |

**Figure 3.17** Relative Frequency Histogram for the Math SAT Data

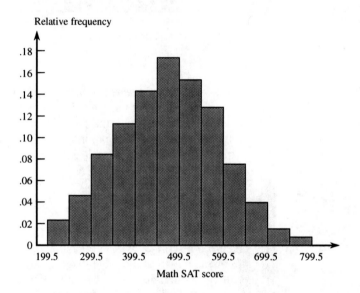

last interval, 750 to 800 as if it were 750 to 799 so that all of the score ranges in the frequency distribution are the same width. Also note that the rectangle representing the score range 400 to 449 actually extends from 399.5 to 449.5 on the score scale. This is similar to what happens in histograms for discrete numerical data where there is no grouping. For example, in Figure 3.16 the rectangle representing 2 is centered at 2 but extends from 1.5 to 2.5 on the number of partners scale.

■

## ▪ Frequency Distributions and Histograms for Continuous Numerical Data

The difficulty in constructing tabular or graphical displays with continuous data, such as observations on reaction time (in seconds) or fuel efficiency (in miles per gallon), is that there are no natural categories. The way out of this dilemma is to define our own categories. For fuel efficiency data, suppose that we mark some intervals on a horizontal miles-per-gallon measurement axis, as pictured in Figure 3.18. Each data value should fall in exactly one of these intervals. If the smallest observation was 25.3 and the largest was 29.8, we might use intervals of width 0.5, with the first interval starting at 25.0 and the last interval ending at 30.0. The resulting intervals are called **class intervals**, or just **classes**. The class intervals play the same role that the categories or individual values played in frequency distributions for categorical or discrete numerical data.

**Figure 3.18** Suitable class intervals for miles-per-gallon data.

| | | | | | | | | | | |
|---|---|---|---|---|---|---|---|---|---|---|
| 25.0 | 25.5 | 26.0 | 26.5 | 27.0 | 27.5 | 28.0 | 28.5 | 29.0 | 29.5 | 30.0 |

There is one further difficulty we need to address. Where should we place an observation such as 27.0, which falls on a boundary between classes? Our convention is to define intervals so that such an observation is placed in the upper rather than the lower class interval. Thus, in a frequency distribution, one class might be 26.5 to <27.0, where the symbol < is a substitute for the phrase *less than*. This class will contain all observations that are greater than or equal to 26.5 and less than 27.0. The observation 27.0 would then fall in the class 27.0 to <27.5.

## Example 3.14   Enrollments at Public Universities

● States differ widely in the percentage of college students who are enrolled in public institutions. The National Center for Education Statistics provided the accompanying data on this percentage for the 50 U.S. states for fall 2002.

**Percentage of College Students Enrolled in Public Institutions**

| | | | | | | | | | | | |
|---|---|---|---|---|---|---|---|---|---|---|---|
| 86 | 96 | 66 | 86 | 80 | 78 | 62 | 81 | 77 | 81 | 77 | 76 |
| 73 | 69 | 76 | 90 | 78 | 82 | 70 | 83 | 46 | 80 | 78 | 93 |
| 66 | 91 | 76 | 86 | 58 | 81 | 91 | 57 | 81 | 88 | 71 | 86 |
| 84 | 57 | 44 | 82 | 79 | 67 | 86 | 75 | 55 | 75 | 80 | 80 |
| 85 | 69 | | | | | | | | | | |

The smallest observation is 44 (Rhode Island) and the largest is 96 (Alaska). It is reasonable to start the first class interval at 40 and let each interval have a width of 10. This gives class intervals of 40 to <50, 50 to <60, 60 to <70, 70 to <80, 80 to <90, and 90 to <100.

Table 3.3 displays the resulting frequency distribution, along with the relative frequencies.

Various relative frequencies can be combined to yield other interesting information. For example,

$$\begin{pmatrix} \text{proportion of states} \\ \text{with percent in public} \\ \text{institutions less than 60} \end{pmatrix} = \begin{pmatrix} \text{proportion in 40} \\ \text{to <50 class} \end{pmatrix} + \begin{pmatrix} \text{proportion in 50} \\ \text{to <60 class} \end{pmatrix}$$
$$= .04 + .08 = .12 \, (12\%)$$

● Data set available online

**Table 3.3**    Frequency Distribution for Percentage of
College Students Enrolled in Public Institutions

| Class Interval | Frequency | Relative Frequency |
|---|---|---|
| 40 to <50 | 2 | .04 |
| 50 to <60 | 4 | .08 |
| 60 to <70 | 6 | .12 |
| 70 to <80 | 14 | .28 |
| 80 to <90 | 19 | .38 |
| 90 to <100 | 5 | .10 |
| | 50 | 1.00 |

and

$$\begin{pmatrix} \text{proportion of states} \\ \text{with percent in} \\ \text{public institutions} \\ \text{between 60 and 90} \end{pmatrix} = \begin{pmatrix} \text{proportion} \\ \text{in 60 to} \\ <70 \text{ class} \end{pmatrix} + \begin{pmatrix} \text{proportion} \\ \text{in 70 to} \\ <80 \text{ class} \end{pmatrix} + \begin{pmatrix} \text{proportion} \\ \text{in 80 to} \\ <90 \text{ class} \end{pmatrix}$$

$$= .12 + .28 + .38 = .78 \,(78\%)$$

■

There are no set rules for selecting either the number of class intervals or the length of the intervals. Using a few relatively wide intervals will bunch the data, whereas using a great many relatively narrow intervals may spread the data over too many intervals, so that no interval contains more than a few observations. Neither type of distribution will give an informative picture of how values are distributed over the range of measurement, and interesting features of the data set may be missed. In general, with a small amount of data, relatively few intervals, perhaps between 5 and 10, should be used. With a large amount of data, a distribution based on 15 to 20 (or even more) intervals is often recommended. The quantity

$$\sqrt{\text{number of observations}}$$

is often used as an estimate of an appropriate number of intervals: 5 intervals for 25 observations, 10 intervals when the number of observations is 100, and so on.

Two people making reasonable and similar choices for the number of intervals, their width, and the starting point of the first interval will usually obtain similar histograms of the data.

## ■ Cumulative Relative Frequencies and Cumulative Relative Frequency Plots

Rather than wanting to know what proportion of the data fall in a particular class, we often wish to determine the proportion falling below a specified value. This is easily done when the value is a class boundary. Consider the following classes and relative frequencies:

| Class | 0 to <25 | 25 to <50 | 50 to <75 | 75 to <100 | 100 to <125 | ... |
|---|---|---|---|---|---|---|
| Rel. freq. | .05 | .10 | .18 | .25 | .20 | ... |

Then

proportion of observations less than 75 = proportion in one of the first three classes
$$= .05 + .10 + .18$$
$$= .33$$

Similarly,

proportion of observations less than 100 = .05 + .10 + .18 + .25 = .33 + .25 = .58

Each such sum of relative frequencies is called a **cumulative relative frequency**. Notice that the cumulative relative frequency .58 is the sum of the previous cumulative relative frequency .33 and the "current" relative frequency .25. The use of cumulative relative frequencies is illustrated in Example 3.15.

## Example 3.15   Bicycle Accidents

In 1996, 50 bicycle riders died in fatal accidents in the state of New York. Table 3.4 gives a relative frequency distribution for the ages of these 50 riders (New York Department of Health). The table also includes a column of cumulative relative frequencies.

**Table 3.4**   Frequency Distribution with Cumulative Relative Frequencies

| Age at Death | Frequency | Relative Frequency | Cumulative Relative Frequency |
|---|---|---|---|
| 5 to <10 | 4 | .08 | .08 |
| 10 to <15 | 4 | .08 | .16 ← .08 + .08 |
| 15 to <20 | 7 | .14 | .30 ← .08 + .08 + .14 |
| 20 to <25 | 4 | .08 | .38 |
| 25 to <45 | 19 | .38 | .76 |
| 45 to <65 | 9 | .18 | .94 |
| 65 to <90 | 3 | .06 | 1.00 |

The proportion of bicycle deaths that were riders less than 25 years of age is .38 (or 38%), the cumulative relative frequency for the 20 to <25 group. What about the proportion of bicycle deaths of riders younger than 35 years old? Because 35 is not the endpoint of one of the intervals in the frequency distribution, we can only estimate this proportion from the information given. The value 35 is halfway between the endpoints of the 25 to 45 interval, so it is reasonable to estimate that half of the relative frequency of .38 for this interval belongs in the 25 to 35 range. Then

estimate of proportion younger than 35 = $.08 + .08 + .14 + .08 + \frac{1}{2}(.38) = .57$

This proportion could also have been computed using the cumulative relative frequencies as

estimate of proportion younger than 35 = $.38 + \frac{1}{2}(.38) = .38 + .19 = .57$

Similarly, since 50 is one-fourth of the way from 45 to 65,

estimate of proportion younger than $50 = .76 + \frac{1}{4}(.18) = .76 + .045 = .805$

◼

A **cumulative relative frequency plot** is just a graph of the cumulative relative frequencies against the upper endpoint of the corresponding interval. The pairs

(upper endpoint of interval, cumulative relative frequency)

are plotted as points on a rectangular coordinate system, and successive points in the plot are connected by a line segment. For the bicycle accident data of Example 3.15, the plotted points would be

| | | | |
|---|---|---|---|
| (10, .08) | (15, .16) | (20, .30) | (25, .38) |
| (45, .76) | (65, .94) | (90, 1.00) | |

One additional point, the pair (lower endpoint of first interval, 0), is also included in the plot (for the bicycle accident data, this would be the point (5, 0)), and then points are connected by line segments. Figure 3.19 shows the cumulative relative frequency plot for the bicycle accident data. The cumulative relative frequency plot can be used to obtain approximate answers to questions such as

What proportion of the observations is smaller than a particular value?

and

What value separates the smallest *p* percent from the larger values?

For example, to determine the approximate proportion of the bicycle fatalities that were for people younger than 55, we would follow a vertical line up from 55 on the *x* axis and then read across to obtain the corresponding cumulative relative frequency, as illustrated in Figure 3.20(a). Approximately .84, or 84%, of the fatalities were for people younger than 55. Similarly, to find the age value that separates the youngest 30% of the fatalities from the higher ages, start at .30 on the cumulative relative frequency axis and move across and then down to find the corresponding age, as shown in Figure 3.20(b). Approximately 30% of the fatalities were for people younger than 20.

**Figure 3.19** Cumulative relative frequency plot for the bicycle accident data of Example 3.15.

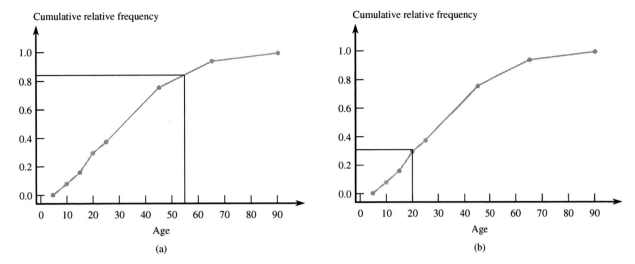

**Figure 3.20**   Using the cumulative relative frequency plot: (a) determining the approximate proportion of bicycle fatalities that were for people 55 or younger; (b) finding the age that separates the youngest 30% of bicycle fatalities from the oldest 70%.

## ■ Histograms for Continuous Numerical Data .................................................

When the class intervals in a frequency distribution are all of equal width, it is easy to construct a histogram using the information in a frequency distribution.

### Histogram for Continuous Numerical Data When the Class Interval Widths Are Equal

**When to Use**

Continuous numerical data. Works well, even for large data sets.

**How to Construct**

1. Mark the boundaries of the class intervals on a horizontal axis.
2. Use either frequency or relative frequency on the vertical axis.
3. Draw a rectangle for each class directly above the corresponding interval (so that the edges are at the class boundaries). The height of each rectangle is the frequency or relative frequency of the corresponding class interval.

**What to Look For**

- Central or typical value
- Extent of spread or variation
- General shape
- Location and number of peaks
- Presence of gaps and outliers

# Example 3.16   TV Viewing Habits of Children

The article "Early Television Exposure and Subsequent Attention Problems in Children" (*Pediatrics,* April 2004) investigated the television viewing habits of children in the United States. Table 3.5 gives approximate relative frequencies (read from graphs that appeared in the article) for the number of hours spent watching TV per day for a sample of children at age 1 year and a sample of children at age 3 years. The data summarized in the article were obtained as part of a large scale national survey.

**Table 3.5**   Relative Frequency Distribution for Number of Hours Spent Watching TV per Day

| TV Hours per Day | Age 1 Year Relative Frequency | Age 3 Years Relative Frequency |
|---|---|---|
| 0 to <2 | .270 | .630 |
| 2 to <4 | .390 | .195 |
| 4 to <6 | .190 | .100 |
| 6 to <8 | .085 | .025 |
| 8 to <10 | .030 | .020 |
| 10 to <12 | .020 | .015 |
| 12 to <14 | .010 | .010 |
| 14 to <16 | .005 | .005 |

Figure 3.21(a) is the relative frequency histogram for the 1-year-old children and Figure 3.21(b) is the relative frequency histogram for 3-year-old children. Notice that both histograms have a single peak with the majority of children in both age groups concentrated in the smaller TV hours intervals. Both histograms are quite stretched out at the upper end, indicating some young children watch a lot of TV.

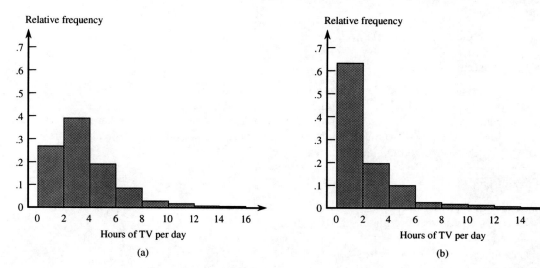

**Figure 3.21**   Histogram of TV hours per day: (a) 1-year-old children; (b) 3-year-old children.

The big difference between the two histograms is at the low end, with a much higher proportion of 3-year-old children falling in the 0 to 2 TV hours interval than is the case for 1-year-old children. A typical number of TV hours per day for 1-year-old children would be somewhere between 2 and 4 hours, whereas a typical number of TV hours for 3-year-old children is in the 0 to 2 hour interval.

■

■ **Class Intervals of Unequal Widths**   Figure 3.22 shows a data set in which a great many observations are concentrated at the center of the set, with only a few outlying, or stray, values both below and above the main body of data. If a frequency distribution is based on short intervals of equal width, a great many intervals will be required to capture all observations, and many of them will contain no observations (0 frequency). On the other hand, only a few wide intervals will capture all values, but then most of the observations will be grouped into a few intervals. Neither choice yields an informative description of the distribution. In such situations, it is best to use a combination of wide class intervals where there are few data points and shorter intervals where there are many data points.

**Figure 3.22** Three choices of class intervals for a data set with outliers: (a) many short intervals of equal width; (b) a few wide intervals of equal width; (c) intervals of unequal width.

### Constructing a Histogram for Continuous Data When Class Interval Widths Are Unequal

In this case, frequencies or relative frequencies should not be used on the vertical axis. Instead, the height of each rectangle, called the **density** for the class, is given by

$$\text{density} = \text{rectangle height} = \frac{\text{relative frequency of class interval}}{\text{class interval width}}$$

The vertical axis is called the **density scale**.

■

*The use of the density scale to construct the histogram ensures that the area of each rectangle in the histogram will be proportional to the corresponding relative frequency.* The formula for density can also be used when class widths are equal. However, when the intervals are of equal width, the extra arithmetic required to obtain the densities is unnecessary.

## Example 3.17  Misreporting Grade Point Average

When people are asked for the values of characteristics such as age or weight, they sometimes shade the truth in their responses. The article "Self-Reports of Academic Performance" (*Social Methods and Research* [November 1981]: 165–185) focused on such characteristics as SAT scores and grade point average (GPA). For each student in a sample, the difference in GPA (reported–actual) was determined. Positive differences resulted from individuals reporting GPAs larger than the correct values. Most differences were close to 0, but there were some rather gross errors. Because of this, the frequency distribution based on unequal class widths shown in Table 3.6 gives an informative yet concise summary.

**Table 3.6** Frequency Distribution for Errors in Reported GPA

| Class Interval | Relative Frequency | Width | Density |
|---|---|---|---|
| −2.0 to <−0.4 | .023 | 1.6 | 0.014 |
| −0.4 to <−0.2 | .055 | .2 | 0.275 |
| −0.2 to <−0.1 | .097 | .1 | 0.970 |
| −0.1 to <0 | .210 | .1 | 2.100 |
| 0 to <0.1 | .189 | .1 | 1.890 |
| 0.1 to <0.2 | .139 | .1 | 1.390 |
| 0.2 to <0.4 | .116 | .2 | 0.580 |
| 0.4 to <2.0 | .171 | 1.6 | 0.107 |

Figure 3.23 displays two histograms based on this frequency distribution. The histogram in Figure 3.23(a) is correctly drawn, with density used to determine the height of each bar. The histogram in Figure 3.23(b) has height equal to relative

**Figure 3.23** Histograms for errors in reporting GPA: (a) a correct picture (height = density); (b) an incorrect picture (height = relative frequency).

frequency and is therefore not correct. In particular, this second histogram considerably exaggerates the incidence of grossly overreported and underreported values—the areas of the two most extreme rectangles are much too large. The eye is naturally drawn to large areas, so it is important that the areas correctly represent the relative frequencies.

■

## ■ Histogram Shapes

General shape is an important characteristic of a histogram. In describing various shapes it is convenient to approximate the histogram itself with a smooth curve (called a *smoothed histogram*). This is illustrated in Figure 3.24.

**Figure 3.24** Approximating a histogram with a smooth curve.

One description of general shape relates to the number of peaks, or **modes**.

A histogram is said to be **unimodal** if it has a single peak, **bimodal** if it has two peaks, and **multimodal** if it has more than two peaks.

■

These shapes are illustrated in Figure 3.25.

**Figure 3.25** Smoothed histograms with various numbers of modes: (a) unimodal; (b) bimodal; (c) multimodal.

(a)          (b)          (c)

Bimodality can occur when the data set consists of observations on two quite different kinds of individuals or objects. For example, consider a large data set consisting of driving times for automobiles traveling between San Luis Obispo, California, and Monterey, California. This histogram would show two peaks, one for those cars that took the inland route (roughly 2.5 hr) and another for those cars traveling up the coast highway (3.5–4 hr). However, bimodality does not automatically follow in such situations. Bimodality will occur in the histogram of the combined groups only if the centers of the two separate histograms are far apart relative to the variability in the two data sets. Thus, a large data set consisting of heights of college students would probably not produce a bimodal histogram because the typical height for males (about 69 in.) and the typical height for females (about 66 in.) are not very far apart. Many histograms encountered in practice are unimodal, and multimodality is rather rare.

Unimodal histograms come in a variety of shapes. A unimodal histogram is **symmetric** if there is a vertical line of symmetry such that the part of the histogram to the left of the line is a mirror image of the part to the right. (Bimodal and multimodal

**Figure 3.26** Several symmetric unimodal smoothed histograms.

histograms can also be symmetric in this way.) Several different symmetric smoothed histograms are shown in Figure 3.26.

Proceeding to the right from the peak of a unimodal histogram, we move into what is called the **upper tail** of the histogram. Going in the opposite direction moves us into the **lower tail**.

A unimodal histogram that is not symmetric is said to be **skewed**. If the upper tail of the histogram stretches out much farther than the lower tail, then the distribution of values is **positively skewed**. If, on the other hand, the lower tail is much longer than the upper tail, the histogram is **negatively skewed**.

These two types of skewness are illustrated in Figure 3.27. Positive skewness is much more frequently encountered than is negative skewness. An example of positive skewness occurs in the distribution of single-family home prices in Los Angeles County; most homes are moderately priced (at least for California), whereas the relatively few homes in Beverly Hills and Malibu have much higher price tags.

**Figure 3.27** Two examples of skewed smoothed histograms: (a) positive skew; (b) negative skew.

(a)                                     (b)

One rather specific shape, a **normal curve**, arises more frequently than any other in statistical applications. Many histograms can be well approximated by a normal curve (e.g., characteristics such as arm span and brain weight). Here we briefly mention several of the most important qualitative properties of such a curve, postponing a more detailed discussion until Chapter 7. A normal curve is both symmetric and bell shaped; it looks like the curve in Figure 3.28(a). However, not all bell-shaped curves are normal. In a normal curve, starting from the top of the bell the height of the curve decreases at a well-defined rate when moving toward either tail. (This rate of decrease is specified by a certain mathematical function.)

A curve with tails that do not decline as rapidly as the tails of a normal curve is called **heavy-tailed** (compared to the normal curve). Similarly, a curve with tails that

**Figure 3.28** Three examples of bell-shaped histograms: (a) normal; (b) heavy-tailed; (c) light-tailed.

(a)                    (b)                    (c)

decrease more rapidly than the normal tails is called **light-tailed**. Figures 3.28(b) and 3.28(c) illustrate these possibilities. The reason that we are concerned about the tails in a distribution is that many inferential procedures that work well (i.e., they result in accurate conclusions) when the population distribution is approximately normal do poorly when the population distribution is heavy tailed.

## ■ Do Sample Histograms Resemble Population Histograms? ........................

Sample data are usually collected to make inferences about a population. The resulting conclusions may be in error if the sample is unrepresentative of the population. So how similar might a histogram of sample data be to the histogram of all population values? Will the two histograms be centered at roughly the same place and spread out to about the same extent? Will they have the same number of peaks, and will these occur at approximately the same places?

A related issue concerns the extent to which histograms based on different samples from the same population resemble one another. If two different sample histograms can be expected to differ from one another in obvious ways, then at least one of them might differ substantially from the population histogram. If the sample differs substantially from the population, conclusions about the population based on the sample are likely to be incorrect. **Sampling variability**—the extent to which samples differ from one another and from the population—is a central idea in statistics. Example 3.18 illustrates such variability in histogram shapes.

........................................................................................................................

# Example 3.18 What You Should Know About Bus Drivers . . .

**Table 3.7**  Frequency Distribution for Number of Accidents by Bus Drivers

| Number of Accidents | Frequency | Relative Frequency |
|---|---|---|
| 0 | 117 | .165 |
| 1 | 157 | .222 |
| 2 | 158 | .223 |
| 3 | 115 | .162 |
| 4 | 78 | .110 |
| 5 | 44 | .062 |
| 6 | 21 | .030 |
| 7 | 7 | .010 |
| 8 | 6 | .008 |
| 9 | 1 | .001 |
| 10 | 3 | .004 |
| 11 | 1 | .001 |
| | 708 | .998 |

● A sample of 708 bus drivers employed by public corporations was selected, and the number of traffic accidents in which each bus driver was involved during a 4-year period was determined ("Application of Discrete Distribution Theory to the Study of Noncommunicable Events in Medical Epidemiology," in *Random Counts in Biomedical and Social Sciences,* G. P. Patil, ed. [University Park, PA: Pennsylvania State University Press, 1970]). A listing of the 708 sample observations might look like this:

3 0 6 0 0 2 1 4 1 . . . 6 0 2

The frequency distribution (Table 3.7) shows that 117 of the 708 drivers had no accidents, a relative frequency of 117/708 = .165 (or 16.5%). Similarly, the proportion of sampled drivers who had 1 accident is .222 (or 22.2%). The largest sample observation was 11.

Although the 708 observations actually constituted a sample from the population of all bus drivers, we will regard the 708 observations as constituting the entire population. The first histogram in Figure 3.29, then, represents the population histogram. The other four histograms in Figure 3.29 are based on four different samples of 50 observations each

● Data set available online

**Figure 3.29** Comparison of population and sample histograms for number of accidents.

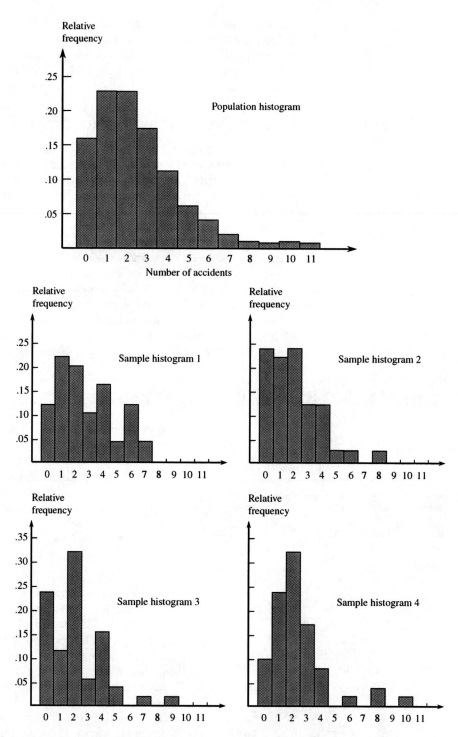

from this population. The five histograms certainly resemble one another in a general way, but some dissimilarities are also obvious. The population histogram rises to a peak and then declines smoothly, whereas the sample histograms tend to have more peaks, valleys, and gaps. Although the population data set contained an observation of 11, none of the four samples did. In fact, in the first two samples, the largest observations were 7 and 8, respectively. In Chapters 8–15 we will see how sampling variability can be described and incorporated into conclusions based on inferential methods.

■

■ Exercises 3.22–3.34 ······························································································

3.22 ● Medicare's new medical plans offer a wide range of variations and choices for seniors when picking a drug plan (*San Luis Obispo Tribune,* November 25, 2005). The monthly cost for a stand-alone drug plan varies from plan to plan and from state to state. The accompanying table gives the premium for the plan with the lowest cost for each state.

| State | Cost per Month (dollars) |
|---|---|
| Alabama | 14.08 |
| Alaska | 20.05 |
| Arizona | 6.14 |
| Arkansas | 10.31 |
| California | 5.41 |
| Colorado | 8.62 |
| Connecticut | 7.32 |
| Delaware | 6.44 |
| District of Columbia | 6.44 |
| Florida | 10.35 |
| Georgia | 17.91 |
| Hawaii | 17.18 |
| Idaho | 6.33 |
| Illinois | 13.32 |
| Indiana | 12.30 |
| Iowa | 1.87 |
| Kansas | 9.48 |
| Kentucky | 12.30 |
| Louisiana | 17.06 |
| Maine | 19.60 |
| Maryland | 6.44 |
| Massachusetts | 7.32 |
| Michigan | 13.75 |
| Minnesota | 1.87 |
| Mississippi | 11.60 |
| Missouri | 10.29 |
| Montana | 1.87 |
| Nebraska | 1.87 |
| Nevada | 6.42 |

| State | Cost per Month (dollars) |
|---|---|
| New Hampshire | 19.60 |
| New Jersey | 4.43 |
| New Mexico | 10.65 |
| New York | 4.10 |
| North Carolina | 13.27 |
| North Dakota | 1.87 |
| Ohio | 14.43 |
| Oklahoma | 10.07 |
| Oregon | 6.93 |
| Pennsylvania | 10.14 |
| Rhode Island | 7.32 |
| South Carolina | 16.57 |
| South Dakota | 1.87 |
| Tennessee | 14.08 |
| Texas | 10.31 |
| Utah | 6.33 |
| Vermont | 7.32 |
| Virginia | 8.81 |
| Washington | 6.93 |
| West Virginia | 10.14 |
| Wisconsin | 11.42 |
| Wyoming | 1.87 |

a. Use class intervals of $0 to <$3, $3 to <$6, $6 to <$9 etc., to create a relative frequency distribution for these data.
b. Construct a histogram and comment on its shape.
c. Using the relative frequency distribution or the histogram, determine the proportion of the states that have a minimum monthly plan of less than $13.00 a month.

3.23 ● The following two relative frequency distributions were constructed using data that appeared in the report "Undergraduate Students and Credit Cards in 2004 (Nellie

Mae, May 2005). One relative frequency distribution is based on credit bureau data for a random sample of 1413 college students, while the other is based on the result of a survey completed by 132 of the 1260 college students who received the survey.

**Credit Card Balance (dollars)— Credit Bureau Data**

| | Relative Frequency |
|---|---|
| 0 to <100 | .18 |
| 100 to <500 | .19 |
| 500 to <1000 | .14 |
| 1000 to <2000 | .16 |
| 2000 to <3000 | .10 |
| 3000 to <7000 | .16 |
| 7000 or more | .07 |

**Credit Card Balance (dollars)— Survey Data**

| | Relative Frequency |
|---|---|
| 0 to <100 | .18 |
| 100 to <500 | .22 |
| 500 to <1000 | .17 |
| 1000 to <2000 | .22 |
| 2000 to <3000 | .07 |
| 3000 to <7000 | .14 |
| 7000 or more | .00 |

a. Construct a histogram for the credit bureau data. For purposes of constructing the histogram, assume that none of the students in the sample had a balance higher than 15,000 and that the last interval can be regarded as 7000 to < 15,000. Be sure to use the density scale when constructing the histogram.
b. Construct a histogram for the survey data. Use the same scale that you used for the histogram in part (a) so that it will be easy to compare the two histograms.
c. Comment on the similarities and differences in the histograms from Parts (a) and (b).
d. Do you think the high nonresponse rate for the survey may have contributed to the observed differences in the two histograms? Explain.

3.24 ● People suffering from Alzheimer's disease often have difficulty performing basic activities of daily living (ADLs). In one study ("Functional Status and Clinical Findings in Patients with Alzheimer's Disease," *Journal of Gerontology* [1992]: 177–182), investigators focused on

six such activities: dressing, bathing, transferring, toileting, walking, and eating. Here are data on the number of ADL impairments for each of 240 patients:

| Number of impairments | 0 | 1 | 2 | 3 | 4 | 5 | 6 |
|---|---|---|---|---|---|---|---|
| Frequency | 100 | 43 | 36 | 17 | 24 | 9 | 11 |

a. Determine the relative frequencies that correspond to the given frequencies.
b. What proportion of these patients had at most two impairments?
c. Use the result of Part (b) to determine what proportion of patients had more than two impairments.
d. What proportion of the patients had at least four impairments?

**3.25** ● ▼ *USA Today* (July 2, 2001) gave the following information regarding cell phone use for men and women:

| Average Number of Minutes Used per Month | Relative Frequency | |
|---|---|---|
| | Men | Women |
| 0 to <200 | .56 | .61 |
| 200 to <400 | .18 | .18 |
| 400 to <600 | .10 | .13 |
| 600 to <800 | .16 | .08 |

a. Construct a relative frequency histogram for average number of minutes used per month for men. How would you describe the shape of this histogram?
b. Construct a relative frequency histogram for average number of minutes used per month for women. Is the distribution for average number of minutes used per month similar for men and women? Explain.
c. What proportion of men average less than 400 minutes per month?
d. Estimate the proportion of men that average less than 500 minutes per month.
e. Estimate the proportion of women that average 450 minutes or more per month.

3.26 ● U.S. Census data for San Luis Obispo County, California, were used to construct the following frequency distribution for commute time (in minutes) of working adults (the given frequencies were read from a graph that appeared in the *San Luis Obispo Tribune* [September 1, 2002] and so are only approximate):

| Commute Time | Frequency |
|---|---|
| 0 to <5 | 5,200 |
| 5 to <10 | 18,200 |
| 10 to <15 | 19,600 |
| 15 to <20 | 15,400 |
| 20 to <25 | 13,800 |
| 25 to <30 | 5,700 |
| 30 to <35 | 10,200 |
| 35 to <40 | 2,000 |
| 40 to <45 | 2,000 |
| 45 to <60 | 4,000 |
| 60 to <90 | 2,100 |
| 90 to <120 | 2,200 |

a. Notice that not all intervals in the frequency distribution are equal in width. Why do you think that unequal width intervals were used?
b. Construct a table that adds a relative frequency and a density column to the given frequency distribution.
c. Use the densities computed in Part (b) to construct a histogram for this data set. (Note: The newspaper displayed an incorrectly drawn histogram based on frequencies rather than densities!) Write a few sentences commenting on the important features of the histogram.
d. Compute the cumulative relative frequencies, and construct a cumulative relative frequency plot.
e. Use the cumulative relative frequency plot constructed in Part (d) to answer the following questions.
   i. Approximately what proportion of commute times were less than 50 min?
   ii. Approximately what proportion of commute times were greater than 22 min?
   iii. What is the approximate commute time value that separates the shortest 50% of commute times from the longest 50%?

**3.27** ● The article "Determination of Most Representative Subdivision" (*Journal of Energy Engineering* [1993]: 43–55) gave data on various characteristics of subdivisions that could be used in deciding whether to provide electrical power using overhead lines or underground lines. Data on the variable $x$ = total length of streets within a subdivision are as follows:

| | | | | | | | |
|---|---|---|---|---|---|---|---|
| 1280 | 5320 | 4390 | 2100 | 1240 | 3060 | 4770 | 1050 |
| 360 | 3330 | 3380 | 340 | 1000 | 960 | 1320 | 530 |
| 3350 | 540 | 3870 | 1250 | 2400 | 960 | 1120 | 2120 |
| 450 | 2250 | 2320 | 2400 | 3150 | 5700 | 5220 | 500 |
| 1850 | 2460 | 5850 | 2700 | 2730 | 1670 | 100 | 5770 |
| 3150 | 1890 | 510 | 240 | 396 | 1419 | 2109 | |

a. Construct a stem-and-leaf display for these data using the thousands digit as the stem. Comment on the various features of the display.
b. Construct a histogram using class boundaries of 0 to 1000, 1000 to 2000, and so on. How would you describe the shape of the histogram?
c. What proportion of subdivisions has total length less than 2000? between 2000 and 4000?

**3.28** Student loans can add up, especially for those attending professional schools to study in such areas as medicine, law, or dentistry. Researchers at the University of Washington studied medical students and gave the following information on the educational debt of medical students on completion of their residencies (*Annals of Internal Medicine* [March 2002]: 384–398):

| Educational Debt (dollars) | Relative Frequency |
|---|---|
| 0 to <5000 | .427 |
| 5000 to <20,000 | .046 |
| 20,000 to <50,000 | .109 |
| 50,000 to <100,000 | .232 |
| 100,000 or more | .186 |

a. What are two reasons that it would be inappropriate to construct a histogram using relative frequencies to determine the height of the bars in the histogram?
b. Suppose that no student had an educational debt of $150,000 or more upon completion of his or her residency, so that the last class in the relative frequency distribution would be 100,000 to <150,000. Summarize this distribution graphically by constructing a histogram of the educational debt data. (Don't forget to use the density scale for the heights of the bars in the histogram, because the interval widths aren't all the same.)
c. Based on the histogram of Part (b), write a few sentences describing the educational debt of medical students completing their residencies.

**Bold** exercises answered in back   ● Data set available online but not required   ▼ Video solution available

**3.29** An exam is given to students in an introductory statistics course. What is likely to be true of the shape of the histogram of scores if:

**a.** the exam is quite easy?

**b.** the exam is quite difficult?

**c.** half the students in the class have had calculus, the other half have had no prior college math courses, and the exam emphasizes mathematical manipulation?

Explain your reasoning in each case.

**3.30** ● The paper "Lessons from Pacemaker Implanta-tions" (*Journal of the American Medical Association* [1965]: 231–232) gave the results of a study that followed 89 heart patients who had received electronic pacemakers. The time (in months) to the first electrical malfunction of the pacemaker was recorded:

```
24  20  16  32  14  22   2  12  24   6  10  20
 8  16  12  24  14  20  18  14  16  18  20  22
24  26  28  18  14  10  12  24   6  12  18  16
34  18  20  22  24  26  18   2  18  12  12   8
24  10  14  16  22  24  22  20  24  28  20  22
26  20   6  14  16  18  24  18  16   6  16  10
14  18  24  22  28  24  30  34  26  24  22  28
30  22  24  22  32
```

**a.** Summarize these data in the form of a frequency dis-tribution, using class intervals of 0 to <6, 6 to <12, and so on.

**b.** Compute the relative frequencies and cumulative rela-tive frequencies for each class interval of the frequency distribution of Part (a).

**c.** Show how the relative frequency for the class interval 12 to <18 could be obtained from the cumulative relative frequencies.

**d.** Use the cumulative relative frequencies to give approx-imate answers to the following:

　**i.** What proportion of those who participated in the study had pacemakers that did not malfunction within the first year?

　**ii.** If the pacemaker must be replaced as soon as the first electrical malfunction occurs, approximately what proportion required replacement between 1 and 2 years after implantation?

**e.** Construct a cumulative relative frequency plot, and use it to answer the following questions.

　**i.** What is the approximate time at which about 50% of the pacemakers had failed?

　**ii.** What is the approximate time at which only about 10% of the pacemakers initially implanted were still functioning?

**3.31** The clearness index was determined for the skies over Baghdad for each of the 365 days during a particular year ("Contribution to the Study of the Solar Radiation Climate of the Baghdad Environment," *Solar Energy* [1990]: 7–12). The accompanying table summarizes the resulting data:

| Clearness Index | Number of Days (frequency) |
|---|---|
| 0.15 to <0.25 | 8 |
| 0.25 to <0.35 | 14 |
| 0.35 to <0.45 | 28 |
| 0.45 to <0.50 | 24 |
| 0.50 to <0.55 | 39 |
| 0.55 to <0.60 | 51 |
| 0.60 to <0.65 | 106 |
| 0.65 to <0.70 | 84 |
| 0.70 to <0.75 | 11 |

**a.** Determine the relative frequencies and draw the corre-sponding histogram. (Be careful here—the intervals do not all have the same width.)

**b.** Cloudy days are those with a clearness index smaller than 0.35. What proportion of the days was cloudy?

**c.** Clear days are those for which the index is at least 0.65. What proportion of the days was clear?

**3.32** How does the speed of a runner vary over the course of a marathon (a distance of 42.195 km)? Consider deter-mining both the time to run the first 5 km and the time to run between the 35 km and 40 km points, and then sub-tracting the 5-km time from the 35–40-km time. A posi-tive value of this difference corresponds to a runner slow-ing down toward the end of the race. The histogram on page 113 is based on times of runners who participated in several different Japanese marathons ("Factors Affecting Runners' Marathon Performance," *Chance* [Fall, 1993]: 24–30). What are some interesting features of this histo-gram? What is a typical difference value? Roughly what proportion of the runners ran the late distance more quickly than the early distance?

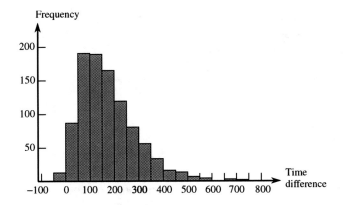

| Class Interval | Frequency | | | | |
|---|---|---|---|---|---|
| | I | II | III | IV | V |
| 0 to <10 | 5 | 40 | 30 | 15 | 6 |
| 10 to <20 | 10 | 25 | 10 | 25 | 5 |
| 20 to <30 | 20 | 10 | 8 | 8 | 6 |
| 30 to <40 | 30 | 8 | 7 | 7 | 9 |
| 40 to <50 | 20 | 7 | 7 | 20 | 9 |
| 50 to <60 | 10 | 5 | 8 | 25 | 23 |
| 60 to <70 | 5 | 5 | 30 | 10 | 42 |

**3.33** Construct a histogram corresponding to each of the five frequency distributions, I–V, given in the following table, and state whether each histogram is symmetric, bimodal, positively skewed, or negatively skewed:

**3.34** Using the five class intervals 100 to 120, 120 to 140, . . . , 180 to 200, devise a frequency distribution based on 70 observations whose histogram could be described as follows:
a. symmetric          c. positively skewed
b. bimodal             d. negatively skewed

**Bold** exercises answered in back     ● Data set available online but not required     ▼ Video solution available

---

## 3.4   Displaying Bivariate Numerical Data

A bivariate data set consists of measurements or observations on two variables, $x$ and $y$. For example, $x$ might be distance from a highway and $y$ the lead content of soil at that distance. When both $x$ and $y$ are numerical variables, each observation consists of a pair of numbers, such as (14, 5.2) or (27.63, 18.9). The first number in a pair is the value of $x$, and the second number is the value of $y$.

An unorganized list of bivariate data yields little information about the distribution of either the $x$ values or the $y$ values separately and even less information about how the two variables are related to one another. Just as graphical displays can be used to summarize univariate data, they can also help with bivariate data. The most important graph based on bivariate numerical data is a **scatterplot**.

In a scatterplot each observation (pair of numbers) is represented by a point on a rectangular coordinate system, as shown in Figure 3.30(a). The horizontal axis is identified with values of $x$ and is scaled so that any $x$ value can be easily located. Similarly, the vertical or $y$ axis is marked for easy location of $y$ values. The point corresponding

**Figure 3.30** Constructing a scatterplot: (a) rectangular coordinate system; (b) point corresponding to (4.5, 15).

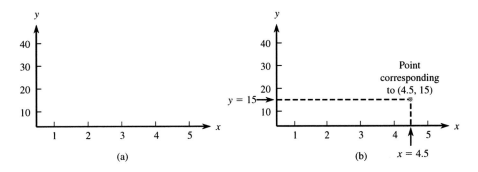

to any particular (x, y) pair is placed where a vertical line from the value on the x axis meets a horizontal line from the value on the y axis. Figure 3.30(b) shows the point representing the observation (4.5, 15); it is above 4.5 on the horizontal axis and to the right of 15 on the vertical axis.

........................................................................................................................

## Example 3.19 Olympic Figure Skating

● Do tall skaters have an advantage when it comes to earning high artistic scores in figure skating competitions? Data on $x$ = height (in cm) and $y$ = artistic score in the free skate for both male and female singles skaters at the 2006 Winter Olympics are shown in the accompanying table. (Data set courtesy of John Walker.)

| Name | Gender | Height | Artistic |
|------|--------|--------|----------|
| PLUSHENKO Yevgeny | M | 178 | 41.2100 |
| BUTTLE Jeffrey | M | 173 | 39.2500 |
| LYSACEK Evan | M | 177 | 37.1700 |
| LAMBIEL Stephane | M | 176 | 38.1400 |
| SAVOIE Matt | M | 175 | 35.8600 |
| WEIR Johnny | M | 172 | 37.6800 |
| JOUBERT Brian | M | 179 | 36.7900 |
| VAN DER PERREN Kevin | M | 177 | 33.0100 |
| TAKAHASHI Daisuke | M | 165 | 36.6500 |
| KLIMKIN Ilia | M | 170 | 32.6100 |
| ZHANG Min | M | 176 | 31.8600 |
| SAWYER Shawn | M | 163 | 34.2500 |
| LI Chengjiang | M | 170 | 28.4700 |
| SANDHU Emanuel | M | 183 | 35.1100 |
| VERNER Tomas | M | 180 | 28.6100 |
| DAVYDOV Sergei | M | 159 | 30.4700 |
| CHIPER Gheorghe | M | 176 | 32.1500 |
| DINEV Ivan | M | 174 | 29.2500 |
| DAMBIER Frederic | M | 163 | 31.2500 |
| LINDEMANN Stefan | M | 163 | 31.0000 |
| KOVALEVSKI Anton | M | 171 | 28.7500 |
| BERNTSSON Kristoffer | M | 175 | 28.0400 |
| PFEIFER Viktor | M | 180 | 28.7200 |
| TOTH Zoltan | M | 185 | 25.1000 |
| ARAKAWA Shizuka | F | 166 | 39.3750 |
| COHEN Sasha | F | 157 | 39.0063 |
| SLUTSKAYA Irina | F | 160 | 38.6688 |
| SUGURI Fumie | F | 157 | 37.0313 |
| ROCHETTE Joannie | F | 157 | 35.0813 |
| MEISSNER Kimmie | F | 160 | 33.4625 |
| HUGHES Emily | F | 165 | 31.8563 |

● Data set available online

| Name | Gender | Height | Artistic |
|------|--------|--------|----------|
| MEIER Sarah | F | 164 | 32.0313 |
| KOSTNER Carolina | F | 168 | 34.9313 |
| SOKOLOVA Yelena | F | 162 | 31.4250 |
| YAN Liu | F | 164 | 28.1625 |
| LEUNG Mira | F | 168 | 26.7000 |
| GEDEVANISHVILI Elene | F | 159 | 31.2250 |
| KORPI Kiira | F | 166 | 27.2000 |
| POYKIO Susanna | F | 159 | 31.2125 |
| ANDO Miki | F | 162 | 31.5688 |
| EFREMENKO Galina | F | 163 | 26.5125 |
| LIASHENKO Elena | F | 160 | 28.5750 |
| HEGEL Idora | F | 166 | 25.5375 |
| SEBESTYEN Julia | F | 164 | 28.6375 |
| KARADEMIR Tugba | F | 165 | 23.0000 |
| FONTANA Silvia | F | 158 | 26.3938 |
| PAVUK Viktoria | F | 168 | 23.6688 |
| MAXWELL Fleur | F | 160 | 24.5438 |

Figure 3.31(a) gives a scatterplot of the data. Looking at the data and the scatterplot, we can see that

1. Several observations have identical $x$ values but different $y$ values (e.g. $x = 176$ cm for both Stephane Lambiel and Min Zhang, but Lambiel's artistic score was 38.1400 and Zhang's artistic score was 31.8600). Thus, the value of $y$ is *not* determined *solely* by the value of $x$ but by various other factors as well.
2. At any given height there is quite a bit of variability in artistic score. For example, for those skaters with height 160 cm, artistic scores ranged from a low of about 24.5 to a high of about 39.
3. There is no noticeable tendency for artistic score to increase as height increases. There does not appear to be a strong relationship between height and artistic score.

   The data set used to construct the scatter plot included data for both male and female skaters. Figure 3.31(b) shows a scatterplot of the (height, artistic score) pairs with observations for male skaters shown in blue and observations for female skaters shown in orange. Not surprisingly, the female skaters tend to be shorter than the male skaters (the observations for females tend to be concentrated toward the left side of the scatterplot). Careful examination of this plot shows that while there was no apparent pattern in the combined (male and female) data set, there may be a relationship between height and artistic score for female skaters.

   Figures 3.31(c) and 3.31(d) show separate scatterplots for the male and female skaters, respectively. It is interesting to note that it appears that for female skaters, higher artistic scores seem to be associated with smaller height values, but for men there does not appear to be a relationship between height and artistic score. The relationship between height and artistic score for women is not evident in the scatterplot of the combined data.

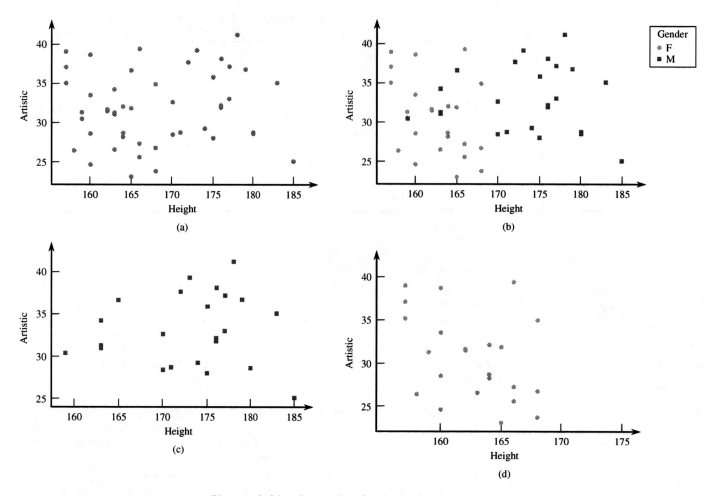

**Figure 3.31** Scatterplots for the data of Example 3.19: (a) scatterplot of data; (b) scatterplot of data with observations for males and females distinguished by color; (c) scatterplot for male skaters; (d) scatterplot for female skaters. ■

    The horizontal and vertical axes in the scatterplots of Figure 3.31 do not intersect at the point (0, 0). In many data sets, the values of $x$ or of $y$ or of both variables differ considerably from 0 relative to the ranges of the values in the data set. For example, a study of how air conditioner efficiency is related to maximum daily outdoor temperature might involve observations at temperatures of 80°, 82°, . . . , 98°, 100°. In such cases, the plot will be more informative if the axes intersect at some point other than (0, 0) and are marked accordingly. This is illustrated in Example 3.20.

.........................................................................................................

# Example 3.20 Taking Those "Hard" Classes Pays Off

    ⦿ The report titled "2005 College Bound Seniors" (College Board, 2005) included the accompanying table showing the average score on the verbal section of the SAT for groups of high school seniors completing different numbers of years of study in six core academic subjects (arts and music, English, foreign languages, mathematics, natural sciences, and social sciences and history). Figure 3.32(a) and (b) show two scatterplots of $x$ = total number of years of study and $y$ = average verbal SAT score. The scatterplots were produced by the statistical computer package MINITAB. In Figure 3.32(a), we let MINITAB select the scale for both axes. Figure 3.32(b) was obtained by specifying that the axes would intersect at the point (0, 0). The second plot does not make effective use of space. It is more crowded than the first plot, and such crowding can make it more difficult to see the general nature of any relationship. For example, it can be more difficult to spot curvature in a crowded plot.

| Years of Study | Average Verbal SAT Score |
|---|---|
| 14 | 446 |
| 15 | 453 |
| 16 | 459 |
| 17 | 467 |
| 18 | 484 |
| 19 | 501 |
| 20 | 545 |

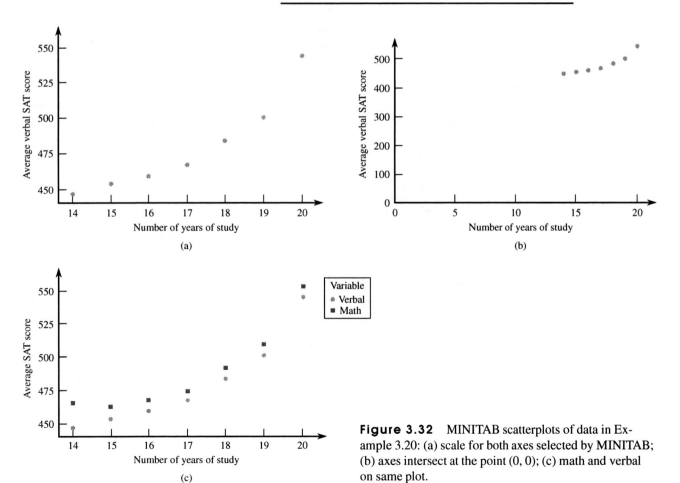

**Figure 3.32**  MINITAB scatterplots of data in Example 3.20: (a) scale for both axes selected by MINITAB; (b) axes intersect at the point (0, 0); (c) math and verbal on same plot.

The scatterplot for average verbal SAT score exhibits a fairly strong curved pattern, indicating that there is a strong relationship between average verbal SAT score and the total number of years of study in the six core academic subjects. Although the pattern in the plot is curved rather than linear, it is still easy to see that the average verbal SAT score increases as the number of years of study increases. Figure 3.32(c) shows a scatterplot with the average verbal SAT scores represented by orange dots and the average math SAT scores represented by blue squares. From this plot we can see that while the average math SAT scores tend to be higher than the average verbal scores at all of the values of total number of years of study, the general curved form of the relationship is similar.

■

In Chapter 5, methods for summarizing bivariate data when the scatterplot reveals a pattern are introduced. Linear patterns are relatively easy to work with. A curved pattern, such as the one in Example 3.20, is a bit more complicated to analyze, and methods for summarizing such nonlinear relationships are developed in Section 5.4.

## ■ Time Series Plots

Data sets often consist of measurements collected over time at regular intervals so that we can learn about change over time. For example, stock prices, sales figures, and other socio-economic indicators might be recorded on a weekly or monthly basis. A **time-series plot** (sometimes also called a time plot) is a simple graph of data collected over time that can be invaluable in identifying trends or patterns that might be of interest.

A time-series plot can be constructed by thinking of the data set as a bivariate data set, where $y$ is the variable observed and $x$ is the time at which the observation was made. These $(x, y)$ pairs are plotted as in a scatterplot. Consecutive observations are then connected by a line segment; this aids in spotting trends over time.

## Example 3.21   The Cost of Christmas

The article "'12 Days' of Gifts Will Run You $18,348" (*The New York Times,* December 24, 2005) described the Christmas Price Index and how it has changed over time. The Christmas Price Index is computed each year by PNC Advisors, and it reflects the cost of the giving all of the gifts described in the popular Christmas song "The Twelve Days of Christmas." For 2005, with the threat of avian flu complicating the shipment of birds such as the song's turtle doves and French hens, the Christmas Price index hit an all-time high of $18,348.87. A time-series plot of the Christmas Price Index for the past 21 years appears on the PNC web site (www.pncchristmaspriceindex.com) and the data given there were used to construct the time-series plot of Figure 3.33. The plot shows an upward trend in the index from 1984 until 1994. A dramatic drop in the cost occurred in 1995, but there has been a clear upward trend in the index since then. You can visit the web site to see individual time-series plots for each of the twelve gifts that are used to determine the Christmas Price Index (a partridge in a pear tree, two turtle doves, etc.). See if you can figure out what caused the dramatic decline in 1995.

**Figure 3.33** Time-series plot for the Christmas Price Index data of Example 3.21.

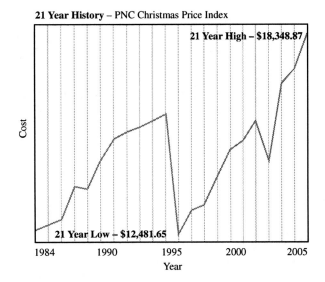

■

.............................................................................................................................

# Example 3.22 Education Level and Income—Stay in School!

The time-series plot shown in Figure 3.34 appears on the U.S. Census Bureau web site. It shows the average earnings of workers by educational level as a proportion of the average earnings of a high school graduate over time. For example, we can see from this plot that in 1993 the average earnings for people with bachelor's degrees was about 1.5 times the average for high school graduates. In that same year, the average earnings for those who were not high school graduates was only about 75%

**Figure 3.34** Time-series plot for average earnings as a proportion of the average earnings of high school graduates.

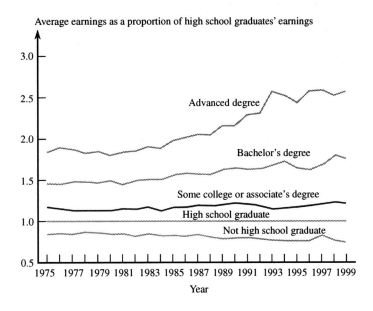

(a proportion of .75) of the average for high school graduates. The time-series plot also shows that the gap between the average earnings for high school graduates and those with a bachelor's degree or an advanced degree widened during the 1990s.

■

## Exercises 3.35–3.45 ...........................................................................................

**3.35** Does the size of a transplanted organ matter? A study that attempted to answer this question ("Minimum Graft Size for Successful Living Donor Liver Transplantation," *Transplantation* [1999]:1112–1116) presented a scatterplot much like the following ("graft weight ratio" is the weight of the transplanted liver relative to the ideal size liver for the recipient):

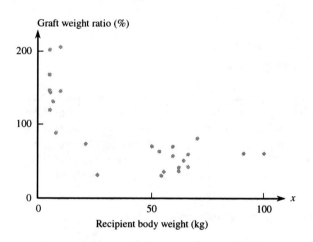

**a.** Discuss interesting features of this scatterplot.
**b.** Why do you think the overall relationship is negative?

**3.36** Data on $x$ = poverty rate (%) and $y$ = high school dropout rate (%) for the 50 U.S. states and the District of Columbia were used to construct the following scatterplot (*Chronicle of Higher Education*, August 31, 2001):

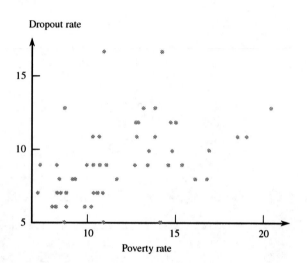

Write a few sentences commenting on this scatterplot. Would you describe the relationship between poverty rate and dropout rate as positive ($y$ tends to increase as $x$ increases), negative ($y$ tends to decrease as $x$ increases), or as having no discernible relationship between $x$ and $y$?

**3.37** ◈ ▼ A number of studies concerning muscular efficiency in humans have used competitive cyclists as subjects. It had previously been observed that variation in efficiency could not be explained by differences in cycling technique. The paper "Cycling Efficiency Is Related to the Percentage of Type I Muscle Fibers" (*Medicine and Science in Sports and Exercise* [1992]: 782–788) reported the accompanying data on $x$ = percentage of type I (slow twitch) muscle fibers and $y$ = cycling gross efficiency (the ratio of work accomplished per minute to caloric expenditure):

| Observation | x | y |
|---|---|---|
| 1 | 32 | 18.3 |
| 2 | 37 | 18.9 |
| 3 | 38 | 19.0 |
| 4 | 40 | 20.9 |
| 5 | 45 | 21.4 |
| 6 | 50 | 20.5 |
| 7 | 50 | 20.1 |
| 8 | 54 | 20.1 |
| 9 | 54 | 20.8 |
| 10 | 55 | 20.5 |
| 11 | 61 | 19.9 |
| 12 | 63 | 20.5 |
| 13 | 63 | 20.6 |
| 14 | 64 | 22.1 |
| 15 | 64 | 21.9 |
| 16 | 70 | 21.2 |
| 17 | 70 | 20.5 |
| 18 | 75 | 22.7 |
| 19 | 76 | 22.8 |

**a.** Construct a scatterplot of the data in which the axes intersect at the point (0, 16). How would you describe the pattern in the plot?
**b.** Does it appear that the value of cycling gross efficiency is determined solely by the percentage of type I muscle fibers? Explain.

3.38 ● The article "Exhaust Emissions from Four-Stroke Lawn Mower Engines" (*Journal of the Air and Water Management Association* [1997]: 945–952) reported data from a study in which both a baseline gasoline and a reformulated gasoline were used. Consider the following observations on age (in years) and $NO_x$ emissions (in grams per kilowatt-hour):

| Engine | Age | Baseline | Reformulated |
|---|---|---|---|
| 1 | 0 | 1.72 | 1.88 |
| 2 | 0 | 4.38 | 5.93 |
| 3 | 2 | 4.06 | 5.54 |
| 4 | 11 | 1.26 | 2.67 |
| 5 | 7 | 5.31 | 6.53 |
| 6 | 16 | 0.57 | 0.74 |
| 7 | 9 | 3.37 | 4.94 |
| 8 | 0 | 3.44 | 4.89 |
| 9 | 12 | 0.74 | 0.69 |
| 10 | 4 | 1.24 | 1.42 |

a. Construct a scatterplot of emissions versus age for the baseline gasoline.
b. Construct a scatterplot of emissions versus age for the reformulated gasoline.
c. Do age and emissions appear to be related? If so, in what way?
d. Comment on the similarities and differences in the two scatterplots of Parts (a) and (b).

**3.39** ▼ One factor in the development of tennis elbow, a malady that strikes fear into the hearts of all serious players of that sport (including one of the authors), is the impact-induced vibration of the racket-and-arm system at ball contact. It is well known that the likelihood of getting tennis elbow depends on various properties of the racket used. Consider the accompanying scatterplot of $x$ = racket resonance frequency (in hertz) and $y$ = sum of peak-to-peak accelerations (a characteristic of arm vibration, in meters per second per second) for $n$ = 23 different rackets ("Transfer of Tennis Racket Vibrations into the Human Forearm," *Medicine and Science in Sports and Exercise* [1992]: 1134–1140). Discuss interesting features of the data and of the scatterplot.

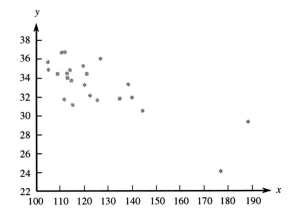

3.40 ● Stress can affect the physiology and behavior of animals, just as it can with humans (as many of us know all too well). The accompanying data on $x$ = plasma cortisol concentration (in milligrams of cortisol per milliliter of plasma) and $y$ = oxygen consumption rate (in milligrams per kilogram per hour) for juvenile steelhead after three 2-min disturbances were read from a graph in the paper "Metabolic Cost of Acute Physical Stress in Juvenile Steelhead" (*Transactions of the American Fisheries Society* [1987]: 257–263). The paper also included data for unstressed fish.

| x | 25 | 36 | 48 | 59 | 62 | 72 | 80 | 100 | 100 | 137 |
|---|----|----|----|----|----|----|----|-----|-----|-----|
| y | 155 | 184 | 180 | 220 | 280 | 163 | 230 | 222 | 241 | 350 |

a. Is the value of y determined solely by the value of x? Explain your reasoning.
b. Construct a scatterplot of the data.
c. Does an increase in plasma cortisol concentration appear to be accompanied by a change in oxygen consumption rate? Comment.

**3.41** ● The National Telecommunications and Information Administration published a report titled "Falling Through the Net: Toward Digital Inclusion" (U.S. Department of Commerce, October 2000) that included the following information on access to computers in the home:

| Year | Percentage of Households with a Computer |
|------|------------------------------------------|
| 1985 | 8.2 |
| 1990 | 15.0 |
| 1994 | 22.8 |
| 1995 | 24.1 |
| 1998 | 36.6 |
| 1999 | 42.1 |
| 2000 | 51.0 |

a. Construct a time-series plot for these data. Be careful —the observations are not equally spaced in time. The points in the plot should not be equally spaced along the x axis.
b. Comment on any trend over time.

3.42 According to the National Association of Home Builders, the average size of a home in 1950 was 983 ft$^2$. The average size increased to 1500 ft$^2$ in 1970, 2080 ft$^2$ in 1990; and 2330 ft$^2$ in 2003 (*San Luis Obispo Tribune*, October 16, 2005).
a. Construct a time-series plot that shows how the average size of a home has changed over time.
b. If the trend of the time-series plot were to continue, what would you predict the average home size to be in 2010?

**3.43** An article that appeared in *USA Today* (September 3, 2003) included a graph similar to the one shown here summarizing responses from polls conducted in 1978, 1991, and 2003 in which a sample of American adults were

asked whether or not it was a good time or a bad time to buy a house.
a. Construct a time-series plot that shows how the percentage that thought it was a good time to buy a house has changed over time.
b. Add a new line to the plot from Part (a) showing the percentage that thought it was a bad time to buy a house over time. Be sure to label the lines clearly.
**c.** Which graph, the given bar chart or the time-series plot, best shows the trend over time?

3.44 ● Some days of the week are more dangerous than others, according to Traffic Safety Facts produced by the National Highway Traffic Safety Administration. Average number of fatalities per day for each day of the week are shown in the accompanying table.

**Average Fatalities per Day (day of the week)**

| | Mon | Tue | Wed | Thurs | Fri | Sat | Sun |
|------|-----|-----|-----|-------|-----|-----|-----|
| 1978–1982 | 103 | 101 | 107 | 116 | 156 | 201 | 159 |
| 1983–1987 | 98 | 96 | 99 | 108 | 140 | 174 | 140 |
| 1988–1992 | 97 | 94 | 97 | 106 | 139 | 168 | 135 |
| 1993–1997 | 97 | 93 | 96 | 102 | 129 | 148 | 127 |
| 1998–2002 | 99 | 96 | 98 | 104 | 129 | 149 | 130 |
| Total | 99 | 96 | 100 | 107 | 138 | 168 | 138 |

a. Using the midpoint of each year range (e.g., 1980 for the 1978–1982 range), construct a time-series plot that shows the average fatalities over time for each day of the week. Be sure to label each line clearly as to which day of the week it represents.

b. Write a sentence or two commenting on the difference in average number of fatalities for the days of the week. What is one possible reason for the differences?

c. Write a sentence or two commenting on the change in average number of fatalities over time. What is one possible reason for the change?

**3.45** The accompanying time-series plot of movie box office totals (in millions of dollars) over 18 weeks of summer for both 2001 and 2002 appeared in *USA Today* (September 3, 2002):

**Giving at the box office**
Box office comparisons for the summer of 2002 vs. 2001:
2001
2002
1 – projected
Source: Nielsen EDI
By Karl Gelles, USA TODAY

Patterns that tend to repeat on a regular basis over time are called seasonal patterns. Describe any seasonal patterns that you see in the summer box office data. Hint: Look for patterns that seem to be consistent from year to year.

**Bold** exercises answered in back    ● Data set available online but not required    ▼ Video solution available

---

# Interpreting and Communicating the Results of Statistical Analyses

A graphical display, when used appropriately, can be a powerful tool for organizing and summarizing data. By sacrificing some of the detail of a complete listing of a data set, important features of the data distribution are more easily seen and more easily communicated to others.

## ■ Communicating the Results of Statistical Analyses

When reporting the results of a data analysis, a good place to start is with a graphical display of the data. A well-constructed graphical display is often the best way to highlight the essential characteristics of the data distribution, such as shape and spread for numerical data sets or the nature of the relationship between the two variables in a bivariate numerical data set.

For effective communication with graphical displays, some things to remember are:

- Be sure to select a display that is appropriate for the given type of data.
- Be sure to include scales and labels on the axes of graphical displays.
- In comparative plots, be sure to include labels or a legend so that it is clear which parts of the display correspond to which samples or groups in the data set.
- Although it is sometimes a good idea to have axes that don't cross at (0, 0) in a scatterplot, the vertical axis in a bar chart or a histogram should always start at 0 (see the cautions and limitations later in this section for more about this).

* Keep your graphs simple. A simple graphical display is much more effective than one that has a lot of extra "junk." Most people will not spend a great deal of time studying a graphical display, so its message should be clear and straightforward.
* Keep your graphical displays honest. People tend to look quickly at graphical displays so it is important that a graph's first impression is an accurate and honest portrayal of the data distribution. In addition to the graphical display itself, data analysis reports usually include a brief discussion of the features of the data distribution based on the graphical display.
* For categorical data, this discussion might be a few sentences on the relative proportion for each category, possibly pointing out categories that were either common or rare compared to other categories.
* For numerical data sets, the discussion of the graphical display usually summarizes the information that the display provides on three characteristics of the data distribution: center or location, spread, and shape.
* For bivariate numerical data, the discussion of the scatterplot would typically focus on the nature of the relationship between the two variables used to construct the plot.
* For data collected over time, any trends or patterns in the time-series plot would be described.

## ■ Interpreting the Results of Statistical Analyses

The use of graphical data displays is quite common in newspapers, magazines, and journals, so it is important to be able to extract information from such displays. For example, data on test scores for a standardized math test given to eighth-graders in 37 states, 2 territories (Guam and the Virgin Islands), and the District of Columbia were presented in the August 13, 1992, edition of *USA Today*. Figure 3.35 gives both

**Figure 3.35**   Stem-and-leaf display and histogram for math test scores.

a stem-and-leaf display and a histogram summarizing these data. Careful examination of these displays reveals the following:

1. Most of the participating states had average eighth-grade math scores between 240 and 280. We would describe the shape of this display as negatively skewed, because of the longer tail on the low end of the distribution.
2. Three of the average scores differed substantially from the others. These turn out to be 218 (Virgin Islands), 229 (District of Columbia), and 230 (Guam). These three scores could be described as outliers. It is interesting to note that the three unusual values are from the areas that are not states.
3. There do not appear to be any outliers on the high side.
4. A "typical" average math score for the 37 states would be somewhere around 260.
5. There is quite a bit of variability in average score from state to state.

How would the displays have been different if the two territories and the District of Columbia had not participated in the testing? The resulting histogram is shown in Figure 3.36. Note that the display is now more symmetric, with no noticeable outliers. The display still reveals quite a bit of state-to-state variability in average score, and 260 still looks reasonable as a "typical" average score. Now suppose that the two highest values among the 37 states (Montana and North Dakota) had been even higher. The stem-and-leaf display might then look like the one given in Figure 3.37. In this stem-and-leaf display, two values stand out from the main part of the display. This would catch our attention and might cause us to look carefully at these two states to determine what factors may be related to high math scores.

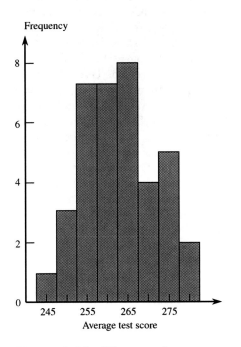

**Figure 3.36** Histogram frequency for the modified math score data.

```
24H | 79
25L | 014
25H | 6667779999
26L | 0003344
26H | 55778
27L | 12233              Stem:  Tens
27H | 667               Leaf:  Ones
28L |
28H |
29L |
29H | 68
```

**Figure 3.37** Stem-and-leaf display for modified math score data.

## ■ What to Look for in Published Data

Here are some questions you might ask yourself when attempting to extract information from a graphical data display:

- Is the chosen display appropriate for the type of data collected?
- For graphical displays of univariate numerical data, how would you describe the shape of the distribution, and what does this say about the variable being summarized?
- Are there any outliers (noticeably unusual values) in the data set? Is there any plausible explanation for why these values differ from the rest of the data? (The presence of outliers often leads to further avenues of investigation.)
- Where do most of the data values fall? What is a typical value for the data set? What does this say about the variable being summarized?
- Is there much variability in the data values? What does this say about the variable being summarized?

Of course, you should always think carefully about how the data were collected. If the data were not gathered in a reasonable manner (based on sound sampling methods or experimental design principles), you should be cautious in formulating any conclusions based on the data.

Consider the histogram in Figure 3.38, which is based on data published by the National Center for Health Statistics. The data set summarized by this histogram consisted of 1990 infant mortality rates (deaths per 1000 live births) for the 50 states in the United States. A histogram is an appropriate way of summarizing these data (although with only 50 observations, a stem-and-leaf display would also have been reasonable). The histogram itself is slightly positively skewed, with most mortality rates between 7.5 and 12. There is quite a bit of variability in infant mortality rate from state to state—perhaps more than we might have expected. This variability might be explained by differences in economic conditions or in access to health care. We may want to look further into these issues. Although there are no obvious outliers, the upper tail is a little longer than the lower tail. The three largest values in the data set are 12.1 (Alabama), 12.3 (Georgia), and 12.8 (South Carolina)—all Southern states. Again, this may suggest some interesting questions that deserve further investigation. A typical infant mortality rate would be about 9.5 deaths per 1000 live births. This represents an improvement, because researchers at the National Center for Health Statistics stated that the overall rate for 1988 was 10 deaths per 1000 live births. However, they also point out that the United States still ranked 22 out of 24 industrialized nations surveyed, with only New Zealand and Israel having higher infant mortality rates.

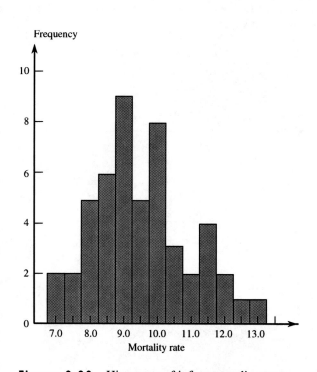

**Figure 3.38** Histogram of infant mortality rates.

## ■ A Word to the Wise: Cautions and Limitations

When constructing and interpreting graphical displays, you need to keep in mind these things:

1. Areas should be proportional to frequency, relative frequency, or magnitude of the number being represented. The eye is naturally drawn to large areas in graphical displays, and it is natural for the observer to make informal comparisons based on area. Correctly constructed graphical displays, such as pie charts, bar charts, and histograms, are designed so that the areas of the pie slices or the bars are proportional to frequency or relative frequency. Sometimes in an effort to make graphical displays more interesting, designers lose sight of this important principle, and the resulting graphs are misleading. For example, consider the following graph (*USA Today,* October 3, 2002):

By Marcy E. Mullins, USA TODAY

   In trying to make the graph more visually interesting by replacing the bars of a bar chart with milk buckets, areas are distorted. For example, the two buckets for 1980 represent 32 cows, whereas the one bucket for 1970 represents 19 cows. This is misleading because 32 is not twice as big as 19. Other areas are distorted as well.

   Another common distortion occurs when a third dimension is added to bar charts or pie charts. For example, the pie chart for the college choice data of Exercise 3.1 is reproduced here along with a three-dimensional version created by Excel. The three-dimensional version distorts the areas and, as a consequence, is much more difficult to interpret correctly.

**Mortgage rates creep up**

30-year mortgage rates:

Source: Freddie Mac

By Quin Tian, USA TODAY

2. Be cautious of graphs with broken axes. Although it is common to see scatterplots with broken axes, be extremely cautious of time-series plots, bar charts, or histograms with broken axes. The use of broken axes in a scatterplot does not distort information about the nature of the relationship in the bivariate data set used to construct the display. On the other hand, in time-series plots, broken axes can sometimes exaggerate the magnitude of change over time. Although it is not always inadvisable to break the vertical axis in a time-series plot, it is something you should watch for, and if you see a time-series plot with a broken axis, as in the accompanying time-series plot of mortgage rates (*USA Today,* October 25, 2002), you should pay particular attention to the scale on the vertical axis and take extra care in interpreting the graph:

In bar charts and histograms, the vertical axis (which represents frequency, relative frequency, or density) should *never* be broken. If the vertical axis is broken in this type of graph, the resulting display will violate the "proportional area" principle and the display will be misleading. For example, the accompanying bar chart is similar to one appearing in an advertisement for a software product designed to help teachers raise student test scores. By starting the vertical axis at 50, the gain for students using the software is exaggerated. Areas of the bars are not proportional to the magnitude of the numbers represented—the area for the rectangle representing 68 is more than three times the area of the rectangle representing 55!

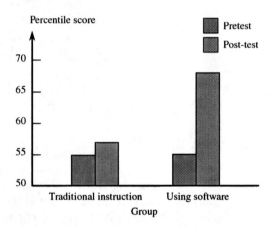

3. Watch out for unequal time spacing in time-series plots. If observations over time are not made at regular time intervals, special care must be taken in constructing the time-series plot. Consider the accompanying time-series plot, which is similar to one appearing in the *San Luis Obispo Tribune* (September 22, 2002) in an article on online banking:

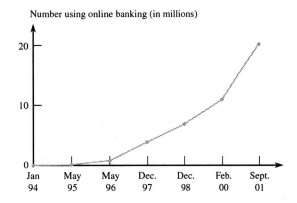

Notice that the intervals between observations are irregular, yet the points in the plot are equally spaced along the time axis. This makes it difficult to make a coherent assessment of the rate of change over time. This could have been remedied by spacing the observations differently along the time axis, as shown in the following plot:

4. Be careful how you interpret patterns in scatterplots. A strong pattern in a scatterplot means that the two variables tend to vary together in a predictable way, but it does not mean that there is a cause-and-effect relationship between the two variables. We will consider this point further in Chapter 5, but in the meantime, when describing patterns in scatterplots, be careful not to use wording that implies that changes in one variable *cause* changes in the other.

5. Make sure that a graphical display creates the right first impression. For example, consider the graph at left from *USA Today* (June 25, 2001). Although this graph does not violate the proportional area principle, the way the "bar" for the "none" category is displayed makes this graph difficult to read, and a quick glance at this graph would leave the reader with an incorrect impression.

## A c t i v i t y   **3.1**    Locating States

**Background:** A newspaper article bemoaning the state of students' knowledge of geography claimed that more students could identify the island where the 2002 season of the TV show *Survivor* was filmed than could locate Vermont on a map of the United States. In this activity, you will collect data that will allow you to estimate the proportion of students that can correctly locate the states of Vermont and Nebraska.

1. Working as a class, decide how you will select a sample that you think will be representative of the students from your school.

2. Use the sampling method from Step 1 to obtain the subjects for this study. Subjects should be shown the accompanying map of the United States and asked to point out the state of Vermont. After the subject has given his or her answer, ask the subject to point out the state of Nebraska. For each subject, record whether or not Vermont was correctly identified and whether or not Nebraska was correctly identified.

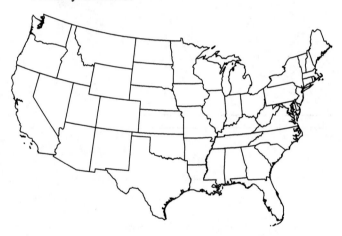

3. When the data collection process is complete, summarize the resulting data in a table like the one shown here:

| Response | Frequency |
| --- | --- |
| Correctly identified both states | |
| Correctly identified Vermont but not Nebraska | |
| Correctly identified Nebraska but not Vermont | |
| Did not correctly identify either state | |

4. Construct a pie chart that summarizes the data in the table from Step 3.

5. What proportion of sampled students were able to correctly identify Vermont on the map?

6. What proportion of sampled students were able to correctly identify Nebraska on the map?

7. Construct a comparative bar chart that shows the proportion correct and the proportion incorrect for each of the two states considered.

8. Which state, Vermont or Nebraska, is closer to the state in which your school is located? Based on the pie chart, do you think that the students at your school were better able to identify the state that was closer than the one that was farther away? Justify your answer.

9. Write a paragraph commenting on the level of knowledge of U.S. geography demonstrated by the students participating in this study.

10. Would you be comfortable generalizing your conclusions in Step 8 to the population of students at your school? Explain why or why not.

## A c t i v i t y   **3.2**    Bean Counters!

**Materials needed:** A large bowl of dried beans (or marbles, plastic beads, or any other small, fairly regular objects) and a coin.

In this activity, you will investigate whether people can hold more in the right hand or in the left hand.

1. Flip a coin to determine which hand you will measure first. If the coin lands heads side up, start with the right hand. If the coin lands tails side up, start with the left hand. With the designated hand, reach into the bowl and grab as many beans as possible. Raise the hand over the bowl and

count to 4. If no beans drop during the count to 4, drop the beans onto a piece of paper and record the number of beans grabbed. If any beans drop during the count, restart the count. That is, you must hold the beans for a count of 4 without any beans falling before you can determine the number grabbed. Repeat the process with the other hand, and then record the following information: (1) right-hand number, (2) left-hand number, and (3) dominant hand (left or right, depending on whether you are left- or right-handed).

2. Create a class data set by recording the values of the three variables listed in Step 1 for each student in your class.

3. Using the class data set, construct a comparative stem-and-leaf display with the right-hand counts displayed on the right and the left-hand counts displayed on the left of the stem-and-leaf display. Comment on the interesting features of the display and include a comparison of the right-hand count and left-hand count distributions.

4. Now construct a comparative stem-and-leaf display that allows you to compare dominant-hand count to non-dominant-hand count. Does the display support the theory that dominant-hand count tends to be higher than non-dominant-hand count?

5. For each observation in the data set, compute the difference

dominant-hand count − nondominant-hand count

Construct a stem-and-leaf display of the differences. Comment on the interesting features of this display.

6. Explain why looking at the distribution of the differences (Step 5) provides more information than the comparative stem-and-leaf display (Step 4). What information is lost in the comparative display that is retained in the display of the differences?

# Summary of Key Concepts and Formulas

| Term or Formula | Comment |
| --- | --- |
| Frequency distribution | A table that displays frequencies, and sometimes relative and cumulative relative frequencies, for categories (categorical data), possible values (discrete numerical data), or class intervals (continuous data). |
| Comparative bar chart | Two or more bar charts that use the same set of horizontal and vertical axes. |
| Pie chart | A graph of a frequency distribution for a categorical data set. Each category is represented by a slice of the pie, and the area of the slice is proportional to the corresponding frequency or relative frequency. |
| Segmented bar chart | A graph of a frequency distribution for a categorical data set. Each category is represented by a segment of the bar, and the area of the segment is proportional to the corresponding frequency or relative frequency. |
| Stem-and-leaf display | A method of organizing numerical data in which the stem values (leading digit(s) of the observations) are listed in a column, and the leaf (trailing digit(s)) for each observation is then listed beside the corresponding stem. Sometimes stems are repeated to stretch the display. |
| Histogram | A picture of the information in a frequency distribution for a numerical data set. A rectangle is drawn above each possible value (discrete data) or class interval. The rectangle's area is proportional to the corresponding frequency or relative frequency. |

| Term or Formula | Comment |
|---|---|
| Histogram shapes | A (smoothed) histogram may be unimodal (a single peak), bimodal (two peaks), or multimodal. A unimodal histogram may be symmetric, positively skewed (a long right or upper tail), or negatively skewed. A frequently occurring shape is the normal curve. |
| Cumulative relative frequency plot | A graph of a cumulative relative frequency distribution. |
| Scatter plot | A picture of bivariate numerical data in which each observation $(x, y)$ is represented as a point with respect to a horizontal $x$ axis and a vertical $y$ axis. |
| Time series plot | A picture of numerical data collected over time |

# Chapter Review Exercises 3.46–3.64

**Thomson**NOW Know exactly what to study! Take a pre-test and receive your Personalized Learning Plan.

**3.46** Each year the College Board publishes a profile of students taking the SAT. In the report "2005 College Bound Seniors: Total Group Profile Report," the average SAT scores were reported for three groups defined by first language learned. Use the data in the accompanying table to construct a bar chart of the average verbal SAT score for the three groups.

| First Language Learned | Average Verbal SAT |
|---|---|
| English | 519 |
| English and another language | 486 |
| A language other than English | 462 |

**3.47** The report referenced in Exercise 3.46 also gave average math SAT scores for the three language groups, as shown in the following table.

| First Language Learned | Average Math SAT |
|---|---|
| English | 521 |
| English and another language | 513 |
| A language other than English | 521 |

Construct a comparative bar chart for the average verbal and math scores for the three language groups. Write a few sentences describing the differences and similarities between the three language groups as shown in the bar chart.

**3.48** Each student in a sample of 227 boys and 251 girls was asked what he or she thought was most important: getting good grades, being popular, or being good at sports. The resulting data, from the paper "The Role of Sport as a Social Determinant for Children" (*Research Quarterly for Exercise and Sport* [1992]: 418–424), are summarized in the accompanying table:

| Most Important | Boys Frequency | Boys Relative Frequency | Girls Frequency | Girls Relative Frequency |
|---|---|---|---|---|
| Grades | 117 | .515 | 130 | .518 |
| Popular | 50 | .220 | 91 | .363 |
| Sports | 60 | .264 | 30 | .120 |

Construct a comparative bar chart for this data set. Remember to use relative frequency when constructing the bar chart because the two group sizes are not the same.

**3.49** The paper "Community Colleges Start to Ask, Where Are the Men?" (*Chronicle of Higher Education*, June 28, 2002) gave data on gender for community college students. It was reported that 42% of students enrolled at community colleges nationwide were male and

58% were female. Construct a segmented bar graph for these data.

**3.50** ● The article "Tobacco and Alcohol Use in G-Rated Children's Animated Films" (*Journal of the American Medical Association* [1999]: 1131–1136) reported exposure to tobacco and alcohol use in all G-rated animated films released between 1937 and 1997 by five major film studios. The researchers found that tobacco use was shown in 56% of the reviewed films. Data on the total tobacco exposure time (in seconds) for films with tobacco use produced by Walt Disney, Inc., were as follows:

223  176  548  37  158  51  299  37  11  165
74  92  6  23  206  9

Data for 11 G-rated animated films showing tobacco use that were produced by MGM/United Artists, Warner Brothers, Universal, and Twentieth Century Fox were also given. The tobacco exposure times (in seconds) for these films was as follows:

205  162  6  1  117  5  91  155  24  55  17

Construct a comparative stem-and-leaf display for these data. Comment on the interesting features of this display.

**3.51** ● The accompanying data on household expenditures on transportation for the United Kingdom appeared in "Transport Statistics for Great Britain: 2002 Edition" (in *Family Spending: A Report on the Family Expenditure Survey* [The Stationary Office, 2002]). Expenditures (in pounds per week) included costs of purchasing and maintaining any vehicles owned by members of the household and any costs associated with public transportation and leisure travel.

| Year | Average Transportation Expenditure | Percentage of Household Expenditures for Transportation |
|------|-----|-----|
| 1990 | 247.20 | 16.2 |
| 1991 | 259.00 | 15.3 |
| 1992 | 271.80 | 15.8 |
| 1993 | 276.70 | 15.6 |
| 1994 | 283.60 | 15.1 |
| 1995 | 289.90 | 14.9 |
| 1996 | 309.10 | 15.7 |
| 1997 | 328.80 | 16.7 |
| 1998 | 352.20 | 17.0 |
| 1999 | 359.40 | 17.2 |
| 2000 | 385.70 | 16.7 |

a. Construct time-series plots of the transportation expense data and the percent of household expense data.
**b.** Do the time-series plots of Part (a) support the statement that follows? Explain why or why not. Statement: Although actual expenditures have been increasing, the percentage of the total household expenditures that was for transportation has remained relatively stable.

**3.52** The web site PollingReport.com gave data from a CBS news poll conducted in December 1999. In the survey described, people were asked the following question: "All things considered, in our society today, do you think there are more advantages in being a man, more advantages in being a woman, or are there no more advantages in being one than the other?" Responses for men and for women are summarized in the following table:

| Response | Relative Frequency | |
|----------|--------|-----|
|  | Women | Men |
| Advantage in being a man | .57 | .41 |
| Advantage in being a woman | .06 | .14 |
| No advantage | .33 | .40 |
| Don't know | .04 | .05 |

Construct a comparative bar chart for the response, and write a few sentences describing the differences in the response distribution for men and women.

**3.53** The same poll described in Exercise 3.52 also asked the question, "What about salaries? These days, if a man and a woman are doing the same work, do you think the man generally earns more, the woman generally earns more, or that both earn the same amount?" The resulting data are shown in the following table:

| Response | Relative Frequency | |
|----------|--------|-----|
|  | Women | Men |
| Man earns more | .70 | .59 |
| Woman earns more | .01 | .01 |
| Both earn the same | .25 | .34 |
| Don't know | .04 | .06 |

a. Construct a comparative bar chart that allows the responses for women and men to be compared.

b. Construct two pie charts, one summarizing the responses for women and one summarizing the responses for men.

c. Is it easier to compare the responses of women and men by looking at the comparative bar chart or the two pie charts? Explain.

d. Write a brief paragraph describing the difference between women and men with respect to the way they answered this question.

**3.54** The article "The Healthy Kids Survey: A Look at the Findings" (*San Luis Obispo Tribune*, October 25, 2002) gave the accompanying information for a sample of fifth graders in San Luis Obispo County. Responses are to the question:

"After school, are you home alone without adult supervision?"

| Response | Percentage |
| --- | --- |
| Never | 8 |
| Some of the time | 15 |
| Most of the time | 16 |
| All of the time | 61 |

a. Summarize these data using a pie chart.

b. Construct a segmented bar chart for these data.

c. Which graphing method—the pie chart or the segmented bar chart—do you think does a better job of conveying information about response? Explain.

**3.55** "If you were taking a new job and had your choice of a boss, would you prefer to work for a man or a woman?" That was the question posed to individuals in a sample of 576 employed adults (*Gallup at a Glance*, October 16, 2002). Responses are summarized in the following table:

| Response | Frequency |
| --- | --- |
| Prefer to work for a man | 190 |
| Prefer to work for a woman | 92 |
| No difference | 282 |
| No opinion | 12 |

**a.** Construct a pie chart to summarize this data set, and write a sentence or two summarizing how people responded to this question.

b. Summarize the given data using a segmented bar chart.

**3.56** The accompanying stem-and-leaf display shows observations on average shower flow rate (in liters per minute) for a sample of 129 houses in Perth, Australia ("An Application of Bayes Methodology to the Analysis of Diary Records from a Water Use Study," *Journal of the American Statistical Association* [1987]: 705–711).

```
 2 | 23
 3 | 2344567789
 4 | 01356889
 5 | 000011144455666789
 6 | 000012222334445666777899999
 7 | 00012233455555668
 8 | 02233448
 9 | 012233335666788
10 | 2344455688
11 | 2335999
12 | 37
13 | 8           Stem: Ones
14 | 36          Leaf: Tenths
15 | 0035
16 |
17 |
18 | 9
```

a. What is the smallest flow rate in the sample?

b. If one additional house yielded a flow rate of 8.9, where would this observation be placed on the display?

c. What is a typical, or representative, flow rate?

d. Does the display appear to be highly concentrated, or quite spread out?

e. Does the distribution of values in the display appear to be reasonably symmetric? If not, how would you describe the departure from symmetry?

f. Does the data set appear to contain any outliers (observations far removed from the bulk of the data)?

**3.57** ● Disparities among welfare payments by different states have been the source of much political controversy. The accompanying table reports average payment per person (in dollars) in the Aid to Families with Dependent Children Program for the 1990 fiscal year. Construct a relative frequency distribution for these data using equal interval widths. Draw the histogram corresponding to your frequency distribution.

| State | Average Welfare Payment ($) |
| --- | --- |
| Alaska | 244.90 |
| California | 218.31 |
| Arizona | 93.57 |
| Montana | 114.95 |

| State | Average Welfare Payment ($) |
|---|---|
| Texas | 56.79 |
| Nebraska | 115.15 |
| Minnesota | 171.75 |
| Arkansas | 65.96 |
| Alabama | 39.62 |
| Illinois | 112.28 |
| Indiana | 92.43 |
| New Hampshire | 164.20 |
| Rhode Island | 179.37 |
| New Jersey | 121.99 |
| Delaware | 113.66 |
| North Carolina | 91.95 |
| Florida | 95.43 |
| Washington | 160.41 |
| Idaho | 97.93 |
| Utah | 118.36 |
| Colorado | 111.20 |
| Oklahoma | 96.98 |
| South Dakota | 95.52 |
| Iowa | 129.58 |
| Louisiana | 55.81 |
| Tennessee | 65.93 |
| Wisconsin | 155.04 |
| Ohio | 115.26 |
| Vermont | 183.36 |
| Connecticut | 205.86 |
| Pennsylvania | 127.70 |
| Maryland | 132.86 |
| South Carolina | 71.91 |
| Hawaii | 187.71 |
| Oregon | 135.99 |
| Nevada | 100.25 |
| Wyoming | 113.84 |
| New Mexico | 81.87 |
| Kansas | 113.88 |
| North Dakota | 130.49 |
| Missouri | 91.93 |
| Mississippi | 40.22 |
| Kentucky | 85.21 |
| Michigan | 154.75 |
| Maine | 150.12 |
| Massachusetts | 200.99 |
| New York | 193.48 |
| West Virginia | 82.94 |
| Virginia | 97.98 |
| Georgia | 91.31 |

**3.58** ● 2005 was a record year for hurricane devastation in the United States (*San Luis Obispo Tribune*, November 30, 2005). Of the 26 tropical storms and hurricanes in the season, 4 hurricanes hit the mainland: Dennis, Katrina, Rita, and Wilma. The U.S. insured catastrophic losses since 1989 (approximate values read from a graph that appeared in the *San Luis Obispo Tribune*, November 30, 2005) are as follows:

| Year | Cost (in billions of dollars) |
|---|---|
| 1989 | 7.5 |
| 1990 | 2.5 |
| 1991 | 4.0 |
| 1992 | 22.5 |
| 1993 | 5.0 |
| 1994 | 18.0 |
| 1995 | 9.0 |
| 1996 | 8.0 |
| 1997 | 2.6 |
| 1998 | 10.0 |
| 1999 | 9.0 |
| 2000 | 3.0 |
| 2001 | 27.0 |
| 2002 | 5.0 |
| 2003 | 12.0 |
| 2004 | 28.5 |
| 2005 | 56.8 |

Construct a time-series plot that shows the insured catastrophic loss over time. What do you think causes the peaks in the graph?

**3.59** ● Each observation in the following data set is the number of housing units (homes or condominiums) sold during November 1992 in a region corresponding to a particular Orange County, California, ZIP code:

```
25  18  16   6  26  11  29   7   5  15  12  37
35  11  16  35  20  27  17  30  10  16  28  13
26  11  12   8   9  29   0  20  30  12  45  26
21  30  18  31   0  46  47  14  13  29  11  18
10  27   5  18  67  21  35  48  42  70  43   0
30  17  35  40  61  18  17  17
```

Construct a stem-and-leaf display, and comment on any interesting features.

3.60 Each murder committed in Utah during the period 1978–1990 was categorized by day of the week, resulting in the following frequencies: Sunday, 109; Monday, 73; Tuesday, 97; Wednesday, 95; Thursday, 83; Friday, 107; Saturday, 100.

a. Construct the corresponding frequency distribution.

b. What proportion of these murders was committed on a weekend day—that is, Friday, Saturday, or Sunday?

c. Do these data suggest that a murder is more likely to be committed on some days than on other days? Explain your reasoning.

**3.61** An article in the *San Luis Obispo Tribune* (November 20, 2002) stated that 39% of those with critical housing needs (those who pay more than half their income for housing) lived in urban areas, 42% lived in suburban areas, and the rest lived in rural areas. Construct a pie chart that shows the distribution of type of residential area (urban, suburban, or rural) for those with critical housing needs.

**3.62** ● Living-donor kidney transplants are becoming more common. Often a living donor has chosen to donate a kidney to a relative with kidney disease. The following data appeared in a *USA Today* article on organ transplants ("Kindness Motivates Newest Kidney Donors," June 19, 2002):

**Number of Kidney Transplants**

| Year | Living-Donor to Relative | Living-Donor to Unrelated Person |
|------|--------------------------|-----------------------------------|
| 1994 | 2390 | 202 |
| 1995 | 2906 | 400 |
| 1996 | 2916 | 526 |
| 1997 | 3144 | 607 |
| 1998 | 3324 | 814 |
| 1999 | 3359 | 930 |
| 2000 | 3679 | 1325 |
| 2001 | 3879 | 1399 |

a. Construct a time-series plot for the number of living-donor kidney transplants where the donor is a relative of the recipient. Describe the trend in this plot.

b. Use the data from 1994 and 2001 to construct a comparative bar chart for the type of donation (relative or unrelated). Write a few sentences commenting on your display.

**3.63** ● Many nutritional experts have expressed concern about the high levels of sodium in prepared foods. The following data on sodium content (in milligrams) per frozen meal appeared in the article "Comparison of 'Light' Frozen Meals" (*Boston Globe,* April 24, 1991):

| | | | | | | | | |
|---|---|---|---|---|---|---|---|---|
| 720 | 530 | 800 | 690 | 880 | 1050 | 340 | 810 | 760 |
| 300 | 400 | 680 | 780 | 390 | 950 | 520 | 500 | 630 |
| 480 | 940 | 450 | 990 | 910 | 420 | 850 | 390 | 600 |

Two histograms for these data are shown:

a. Do the two histograms give different impressions about the distribution of values?

b. Use each histogram to determine approximately the proportion of observations that are less than 800, and compare to the actual proportion.

3.64 ● Americium 241 ($^{241}$Am) is a radioactive material used in the manufacture of smoke detectors. The article "Retention and Dosimetry of Injected $^{241}$Am in Beagles" (*Radiation Research* [1984]: 564–575) described a study in which 55 beagles were injected with a dose of $^{241}$Am (proportional to each animal's weight). Skeletal retention of $^{241}$Am (in microcuries per kilogram) was recorded for each beagle, resulting in the following data:

| | | | | | | |
|---|---|---|---|---|---|---|
| 0.196 | 0.451 | 0.498 | 0.411 | 0.324 | 0.190 | 0.489 |
| 0.300 | 0.346 | 0.448 | 0.188 | 0.399 | 0.305 | 0.304 |
| 0.287 | 0.243 | 0.334 | 0.299 | 0.292 | 0.419 | 0.236 |
| 0.315 | 0.447 | 0.585 | 0.291 | 0.186 | 0.393 | 0.419 |

| | | | | | | |
|---|---|---|---|---|---|---|
| 0.335 | 0.332 | 0.292 | 0.375 | 0.349 | 0.324 | 0.301 |
| 0.333 | 0.408 | 0.399 | 0.303 | 0.318 | 0.468 | 0.441 |
| 0.306 | 0.367 | 0.345 | 0.428 | 0.345 | 0.412 | 0.337 |
| 0.353 | 0.357 | 0.320 | 0.354 | 0.361 | 0.329 | |

a. Construct a frequency distribution for these data, and draw the corresponding histogram.
b. Write a short description of the important features of the shape of the histogram.

Mentor

Do you need a live tutor for homework problems?

**Thomson**NOW
Are you ready? Take your exam-prep post-test now.

# Chapter 4

# Numerical Methods for Describing Data

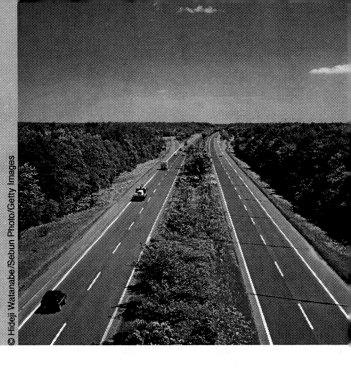

© Hideji Watanabe/Sebun Photo/Getty Images

In 2006, Medicare introduced a new prescription drug program. The article "Those Most in Need May Miss Drug Benefit Sign-Up" (*USA Today,* May 9, 2006) notes that just two weeks before the enrollment deadline only 24% of those eligible for low-income subsidies under this program had signed up. The article also gave the percentage of those eligible who had signed up in each of 49 states and the District of Columbia (information was not available for Vermont):

| | | | | | | | | | | | |
|---|---|---|---|---|---|---|---|---|---|---|---|
| 24 | 27 | 12 | 38 | 21 | 26 | 23 | 33 | 19 | 19 | 26 | 28 |
| 16 | 21 | 28 | 20 | 21 | 41 | 22 | 16 | 29 | 26 | 22 | 16 |
| 27 | 22 | 19 | 22 | 22 | 22 | 30 | 20 | 21 | 34 | 26 | 20 |
| 25 | 19 | 17 | 21 | 27 | 19 | 27 | 34 | 20 | 30 | 20 | 21 |
| 14 | 18 | | | | | | | | | | |

What is a typical value for this data set? Is the nationwide figure of 24% representative of the individual state percentages? The enrollment percentages differ widely from state to state, ranging from a low of 12% (Arizona) to a high of 41% (Kentucky). How might we summarize this variability numerically? In this chapter we show how to calculate numerical summary measures that describe more precisely both the center and the extent of spread in a data set. In Section 4.1 we introduce the mean and the median, the two most widely used measures of the center of a distribution. The variance and the standard deviation are presented in Section 4.2 as measures of variability. In later sections we discuss several techniques for using such summary measures to describe other characteristics of the data.

## 4.1 Describing the Center of a Data Set

When describing numerical data, it is common to report a value that is representative of the observations. Such a number describes roughly where the data are located or "centered" along the number line, and it is called a measure of center. The two most popular measures of center are the *mean* and the *median*.

### ▪ The Mean

The **mean** of a set of numerical observations is just the familiar arithmetic average: the sum of the observations divided by the number of observations. It is helpful to have concise notation for the variable on which observations were made, the sample size, and the individual observations. Let

$x$ = the variable for which we have sample data
$n$ = the number of observations in the sample (the sample size)
$x_1$ = the first observation in the sample
$x_2$ = the second observation in the sample
$\vdots$
$x_n$ = the $n$th (last) observation in the sample

For example, we might have a sample consisting of $n = 4$ observations on $x =$ battery lifetime (in hours):

$$x_1 = 5.9 \qquad x_2 = 7.3 \qquad x_3 = 6.6 \qquad x_4 = 5.7$$

Notice that the value of the subscript on $x$ has no relationship to the magnitude of the observation. In this example, $x_1$ is just the first observation in the data set and not necessarily the smallest observation, and $x_n$ is the last observation but not necessarily the largest.

The sum of $x_1, x_2, \ldots, x_n$ can be denoted by $x_1 + x_2 + \cdots + x_n$, but this is cumbersome. The Greek letter $\Sigma$ is traditionally used in mathematics to denote summation. In particular, $\Sigma x$ denotes the sum of all the $x$ values in the data set under consideration.*

---

**DEFINITION**

The **sample mean** of a sample of numerical observations $x_1, x_2, \ldots, x_n$, denoted by $\bar{x}$ is

$$\bar{x} = \frac{\text{sum of all observations in the sample}}{\text{number of observations in the sample}} = \frac{x_1 + x_2 + \cdots + x_n}{n} = \frac{\Sigma x}{x}$$

---

*It is also common to see $\Sigma x$ written as $\Sigma x_i$ or even as $\sum\limits_{i=1}^{n} x_i$, but for simplicity we will usually omit the summation indices.

# Example 4.1    Improving Knee Extension

● Increasing joint extension is one goal of athletic trainers. In a study to investigate the effect of a therapy that uses ultrasound and stretching (Trae Tashiro, Masters Thesis, University of Virginia, 2004) passive knee extension was measured after treatment. Passive knee extension (in degrees) is given for each of 10 participants in the study:

$$x_1 = 59 \quad x_2 = 46 \quad x_3 = 64 \quad x_4 = 49 \quad x_5 = 56$$
$$x_6 = 70 \quad x_7 = 45 \quad x_8 = 52 \quad x_9 = 63 \quad x_{10} = 52$$

The sum of these sample values is $59 + 46 + 64 + \cdots + 52 = 556$, and the sample mean passive knee extension is

$$\bar{x} = \frac{\Sigma x}{n} = \frac{556}{10} = 55.6$$

We would report $55.6°$ as a representative value of passive knee extension for this sample (even though there is no person in the sample that actually had a passive knee extension of $55.6°$).

■

The data values in Example 4.1 were all integers, yet the mean was given as 55.6. It is common to use more digits of decimal accuracy for the mean. This allows the value of the mean to fall between possible observable values (e.g., the average number of children per family could be 1.8, whereas no single family will have 1.8 children).

The sample mean $\bar{x}$ is computed from sample observations, so it is a characteristic of the particular sample in hand. It is customary to use Roman letters to denote sample characteristics, as we have done with $\bar{x}$. Characteristics of the population are usually denoted by Greek letters. One of the most important of such characteristics is the population mean.

> **D E F I N I T I O N**
>
> The **population mean**, denoted by $\mu$, is the average of all $x$ values in the entire population.

For example, the true average fuel efficiency for all 600,000 cars of a certain type under specified conditions might be $\mu = 27.5$ mpg. A sample of $n = 5$ cars might yield efficiencies of 27.3, 26.2, 28.4, 27.9, 26.5, from which we obtain $\bar{x} = 27.26$ for this particular sample (somewhat smaller than $\mu$). However, a second sample might give $\bar{x} = 28.52$, a third $\bar{x} = 26.85$, and so on. The value of $\bar{x}$ varies from sample to sample, whereas there is just one value for $\mu$. We shall see subsequently how the value of $\bar{x}$ from a particular sample can be used to draw various conclusions about the value of $\mu$.

● Data set available online

Example 4.2 illustrates how the value of $\bar{x}$ from a particular sample can differ from the value of $\mu$ and how the value of $\bar{x}$ differs from sample to sample.

# Example 4.2   County Population Sizes

The 50 states plus the District of Columbia contain 3137 counties. Let $x$ denote the number of residents of a county. Then there are 3137 values of the variable $x$ in the population. The sum of these 3137 values is 293,655,404 (2004 Census Bureau estimate), so the population average value of $x$ is

$$\mu = \frac{293,655,404}{3137} = 93,610.27 \text{ residents per county}$$

We used the Census Bureau web site to select three different samples at random from this population of counties, with each sample consisting of five counties. The results appear in Table 4.1, along with the sample mean for each sample. Not only are the three $\bar{x}$ values different from one another—because they are based on three different samples and the value of $\bar{x}$ depends on the $x$ values in the sample—but also none of the three values comes close to the value of the population mean, $\mu$. If we did not know the value of $\mu$ but had only Sample 1 available, we might use $\bar{x}$ as an *estimate* of $\mu$, but our estimate would be far off the mark.

**Table 4.1**   Three Samples from the Population of All U.S. Counties
($x$ = number of residents)

| Sample 1 | | Sample 2 | | Sample 3 | |
|---|---|---|---|---|---|
| County | x Value | County | x Value | County | x Value |
| Fayette, TX | 22,513 | Stoddard, MO | 29,773 | Chattahoochee, GA | 13,506 |
| Monroe, IN | 121,013 | Johnston, OK | 10,440 | Petroleum, MT | 492 |
| Greene, NC | 20,219 | Sumter, AL | 14,141 | Armstrong, PA | 71,395 |
| Shoshone, ID | 12,827 | Milwaukee, WI | 928,018 | Smith, MI | 14,306 |
| Jasper, IN | 31,624 | Albany, WY | 31,473 | Benton, MO | 18,519 |
| $\sum x = 208,196$ | | $\sum x = 1,013,845$ | | $\sum x = 118,218$ | |
| $\bar{x} = 41,639.2$ | | $\bar{x} = 202,769.0$ | | $\bar{x} = 23,643.6$ | |

Alternatively, we could combine the three samples into a single sample with $n = 15$ observations:

$$x_1 = 22,513, \ldots, x_5 = 31,624, \ldots, x_{15} = 18,519$$
$$\sum x = 1,340,259$$
$$\bar{x} = \frac{1,340,259}{15} = 89,350.6$$

This value is closer to the value of $\mu$ but is still somewhat unsatisfactory as an estimate. The problem here is that the population of $x$ values exhibits a lot of variability (the largest value is $x = 9,937,739$ for Los Angeles County, California, and the smallest value is $x = 52$ for Loving County, Texas, which evidently few people love). Therefore, it is difficult for a sample of 15 observations, let alone just 5, to be reasonably representative of the population. In Chapter 9 you will see how to take variability into account when deciding on a sample size.

■

One potential drawback to the mean as a measure of center for a data set is that its value can be greatly affected by the presence of even a single *outlier* (an unusually large or small observation) in the data set.

## Example 4.3   Number of Visits to a Class Web Site

● Forty students were enrolled in a section of a general education course in statistical reasoning during the fall quarter of 2002 at Cal Poly. The instructor made course materials, grades, and lecture notes available to students on a class web site, and course management software kept track of how often each student accessed any of the web pages on the class site. One month after the course began, the instructor requested a report that indicated how many times each student had accessed a web page on the class site. The 40 observations were:

| 20 | 37 | 4 | 20 | 0 | 84 | 14 | 36 | 5 | 331 | 19 | 0 |
|----|----|----|----|----|----|----|----|----|-----|----|----|
| 0  | 22 | 3  | 13 | 14 | 36 | 4  | 0  | 18 | 8   | 0  | 26 |
| 4  | 0  | 5  | 23 | 19 | 7  | 12 | 8  | 13 | 16  | 21 | 7  |
| 13 | 12 | 8  | 42 |    |    |    |    |    |     |    |    |

The sample mean for this data set is $\bar{x} = 23.10$. Figure 4.1 is a MINITAB dotplot of the data. Many would argue that 23.10 is not a very representative value for this sample, because 23.10 is larger than most of the observations in the data set—only 7 of 40 observations, or 17.5%, are larger than 23.10. The two outlying values of 84 and 331 (no, that wasn't a typo!) have a substantial impact on the value of $\bar{x}$.

**Figure 4.1**   A MINITAB dotplot of the data in Example 4.3

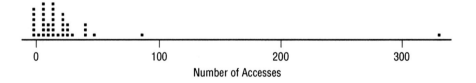

Number of Accesses

■

We now turn our attention to a measure of center that is not so sensitive to outliers —the median.

## ■ The Median

The median strip of a highway divides the highway in half, and the median of a numerical data set does the same thing for a data set. Once the data values have been listed in order from smallest to largest, the **median** is the middle value in the list, and it divides the list into two equal parts. Depending on whether the sample size $n$ is even or odd, the process of determining the median is slightly different. When $n$ is an odd number (say, 5), the sample median is the single middle value. But when $n$ is even (say, 6), there are two middle values in the ordered list, and we average these two middle values to obtain the sample median.

---

**D EFINITION**

The **sample median** is obtained by first ordering the $n$ observations from smallest to largest (with any repeated values included, so that every sample observation appears in the ordered list). Then

$$\text{sample median} = \begin{cases} \text{the single middle value if } n \text{ is odd} \\ \text{the average of the middle two values if } n \text{ is even} \end{cases}$$

---

## Example 4.4   Web Site Data Revised

The sample size for the web site access data of Example 4.3 was $n = 40$, an even number. The median is the average of the 20th and 21st values (the middle two) in the ordered list of the data. Arranging the data in order from smallest to largest produces the following ordered list:

| 0 | 0 | 0 | 0 | 0 | 0 | 3 | 4 | 4 | 4 | 5 | 5 |
|---|---|---|---|---|---|---|---|---|---|---|---|
| 7 | 7 | 8 | 8 | 8 | 12 | 12 | 13 | 13 | 13 | 14 | 14 |
| 16 | 18 | 19 | 19 | 20 | 20 | 21 | 22 | 23 | 26 | 36 | 36 |
| 37 | 42 | 84 | 331 | | | | | | | | |

The median can now be determined:

$$median = \frac{13 + 13}{2} = 13$$

Looking at the dotplot (Figure 4.1), we see that this value appears to be somewhat more typical of the data than $\bar{x} = 23.10$ is.

■

The sample mean can be sensitive to even a single value that lies far above or below the rest of the data. The value of the mean is pulled out toward such an outlying value or values. The median, on the other hand, is quite *in*sensitive to outliers. For example, the largest sample observation (331) in Example 4.3 can be increased by an arbitrarily large amount without changing the value of the median. Similarly, an increase in the second or third largest observations does not affect the median, nor would a decrease in several of the smallest observations.

This stability of the median is what sometimes justifies its use as a measure of center in some situations. For example, the article "Educating Undergraduates on Using Credit Cards" (Nellie Mae, 2005) reported that the mean credit card debt for undergraduate students in 2001 was $2327, whereas the median credit card debt was only $1770. In this case, the small percentage of students with unusually high credit card debt may be resulting in a mean that is not representative of a typical student credit card debt.

## ■ Comparing the Mean and the Median

Figure 4.2 presents several smoothed histograms that might represent either a distribution of sample values or a population distribution. Pictorially, the median is the value on the measurement axis that separates the histogram into two parts, with .5 (50%) of the area under each part of the curve. The mean is a bit harder to visualize. If the histogram were balanced on a triangle (a fulcrum), it would tilt unless the triangle was positioned at the mean. The mean is the balance point for the distribution.

**Figure 4.2**  The mean and the median.

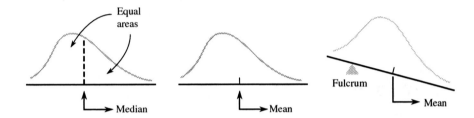

When the histogram is symmetric, the point of symmetry is both the dividing point for equal areas and the balance point, and the mean and the median are equal. However, when the histogram is unimodal (single-peaked) with a longer upper tail (positively skewed), the outlying values in the upper tail pull the mean up, so it generally lies above the median. For example, an unusually high exam score raises the mean but does not affect the median. Similarly, when a unimodal histogram is negatively skewed, the mean is generally smaller than the median (see Figure 4.3).

**Figure 4.3**  Relationship between the mean and the median.

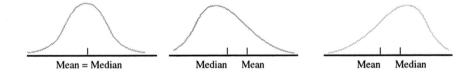

## ■ Trimmed Means

The extreme sensitivity of the mean to even a single outlier and the extreme insensitivity of the median to a substantial proportion of outliers can sometimes make both of them suspect as a measure of center. A *trimmed mean* is a compromise between these two extremes.

> **D E F I N I T I O N**
>
> A **trimmed mean** is computed by first ordering the data values from smallest to largest, deleting a selected number of values from each end of the ordered list, and finally averaging the remaining values.
>
> The **trimming percentage** is the percentage of values deleted from *each* end of the ordered list.

Sometimes the number of observations to be deleted from each end of the data set is specified. Then the corresponding trimming percentage is calculated as

$$\text{trimming percentage} = \left( \frac{\text{number deleted from each end}}{n} \right) \cdot 100$$

In other cases, the trimming percentage is specified and then used to determine how many observations to delete from each end, with

$$\text{number deleted from each end} = (\text{trimming percentage}) \cdot n$$

If the number of observations to be deleted from each end resulting from this calculation is not an integer, it can be rounded to the nearest integer (which changes the trimming percentage a bit).

## Example 4.5  NBA Salaries

● *USA Today* (December 17, 2003) published salaries of NBA players for the 2003–2004 season. Salaries for the players of the Chicago Bulls were

| Player | 2003–2004 Salary |
| --- | --- |
| Antonio Davis | $12,000,000 |
| Eddie Robinson | 6,246,950 |
| Jerome Williams | 5,400,000 |
| Scottie Pippen | 4,917,000 |
| Tyson Chandler | 3,804,360 |
| Marcus Fizer | 3,727,000 |
| Jay Williams | 3,710,000 |
| Eddy Curry | 3,080,000 |
| Jamal Crawford | 2,578,000 |
| Kirk Hinrich | 2,098,600 |
| Corie Blount | 1,600,000 |
| Kendall Gill | 1,070,000 |
| Chris Jefferies | 840,360 |
| Rick Brunson | 813,679 |
| Linton Johnson | 366,931 |

A MINITAB dotplot of these data is shown in Figure 4.4. Because the data distribution is not symmetric and there are outliers, a trimmed mean is a reasonable choice for describing the center of this data set.

There are 15 observations in this data set. Deleting the two largest and the two smallest observations from the data set and then averaging the remaining values

● Data set available online

**Figure 4.4** A MINITAB dotplot of the data in Example 4.5.

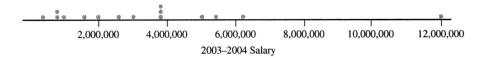

2003–2004 Salary

would result in a $\left(\dfrac{2}{15}\right)(100) = 13\%$ trimmed mean. For the Bulls salary data, the two largest salaries are \$12,000,000 and \$6,246,950 and the two smallest are \$813,679 and \$366,931. The average of the remaining 11 observations is

$$13\% \text{ trimmed mean} = \frac{5,400,000 + \cdots + 840,360}{11} = \frac{32,825,320}{11} = 2,984,120$$

The mean (\$3,483,525) is larger than the trimmed mean because of the unusually large values in the data set, and the trimmed mean is closer to the median salary value (\$3,080,000).

For the LA Lakers, the difference between the mean (\$4,367,343) and the 13% trimmed mean (\$2,233,061) is even more dramatic because during the 2003–2004 season one player on the Lakers earned over \$26 million and another player earned over \$13 million.

■

## ■ Categorical Data

The natural numerical summary quantities for a categorical data set are the relative frequencies for the various categories. Each relative frequency is the proportion (fraction) of responses that are in the corresponding category. Often there are only two possible responses (a *dichotomy*)—for example, male or female, does or does not have a driver's license, did or did not vote in the last election. It is convenient in such situations to label one of the two possible responses S (for success) and the other F (for failure). As long as further analysis is consistent with the labeling, it does not matter which category is assigned the S label. When the data set is a sample, the fraction of S's in the sample is called the *sample proportion of successes*.

> **DEFINITION**
>
> The **sample proportion of successes**, denoted by $p$, is
>
> $$p = \text{sample proportion of successes} = \frac{\text{number of S's in the sample}}{n}$$
>
> where $S$ is the label used for the response designated as success.

# Example 4.6   Can You Hear Me Now?

© Royalty-Free/Getty Images

It is not uncommon for a cell phone user to complain about the quality of his or her service provider. Suppose that each person in a sample of $n = 15$ cell phone users is asked if he or she is satisfied with the cell phone service. Each response is classified as S (satisfied) or F (not satisfied). The resulting data are:

$$\text{S  F  S  S  S  F  F  S  S  F}$$
$$\text{S  S  S  F  F}$$

This sample contains nine S's, so

$$p = \frac{9}{15} = .60$$

That is, 60% of the sample responses are S's. Of those surveyed, 60% are satisfied with their cell phone service.

■

The Greek letter $\pi$ is used to denote the **population proportion of S's.**\* We will see later how the value of $p$ from a particular sample can be used to make inferences about $\pi$.

■ Exercises 4.1–4.14 ............................................................................

**4.1** ● ▼ The Highway Loss Data Institute publishes data on repair costs resulting from a 5-mph crash test of a car moving forward into a flat barrier. The following table gives data for 10 midsize luxury cars tested in October 2002:

| Model | Repair Cost |
|---|---|
| Audi A6 | 0 |
| BMW 328i | 0 |
| Cadillac Catera | 900 |
| Jaguar X | 1254 |
| Lexus ES300 | 234 |
| Lexus IS300 | 979 |
| Mercedes C320 | 707 |
| Saab 9-5 | 670 |
| Volvo S60 | 769 |
| Volvo S80 | 4194* |

*Included cost to replace airbags, which deployed.

Compute the values of the mean and the median. Why are these values so different? Which of the mean and median is more representative of the data set, and why?

**4.2** ● *USA Today* (May 9, 2006) published the accompanying average weekday circulation for the six month period ending March 31, 2006 for the top 20 newspapers in the country:

| | | | | |
|---|---|---|---|---|
| 2,272,815 | 2,049,786 | 1,142,464 | 851,832 | 724,242 |
| 708,477 | 673,379 | 579,079 | 513,387 | 438,722 |
| 427,771 | 398,329 | 398,246 | 397,288 | 365,011 |
| 362,964 | 350,457 | 345,861 | 343,163 | 323,031 |

a. Which of the mean or the median do you think will be larger for this data set? Explain.
b. Compute the values of the mean and the median of this data set.

\*Note that we are using the symbol $\pi$ to represent a population proportion and *not* as the mathematical constant $\pi = 3.14\ldots$ Some statistics books use the symbol $p$ for the population proportion and $\hat{p}$ for the sample proportion.

**Bold** exercises answered in back        ● Data set available online but not required        ▼ Video solution available

c. Of the mean and median, which does the best job of describing a typical value for this data set?

d. Explain why it would not be reasonable to generalize from this sample of 20 newspapers to the population of daily newspapers in the United States.

**4.3** ● Bidri is a popular and traditional art form in India. Bidri articles (bowls, vessels, and so on) are made by casting from an alloy containing primarily zinc along with some copper. Consider the following observations on copper content (%) for a sample of Bidri artifacts in London's Victoria and Albert Museum ("Enigmas of Bidri," *Surface Engineering* [2005]: 333–339), listed in increasing order:

2.0  2.4  2.5  2.6  2.6  2.7  2.7  2.8  3.0  3.1
3.2  3.3  3.3  3.4  3.4  3.6  3.6  3.6  3.6  3.7
4.4  4.6  4.7  4.8  5.3  10.1

a. Construct a dotplot for these data.

b. Calculate the mean and median copper content.

c. Will an 8% trimmed mean be larger or smaller than the mean for this data set? Explain your reasoning.

**4.4** ● The chapter introduction gave the accompanying data on the percentage of those eligible for a low-income subsidy who had signed up for a Medicare drug plan in each of 49 states (information was not available for Vermont) and the District of Columbia (*USA Today,* May 9, 2006).

| 24 | 27 | 12 | 38 | 21 | 26 | 23 | 33 |
|----|----|----|----|----|----|----|----|
| 19 | 19 | 26 | 28 | 16 | 21 | 28 | 20 |
| 21 | 41 | 22 | 16 | 29 | 26 | 22 | 16 |
| 27 | 22 | 19 | 22 | 22 | 22 | 30 | 20 |
| 21 | 34 | 26 | 20 | 25 | 19 | 17 | 21 |
| 27 | 19 | 27 | 34 | 20 | 30 | 20 | 21 |
| 14 | 18 |    |    |    |    |    |    |

a. Compute the mean for this data set.

b. The article stated that nationwide, 24% of those eligible had signed up. Explain why the mean of this data set from Part (a) is not equal to 24. (No information was available for Vermont, but that is not the reason that the mean differs—the 24% was calculated excluding Vermont.)

**4.5** ● The U.S. Department of Transportation reported the number of speeding-related crash fatalities for the 20 dates that had the highest number of these fatalities between 1994 and 2003 (*Traffic Safety Facts,* July 2005).

| Date | Speeding-Related Fatalities | Date | Speeding-Related Fatalities |
|------|------|------|------|
| Jan 1 | 521 | Aug 17 | 446 |
| Jul 4 | 519 | Dec 24 | 436 |
| Aug 12 | 466 | Aug 25 | 433 |
| Nov 23 | 461 | Sep 2 | 433 |
| Jul 3 | 458 | Aug 6 | 431 |
| Dec 26 | 455 | Aug 10 | 426 |
| Aug 4 | 455 | Sept 21 | 424 |
| Aug 31 | 446 | Jul 27 | 422 |
| May 25 | 446 | Sep 14 | 422 |
| Dec 23 | 446 | May 27 | 420 |

a. Compute the mean number of speeding-related fatalities for these 20 days.

b. Compute the median number of speeding-related fatalities for these 20 days.

c. Explain why it is not reasonable to generalize from this sample of 20 days to the other 345 days of the year.

4.6 The ministry of Health and Long-Term Care in Ontario, Canada, publishes information on its web site (www.health.gov.on.ca) on the time that patients must wait for various medical procedures. For two cardiac procedures completed in fall of 2005 the following information was provided:

| | Number of Completed Procedures | Median Wait Time (days) | Mean Wait Time (days) | 90% Completed Within (days) |
|---|---|---|---|---|
| Angioplasty | 847 | 14 | 18 | 39 |
| Bypass surgery | 539 | 13 | 19 | 42 |

a. The median wait time for angioplasty is greater than the median wait time for bypass surgery but the mean wait time is shorter for angioplasty than for bypass surgery. What does this suggest about the distribution of wait times for these two procedures?

b. Is it possible that another medical procedure might have a median wait time that is greater than the time reported for "90% completed within"? Explain.

**4.7 ● ▼** Medicare's new medical plans offer a wide range of variations and choices for seniors when picking a drug plan (*San Luis Obispo Tribune*, November 25, 2005). The monthly cost for a stand-alone drug plan can vary from a low of $1.87 in Montana, Wyoming, North Dakota, South Dakota, Nebraska, Minnesota and Iowa to a high of $104.89. Here are the lowest and highest monthly premiums for stand-alone Medicare drug plans for each state:

| State | $ Low | $ High |
|---|---|---|
| Alabama | 14.08 | 69.98 |
| Alaska | 20.05 | 61.93 |
| Arizona | 6.14 | 64.86 |
| Arkansas | 10.31 | 67.98 |
| California | 5.41 | 66.08 |
| Colorado | 8.62 | 65.88 |
| Connecticut | 7.32 | 65.58 |
| Delaware | 6.44 | 68.91 |
| District of Columbia | 6.44 | 68.91 |
| Florida | 10.35 | 104.89 |
| Georgia | 17.91 | 73.17 |
| Hawaii | 17.18 | 64.43 |
| Idaho | 6.33 | 68.88 |
| Illinois | 13.32 | 65.04 |
| Indiana | 12.30 | 70.72 |
| Iowa | 1.87 | 99.90 |
| Kansas | 9.48 | 67.88 |
| Kentucky | 12.30 | 70.72 |
| Louisiana | 17.06 | 70.59 |
| Maine | 19.60 | 65.39 |
| Maryland | 6.44 | 68.91 |
| Massachusetts | 7.32 | 65.58 |
| Michigan | 13.75 | 65.69 |
| Minnesota | 1.87 | 99.90 |
| Mississippi | 11.60 | 70.59 |
| Missouri | 10.29 | 68.26 |
| Montana | 1.87 | 99.90 |
| Nebraska | 1.87 | 99.90 |
| Nevada | 6.42 | 64.63 |
| New Hampshire | 19.60 | 65.39 |
| New Jersey | 4.43 | 66.53 |
| New Mexico | 10.65 | 62.38 |
| New York | 4.10 | 85.02 |
| North Carolina | 13.27 | 65.03 |
| North Dakota | 1.87 | 99.90 |
| Ohio | 14.43 | 68.05 |
| Oklahoma | 10.07 | 70.79 |
| Oregon | 6.93 | 64.99 |

| State | $ Low | $ High |
|---|---|---|
| Pennsylvania | 10.14 | 68.61 |
| Rhode Island | 7.32 | 65.58 |
| South Carolina | 16.57 | 69.72 |
| South Dakota | 1.87 | 99.90 |
| Tennessee | 14.08 | 69.98 |
| Texas | 10.31 | 68.41 |
| Utah | 6.33 | 68.88 |
| Vermont | 7.32 | 65.58 |
| Virginia | 8.81 | 68.61 |
| Washington | 6.93 | 64.99 |
| West Virginia | 10.14 | 68.61 |
| Wisconsin | 11.42 | 63.23 |
| Wyoming | 1.87 | 99.90 |

Which of the following can be determined from the data? If it can be determined, calculate the requested value. If it cannot be determined, explain why not.
**a.** the median premium cost in Colorado
**b.** the number of plan choices in Virginia
**c.** the state(s) with the largest difference in cost between plans
**d.** the state(s) with the choice with the highest premium cost
**e.** the state for which the minimum premium cost is greatest
**f.** the mean of the minimum cost of all states beginning with the letter "M"

**4.8** *Note: This exercise requires the use of a computer.* Refer to the Medicare drug plan premium data of Exercise 4.7.
**a.** Construct a dotplot or a stem-and-leaf display of the lowest premium cost data.
**b.** Based on the display in Part (a), which of the following would you expect to be the case for the lowest cost premium data?
   i. the mean will be less than the median
   ii. the mean will be approximately equal to the median
   iii. the mean will be greater than the median
**c.** Compute the mean and median for the lowest cost premium data.
**d.** Construct an appropriate graphical display for the highest cost premium data.
**e.** Compute the mean and median for the highest cost premium data.

**4.9** Houses in California are expensive, especially on the Central Coast where the air is clear, the ocean is blue, and the scenery is stunning. The median home price in San Luis Obispo County reached a new high in July 2004 soaring to $452,272 from $387,120 in March 2004. (*San Luis Obispo Tribune*, April 28, 2004). The article included two quotes from people attempting to explain why the median price had increased. Richard Watkins, chairman of the Central Coast Regional Multiple Listing Services was quoted as saying "There have been some fairly expensive houses selling, which pulls the median up." Robert Kleinhenz, deputy chief economist for the California Association of Realtors explained the volatility of house prices by stating: "Fewer sales means a relatively small number of very high or very low home prices can more easily skew medians." Are either of these statements correct? For each statement that is incorrect, explain why it is incorrect and propose a new wording that would correct any errors in the statement.

4.10  Consider the following statement: More than 65% of the residents of Los Angeles earn less than the average wage for that city. Could this statement be correct? If so, how? If not, why not?

**4.11 ▼** A sample consisting of four pieces of luggage was selected from among those checked at an airline counter, yielding the following data on $x$ = weight (in pounds):

$x_1 = 33.5$, $x_2 = 27.3$, $x_3 = 36.7$, $x_4 = 30.5$

Suppose that one more piece is selected; denote its weight by $x_5$. Find a value of $x_5$ such that $\bar{x}$ = sample median.

4.12  Suppose that 10 patients with meningitis received treatment with large doses of penicillin. Three days later, temperatures were recorded, and the treatment was considered successful if there had been a reduction in a patient's temperature. Denoting success by S and failure by F, the 10 observations are

S   S   F   S   S   S   F   F   S   S

a.  What is the value of the sample proportion of successes?
b.  Replace each S with a 1 and each F with a 0. Then calculate $\bar{x}$ for this numerically coded sample. How does $\bar{x}$ compare to $p$?
c.  Suppose that it is decided to include 15 more patients in the study. How many of these would have to be S's to give $p = .80$ for the entire sample of 25 patients?

**4.13**  An experiment to study the lifetime (in hours) for a certain type of component involved putting 10 components into operation and observing them for 100 hr. Eight of the components failed during that period, and those lifetimes were recorded. The lifetimes of the two components still functioning after 100 hr are recorded as 100+. The resulting sample observations were

48   79   100+   35   92   86   57   100+   17   29

Which of the measures of center discussed in this section can be calculated, and what are the values of those measures?

4.14  An instructor has graded 19 exam papers submitted by students in a class of 20 students, and the average so far is 70. (The maximum possible score is 100.) How high would the score on the last paper have to be to raise the class average by 1 point? By 2 points?

**Bold** exercises answered in back     ● Data set available online but not required     ▼ Video solution available

---

## 4.2   Describing Variability in a Data Set

Reporting a measure of center gives only partial information about a data set. It is also important to describe the spread of values about the center. The three different samples displayed in Figure 4.5 all have mean = median = 45. There is much variability in the first sample compared to the third sample. The second sample shows less variability than the first and more variability than the third; most of the variability in the second sample is due to the two extreme values being so far from the center.

**Figure 4.5** Three samples with the same center and different amounts of variability.

Sample

1.   20, 40, 50, 30, 60, 70

2.   47, 43, 44, 46, 20, 70

3.   44, 43, 40, 50, 47, 46

Mean = Median

The simplest numerical measure of variability is the range.

> **DEFINITION**
>
> The **range** of a data set is defined as
>
> range = largest observation − smallest observation

In general, more variability will be reflected in a larger range. However, variability is a characteristic of the entire data set, and each observation contributes to variability. The first two samples plotted in Figure 4.5 both have a range of 50, but there is less variability in the second sample.

## ■ Deviations from the Mean

The most common measures of variability describe the extent to which the sample observations deviate from the sample mean $\bar{x}$. Subtracting $\bar{x}$ from each observation gives a set of deviations from the mean.

> **DEFINITION**
>
> The $n$ **deviations from the sample mean** are the differences
>
> $$(x_1 - \bar{x}), (x_2 - \bar{x}), \ldots, (x_n - \bar{x})$$

A particular deviation is positive if the corresponding $x$ value is greater than $\bar{x}$ and negative if the $x$ value is less than $\bar{x}$.

## Example 4.7   Acrylamide Levels in French Fries

● Research by the Food and Drug Administration (FDA) shows that acrylamide (a possible cancer-causing substance) forms in high-carbohydrate foods cooked at high temperatures and that acrylamide levels can vary widely even within the same brand of food (Associated Press, December 6, 2002). FDA scientists analyzed McDonald's

● Data set available online

french fries purchased at seven different locations and found the following acrylamide levels:

497     193     328     155     326     245     270

For this data set, $\sum x = 2014$ and $\bar{x} = 287.714$. Table 4.2 displays the data along with the corresponding deviations, formed by subtracting $\bar{x} = 287.714$ from each observation. Three of the deviations are positive because three of the observations are larger than $\bar{x}$. The negative deviations correspond to observations that are smaller than $\bar{x}$. Some of the deviations are quite large in magnitude (209.286 and $-132.714$, for example), indicating observations that are far from the sample mean.

**Table 4.2**   Deviations from the Mean for the Acrylamide Data

| Observation (x) | Deviation (x − x̄) |
|---|---|
| 497 | 209.286 |
| 193 | −94.714 |
| 328 | 40.286 |
| 155 | −132.714 |
| 326 | 38.286 |
| 245 | −42.714 |
| 270 | −17.714 |

■

In general, the greater the amount of variability in the sample, the larger the magnitudes (ignoring the signs) of the deviations. We now consider how to combine the deviations into a single numerical measure of variability. A first thought might be to calculate the average deviation, by adding the deviations together (this sum can be denoted compactly by $\sum(x - \bar{x})$) and then dividing by $n$. This does not work, though, because negative and positive deviations counteract one another in the summation.

Except for the effects of rounding in computing the deviations, it is always true that

$$\sum(x - \bar{x}) = 0$$

Since this sum is zero, the average deviation is always zero and so it cannot be used as a measure of variability.

■

As a result of rounding, the value of the sum of the seven deviations in Example 4.7 is $\sum(x - \bar{x}) = .002$. If we used even more decimal accuracy in computing $\bar{x}$ the sum would be even closer to 0.

## ■ The Variance and Standard Deviation

The customary way to prevent negative and positive deviations from counteracting one another is to square them before combining. Then deviations with opposite signs but with the same magnitude, such as $+20$ and $-20$, make identical contributions to variability. The squared deviations are $(x_1 - \bar{x})^2, (x_2 - \bar{x})^2, \ldots, (x_n - \bar{x})^2$ and their sum is

$$(x_1 - \bar{x})^2 + (x_2 - \bar{x})^2 + \cdots + (x_n - \bar{x})^2 = \sum(x - \bar{x})^2$$

Common notation for $\sum(x - \bar{x})^2$ is $S_{xx}$. Dividing this sum by the sample size $n$ gives the average squared deviation. Although this seems to be a reasonable measure of variability, we use a divisor slightly smaller than $n$. (The reason for this will be explained later in this section and in Chapter 9.)

> **DEFINITION**
>
> The **sample variance**, denoted by $s^2$, is the sum of squared deviations from the mean divided by $n - 1$. That is,
>
> $$s^2 = \frac{\sum(x - \bar{x})^2}{n - 1} = \frac{S_{xx}}{n - 1}$$
>
> The **sample standard deviation** is the positive square root of the sample variance and is denoted by $s$.

A large amount of variability in the sample is indicated by a relatively large value of $s^2$ or $s$, whereas a value of $s^2$ or $s$ close to 0 indicates a small amount of variability. Notice that whatever unit is used for $x$ (such as pounds or seconds), the squared deviations and therefore $s^2$ are in squared units. Taking the square root gives a measure expressed in the same units as $x$. Thus, for a sample of heights, the standard deviation might be $s = 3.2$ in., and for a sample of textbook prices, it might be $s = \$12.43$.

## Example 4.8  French Fries Revisited

Let's continue using the acrylamide data and the computed deviations from the mean given in Example 4.7 to obtain the sample variance and standard deviation. Table 4.3 shows the observations, deviations from the mean, and squared deviations.

**Table 4.3**  Deviations and Squared Deviations for the Acrylamide Data

| Observation (x) | Deviation (x − x̄) | Squared Deviation (x − x̄)² |
|---|---|---|
| 497 | 209.286 | 43800.630 |
| 193 | −94.714 | 8970.742 |
| 328 | 40.286 | 1622.962 |
| 155 | −132.714 | 17613.006 |
| 326 | 38.286 | 1465.818 |
| 245 | −42.714 | 1824.486 |
| 270 | −17.714 | 313.786 |
| | | $\sum(x - \bar{x})^2 = 75{,}611.429$ |

 Step-by-step technology instructions available online

Combining the squared deviations to compute the values of $s^2$ and $s$ gives

$$\sum(x - \bar{x})^2 = S_{xx} = 75,611.429$$

and

$$s^2 = \frac{\sum(x - \bar{x})^2}{n - 1} = \frac{75,611.429}{7 - 1} = \frac{75,611.429}{6} = 12,601.904$$

$$s = \sqrt{12,601.904} = 112.258$$

■

The computation of $s^2$ can be a bit tedious, especially if the sample size is large. Fortunately, many calculators and computer software packages compute the variance and standard deviation upon request. One commonly used statistical computer package is MINITAB. The output resulting from using the MINITAB Describe command with the acrylamide data follows. MINITAB gives a variety of numerical descriptive measures, including the mean, the median, and the standard deviation.

**Descriptive Statistics: acrylamide**

| Variable | N | Mean | Median | TrMean | StDev | SE Mean |
|---|---|---|---|---|---|---|
| acrylamide | 7 | 287.7 | 270.0 | 287.7 | 112.3 | 42.4 |

| Variable | Minimum | Maximum | Q1 | Q3 |
|---|---|---|---|---|
| acrylamide | 155.0 | 497.0 | 193.0 | 328.0 |

The standard deviation can be informally interpreted as the size of a "typical" or "representative" deviation from the mean. Thus, in Example 4.8, a typical deviation from $\bar{x}$ is about 112.3; some observations are closer to $\bar{x}$ than 112.3 and others are farther away. We computed $s = 112.3$ in Example 4.8 without saying whether this value indicated a large or a small amount of variability. At this point, it is better to use $s$ for comparative purposes than for an absolute assessment of variability. If we obtained a sample of acrylamide level values for a second set of McDonald's french fries and computed $s = 104.6$, then we would conclude that our original sample has more variability than our second sample.

There are measures of variability for the entire population that are analogous to $s^2$ and $s$ for a sample. These measures are called the **population variance** and the **population standard deviation** and are denoted by $\sigma^2$ and $\sigma$, respectively. (We again use a lowercase Greek letter for a population characteristic.) As with $s$, the value of $\sigma$ can be used for comparative purposes.

In many statistical procedures, we would like to use the value of $\sigma$, but unfortunately it is not usually known. Therefore, in its place we must use a value computed from the sample that we hope is close to $\sigma$ (i.e., a good *estimate* of $\sigma$). We use the divisor $(n - 1)$ in $s^2$ rather than $n$ because, on average, the resulting value tends to be a bit closer to $\sigma^2$. We will say more about this in Chapter 9.

An alternative rationale for using $(n - 1)$ is based on the property $\sum(x - \bar{x}) = 0$. Suppose that $n = 5$ and that four of the deviations are

$$x_1 - \bar{x} = -4 \qquad x_2 - \bar{x} = 6 \qquad x_3 - \bar{x} = 1 \qquad x_5 - \bar{x} = -8$$

Then, because the sum of these four deviations is $-5$, the remaining deviation must be $x_4 - \bar{x} = 5$ (so that the sum of all five is 0). Although there are five deviations, only four of them contain independent information about variability. More generally, once any $(n-1)$ of the deviations are available, the value of the remaining deviation is determined. The $n$ deviations actually contain only $(n-1)$ independent pieces of information about variability. Statisticians express this by saying that $s^2$ and $s$ are based on $(n-1)$ *degrees of freedom* (df).

## ■ The Interquartile Range

As with $\bar{x}$, the value of $s$ can be greatly affected by the presence of even a single unusually small or large observation. The *interquartile range* is a measure of variability that is resistant to the effects of outliers. It is based on quantities called *quartiles*. The *lower quartile* separates the bottom 25% of the data set from the upper 75%, and the *upper quartile* separates the top 25% from the bottom 75%. The *middle quartile* is the median, and it separates the bottom 50% from the top 50%. Figure 4.6 illustrates the locations of these quartiles for a smoothed histogram.

**Figure 4.6**  The quartiles for a smoothed histogram.

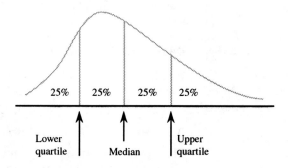

The quartiles for sample data are obtained by dividing the $n$ ordered observations into a lower half and an upper half; if $n$ is odd, the median is excluded from both halves. The two extreme quartiles are then the medians of the two halves. (Note: The median is only temporarily excluded for the purpose of computing quartiles. It is not excluded from the data set.)

> **D EFINITION** *
>
>   **lower quartile** = median of the lower half of the sample
>   **upper quartile** = median of the upper half of the sample
> (If $n$ is odd, the median of the entire sample is excluded from both halves.)
>
> The **interquartile range (iqr)**, a measure of variability that is not as sensitive to the presence of outliers as the standard deviation, is given by
>   **iqr = upper quartile − lower quartile**
>
> * There are several other sensible ways to define quartiles. Some calculators and software packages use an alternate definition.

The resistant nature of the interquartile range follows from the fact that up to 25% of the smallest sample observations and up to 25% of the largest sample observations can be made more extreme without affecting the value of the interquartile range.

# Example 4.9   Hospital Cost-to-Charge Ratios

● The Oregon Department of Health Services publishes cost-to-charge ratios for hospitals in Oregon on its web site. The cost-to-charge ratio is computed as the ratio of the actual cost of care to what the hospital actually bills for care, and the ratio is usually expressed as a percentage. A cost-to-charge ratio of 60% means that the actual cost is 60% of what was billed. The ratios for inpatient services in 2002 at 31 hospitals in Oregon were:

| 68 | 76 | 60 | 88 | 69 | 80 | 75 | 67 | 71 | 100 |
| 63 | 62 | 71 | 74 | 64 | 48 | 100 | 72 | 65 | 50 |
| 72 | 100 | 63 | 45 | 54 | 60 | 75 | 57 | 74 | 84 |
| 83 | | | | | | | | | |

Figure 4.7 gives a stem-and-leaf display of the data.

**Figure 4.7**   MINITAB stem-and-leaf display of hospital cost-to-charge ratio data in Example 4.9.

**Stem-and-Leaf Display: Cost-to-Charge**
Stem-and-leaf of Cost-to-Charge N = 31
Leaf Unit = 1.0

```
 4  58
 5  04
 5  7
 6  002334
 6  5789
 7  112244
 7  556
 8  034
 8  8
 9
 9
10  000
```

The sample size $n = 31$ is an odd number, so the median is excluded from both halves of the sample when computing the quartiles.

**Ordered Data**

Lower half   45   48   50   54   57   60   60   **62**   63   63   64   65   67   68   69
Median                                                   **71**
Upper half   71   72   72   74   74   75   75   **76**   80   83   84   88   100   100   100

Each half of the sample contains 15 observations. The lower quartile is just the median of the lower half of the sample (62 for this data set), and the upper quartile is the median of the upper half (76 for this data set). This gives

lower quartile = 62
upper quartile = 76
iqr = 76 − 62 = 14

● Data set available online

The sample mean and standard deviation for this data set are 70.65 and 14.11, respectively. If we were to change the two smallest values from 45 and 48 to 25 and 28 (so that they still remain the two smallest values), the median and interquartile range would not be affected, whereas the mean and the standard deviation would change to 69.35 and 16.99, respectively.

■

The **population interquartile range** is the difference between the upper and lower population quartiles. If a histogram of the data set under consideration (whether a population or a sample) can be reasonably well approximated by a normal curve, then the relationship between the standard deviation (sd) and the interquartile range is roughly sd = iqr/1.35. A value of the standard deviation much larger than iqr/1.35 suggests a histogram with heavier (or longer) tails than a normal curve. For the hospital cost-to-charge data of Example 4.9, we had $s = 14.11$, whereas iqr/1.35 = 14/1.35 = 10.37. This suggests that the distribution of sample values is indeed heavy-tailed compared to a normal curve, as can be seen in the stem-and-leaf display.

## ■ Exercises 4.15–4.28 ...........................................................................

**4.15** A sample of $n = 5$ college students yielded the following observations on number of traffic citations for a moving violation during the previous year:

$$x_1 = 1 \qquad x_2 = 0 \qquad x_3 = 0 \qquad x_4 = 3 \qquad x_5 = 2$$

Calculate $s^2$ and $s$.

4.16 Give two sets of five numbers that have the same mean but different standard deviations, and give two sets of five numbers that have the same standard deviation but different means.

**4.17** Going back to school can be an expensive time for parents—second only to the Christmas holiday season in terms of spending (*San Luis Obispo Tribune*, August 18, 2005). Parents spend an average of $444 on their children at the beginning of the school year stocking up on clothes, notebooks, and even iPods. Of course, not every parent spends the same amount of money and there is some variation. Do you think a data set consisting of the amount spent at the beginning of the school year for each student at a particular elementary school would have a large or a small standard deviation? Explain.

4.18 The article "Rethink Diversification to Raise Returns, Cut Risk" (*San Luis Obispo Tribune*, January 21, 2006) included the following paragraph:

In their research, Mulvey and Reilly compared the results of two hypothetical portfolios and used actual data from 1994 to 2004 to see what returns they would achieve. The first portfolio invested in Treasury bonds, domestic stocks, international stocks, and cash. Its 10-year average annual return was 9.85 percent, and its volatility—measured as the standard deviation of annual returns—was 9.26 percent. When Mulvey and Reilly shifted some assets in the portfolio to include funds that invest in real estate, commodities, and options, the 10-year return rose to 10.55 percent while the standard deviation fell to 7.97 percent. In short, the more diversified portfolio had a slightly better return and much less risk.

Explain why the standard deviation is a reasonable measure of volatility and why it is reasonable to interpret a smaller standard deviation as meaning less risk.

**4.19** ● The U.S. Department of Transportation reported the accompanying data on the number of speeding-related crash fatalities during holiday periods for the years from 1994 to 2003 (*Traffic Safety Facts*, July 20, 2005).

**Speeding-Related Fatalities**

| Holiday Period | 1994 | 1995 | 1996 | 1997 | 1998 | 1999 | 2000 | 2001 | 2002 | 2003 |
|---|---|---|---|---|---|---|---|---|---|---|
| New Year's Day | 141 | 142 | 178 | 72 | 219 | 138 | 171 | 134 | 210 | 70 |
| Memorial Day | 193 | 178 | 185 | 197 | 138 | 183 | 156 | 190 | 188 | 181 |
| July 4th | 178 | 219 | 202 | 179 | 169 | 176 | 219 | 64 | 234 | 184 |
| Labor Day | 183 | 188 | 166 | 179 | 162 | 171 | 180 | 138 | 202 | 189 |
| Thanksgiving | 212 | 198 | 218 | 210 | 205 | 168 | 187 | 217 | 210 | 202 |
| Christmas | 152 | 129 | 66 | 183 | 134 | 193 | 155 | 210 | 60 | 198 |

**a.** Compute the standard deviation for the New Year's Day data.

**b.** Without computing the standard deviation of the Memorial Day data, explain whether the standard deviation for the Memorial Day data would be larger or smaller than the standard deviation of the New Year's Day data.

**c.** Memorial Day and Labor Day are holidays that always occur on Monday and Thanksgiving always occurs on a Thursday, whereas New Year's Day, July 4th and Christmas do not always fall on the same day of the week every year. Based on the given data, is there more or less variability in the speeding-related crash fatality numbers from year to year for same day of the week holiday periods than for holidays that can occur on different days of the week? Support your answer with appropriate measures of variability.

**4.20** The ministry of Health and Long-Term Care in Ontario, Canada publishes information on the time that patients must wait for various medical procedures on its web site (www.health.gov.on.ca). For two cardiac procedures completed in fall of 2005 the following information was provided:

| Procedure | Number of Completed Procedures | Median Wait Time (days) | Mean Wait Time (days) | 90% Completed Within (days) |
|---|---|---|---|---|
| Angioplasty | 847 | 14 | 18 | 39 |
| Bypass surgery | 539 | 13 | 19 | 42 |

**a.** Which of the following must be true for the lower quartile of the data set consisting of the 847 wait times for angioplasty?

   i. The lower quartile is less than 14.
   ii. The lower quartile is between 14 and 18.
   iii. The lower quartile is between 14 and 39.
   iv. The lower quartile is greater than 39.

**b.** Which of the following must be true for the upper quartile of the data set consisting of the 539 wait times for bypass surgery?

   i. The upper quartile is less than 13.
   ii. The upper quartile is between 13 and 19.
   iii. The upper quartile is between 13 and 42.
   iv. The upper quartile is greater than 42.

**c.** Which of the following must be true for the 95th percentile of the data set consisting of the 539 wait times for bypass surgery?

   i. The 95th percentile is less than 13.
   ii. The 95th percentile is between 13 and 19.
   iii. The 95th percentile is between 13 and 42.
   iv. The 95th percentile is greater than 42.

**4.21** The accompanying table shows the low price, the high price, and the average price of homes in fifteen communities in San Luis Obispo County between January 1, 2004 and August 1, 2004 (*San Luis Obispo Tribune*, September 5, 2004).

| Community | Average Price | Number Sold | Low | High |
|---|---|---|---|---|
| Cayucos | $937,366 | 31 | $380,000 | $2,450,000 |
| Pismo Beach | $804,212 | 71 | $439,000 | $2,500,000 |
| | | | | *(continued)* |

| Community | Average Price | Number Sold | Low | High |
|---|---|---|---|---|
| Cambria | $728,312 | 85 | $340,000 | $2,000,000 |
| Avila Beach | $654,918 | 16 | $475,000 | $1,375,000 |
| Morro Bay | $606,456 | 114 | $257,000 | $2,650,000 |
| Arroyo Grande | $595,577 | 214 | $178,000 | $1,526,000 |
| Templeton | $578,249 | 89 | $265,000 | $2,350,000 |
| San Luis Obispo | $557,628 | 277 | $258,000 | $2,400,000 |
| Nipomo | $528,572 | 138 | $263,000 | $1,295,000 |
| Los Osos | $511,866 | 123 | $140,000 | $3,500,000 |
| Santa Margarita | $430,354 | 22 | $290,000 | $583,000 |
| Atascadero | $420,603 | 270 | $140,000 | $1,600,000 |
| Grover Beach | $416,405 | 97 | $242,000 | $720,000 |
| Paso Robles | $412,584 | 439 | $170,000 | $1,575,000 |
| Oceano | $390,354 | 59 | $177,000 | $1,350,000 |

**a.** Explain why the average price for the combined areas of Los Osos and Morro Bay is not just the average of $511,866 and $606,456.
**b.** Houses sold in Grover Beach and Paso Robles have very similar average prices. Based on the other information given, which is likely to have the higher standard deviation for price?
**c.** Consider houses sold in Grover Beach and Paso Robles. Based on the other information given, which is likely to have the higher median price?

**4.22** ◉ Cost-to-charge ratios (see Example 4.9 for a definition of this ratio) were reported for the 10 hospitals in California with the lowest ratios (*San Luis Obispo Tribune,* December 15, 2002). These ratios represent the 10 hospitals with the highest markup, because for these hospitals, the actual cost was only a small percentage of the amount billed. The 10 cost-to-charge values (percentages) were

| | | | | | |
|---|---|---|---|---|---|
| 8.81 | 10.26 | 10.20 | 12.66 | 12.86 | 12.96 |
| 13.04 | 13.14 | 14.70 | 14.84 | | |

**a.** Compute the variance and standard deviation for this data set.
**b.** If cost-to-charge data were available for all hospitals in California, would the standard deviation of this data set be larger or smaller than the standard deviation computed in

Part (a) for the 10 hospitals with the lowest cost-to-charge values? Explain.
**c.** Explain why it would not be reasonable to use the data from the sample of 10 hospitals in Part (a) to draw conclusions about the population of all hospitals in California.

**4.23** ◉ In 1997 a woman sued a computer keyboard manufacturer, charging that her repetitive stress injuries were caused by the keyboard (*Genessey v. Digital Equipment Corporation*). The jury awarded about $3.5 million for pain and suffering, but the court then set aside that award as being unreasonable compensation. In making this determination, the court identified a "normative" group of 27 similar cases and specified a reasonable award as one within 2 standard deviations of the mean of the awards in the 27 cases. The 27 award amounts were (in thousands of dollars)

| | | | | | | | |
|---|---|---|---|---|---|---|---|
| 37 | 60 | 75 | 115 | 135 | 140 | 149 | 150 |
| 238 | 290 | 340 | 410 | 600 | 750 | 750 | 750 |
| 1050 | 1100 | 1139 | 1150 | 1200 | 1200 | 1250 | 1576 |
| 1700 | 1825 | 2000 | | | | | |

What is the maximum possible amount that could be awarded under the "2-standard deviations rule"?

**4.24** ◉ The Highway Loss Data Institute reported the following repair costs resulting from crash tests conducted in October 2002. The given data are for a 5-mph crash into a flat surface for both a sample of 10 moderately priced midsize cars and a sample of 14 inexpensive midsize cars.

| Moderately Priced Midsize Cars | 296 | 0 | 1085 | 148 | 1065 |
|---|---|---|---|---|---|
| | 0 | 0 | 341 | 184 | 370 |
| Inexpensive Midsize Cars | 513 | 719 | 364 | 295 | 305 |
| | 335 | 353 | 156 | 209 | 288 |
| | 0 | 0 | 397 | 243 | |

**a.** Compute the standard deviation and the interquartile range for the repair cost of the moderately priced midsize cars.
**b.** Compute the standard deviation and the interquartile range for the repair cost of the inexpensive midsize cars.
**c.** Is there more variability in the repair cost for the moderately priced cars or for the inexpensive midsize cars? Justify your choice.
**d.** Compute the mean repair cost for each of the two types of cars.
**e.** Write a few sentences comparing repair cost for moderately priced and inexpensive midsize cars. Be sure to include information about both center and variability.

**Bold** exercises answered in back    ◉ Data set available online but not required    ▼ Video solution available

**4.25** ◉ ▼ The paper "Total Diet Study Statistics on Element Results" (Food and Drug Administration, April 25, 2000) gave information on sodium content for various types of foods. Twenty-six tomato catsups were analyzed. Data consistent with summary quantities given in the paper were

### Sodium content (mg/kg)

| | | | | | |
|---|---|---|---|---|---|
| 12,148 | 10,426 | 10,912 | 9116 | 13,226 | 11,663 |
| 11,781 | 10,680 | 8457 | 10,788 | 12,605 | 10,591 |
| 11,040 | 10,815 | 12,962 | 11,644 | 10,047 | 10,478 |
| 10,108 | 12,353 | 11,778 | 11,092 | 11,673 | 8758 |
| 11,145 | 11,495 | | | | |

Compute the values of the quartiles and the interquartile range.

**4.26** ◉ The paper referenced in Exercise 4.25 also gave summary quantities for sodium content (in milligrams per kilogram) of chocolate pudding made from instant mix:

3099  3112  2401  2824  2682  2510  2297  3959  3068  3700

a. Compute the mean, the standard deviation, and the interquartile range for sodium content of these chocolate puddings.
b. Based on the interquartile range, is there more or less variability in sodium content for the chocolate pudding data than for the tomato catsup data of Exercise 4.25?

**4.27** ◉ Example 4.9 gave 2002 cost-to-charge ratios for inpatient services at 31 hospitals in Oregon. The same data source also provided the cost-to-charge ratios for outpatient services at these same 31 hospitals:

75  54  50  75  58  56  56  62  66  69  100  57
45  51  53  45  84  45  48  39  51  51  65  100
63  96  54  53  67  52  71

a. Use the given data to compute the quartiles and the interquartile range for the outpatient cost-to-charge ratio.
b. How does the interquartile range compare to the interquartile range for the inpatient cost-to-charge ratio from Example 4.9? Is there more variability in the inpatient or the outpatient ratio?

**4.28** ◉ The standard deviation alone does not measure relative variation. For example, a standard deviation of $1 would be considered large if it is describing the variability from store to store in the price of an ice cube tray. On the other hand, a standard deviation of $1 would be considered small if it is describing store-to-store variability in the price of a particular brand of freezer. A quantity designed to give a relative measure of variability is the *coefficient of variation*. Denoted by CV, the coefficient of variation expresses the standard deviation as a percentage of the mean. It is defined by the formula $CV = 100\left(\dfrac{s}{\bar{x}}\right)$.

Consider two samples. Sample 1 gives the actual weight (in ounces) of the contents of cans of pet food labeled as having a net weight of 8 oz. Sample 2 gives the actual weight (in pounds) of the contents of bags of dry pet food labeled as having a net weight of 50 lb. The weights for the two samples are:

| Sample 1 | 8.3 | 7.1 | 7.6 | 8.1 | 7.6 |
|---|---|---|---|---|---|
| | 8.3 | 8.2 | 7.7 | 7.7 | 7.5 |
| Sample 2 | 52.3 | 50.6 | 52.1 | 48.4 | 48.8 |
| | 47.0 | 50.4 | 50.3 | 48.7 | 48.2 |

a. For each of the given samples, calculate the mean and the standard deviation.
b. Compute the coefficient of variation for each sample. Do the results surprise you? Why or why not?

---

**Bold** exercises answered in back     ◉ Data set available online but not required     ▼ Video solution available

---

## 4.3  Summarizing a Data Set: Boxplots

In Sections 4.1 and 4.2, we looked at ways of describing the center and variability of a data set using numerical measures. It would be nice to have a method of summarizing data that gives more detail than just a measure of center and spread and yet less detail than a stem-and-leaf display or histogram. A *boxplot* is one such technique. It is compact, yet it provides information about the center, spread, and symmetry or skewness of the data. We consider two types of boxplots: the skeletal boxplot and the modified boxplot.

## Construction of a Skeletal Boxplot

1. Draw a horizontal (or vertical) measurement scale.
2. Construct a rectangular box with a left (or lower) edge at the lower quartile and a right (or upper) edge at the upper quartile. The box width is then equal to the iqr.
3. Draw a vertical (or horizontal) line segment inside the box at the location of the median.
4. Extend horizontal (or vertical) line segments, called whiskers, from each end of the box to the smallest and largest observations in the data set.

■

# Example 4.10   Revisiting Hospital Cost-to-Charge Ratios

Let's reconsider the cost-to-charge data for hospitals in Oregon (Example 4.9). The ordered observations are:

**Ordered Data**

Lower half   45   48   50   54   57   60   60   **62**   63   63   64   65   67   68   69

Median                                                      **71**

Upper half   71   72   72   74   74   75   75   **76**   80   83   84   88   100   100   100

To construct a boxplot of these data, we need the following information: the smallest observation, the lower quartile, the median, the upper quartile, and the largest observation. This collection of summary measures is often referred to as the **five-number summary**. For this data set (see Example 4.9), we have

> smallest observation = 45
> lower quartile = median of the lower half = 62
> median = 16th observation in the ordered list = 71
> upper quartile = median of the upper half = 76
> largest observation = 100

Figure 4.8 shows the corresponding boxplot. The median line is somewhat closer to the upper edge of the box than to the lower edge, suggesting a concentration of values in the upper part of the middle half. The upper whisker is a bit longer than the lower whisker. These conclusions are consistent with the stem-and-leaf display of Figure 4.7.

**Figure 4.8**   Skeletal boxplot for the cost-to-charge data of Example 4.10.

| | | | | | | |
|---|---|---|---|---|---|---|
| 40 | 50 | 60 | 70 | 80 | 90 | 100 |

Cost-to-charge ratio

■

The sequence of steps used to construct a skeletal boxplot is easily modified to give information about outliers.

> **DEFINITION**
>
> An observation is an **outlier** if it is more than 1.5(iqr) away from the nearest quartile (the nearest end of the box).
>
> An outlier is **extreme** if it is more than 3(iqr) from the nearest end of the box, and it is **mild** otherwise.

A **modified boxplot** represents mild outliers by shaded circles and extreme outliers by open circles, and the whiskers extend on each end to the most extreme observations that are *not* outliers.

### Construction of a Modified Boxplot

1. Draw a horizontal (or vertical) measurement scale.
2. Construct a rectangular box with a left (or lower) edge is at the lower quartile and whose right (or upper) edge is at the upper quartile. The box width is then equal to the iqr.
3. Draw a vertical (or horizontal) line segment inside the box at the location of the median.
4. Determine if there are any mild or extreme outliers in the data set.
5. Draw whiskers that extend from each end of the box to the most extreme observation that is *not* an outlier.
6. Draw a solid circle to mark the location of any mild outliers in the data set.
7. Draw an open circle to mark the location of any extreme outliers in the data set.

■

....................................................................................................................

# Example 4.11  Golden Rectangles

● The accompanying data came from an anthropological study of rectangular shapes (*Lowie's Selected Papers in Anthropology,* Cora Dubios, ed. [Berkeley, CA: University of California Press, 1960]: 137–142). Observations were made on the variable $x$ = width/length for a sample of $n = 20$ beaded rectangles used in Shoshoni Indian leather handicrafts:

| | | | | | | | | | |
|---|---|---|---|---|---|---|---|---|---|
| .553 | .570 | .576 | .601 | .606 | .606 | .609 | .611 | .615 | .628 |
| .654 | .662 | .668 | .670 | .672 | .690 | .693 | .749 | .844 | .933 |

The quantities needed for constructing the modified boxplot follow:

| | |
|---|---|
| median = .641 | iqr = .681 − .606 = .075 |
| lower quartile = .606 | 1.5(iqr) = .1125 |
| upper quartile = .681 | 3(iqr) = .225 |

Thus,

$$\text{(upper quartile)} + 1.5(\text{iqr}) = .681 + .1125 = .7935$$
$$\text{(lower quartile)} - 1.5(\text{iqr}) = .606 - .1125 = .4935$$

So 0.844 and 0.933 are both outliers on the upper end (because they are larger than 0.7935), and there are no outliers on the lower end (because no observations are smaller than 0.4935). Because

(upper quartile) + 3(iqr) = 0.681 + 0.225 = 0.906

0.933 is an extreme outlier and 0.844 is only a mild outlier. The upper whisker extends to the largest observation that is not an outlier, 0.749, and the lower whisker extends to 0.553. The boxplot is presented in Figure 4.9. The median line is not at the center of the box, so there is a slight asymmetry in the middle half of the data. However, the most striking feature is the presence of the two outliers. These two $x$ values considerably exceed the "golden ratio" of 0.618, used since antiquity as an aesthetic standard for rectangles.

**Figure 4.9** Boxplot for the rectangle data in Example 4.11.

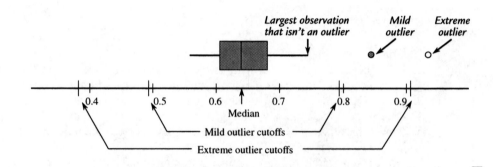

■

·······················································································································

# Example 4.12 State Gross Products

◉ *Highway Statistics 2001* (Federal Highway Administration) gave selected descriptive measures for the 50 U.S. states and the District of Columbia. The 51 observations for gross state product (in billions of dollars) and per capita state product (in dollars) are as follows:

**Gross Product**

| 110 | 24 | 134 | 62 | 1119 | 142 | 142 | 34 | 54 | 419 | 254 | 40 |
|-----|-----|-----|-----|------|-----|-----|-----|-----|-----|-----|-----|
| 31 | 426 | 174 | 85 | 77 | 107 | 129 | 32 | 165 | 239 | 295 | 161 |
| 62 | 163 | 20 | 52 | 63 | 41 | 319 | 48 | 707 | 236 | 17 | 341 |
| 82 | 105 | 364 | 30 | 100 | 21 | 160 | 646 | 60 | 16 | 231 | 193 |
| 40 | 158 | 18 | | | | | | | | | |

**Per Capita GP**

| 25,282 | 39,024 | 28,712 | 24,429 | 34,238 | 35,777 | 43,385 | 45,699 |
|--------|--------|--------|--------|--------|--------|--------|--------|
| 103,647 | 28,106 | 33,259 | 33,813 | 28,183 | 35,294 | 29,452 | 29,710 |
| 29,178 | 27,199 | 29,567 | 25,641 | 32,164 | 38,900 | 30,041 | 34,087 |
| 22,537 | 29,974 | 22,727 | 31,306 | 36,124 | 34,570 | 39,402 | 27,682 |
| 38,934 | 31,275 | 26,645 | 30,343 | 34,558 | 31,993 | 30,328 | 30,364 |
| 26,042 | 28,728 | 29,450 | 32,772 | 28,588 | 27,073 | 34,028 | 33,931 |
| 22,075 | 30,257 | 37,500 | | | | | |

◉ Data set available online

Figure 4.10(a) shows a MINITAB boxplot for gross state product. Note that the upper whisker is longer than the lower whisker and that there are three outliers on the high end (from least extreme to most extreme, they are Texas, New York, and California—not surprising, because these are the three states with the largest population sizes). Figure 4.10(b) shows a MINITAB boxplot of the per capita gross state product (state gross product divided by population size). For this boxplot, the upper whisker is longer than the lower whisker and there are only two outliers on the upper end. The two outliers in this data set are Delaware and Washington, D.C., indicating that, although the three largest states have the highest gross state product, they are not the states with the highest *per capita* gross state product.

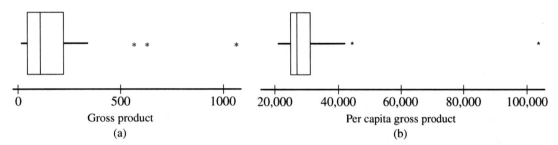

**Figure 4.10**   MINITAB boxplots for the data of Example 4.12: (a) gross state product; (b) per capita gross state product.

Note that MINITAB does not distinguish between mild outliers and extreme outliers in the boxplot. For the per capita gross state product data,

$$\text{lower quartile} = 28{,}183$$
$$\text{upper quartile} = 34{,}558$$
$$\text{iqr} = 34{,}558 - 28{,}183 = 9375$$

Then

$$1.5(\text{iqr}) = 9562.5$$
$$3(\text{iqr}) = 19{,}125$$

The observation for Delaware (45,699) would be a mild outlier, because it is more than 1.5(iqr) but less than 3(iqr) from the upper quartile. The observation for Washington, D.C. (103,647), is an extreme outlier, because it is more than 3(iqr) away from the upper quartile.

For the gross product data,

$$\text{lower quartile} = 41$$
$$\text{upper quartile} = 231$$
$$\text{iqr} = 231 - 41 = 190$$
$$1.5(\text{iqr}) = 285 \qquad 3(\text{iqr}) = 570$$

so the observations for Texas (646) and New York (707) are mild outliers and the observation for California (1119) is an extreme outlier.

■

With two or more data sets consisting of observations on the same variable (e.g., fuel efficiencies for four types of car or weight gains for a control group and a treatment group), **comparative boxplots** (more than one boxplot drawn using the same scale) convey initial impressions concerning similarities and differences between the data sets.

## Example 4.13 NBA Salaries Revisited

The 2003–2004 salaries of NBA players published in *USA Today* (December 17, 2003) were used to construct the comparative boxplot of the salary data for five teams shown in Figure 4.11.

**Figure 4.11** Comparative boxplot for salaries for five NBA teams.

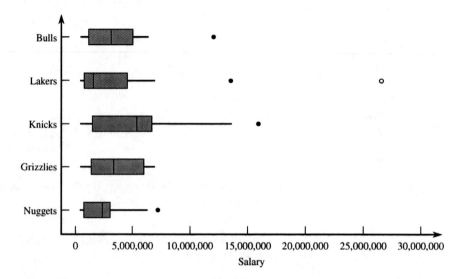

The comparative boxplot reveals some interesting similarities and differences in the salary distributions of the five teams. The minimum salary is about the same for all five teams. The median salary was lowest for the Lakers—in fact the median for the Lakers is about the same as the lower quartile for the Knicks and the Grizzlies, indicating that half of the players on the Lakers have salaries less than about $1.5 million, whereas only about 25% of the Knicks and the Grizzlies have salaries less than about $1.5 million. On the other hand, the Lakers had the player with by far the highest salary and two of the players with the highest three salaries. The Grizzlies were the only team that did not have any salary outliers.

■

## Exercises 4.29–4.35

**4.29** Based on a large national sample of working adults, the U.S. Census Bureau reports the following information on travel time to work for those who do not work at home:

  lower quartile = 7 min
  median = 18 min
  upper quartile = 31 min

Also given was the mean travel time, which was reported as 22.4 min.
**a.** Is the travel time distribution more likely to be approximately symmetric, positively skewed, or negatively skewed? Explain your reasoning based on the given summary quantities.

b. Suppose that the minimum travel time was 1 min and that the maximum travel time in the sample was 205 min. Construct a skeletal boxplot for the travel time data.
c. Were there any mild or extreme outliers in the data set? How can you tell?

4.30 ◉ The technical report "Ozone Season Emissions by State" (U.S. Environmental Protection Agency, 2002) gave the following nitrous oxide emissions (in thousands of tons) for the 48 states in the continental U.S. states:

| 76 | 22 | 40 | 7 | 30 | 5 | 6 | 136 | 72 | 33 | 0 |
|----|----|----|----|----|----|----|----|----|----|----|
| 89 | 136 | 39 | 92 | 40 | 13 | 27 | 1 | 63 | 33 | 60 |
| 27 | 16 | 63 | 32 | 20 | 2 | 15 | 36 | 19 | 39 | 130 |
| 40 | 4 | 85 | 38 | 7 | 68 | 151 | 32 | 34 | 0 | 6 |
| 43 | 89 | 34 | 0 | | | | | | | |

Use these data to construct a boxplot that shows outliers. Write a few sentences describing the important characteristics of the boxplot.

4.31 ◉ ▼ A report from Texas Transportation Institute (Texas A&M University System 2005) on Congestion Reduction Strategies looked into the extra travel time (due to traffic congestion) for commute travel per traveler per year in hours for different urban areas. Below are the data for urban areas that had a population of over 3 million for the year 2002.

| Urban Area | Extra Hours per Traveler per Year |
|------------|----------------------------------|
| Los Angeles | 98 |
| San Francisco | 75 |
| Washington DC | 66 |
| Atlanta | 64 |
| Houston | 65 |
| Dallas, Fort Worth | 61 |
| Chicago | 55 |
| Detroit | 54 |
| Miami | 48 |
| Boston | 53 |
| New York | 50 |
| Phoenix | 49 |
| Philadelphia | 40 |

a. Compute the mean and median values for extra travel hours. Based on the values of the mean and median, is the distribution of extra travel hours likely to be approximately symmetric, positively skewed, or negatively skewed?

b. Construct a modified boxplot for these data and comment on any interesting features of the plot.

4.32 ◉ Shown here are the number of auto accidents per year for every 1000 people in each of 40 occupations (*Knight Ridder Tribune,* June 19, 2004):

| Occupation | Accidents per 1000 | Occupation | Accidents per 1000 |
|------------|---------------------|------------|---------------------|
| Student | 152 | Banking, finance | 89 |
| Physician | 109 | Customer service | 88 |
| Lawyer | 106 | Manager | 88 |
| Architect | 105 | Medical support | 87 |
| Real estate broker | 102 | Computer-related | 87 |
| Enlisted military | 99 | Dentist | 86 |
| Social worker | 98 | Pharmacist | 85 |
| Manual laborer | 96 | Proprietor | 84 |
| Analyst | 95 | Teacher, professor | 84 |
| Engineer | 94 | Accountant | 84 |
| Consultant | 94 | Law enforcement | 79 |
| Sales | 93 | Physical therapist | 78 |
| Military officer | 91 | Veterinarian | 78 |
| Nurse | 90 | Clerical, secretary | 77 |
| School administrator | 90 | Clergy | 76 |
| Skilled laborer | 90 | Homemaker | 76 |
| Librarian | 90 | Politician | 76 |
| Creative arts | 90 | Pilot | 75 |
| Executive | 89 | Firefighter | 67 |
| Insurance agent | 89 | Farmer | 43 |

a. Would you recommend using the standard deviation or the iqr as a measure of variability for this data set?
b. Are there outliers in this data set? If so, which observations are mild outliers? Which are extreme outliers?
c. Draw a modified boxplot for this data set.
d. If you were asked by an insurance company to decide which, if any, occupations should be offered a professional discount on auto insurance, which occupations would you recommend? Explain.

4.33 ◉ ▼ The paper "Relationship Between Blood Lead and Blood Pressure Among Whites and African Americans" (a technical report published by Tulane University School of Public Health and Tropical Medicine, 2000) gave summary quantities for blood lead level (in micrograms per deciliter) for a sample of whites and a sample of African Americans. Data consistent with the given summary quantities follow:

| Whites | 8.3 | 0.9 | 2.9 | 5.6 | 5.8 | 5.4 | 1.2 |
|--------|-----|-----|-----|-----|-----|-----|-----|
|        | 1.0 | 1.4 | 2.1 | 1.3 | 5.3 | 8.8 | 6.6 |
|        | 5.2 | 3.0 | 2.9 | 2.7 | 6.7 | 3.2 |     |
| African | 4.8 | 1.4 | 0.9 | 10.8 | 2.4 | 0.4 | 5.0 |
| Americans | 5.4 | 6.1 | 2.9 | 5.0 | 2.1 | 7.5 | 3.4 |
|         | 13.8 | 1.4 | 3.5 | 3.3 | 14.8 | 3.7 |    |

**a.** Compute the values of the mean and the median for blood lead level for the sample of African Americans. Which of the mean or the median is larger? What characteristic of the data set explains the relative values of the mean and the median?

**b.** Construct a comparative boxplot for blood lead level for the two samples. Write a few sentences comparing the blood lead level distributions for the two samples.

**4.34** ● The article "Compression of Single-Wall Corrugated Shipping Containers Using Fixed and Floating Test Platens" (*Journal of Testing and Evaluation* [1992]: 318–320) described an experiment in which several different types of boxes were compared with respect to compressive strength. Consider the following observations on four different types of boxes (these data are consistent with summary quantities given in the paper):

| Type of Box | Compression Strength (lb) | | | | | |
|-------------|-------|-------|-------|-------|-------|-------|
| 1 | 655.5 | 788.3 | 734.3 | 721.4 | 679.1 | 699.4 |
| 2 | 789.2 | 772.5 | 786.9 | 686.1 | 732.1 | 774.8 |
| 3 | 737.1 | 639.0 | 696.3 | 671.7 | 717.2 | 727.1 |
| 4 | 535.1 | 628.7 | 542.4 | 559.0 | 586.9 | 520.0 |

Construct a boxplot for each type of box. Use the same scale for all four boxplots. Discuss the similarities and differences in the boxplots.

**4.35** ● Blood cocaine concentration (in milligrams per liter) was determined for both a sample of individuals who had died from cocaine-induced excited delirium and a sample of those who had died from a cocaine overdose without excited delirium. The accompanying data are consistent with summary values given in the paper "Fatal Excited Delirium Following Cocaine Use" (*Journal of Forensic Sciences* [1997]: 25–31):

**Excited Delirium**

| 0 | 0 | 0 | 0 | 0.1 | 0.1 | 0.1 | 0.1 | 0.2 | 0.2 |
|---|---|---|---|-----|-----|-----|-----|-----|-----|
| 0.3 | 0.3 | 0.3 | 0.4 | 0.5 | 0.7 | 0.7 | 1.0 | 1.5 | 2.7 |
| 2.8 | 3.5 | 4.0 | 8.9 | 9.2 | 11.7 | 21.0 | | | |

**No Excited Delirium**

| 0 | 0 | 0 | 0 | 0 | 0.1 | 0.1 | 0.1 | 0.1 |
|---|---|---|---|---|-----|-----|-----|-----|
| 0.2 | 0.2 | 0.2 | 0.3 | 0.3 | 0.3 | 0.4 | 0.5 | 0.5 |
| 0.6 | 0.8 | 0.9 | 1.0 | 1.2 | 1.4 | 1.5 | 1.7 | 2.0 |
| 3.2 | 3.5 | 4.1 | 4.3 | 4.8 | 5.0 | 5.6 | 5.9 | 6.0 |
| 6.4 | 7.9 | 8.3 | 8.7 | 9.1 | 9.6 | 9.9 | 11.0 | 11.5 |
| 12.2 | 12.7 | 14.0 | 16.6 | 17.8 | | | | |

**a.** Determine the median, quartiles, and interquartile range for each of the two samples.

**b.** Are there any outliers in either sample? Any extreme outliers?

**c.** Construct a comparative boxplot, and use it as a basis for comparing and contrasting the two samples.

---

**Bold** exercises answered in back ● Data set available online but not required ▼ Video solution available

---

## 4.4 Interpreting Center and Variability: Chebyshev's Rule, the Empirical Rule, and z Scores

The mean and standard deviation can be combined to obtain informative statements about how the values in a data set are distributed and about the relative position of a particular value in a data set. To do this, it is useful to be able to describe how far away a particular observation is from the mean in terms of the standard deviation. For example, we might say that an observation is 2 standard deviations above the mean or that an observation is 1.3 standard deviations below the mean.

# Example 4.14   Standardized Test Scores

Consider a data set of scores on a standardized test with a mean and standard deviation of 100 and 15, respectively. We can make the following statements:

1. Because $100 - 15 = 85$, we say that a score of 85 is "1 standard deviation *below* the mean." Similarly, $100 + 15 = 115$ is "1 standard deviation *above* the mean" (see Figure 4.12).
2. Because 2 standard deviations is $2(15) = 30$, and $100 + 30 = 130$ and $100 - 30 = 70$, scores between 70 and 130 are those *within* 2 standard deviations of the mean (see Figure 4.13).
3. Because $100 + (3)(15) = 145$, scores above 145 exceed the mean by more than 3 standard deviations.

**Figure 4.12**   Values within 1 standard deviation of the mean (Example 4.14).

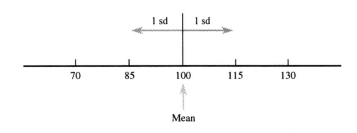

**Figure 4.13**   Values within 2 standard deviations of the mean (Example 4.14).

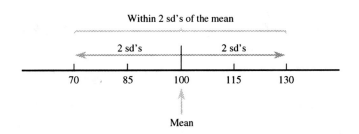

■

Sometimes in published articles, the mean and standard deviation are reported, but a graphical display of the data is not given. However, by using a result called Chebyshev's Rule, we can get a sense of the distribution of data values based on our knowledge of only the mean and standard deviation.

## Chebyshev's Rule

Consider any number $k$, where $k \geq 1$. Then the percentage of observations that are within $k$ standard deviations of the mean is at least $100\left(1 - \dfrac{1}{k^2}\right)\%$. Substituting selected values of $k$ gives the following results.

*(continued)*

| Number of Standard Deviations, $k$ | $1 - \dfrac{1}{k^2}$ | Percentage Within $k$ Standard Deviations of the Mean |
|:---:|:---:|:---:|
| 2 | $1 - \dfrac{1}{4} = .75$ | at least 75% |
| 3 | $1 - \dfrac{1}{9} = .89$ | at least 89% |
| 4 | $1 - \dfrac{1}{16} = .94$ | at least 94% |
| 4.472 | $1 - \dfrac{1}{20} = .95$ | at least 95% |
| 5 | $1 - \dfrac{1}{25} = .96$ | at least 96% |
| 10 | $1 - \dfrac{1}{100} = .99$ | at least 99% |

# Example 4.15 Child Care for Preschool Kids

The article "Piecing Together Child Care with Multiple Arrangements: Crazy Quilt or Preferred Pattern for Employed Parents of Preschool Children?" (*Journal of Marriage and the Family* [1994]: 669–680) examined various modes of care for preschool children. For a sample of families with one such child, it was reported that the mean and standard deviation of child care time per week were approximately 36 hr and 12 hr, respectively. Figure 4.14 displays values that are 1, 2, and 3 standard deviations from the mean.

**Figure 4.14** Measurement scale for child care time (Example 4.15).

| 0 | 12 | 24 | 36 | 48 | 60 | 72 |
|---|----|----|----|----|----|----|
| $\bar{x} - 3s$ | $\bar{x} - 2s$ | $\bar{x} - s$ | $\bar{x}$ | $\bar{x} + s$ | $\bar{x} + 2s$ | $\bar{x} + 3s$ |

Chebyshev's Rule allows us to assert the following:

1. At least 75% of the sample observations must be between 12 and 60 hours (within 2 standard deviations of the mean).
2. Because at least 89% of the observations must be between 0 and 72, at most 11% are outside this interval. Time cannot be negative, so we conclude that at most 11% of the observations exceed 72.
3. The values 18 and 54 are 1.5 standard deviations to either side of $\bar{x}$, so using $k = 1.5$ in Chebyshev's Rule implies that at least 55.6% of the observations must be between these two values. Thus, at most 44.4% of the observations are less than 18—*not* at most 22.2%, because the distribution of values may not be symmetric.

Because Chebyshev's Rule is applicable to any data set (distribution), whether symmetric or skewed, we must be careful when making statements about the proportion above a particular value, below a particular value, or inside or outside an interval that is not centered at the mean. The rule must be used in a conservative fashion. There is another aspect of this conservatism. Whereas the rule states that at least 75% of the observations are within 2 standard deviations of the mean, in many data sets substantially more than 75% of the values satisfy this condition. The same sort of understatement is frequently encountered for other values of *k* (numbers of standard deviations).

## Example 4.16  IQ Scores

Figure 4.15 gives a stem-and-leaf display of IQ scores of 112 children in one of the early studies that used the Stanford revision of the Binet–Simon intelligence scale (*The Intelligence of School Children,* L. M. Terman [Boston: Houghton-Mifflin, 1919]).

Summary quantities include

$$\bar{x} = 104.5 \qquad s = 16.3 \qquad 2s = 32.6 \qquad 3s = 48.9$$

**Figure 4.15** Stem-and leaf display of IQ scores used in Example 4.16.

```
 6 | 1
 7 | 25679
 8 | 0000124555668
 9 | 0000112333446666778889
10 | 00011222223333566677778899999
11 | 00001122333344444477899
12 | 01111123445669
13 | 006
14 | 26                          Stem: Tens
15 | 2                           Leaf:  Ones
```

In Figure 4.15, all observations that are within two standard deviations of the mean are shown in blue. Table 4.4 shows how Chebyshev's Rule can sometimes considerably understate actual percentages.

**Table 4.4**   Summarizing the Distribution of IQ Scores

| *k* = Number of sd's | $\bar{x} \pm ks$ | Chebyshev | Actual |
|---|---|---|---|
| 2 | 71.9 to 137.1 | at least 75% | *the blue* → 96% (108) |
| 2.5 | 63.7 to 145.3 | at least 84% | *leaves in Figure 4.15* 97% (109) |
| 3 | 55.6 to 153.4 | at least 89% | 100% (112) |

■

## ■ Empirical Rule

The fact that statements based on Chebyshev's Rule are frequently conservative suggests that we should look for rules that are less conservative and more precise. The most useful such rule is the **Empirical Rule**, which can be applied whenever the distribution of data values can be reasonably well described by a normal curve (distributions that are "mound" shaped).

### The Empirical Rule

If the histogram of values in a data set can be reasonably well approximated by a normal curve, then

Approximately 68% of the observations are within 1 standard deviation of the mean.
Approximately 95% of the observations are within 2 standard deviations of the mean.
Approximately 99.7% of the observations are within 3 standard deviations of the mean.

The Empirical Rule makes "approximately" instead of "at least" statements, and the percentages for $k = 1$, 2, and 3 standard deviations are much higher than those of Chebyshev's Rule. Figure 4.16 illustrates the percentages given by the Empirical Rule. In contrast to Chebyshev's Rule, dividing the percentages in half is permissible, because a normal curve is symmetric.

**Figure 4.16** Approximate percentages implied by the Empirical Rule.

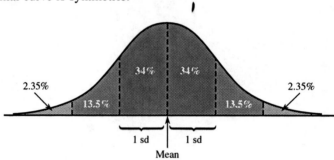

## Example 4.17  Heights of Mothers and the Empirical Rule

One of the earliest articles to argue for the wide applicability of the normal distribution was "On the Laws of Inheritance in Man. I. Inheritance of Physical Characters" (*Biometrika* [1903]: 375–462). Among the data sets discussed in the article was one consisting of 1052 measurements of the heights of mothers. The mean and standard deviation were

$$\bar{x} = 62.484 \text{ in.} \qquad s = 2.390 \text{ in.}$$

The data distribution was described as approximately normal. Table 4.5 contrasts actual percentages with those obtained from Chebyshev's Rule and the Empirical Rule.

**Table 4.5**  Summarizing the Distribution of Mothers' Heights

| Number of sd's | Interval | Actual | Empirical Rule | Chebyshev Rule |
|---|---|---|---|---|
| 1 | 60.094 to 64.874 | 72.1% | 68% | At least 0% |
| 2 | 57.704 to 67.264 | 96.2% | 95% | At least 75% |
| 3 | 55.314 to 69.654 | 99.2% | 99.7% | At least 89% |

Clearly, the Empirical Rule is much more successful and informative in this case than Chebyshev's Rule.

■

Our detailed study of the normal distribution and areas under normal curves in Chapter 7 will enable us to make statements analogous to those of the Empirical Rule for values other than $k = 1, 2,$ or 3 standard deviations. For now, note that it is unusual to see an observation from a normally distributed population that is farther than 2 standard deviations from the mean (only 5%), and it is very surprising to see one that is more than 3 standard deviations away. If you encountered a mother whose height was 72 in., you might reasonably conclude that she was not part of the population described by the data set in Example 4.17.

## ■ Measures of Relative Standing

When you obtain your score after taking an achievement test, you probably want to know how it compares to the scores of others who have taken the test. Is your score above or below the mean, and by how much? Does your score place you among the top 5% of those who took the test or only among the top 25%? Questions of this sort are answered by finding ways to measure the position of a particular value in a data set relative to all values in the set. One such measure involves calculating a *z score*.

> ### DEFINITION
>
> The *z* **score** corresponding to a particular value is
>
> $$z \text{ score} = \frac{\text{value} - \text{mean}}{\text{standard deviation}}$$
>
> The *z* score tells us how many standard deviations the value is from the mean. It is positive or negative according to whether the value lies above or below the mean.

The process of subtracting the mean and then dividing by the standard deviation is sometimes referred to as *standardization,* and a *z* score is one example of what is called a *standardized score.*

## Example 4.18  Relatively Speaking, Which Is the Better Offer?

Suppose that two graduating seniors, one a marketing major and one an accounting major, are comparing job offers. The accounting major has an offer for $45,000 per year, and the marketing student has an offer for $43,000 per year. Summary information about the distribution of offers follows:

Accounting:  mean = 46,000    standard deviation = 1500
Marketing:   mean = 42,500    standard deviation = 1000

Then,

$$\text{accounting } z \text{ score} = \frac{45,000 - 46,000}{1500} = -.67$$

(so $45,000 is .67 standard deviation below the mean), whereas

$$\text{marketing } z \text{ score} = \frac{43,000 - 42,500}{1000} = .5$$

Relative to the appropriate data sets, the marketing offer is actually more attractive than the accounting offer (although this may not offer much solace to the marketing major).

■

The $z$ score is particularly useful when the distribution of observations is approximately normal. In this case, from the Empirical Rule, a $z$ score outside the interval from $-2$ to $+2$ occurs in about 5% of all cases, whereas a $z$ score outside the interval from $-3$ to $+3$ occurs only about 0.3% of the time.

## ■ Percentiles

A particular observation can be located even more precisely by giving the percentage of the data that fall at or below that observation. If, for example, 95% of all test scores are at or below 650, whereas only 5% are above 650, then 650 is called the *95th percentile* of the data set (or of the distribution of scores). Similarly, if 10% of all scores are at or below 400 and 90% are above 400, then the value 400 is the 10th percentile.

> ### D E F I N I T I O N
>
> For any particular number $r$ between 0 and 100, the **rth percentile** is a value such that $r$ percent of the observations in the data set fall at or below that value.

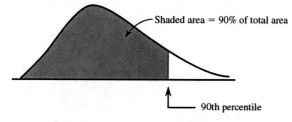

Figure 4.17 illustrates the 90th percentile. We have already met several percentiles in disguise. The median is the 50th percentile, and the lower and upper quartiles are the 25th and 75th percentiles, respectively.

**Figure 4.17** Ninetieth percentile for a smoothed histogram.

## Example 4.19 Variable Cost as a Percentage of Operating Revenue

Variable cost as a percentage of operating revenue is an important indicator of a company's financial health. The article "A Credit Limit Decision Model for Inventory Floor Planning and Other Extended Trade Credit Arrangements" (*Decision Sciences* [1992]: 200–220) reported the following summary data for a sample of 350 corporations:

sample mean = 90.1%    sample median = 91.2%
5th percentile = 78.3%    95th percentile = 98.6%

Thus, half of the sampled firms had variable costs that were less than 91.2% of operating revenues because 91.2 is the 50th percentile. If the distribution of values was perfectly symmetric, the mean and the median would be identical. Further evidence against symmetry is provided by the two other given percentiles. The 5th percentile is 12.9 percentage points below the median, whereas the 95th percentile is only 7.4 percentage points above the median. The histogram given in the article had roughly the shape of the negatively skewed smoothed histogram in Figure 4.18 (the total area under the curve is 1).

**Figure 4.18**  The distribution of variable costs from Example 4.19.

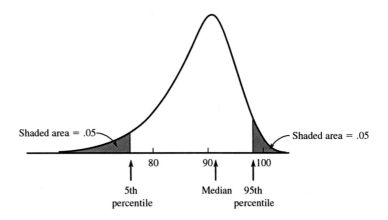

■

## Exercises 4.36–4.50

**4.36**  The average playing time of compact discs in a large collection is 35 min, and the standard deviation is 5 min.
a.  What value is 1 standard deviation above the mean? 1 standard deviation below the mean? What values are 2 standard deviations away from the mean?
b.  Without assuming anything about the distribution of times, at least what percentage of the times are between 25 and 45 min?
c.  Without assuming anything about the distribution of times, what can be said about the percentage of times that are either less than 20 min or greater than 50 min?
d.  Assuming that the distribution of times is normal, approximately what percentage of times are between 25 and 45 min? less than 20 min or greater than 50 min? less than 20 min?

**4.37** ▼ In a study investigating the effect of car speed on accident severity, 5000 reports of fatal automobile accidents were examined, and the vehicle speed at impact was recorded for each one. For these 5000 accidents, the average speed was 42 mph and that the standard deviation was

15 mph. A histogram revealed that the vehicle speed at impact distribution was approximately normal.
**a.**  Roughly what proportion of vehicle speeds were between 27 and 57 mph?
**b.**  Roughly what proportion of vehicle speeds exceeded 57 mph?

**4.38**  The U.S. Census Bureau (2000 census) reported the following relative frequency distribution for travel time to work for a large sample of adults who did not work at home:

| Travel Time (minutes) | Relative Frequency |
|---|---|
| 0 to <5 | .04 |
| 5 to <10 | .13 |
| 10 to <15 | .16 |
| 15 to <20 | .17 |
| 20 to <25 | .14 |
| 25 to <30 | .05 |
| | *(continued)* |

| Travel Time (minutes) | Relative Frequency |
|---|---|
| 30 to <35 | .12 |
| 35 to <40 | .03 |
| 40 to <45 | .03 |
| 45 to <60 | .06 |
| 60 to <90 | .05 |
| 90 or more | .02 |

a. Draw the histogram for the travel time distribution. In constructing the histogram, assume that the last interval in the relative frequency distribution (90 or more) ends at 200; so the last interval is 90 to <200. Be sure to use the density scale to determine the heights of the bars in the histogram because not all the intervals have the same width.

b. Describe the interesting features of the histogram from Part (a), including center, shape, and spread.

c. Based on the histogram from Part (a), would it be appropriate to use the Empirical Rule to make statements about the travel time distribution? Explain why or why not.

d. The approximate mean and standard deviation for the travel time distribution are 27 min and 24 min, respectively. Based on this mean and standard deviation and the fact that travel time cannot be negative, explain why the travel time distribution could not be well approximated by a normal curve.

e. Use the mean and standard deviation given in Part (d) and Chebyshev's Rule to make a statement about
   i. the percentage of travel times that were between 0 and 75 min
   ii. the percentage of travel times that were between 0 and 47 min

f. How well do the statements in Part (e) based on Chebyshev's Rule agree with the actual percentages for the travel time distribution? (Hint: You can estimate the actual percentages from the given relative frequency distribution.)

**4.39** Mobile homes are tightly constructed for energy conservation. This can lead to a buildup of indoor pollutants. The paper "A Survey of Nitrogen Dioxide Levels Inside Mobile Homes" (*Journal of the Air Pollution Control Association* [1988]: 647–651) discussed various aspects of $NO_2$ concentration in these structures.

a. In one sample of mobile homes in the Los Angeles area, the mean $NO_2$ concentration in kitchens during the summer was 36.92 ppb, and the standard deviation was 11.34. Making no assumptions about the shape of the $NO_2$ distribution, what can be said about the percentage of observations between 14.24 and 59.60?

b. Inside what interval is it guaranteed that at least 89% of the concentration observations will lie?

c. In a sample of non–Los Angeles mobile homes, the average kitchen $NO_2$ concentration during the winter was 24.76 ppb, and the standard deviation was 17.20. Do these values suggest that the histogram of sample observations did not closely resemble a normal curve? (Hint: What is $\bar{x} - 2s$?)

**4.40** The article "Taxable Wealth and Alcoholic Beverage Consumption in the United States" (*Psychological Reports* [1994]: 813–814) reported that the mean annual adult consumption of wine was 3.15 gal and that the standard deviation was 6.09 gal. Would you use the Empirical Rule to approximate the proportion of adults who consume more than 9.24 gal (i.e., the proportion of adults whose consumption value exceeds the mean by more than 1 standard deviation)? Explain your reasoning.

**4.41** A student took two national aptitude tests. The national average and standard deviation were 475 and 100, respectively, for the first test and 30 and 8, respectively, for the second test. The student scored 625 on the first test and 45 on the second test. Use $z$ scores to determine on which exam the student performed better relative to the other test takers.

**4.42** Suppose that your younger sister is applying for entrance to college and has taken the SATs. She scored at the 83rd percentile on the verbal section of the test and at the 94th percentile on the math section of the test. Because you have been studying statistics, she asks you for an interpretation of these values. What would you tell her?

**4.43** A sample of concrete specimens of a certain type is selected, and the compressive strength of each specimen is determined. The mean and standard deviation are calculated as $\bar{x} = 3000$ and $s = 500$, and the sample histogram is found to be well approximated by a normal curve.

a. Approximately what percentage of the sample observations are between 2500 and 3500?

b. Approximately what percentage of sample observations are outside the interval from 2000 to 4000?

c. What can be said about the approximate percentage of observations between 2000 and 2500?

d. Why would you not use Chebyshev's Rule to answer the questions posed in Parts (a)–(c)?

**4.44** The paper "Modeling and Measurements of Bus Service Reliability" (*Transportation Research* [1978]: 253–256) studied various aspects of bus service and presented data on travel times from several different routes. The accompanying frequency distribution is for bus travel times from origin to destination on one particular route in Chicago during peak morning traffic periods:

| Class | Frequency | Relative Frequency |
|---|---|---|
| 15 to <16 | 4 | .02 |
| 16 to <17 | 0 | .00 |
| 17 to <18 | 26 | .13 |
| 18 to <19 | 99 | .49 |
| 19 to <20 | 36 | .18 |
| 20 to <21 | 8 | .04 |
| 21 to <22 | 12 | .06 |
| 22 to <23 | 0 | .00 |
| 23 to <24 | 0 | .00 |
| 24 to <25 | 0 | .00 |
| 25 to <26 | 16 | .08 |

a. Construct the corresponding histogram.
b. Compute (approximately) the following percentiles:
   i. 86th          iv. 95th
   ii. 15th         v. 10th
   iii. 90th

**4.45** An advertisement for the "30-in. Wonder" that appeared in the September 1983 issue of the journal *Packaging* claimed that the 30-in. Wonder weighs cases and bags up to 110 lb and provides accuracy to within 0.25 oz. Suppose that a 50-oz weight was repeatedly weighed on this scale and the weight readings recorded. The mean value was 49.5 oz, and the standard deviation was 0.1. What can be said about the proportion of the time that the scale actually showed a weight that was within 0.25 oz of the true value of 50 oz? (Hint: Use Chebyshev's Rule.)

**4.46** Suppose that your statistics professor returned your first midterm exam with only a z score written on it. She also told you that a histogram of the scores was approximately normal. How would you interpret each of the following z scores?
a. 2.2          d. 1.0
b. 0.4          e. 0
c. 1.8

**4.47** The paper "Answer Changing on Multiple-Choice Tests" (*Journal of Experimental Education* [1980]: 18–21) reported that for a group of 162 college students, the average number of responses changed from the correct answer to an incorrect answer on a test containing 80 multiple-choice items was 1.4. The corresponding standard deviation was reported to be 1.5. Based on this mean and standard deviation, what can you tell about the shape of the distribution of the variable *number of answers changed from right to wrong*? What can you say about the number of students who changed at least six answers from correct to incorrect?

**4.48** The average reading speed of students completing a speed-reading course is 450 words per minute (wpm). If the standard deviation is 70 wpm, find the z score associated with each of the following reading speeds.
a. 320 wpm          c. 420 wpm
b. 475 wpm          d. 610 wpm

**4.49** ● ▼ The following data values are 1989 per capita expenditures on public libraries for each of the 50 states:

| | | | | | | |
|---|---|---|---|---|---|---|
| 29.48 | 24.45 | 23.64 | 23.34 | 22.10 | 21.16 | 19.83 |
| 18.01 | 17.95 | 17.23 | 16.53 | 16.29 | 15.89 | 15.85 |
| 13.64 | 13.37 | 13.16 | 13.09 | 12.66 | 12.37 | 11.93 |
| 10.99 | 10.55 | 10.24 | 10.06 | 9.84 | 9.65 | 8.94 |
| 7.70 | 7.56 | 7.46 | 7.04 | 6.58 | 5.98 | 19.81 |
| 19.25 | 19.18 | 18.62 | 14.74 | 14.53 | 14.46 | 13.83 |
| 11.85 | 11.71 | 11.53 | 11.34 | 8.72 | 8.22 | 8.13 |
| 8.01 | | | | | | |

a. Summarize this data set with a frequency distribution. Construct the corresponding histogram.
**b.** Use the histogram in Part (a) to find approximate values of the following percentiles:
i. 50th          iv. 90th
ii. 70th         v. 40th
iii. 10th

**4.50** The accompanying table gives the mean and standard deviation of reaction times (in seconds) for each of two different stimuli:

| | Stimulus 1 | Stimulus 2 |
|---|---|---|
| Mean | 6.0 | 3.6 |
| Standard deviation | 1.2 | 0.8 |

If your reaction time is 4.2 sec for the first stimulus and 1.8 sec for the second stimulus, to which stimulus are you reacting (compared to other individuals) relatively more quickly?

**Bold** exercises answered in back    ● Data set available online but not required    ▼ Video solution available

## 4.5   Interpreting and Communicating the Results of Statistical Analyses

As was the case with the graphical displays of Chapter 3, the primary function of the descriptive tools introduced in this chapter is to help us better understand the variables under study. If we have collected data on the amount of money students spend on textbooks at a particular university, most likely we did so because we wanted to learn about the distribution of this variable (amount spent on textbooks) for the population of interest (in this case, students at the university). Numerical measures of center and spread and boxplots help to enlighten us, and they also allow us to communicate to others what we have learned from the data.

### ■ Communicating the Results of Statistical Analyses

When reporting the results of a data analysis, it is common to start with descriptive information about the variables of interest. It is always a good idea to start with a graphical display of the data, and, as we saw in Chapter 3, graphical displays of numerical data are usually described in terms of center, variability, and shape. The numerical measures of this chapter can help you to be more specific in describing the center and spread of a data set.

When describing center and spread, you must first decide which measures to use. Common choices are to use either the sample mean and standard deviation or the sample median and interquartile range (and maybe even a boxplot) to describe center and spread. Because the mean and standard deviation can be sensitive to extreme values in the data set, they are best used when the distribution shape is approximately symmetric and when there are few outliers. If the data set is noticeably skewed or if there are outliers, then the observations are more spread out in one part of the distribution than in the others. In this situation, a five-number summary or a boxplot conveys more information than the mean and standard deviation do.

### ■ Interpreting the Results of Statistical Analyses

It is relatively rare to find raw data in published sources. Typically, only a few numerical summary quantities are reported. We must be able to interpret these values and understand what they tell us about the underlying data set.

For example, a university recently conducted an investigation of the amount of time required to enter the information contained in an application for admission into the university computer system. One of the individuals who performs this task was asked to note starting time and completion time for 50 randomly selected application forms. The resulting entry times (in minutes) were summarized using the mean, median, and standard deviation:

$$\bar{x} = 7.854$$
$$\text{median} = 7.423$$
$$s = 2.129$$

```
 4 8
 5 0234579
 6 00001234566779
 7 223556688
 8 23334
 9 002
10 011168
11 134
12 2            Stem:  Ones
13             Leaf:  Tenths
14 3
```

**Figure 4.19**   Stem-and-leaf display of data entry times.

What do these summary values tell us about entry times? The average time required to enter admissions data was 7.854 min, but the relatively large standard deviation suggests that many observations differ substantially from this mean. The median tells us that half of the applications required less than 7.423 min to enter. The fact that the mean exceeds the median suggests that some unusually large values in the data set affected the value of the mean. This last conjecture is confirmed by the stem-and-leaf display of the data given in Figure 4.19.

The administrators conducting the data-entry study looked at the outlier 14.3 min and at the other relatively large values in the data set; they found that the five largest values came from applications that were entered before lunch. After talking with the individual who entered the data, the administrators speculated that morning entry times might differ from afternoon entry times because there tended to be more distractions and interruptions (phone calls, etc.) during the morning hours, when the admissions office generally was busier. When morning and afternoon entry times were separated, the following summary statistics resulted:

Morning (based on $n = 20$ applications):   $\bar{x} = 9.093$   median $= 8.743$   $s = 2.329$
Afternoon (based on $n = 30$ applications):   $\bar{x} = 7.027$   median $= 6.737$   $s = 1.529$

Clearly, the average entry time is higher for applications entered in the morning; also, the individual entry times differ more from one another in the mornings than in the afternoons (because the standard deviation for morning entry times, 2.329, is about 1.5 times as large as 1.529, the standard deviation for afternoon entry times).

## ■ What to Look for in Published Data

Here are a few questions to ask yourself when you interpret numerical summary measures.

- Is the chosen summary measure appropriate for the type of data collected? In particular, watch for inappropriate use of the mean and standard deviation with categorical data that has simply been coded numerically.
- If both the mean and the median are reported, how do the two values compare? What does this suggest about the distribution of values in the data set? If only the mean or the median was used, was the appropriate measure selected?
- Is the standard deviation large or small? Is the value consistent with your expectations regarding variability? What does the value of the standard deviation tell you about the variable being summarized?
- Can anything of interest be said about the values in the data set by applying Chebyshev's Rule or the Empirical Rule?

For example, consider a study on smoking and lactation. The journal article "Smoking During Pregnancy and Lactation and Its Effects on Breast Milk Volume" (*American Journal of Clinical Nutrition* [1991]: 1011–1016) reported the following summary values for data collected on daily breast milk volume (in grams) for two groups of nursing mothers:

| Group | Mean | Standard Deviation | Median |
|---|---|---|---|
| Smokers | 693 | 110 | 589.5 |
| Nonsmokers | 961 | 120 | 946 |

Because milk volume is a numerical variable, these descriptive measures reasonably summarize the data set. For nonsmoking mothers, the mean and the median are similar, indicating that the milk volume distribution is approximately symmetric. The average milk volume for smoking mothers is 693, whereas for nonsmoking mothers the mean milk volume is 961—quite a bit higher than for the smoking mothers. The standard deviations for the two groups are similar, suggesting that, although the average milk volume may be lower for smokers, the variability in mothers' milk volume is about the same. Because the median for the smoking group is smaller than the corresponding mean, we suspect that the distribution of milk volume for smoking mothers is positively skewed.

## ■ A Word to the Wise: Cautions and Limitations ...............................................

When computing or interpreting numerical descriptive measures, you need to keep in mind the following:

1. **Measures of center don't tell all.** Although measures of center, such as the mean and the median, do give us a sense of what might be considered a typical value for a variable, this is only one characteristic of a data set. Without additional information about variability and distribution shape, we don't really know much about the behavior of the variable.
2. **Data distributions with different shapes can have the same mean and standard deviation.** For example, consider the following two histograms:

Both histograms summarize data sets that have a mean of 10 and a standard deviation of 2, yet they have different shapes.
3. **Both the mean and the standard deviation are sensitive to extreme values in a data set**, especially if the sample size is small. If a data distribution is skewed or if the data set has outliers, the median and the interquartile range may be a better choice for describing center and spread.
4. **Measures of center and variability describe the values of the variable studied, not the frequencies in a frequency distribution or the heights of the bars in a histogram.** For example, consider the following two frequency distributions and histograms:

| Frequency Distribution A | | Frequency Distribution B | |
|---|---|---|---|
| **Value** | **Frequency** | **Value** | **Frequency** |
| 1 | 10 | 1 | 5 |
| 2 | 10 | 2 | 10 |
| 3 | 10 | 3 | 20 |
| 4 | 10 | 4 | 10 |
| 5 | 10 | 5 | 5 |

Histogram A

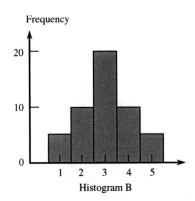

Histogram B

There is more variability in the data summarized by Frequency Distribution and Histogram A than in the data summarized by Frequency Distribution and Histogram B. This is because the values of the variable described by Histogram and Frequency Distribution B are more concentrated near the mean than are the values for the variable described by Histogram and Frequency Distribution A. Don't be misled by the fact that there is no variability in the frequencies in Frequency Distribution A or the heights of the bars in Histogram A.

5. Be careful with boxplots based on small sample sizes. Boxplots convey information about center, variability, and shape, but when the sample size is small, you should be hesitant to overinterpret shape information. It is really not possible to decide whether a data distribution is symmetric or skewed if only a small sample of observations from the distribution is available.

6. Not all distributions are normal (or even approximately normal). Be cautious in applying the Empirical Rule in situations where you are not convinced that the data distribution is at least approximately normal. Using the Empirical Rule in such situations can lead to incorrect statements.

7. Watch out for outliers! Unusual observations in a data set often provide important information about the variable under study, so it is important to consider outliers in addition to describing what is typical. Outliers can also be problematic—both because the values of some descriptive measures are influenced by outliers and because some of the methods for drawing conclusions from data may not be appropriate if the data set has outliers.

## Activity 4.1 Collecting and Summarizing Numerical Data

In this activity, you will work in groups to collect data that will provide information about how many hours per week, on average, students at your school spend engaged in a particular activity. You will use the sampling plan designed in Activity 2.1 to collect the data.

1. With your group, pick one of the following activities to be the focus of your study:
   i. Surfing the web
   ii. Studying or doing homework
   iii. Watching TV
   iv. Exercising
   v. Sleeping

or you may choose a different activity, *subject to the approval of your instructor.*

2. Use the plan developed in Activity 2.1 to collect data on the variable you have chosen for your study.
3. Summarize the resulting data using both numerical and graphical summaries. Be sure to address both center and variability.
4. Write a short article for your school paper summarizing your findings regarding student behavior. Your article should include both numerical and graphical summaries.

## Activity 4.2 Airline Passenger Weights

The article "Airlines Should Weigh Passengers, Bags, NTSB Says" (*USA Today*, February 27, 2004) states that the National Transportation Safety Board recommended that airlines weigh passengers and their bags to prevent overloaded planes from attempting to take off. This recommendation was the result of an investigation into the crash of a small commuter plane in 2003, which determined that too much weight contributed to the crash.

Rather than weighing passengers, airlines currently use estimates of average passenger and luggage weights. After the 2003 accident, this estimate was increased by 10 lbs. for passengers and 5 lbs. for luggage. Although an airplane can fly if it is somewhat overweight if all systems are working properly, if one of the plane's engines fails an overweight plane becomes difficult for the pilot to control.

Assuming that the new estimate of the average passenger weight is accurate, discuss the following questions with a partner and then write a paragraph that answers these questions.

1. What role does variability in passenger weights play in creating a potentially dangerous situation for an airline?
2. Would an airline have a lower risk of a potentially dangerous situation if the variability in passenger weight is large or if it is small?

## Activity 4.3 Boxplot Shapes

In this activity, you will investigate the relationship between boxplot shapes and the corresponding five-number summary. The accompanying figure shows four boxplots, labeled A–D. Also given are four five-number summaries, labeled I–IV. Match each five-number summary to the appropriate boxplot. Note that scales are not included on the boxplots, so you will have to think about what the five-number summary implies about characteristics of the boxplot.

**Five-Number Summaries**

|                | I   | II | III | IV  |
| -------------- | --- | -- | --- | --- |
| Minimum        | 40  | 4  | 0.0 | 10  |
| Lower quartile | 45  | 8  | 0.1 | 34  |
| Median         | 71  | 16 | 0.9 | 44  |
| Upper quartile | 88  | 25 | 2.2 | 82  |
| Maximum        | 106 | 30 | 5.1 | 132 |

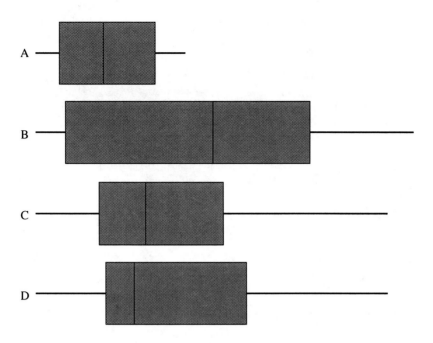

# Summary of Key Concepts and Formulas

| Term or Formula | Comment |
|---|---|
| $x_1, x_2, \dots, x_n$ | Notation for sample data consisting of observations on a variable $x$, where $n$ is the sample size. |
| Sample mean, $\bar{x}$ | The most frequently used measure of center of a sample. It can be very sensitive to the presence of even a single outlier (unusually large or small observation). |
| Population mean, $\mu$ | The average $x$ value in the entire population. |
| Sample median | The middle value in the ordered list of sample observations. (For $n$ even, the median is the average of the two middle values.) It is very insensitive to outliers. |
| Trimmed mean | A measure of center in which the observations are first ordered from smallest to largest, one or more observations are deleted from each end, and the remaining ones are averaged. In terms of sensitivity to outliers, it is a compromise between the mean and the median. |
| Deviations from the mean: $x_1 - \bar{x}, x_2 - \bar{x}, \dots, x_n - \bar{x}$ | Quantities used to assess variability in a sample. Except for rounding effects, $\sum(x - \bar{x}) = 0$. |
| The sample variance $s^2 = \dfrac{\sum(x - \bar{x})^2}{n-1}$ and standard deviation $s = \sqrt{s^2}$ | The most frequently used measures of variability for sample data. |

| Term or Formula | Comment |
|---|---|
| The population variance $\sigma^2$ and standard deviation $\sigma$ | Measures of variability for the entire population. |
| Quartiles and the interquartile range | The lower quartile separates the smallest 25% of the data from the remaining 75%, and the upper quartile separates the largest 25% from the smallest 75%. The interquartile range (iqr), a measure of variability less sensitive to outliers than $s$, is the difference between the upper and lower quartiles. |
| Chebyshev's Rule | This rule states that for any number $k \geq 1$, *at least* $100\left(1 - \dfrac{1}{k^2}\right)$ % of the observations in *any* data set are within $k$ standard deviations of the mean. It is typically conservative in that the actual percentages often considerably exceed the stated lower bound. |
| Empirical Rule | This rule gives the approximate percentage of observations within 1 standard deviation (68%), 2 standard deviations (95%), and 3 standard deviations (99.7%) of the mean when the histogram is well approximated by a normal curve. |
| $z$ score | This quantity gives the distance between an observation and the mean expressed as a certain number of standard deviations. It is positive (negative) if the observation lies above (below) the mean. |
| $r$th percentile | The value such that $r$% of the observations in the data set fall at or below that value. |
| Five-number summary | A summary of a data set that includes the minimum, lower quartile, median, upper quartile, and maximum. |
| Boxplot | A picture that conveys information about the most important features of a numerical data set: center, spread, extent of skewness, and presence of outliers. |

# Chapter Review Exercises 4.51–4.69

**Thomson**NOW  Know exactly what to study! Take a pre-test and receive your Personalized Learning Plan.

**4.51** The *San Luis Obispo Telegram-Tribune* (October 1, 1994) reported the following monthly salaries for supervisors from six different counties: $5354 (Kern), $5166 (Monterey), $4443 (Santa Cruz), $4129 (Santa Barbara), $2500 (Placer), and $2220 (Merced). San Luis Obispo County supervisors are supposed to be paid the average of the two counties among these six in the middle of the salary range. Which measure of center determines this salary, and what is its value? Why is the other measure of center featured in this section not as favorable to these supervisors (although it might appeal to taxpayers)?

**Bold** exercises answered in back   ● Data set available online but not required   ▼ Video solution available

**4.52** ● A sample of 26 offshore oil workers took part in a simulated escape exercise, resulting in the accompanying data on time (in seconds) to complete the escape ("Oxygen Consumption and Ventilation During Escape from an Offshore Platform," *Ergonomics*[1997]: 281–292):

| | | | | | | | | |
|---|---|---|---|---|---|---|---|---|
| 389 | 356 | 359 | 363 | 375 | 424 | 325 | 394 | 402 |
| 373 | 373 | 370 | 364 | 366 | 364 | 325 | 339 | 393 |
| 392 | 369 | 374 | 359 | 356 | 403 | 334 | 397 | |

a. Construct a stem-and-leaf display of the data. Will the sample mean or the sample median be larger for this data set?
b. Calculate the values of the sample mean and median.
c. By how much could the largest time be increased without affecting the value of the sample median? By how much could this value be decreased without affecting the sample median?

**4.53** The *San Luis Obispo Telegram-Tribune* (November 29, 1995) reported the values of the mean and median salary for major league baseball players for 1995. The values reported were $1,110,766 and $275,000.
a. Which of the two given values do you think is the mean and which is the median? Explain your reasoning.
b. The reported mean was computed using the salaries of all major league players in 1995. For the 1995 salaries, is the reported mean the population mean $\mu$ or the sample mean $\bar{x}$? Explain.

**4.54** Because some homes have selling prices that are much higher than most, the median price is usually used to describe a "typical" home price for a given location. The three accompanying quotes are all from the *San Luis Obispo Tribune,* but each gives a different interpretation of the median price of a home in San Luis Obispo County. Comment on each of these statements. (Look carefully. At least one of the statements is incorrect.)
a. "So we have gone from 23 percent to 27 percent of county residents who can afford the median priced home at $278,380 in SLO County. That means that half of the homes in this county cost less than $278,380 and half cost more." (October 11, 2001)
b. "The county's median price rose to $285,170 in the fourth quarter, a 9.6 percent increase from the same period a year ago, the report said. (The median represents the midpoint of a range.)" (February 13, 2002)
c. " 'Your median is going to creep up above $300,000 if there is nothing available below $300,000,' Walker said." (February 26, 2002)

**4.55** ● Although bats are not known for their eyesight, they are able to locate prey (mainly insects) by emitting high-pitched sounds and listening for echoes. A paper appearing in *Animal Behaviour* ("The Echolocation of Flying Insects by Bats" [1960]: 141–154) gave the following distances (in centimeters) at which a bat first detected a nearby insect:

| | | | | | | | | | | |
|---|---|---|---|---|---|---|---|---|---|---|
| 62 | 23 | 27 | 56 | 52 | 34 | 42 | 40 | 68 | 45 | 83 |

a. Compute the sample mean distance at which the bat first detects an insect.
b. Compute the sample variance and standard deviation for this data set. Interpret these values.

**4.56** For the data in Exercise 4.55, subtract 10 from each sample observation. For the new set of values, compute the mean and the deviations from the mean. How do these deviations compare to the deviations from the mean for the original sample? How does $s^2$ for the new values compare to $s^2$ for the old values? In general, what effect does subtracting (or adding) the same number to each observation have on $s^2$ and $s$? Explain.

**4.57** For the data of Exercise 4.55, multiply each data value by 10. How does $s$ for the new values compare to $s$ for the original values? More generally, what happens to $s$ if each observation is multiplied by the same positive constant $c$?

**4.58** ● The percentage of juice lost after thawing for 19 different strawberry varieties appeared in the article "Evaluation of Strawberry Cultivars with Different Degrees of Resistance to Red Scale" (*Fruit Varieties Journal* [1991]: 12–17):

| | | | | | | | | | | | |
|---|---|---|---|---|---|---|---|---|---|---|---|
| 46 | 51 | 44 | 50 | 33 | 46 | 60 | 41 | 55 | 46 | 53 | 53 |
| 42 | 44 | 50 | 54 | 46 | 41 | 48 | | | | | |

a. Are there any observations that are mild outliers? Extreme outliers?
b. Construct a boxplot, and comment on the important features of the plot.

**4.59** ● To understand better the effects of exercise and aging on various circulatory functions, the article "Cardiac Output in Male Middle-Aged Runners" (*Journal of Sports Medicine* [1982]: 17–22) presented data from a study of 21 middle-aged male runners. The following data set gives values of oxygen capacity values (in milliliters per kilogram per minute) while the participants pedaled at a specified rate on a bicycle ergometer:

| 12.81 | 14.95 | 15.83 | 15.97 | 17.90 | 18.27 | 18.34 |
| 19.82 | 19.94 | 20.62 | 20.88 | 20.93 | 20.98 | 20.99 |
| 21.15 | 22.16 | 22.24 | 23.16 | 23.56 | 35.78 | 36.73 |

a. Compute the median and the quartiles for this data set.
b. What is the value of the interquartile range? Are there outliers in this data set?
c. Draw a modified boxplot, and comment on the interesting features of the plot.

4.60 ● The risk of developing iron deficiency is especially high during pregnancy. Detecting such a deficiency is complicated by the fact that some methods for determining iron status can be affected by the state of pregnancy itself. Consider the following data on transferrin receptor concentration for a sample of women with laboratory evidence of overt iron-deficiency anemia ("Serum Transferrin Receptor for the Detection of Iron Deficiency in Pregnancy," *American Journal of Clinical Nutrition* [1991]: 1077–1081):

| 15.2 | 9.3 | 7.6 | 11.9 | 10.4 | 9.7 | 20.4 | 9.4 | 11.5 |
| 16.2 | 9.4 | 8.3 |

Compute the values of the sample mean and median. Why are these values different here? Which one do you regard as more representative of the sample, and why?

4.61 ● The paper "The Pedaling Technique of Elite Endurance Cyclists" (*International Journal of Sport Biomechanics* [1991]: 29–53) reported the following data on single-leg power at a high workload:

| 244 | 191 | 160 | 187 | 180 | 176 | 174 | 205 | 211 |
| 183 | 211 | 180 | 194 | 200 |

a. Calculate and interpret the sample mean and median.
b. Suppose that the first observation had been 204, not 244. How would the mean and median change?
c. Calculate a trimmed mean by eliminating the smallest and the largest sample observations. What is the corresponding trimming percentage?
d. Suppose that the largest observation had been 204 rather than 244. How would the trimmed mean in Part (c) change? What if the largest value had been 284?

4.62 The paper cited in Exercise 4.61 also reported values of single-leg power for a low workload. The sample mean for $n = 13$ observations was $\bar{x} = 119.8$ (actually 119.7692), and the 14th observation, somewhat of an outlier, was 159. What is the value of $\bar{x}$ for the entire sample?

4.63 ● The amount of aluminum contamination (in parts per million) in plastic was determined for a sample of 26 plastic specimens, resulting in the following data ("The Log Normal Distribution for Modeling Quality Data When the Mean Is Near Zero," *Journal of Quality Technology* [1990]: 105–110):

| 30 | 30 | 60 | 63 | 70 | 79 | 87 | 90 | 101 |
| 102 | 115 | 118 | 119 | 119 | 120 | 125 | 140 | 145 |
| 172 | 182 | 183 | 191 | 222 | 244 | 291 | 511 |

Construct a boxplot that shows outliers, and comment on the interesting features of this plot.

4.64 ● The article "Can We Really Walk Straight?" (*American Journal of Physical Anthropology* [1992]: 19–27) reported on an experiment in which each of 20 healthy men was asked to walk as straight as possible to a target 60 m away at normal speed. Consider the following data on cadence (number of strides per second):

| 0.95 | 0.85 | 0.92 | 0.95 | 0.93 | 0.86 | 1.00 | 0.92 |
| 0.85 | 0.81 | 0.78 | 0.93 | 0.93 | 1.05 | 0.93 | 1.06 |
| 1.06 | 0.96 | 0.81 | 0.96 |

Use the methods developed in this chapter to summarize the data; include an interpretation or discussion wherever appropriate. (Note: The author of the paper used a rather sophisticated statistical analysis to conclude that people cannot walk in a straight line and suggested several explanations for this.)

4.65 ● The article "Comparing the Costs of Major Hotel Franchises" (*Real Estate Review* [1992]: 46–51) gave the following data on franchise cost as a percentage of total room revenue for chains of three different types:

| Budget | 2.7 | 2.8 | 3.8 | 3.8 | 4.0 | 4.1 | 5.5 |
| | 5.9 | 6.7 | 7.0 | 7.2 | 7.2 | 7.5 | 7.5 |
| | 7.7 | 7.9 | 7.9 | 8.1 | 8.2 | 8.5 | |
| Midrange | 1.5 | 4.0 | 6.6 | 6.7 | 7.0 | 7.2 | 7.2 |
| | 7.4 | 7.8 | 8.0 | 8.1 | 8.3 | 8.6 | 9.0 |
| First-class | 1.8 | 5.8 | 6.0 | 6.6 | 6.6 | 6.6 | 7.1 |
| | 7.2 | 7.5 | 7.6 | 7.6 | 7.8 | 7.8 | 8.2 |
| | 9.6 | | | | | | |

Construct a boxplot for each type of hotel, and comment on interesting features, similarities, and differences.

**4.66** ● The accompanying data on milk volume (in grams per day) were taken from the paper "Smoking During Pregnancy and Lactation and Its Effects on Breast Milk Volume" (*American Journal of Clinical Nutrition* [1991]: 1011–1016):

| Smoking | 621 | 793 | 593 | 545 | 753 | 655 |
|---|---|---|---|---|---|---|
| mothers | 895 | 767 | 714 | 598 | 693 | |
| Nonsmoking | 947 | 945 | 1086 | 1202 | 973 | 981 |
| mothers | 930 | 745 | 903 | 899 | 961 | |

Compare and contrast the two samples.

**4.67** The *Los Angeles Times* (July 17, 1995) reported that in a sample of 364 lawsuits in which punitive damages were awarded, the sample median damage award was $50,000, and the sample mean was $775,000. What does this suggest about the distribution of values in the sample?

**4.68** ● Age at diagnosis for each of 20 patients under treatment for meningitis was given in the paper "Penicillin in the Treatment of Meningitis" (*Journal of the American Medical Association* [1984]: 1870–1874). The ages (in years) were as follows:

| 18 | 18 | 25 | 19 | 23 | 20 | 69 | 18 | 21 | 18 | 20 | 18 |
|---|---|---|---|---|---|---|---|---|---|---|---|
| 18 | 20 | 18 | 19 | 28 | 17 | 18 | 18 | | | | |

a. Calculate the values of the sample mean and the standard deviation.
b. Calculate the 10% trimmed mean. How does the value of the trimmed mean compare to that of the sample mean? Which would you recommend as a measure of location? Explain.
c. Compute the upper quartile, the lower quartile, and the interquartile range.
d. Are there any mild or extreme outliers present in this data set?
e. Construct the boxplot for this data set.

**4.69** Suppose that the distribution of scores on an exam is closely described by a normal curve with mean 100. The 16th percentile of this distribution is 80.
**a.** What is the 84th percentile?
**b.** What is the approximate value of the standard deviation of exam scores?
**c.** What $z$ score is associated with an exam score of 90?
**d.** What percentile corresponds to an exam score of 140?
**e.** Do you think there were many scores below 40? Explain.

Mentor
Do you need a live tutor for homework problems?

**Thomson**NOW
Are you ready? Take your exam-prep post-test now.

**Bold** exercises answered in back ● Data set available online but not required ▼ Video solution available

# Chapter 5

# Summarizing Bivariate Data

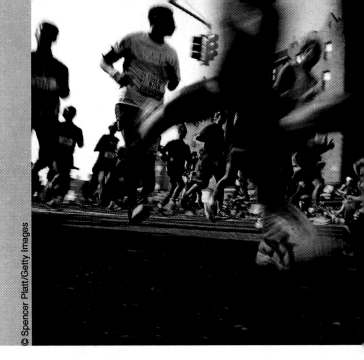

© Spencer Platt/Getty Images

Unusually large brain size at age 2 to 5 years is one indicator that a child may be at risk for autism. Research described in the *Journal of the American Medical Association* (July 2003) investigated whether head circumference at age 6 to 14 months could serve as a predictor of cerebral grey matter at age 2 to 5 years. Data on head circumference (measured at age 6 to 14 months) and cerebral grey matter (measured at age 2 to 5 years) for 17 male children with autism were used to explore the relationship between these two variables.

Questions of interest are: Is there a relationship between head circumference at age 6 to 14 months and the cerebral grey matter measurement at age 2 to 5 years? If so, can a head circumference measurement taken at an early age be used to predict what the grey matter measurement will be, potentially allowing doctors to detect autism at a younger age? How accurate are such predictions of grey matter?

In this chapter, we introduce methods for describing relationships between two numerical variables and for assessing the strength of a relationship. These methods allow us to answer questions such as the ones just posed regarding the relationship between head circumference at age 6 to 14 months and the grey matter measurement at age 2 to 5 years. In Chapter 13, methods of statistical inference for drawing conclusions from data consisting of observations on two variables are developed. The techniques introduced in this chapter are also important stepping stones for analyzing data consisting of observations on three or more variables, the topic of Chapter 14.

# 5.1 Correlation

An investigator is often interested in how two or more attributes of individuals or objects in a population are related to one another. For example, an environmental researcher might wish to know how the lead content of soil varies with distance from a major highway. Researchers in early childhood education might investigate how vocabulary size is related to age. College admissions officers, who must try to predict whether an applicant will succeed in college, might use a model relating college grade point average to high school grades, and ACT or SAT scores.

Recall that a scatterplot of bivariate numerical data gives a visual impression of how strongly $x$ values and $y$ values are related. However, to make precise statements and draw conclusions from data, we must go beyond pictures. A **correlation coefficient** (from *co-* and *relation*) is a numerical assessment of the strength of relationship between the $x$ and $y$ values in a set of $(x, y)$ pairs. In this section, we introduce the most commonly used correlation coefficient.

Figure 5.1 displays several scatterplots that show different relationships between the $x$ and $y$ values. The plot in Figure 5.1(a) suggests a strong *positive relationship* between $x$ and $y$; for every pair of points in the plot, the one with the larger $x$ value also has the larger $y$ value. That is, an increase in $x$ is inevitably paired with an increase in $y$. The plot in Figure 5.1(b) shows a strong tendency for $y$ to increase as $x$ does, but there are a few exceptions. For example, the $x$ and $y$ values of the two points in the extreme upper right-hand corner of the plot go in opposite directions ($x$ increases but $y$ decreases). Nevertheless, a plot such as this would again indicate a rather strong

**Figure 5.1** Scatterplots illustrating various types of relationships: (a) positive linear relation; (b) another positive linear relation; (c) negative linear relation; (d) no relation; (e) curved relation.

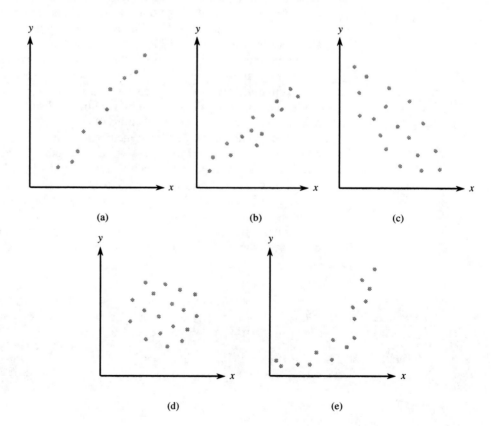

positive relationship. Figure 5.1(c) suggests that $x$ and $y$ are *negatively related*—as $x$ increases, $y$ tends to decrease. The negative relationship in this plot is not as strong as the positive relationship in Figure 5.1(b), although both plots show a well-defined linear pattern. The plot of Figure 5.1(d) indicates no strong relationship between $x$ and $y$; there is no tendency for $y$ either to increase or to decrease as $x$ increases. Finally, as illustrated in Figure 5.1(e), a scatterplot can show evidence of a strong relationship that is curved rather than linear.

## ■ Pearson's Sample Correlation Coefficient

Let $(x_1, y_1)$, $(x_2, y_2)$, . . . , $(x_n, y_n)$ denote a sample of $(x, y)$ pairs. Consider replacing each $x$ value by the corresponding $z$ score, $z_x$ (by subtracting $\bar{x}$ and then dividing by $s_x$) and similarly replacing each $y$ value by its $z$ score. Note that $x$ values that are larger than $\bar{x}$ will have positive $z$ scores and those smaller than $\bar{x}$ will have negative $z$ scores. Also $y$ values larger than $\bar{y}$ will have positive $z$ scores and those smaller will have negative $z$ scores. A common measure of the strength of linear relationship, called Pearson's sample correlation coefficient, is based on the sum of the products of $z_x$ and $z_y$ for each observation in the bivariate data set, $\sum z_x z_y$.

The scatterplot in Figure 5.2(a) indicates a strong positive relationship. A vertical line through $\bar{x}$ and a horizontal line through $\bar{y}$ divide the plot into four regions. In Region I, both $x$ and $y$ exceed their mean values, so the $z$ score for $x$ and the $z$ score for $y$ are both positive numbers. It follows that $z_x z_y$ is positive. The product of the $z$ scores is also positive for any point in Region III, because both $z$ scores are negative there and multiplying two negative numbers gives a positive number. In each of the other two regions, one $z$ score is positive and the other is negative, so $z_x z_y$ is negative. But because the points generally fall in Regions I and III, the products of $z$ scores tend to be positive. Thus, the *sum* of the products is a large positive number.

Similar reasoning for the data displayed in Figure 5.2(b), which exhibits a strong negative relationship, implies that $\sum z_x z_y$ is a large negative number. When there is no strong relationship, as in Figure 5.2(c), positive and negative products tend to counteract one another, producing a value of $\sum z_x z_y$ that is close to 0. In summary, $\sum z_x z_y$ seems to be a reasonable measure of the degree of association between $x$ and $y$; it can be a large positive number, a large negative number, or a number close to 0, depending on whether there is a strong positive, a strong negative, or no strong linear relationship.

Pearson's sample correlation coefficient, denoted $r$, is obtained by dividing $\sum z_x z_y$ by $(n - 1)$.

---

### DEFINITION

**Pearson's sample correlation coefficient $r$ is given by**

$$r = \frac{\sum z_x z_y}{n - 1}$$

Although there are several different correlation coefficients, Pearson's correlation coefficient is by far the most commonly used, and so the name "Pearson's" is often omitted and it is referred to as simply **the correlation coefficient.**

**Figure 5.2** Viewing a scatterplot according to the signs of $z_x$ and $z_y$: (a) a positive relation; (b) a negative relation; (c) no strong relation.

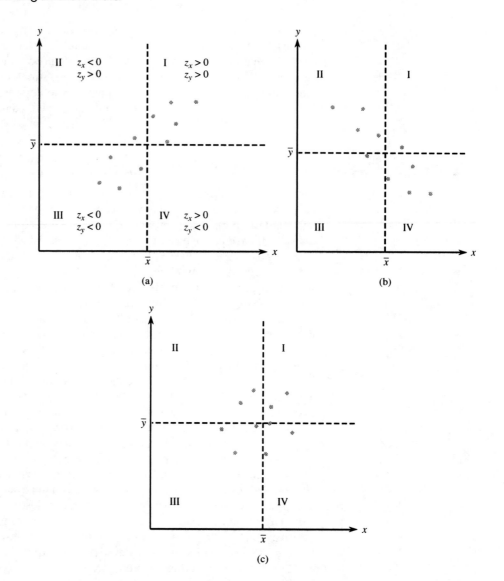

(a)

(b)

(c)

Hand calculation of the correlation coefficient is quite tedious. Fortunately, all statistical software packages and most scientific calculators can compute $r$ once the $x$ and $y$ values have been input.

# Example 5.1    Graduation Rates and Student-Related Expenditures

● The web site www.collegeresults.org publishes data on U.S. colleges and universities. For the six primarily undergraduate public universities in California with enrollments between 10,000 and 20,000, six-year graduation rates and student-related expenditures per full-time student for 2003 were reported as follows:

● Data set available online

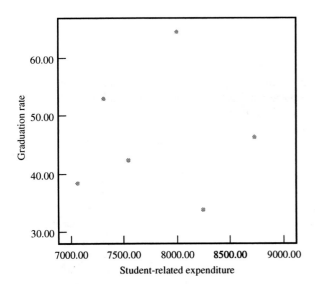

**Figure 5.3**   SPSS scatterplot for the data of Example 5.1.

| Observation | 1 | 2 | 3 | 4 | 5 | 6 |
|---|---|---|---|---|---|---|
| **Graduation rate** | 64.6 | 53.0 | 46.3 | 42.5 | 38.5 | 33.9 |
| **Student-related expenditure** | 8011 | 7323 | 8735 | 7548 | 7071 | 8248 |

Figure 5.3 is a scatterplot of these data generated using SPSS, a widely used statistics package.

Let $x$ denote the student-related expenditure per full-time student and $y$ denote the six-year graduation rate. It is easy to verify that

$$\bar{x} = 7822.67 \quad s_x = 622.71 \quad \bar{y} = 46.47 \quad s_y = 11.03$$

To illustrate the calculation of the correlation coefficient, we begin by computing $z$ scores for each $(x, y)$ pair in the data set. For example, the first observation is $(8011, 64.6)$. The corresponding $z$ scores are

$$z_x = \frac{8011 - 7822.67}{622.71} = 0.30 \quad z_y = \frac{64.6 - 46.47}{11.03} = 1.64$$

The following table shows the $z$ scores and the product $z_x z_y$ for each observation:

| x | y | $z_x$ | $z_y$ | $z_x z_y$ |
|---|---|---|---|---|
| 8011 | 64.6 | 0.30 | 1.64 | 0.50 |
| 7323 | 53.0 | −0.80 | 0.59 | −0.48 |
| 8735 | 46.3 | 1.47 | −0.02 | −0.02 |
| 7548 | 42.5 | −0.44 | −0.36 | 0.16 |
| 7071 | 38.5 | −1.21 | −0.72 | 0.87 |
| 8248 | 33.9 | 0.68 | −1.14 | −0.78 |

$$\sum z_x z_y = 0.25$$

Then, with $n = 6$

$$r = \frac{\sum z_x z_y}{n - 1} = \frac{0.25}{5} = .05$$

SPSS was used to compute the correlation coefficient, producing the following computer output.

**Correlations**

| Gradrate | Pearson Correlation | .050 |
|---|---|---|

Based on the scatterplot and the properties of the correlation coefficient presented in the discussion that follows this example, we conclude that there is at best a very weak positive linear relationship between student-related expenditure and graduation rate for these six universities.

■

## ▪ Properties of *r*

1. *The value of r does not depend on the unit of measurement for either variable.* For example, if $x$ is height, the corresponding $z$ score is the same whether height is expressed in inches, meters, or miles, and thus the value of the correlation coefficient is not affected. The correlation coefficient measures the inherent strength of the linear relationship between two numerical variables.

2. *The value of r does not depend on which of the two variables is considered x.* Thus, if we had let $x =$ graduation rate and $y =$ student related expenditure in Example 5.1, the same value, $r = 0.05$, would have resulted.

3. *The value of r is between $-1$ and $+1$.* A value near the upper limit, $+1$, indicates a substantial positive relationship, whereas an $r$ close to the lower limit, $-1$, suggests a substantial negative relationship. Figure 5.4 shows a useful way to describe the strength of relationship based on $r$. It may seem surprising that a value of $r$ as extreme as $-.5$ or $.5$ should be in the weak category; an explanation for this is given later in the chapter. Even a weak correlation can indicate a meaningful relationship.

**Figure 5.4** Describing the strength of a linear relationship.

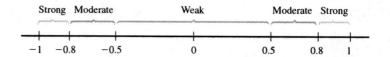

4. *The correlation coefficient $r = 1$ only when all the points in a scatterplot of the data lie exactly on a straight line that slopes upward. Similarly, $r = -1$ only when all the points lie exactly on a downward-sloping line.* Only when there is a perfect linear relationship between $x$ and $y$ in the sample does $r$ take on one of its two possible extreme values.

5. *The value of r is a measure of the extent to which x and y are linearly related*—that is, the extent to which the points in the scatterplot fall close to a straight line. A value of $r$ close to 0 does not rule out *any* strong relationship between $x$ and $y$; there could still be a strong relationship but one that is not linear.

## Example 5.2    Nightingales: Song Repertoire Size and Body Characteristics

For male songbirds, both physical characteristics and the quality of the song play a role in a female's choice of a mate. The authors of the article "Song Repertoire Is Correlated with Body Measures and Arrival Date in Common Nightingales" (*Animal Behaviour* [2005]: 211–217) used data from $n = 20$ nightingales to reach the conclusion that there was a positive correlation between the number of different songs in a nightingale's repertoire and both body weight ($r = .53$) and wing length ($r = .47$), and a negative correlation between repertoire size and arrival date ($r = -.47$). This means that heavier birds tend to know more songs, as do birds with longer wings. The authors of the paper indicated that the observed correlation between repertoire size and body characteristics was unlikely to be due solely to the age of the bird, since all nightingales in the study were more than 3 years old and prior research indicates that repertoire size does not continue to increase with age after the third year.

The negative correlation between repertoire size and arrival date was interpreted as meaning that male nightingales who knew more songs tended to arrive at their breeding habitats earlier than those who knew fewer songs.

■

## Example 5.3 Is Foal Weight Related to Mare Weight?

● Foal weight at birth is an indicator of health, so it is of interest to breeders of thoroughbred horses. Is foal weight related to the weight of the mare (mother)? The accompanying data are from the article "Suckling Behaviour Does Not Measure Milk Intake in Horses" (*Animal Behaviour* [1999]: 673–678):

| Observation | 1 | 2 | 3 | 4 | 5 | 6 | 7 | 8 |
|---|---|---|---|---|---|---|---|---|
| Mare weight ($x$, in kg) | 556 | 638 | 588 | 550 | 580 | 642 | 568 | 642 |
| Foal weight ($y$, in kg) | 129 | 119 | 132 | 123.5 | 112 | 113.5 | 95 | 104 |

| Observation | 9 | 10 | 11 | 12 | 13 | 14 | 15 |
|---|---|---|---|---|---|---|---|
| Mare weight ($x$, in kg) | 556 | 616 | 549 | 504 | 515 | 551 | 594 |
| Foal weight ($y$, in kg) | 104 | 93.5 | 108.5 | 95 | 117.5 | 128 | 127.5 |

MINITAB was used to compute the value of the correlation coefficient (Pearson's) for these data, with the following result:

**Correlations (Pearson)**
Correlation of Mare Weight and Foal Weight = 0.001

A correlation coefficient this close to 0 indicates no linear relationship between mare weight and foal weight. A scatterplot of the data (Figure 5.5) supports the conclusion that mare weight and foal weight are unrelated. From the correlation coefficient alone, we can conclude only that there is no *linear* relationship. We cannot rule out a more complicated curved relationship without also examining the scatterplot.

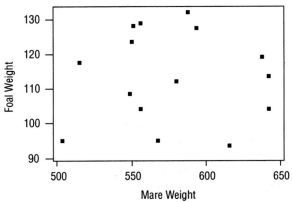

**Figure 5.5** A MINITAB scatterplot of the mare and foal weight data of Example 5.3.

■

## Example 5.4 Age and Marathon Times

● The article "Master's Performance in the New York City Marathon" (*British Journal of Sports Medicine* [2004]: 408–412) gave the following data on the average finishing time by age group for female participants in the 1999 marathon.

♪♪ Step-by-step technology instructions available online    ● Data set available online

| Age Group | Representative Age | Average Finish Time |
|---|---|---|
| 10–19 | 15 | 302.38 |
| 20–29 | 25 | 193.63 |
| 30–39 | 35 | 185.46 |
| 40–49 | 45 | 198.49 |
| 50–59 | 55 | 224.30 |
| 60–69 | 65 | 288.71 |

The scatterplot of average finish time versus representative age is shown in Figure 5.6.

**Figure 5.6** Scatterplot of $y$ = average finish time and $x$ = age for the data of Example 5.4.

Using MINITAB to compute Pearson's correlation coefficient between age and average finish time results in the following:

**Correlations: Age, Average Finish Time**

Pearson correlation of Age and Average Finish Time = 0.038

This example shows the importance of interpreting $r$ as a measure of the strength of a *linear* association. Here, $r$ is not large, but there is a strong nonlinear relationship between age and average finish time. The point is we should not conclude that there is no relationship whatsoever simply because the value of $r$ is small in absolute value.

■

## ■ The Population Correlation Coefficient .............................................................

The sample correlation coefficient $r$ measures how strongly the $x$ and $y$ values in a *sample* of pairs are linearly related to one another. There is an analogous measure of how strongly $x$ and $y$ are related in the entire population of pairs from which the sample was obtained. It is called the **population correlation coefficient** and is denoted $\rho$. (Notice again the use of a Greek letter for a population characteristic and a Roman letter for a sample characteristic.) We will never have to calculate $\rho$ from an entire population of pairs, but it is important to know that $\rho$ satisfies properties paralleling those of $r$:

1. $\rho$ is a number between $-1$ and $+1$ that does not depend on the unit of measurement for either $x$ or $y$, or on which variable is labeled $x$ and which is labeled $y$.
2. $\rho = +1$ or $-1$ if and only if all $(x, y)$ pairs in the population lie exactly on a straight line, so $\rho$ measures the extent to which there is a linear relationship in the population.

In Chapter 13, we show how the sample correlation coefficient $r$ can be used to make an inference concerning the population correlation coefficient $\rho$.

## ■ Correlation and Causation

A value of $r$ close to 1 indicates that relatively large values of one variable tend to be associated with relatively large values of the other variable. This is far from saying that a large value of one variable *causes* the value of the other variable to be large. Correlation measures the extent of association, but *association does not imply causation*. It frequently happens that two variables are highly correlated not because one is causally related to the other but because they are both strongly related to a third variable. Among all elementary school children, the relationship between the number of cavities in a child's teeth and the size of his or her vocabulary is strong and positive. Yet no one advocates eating foods that result in more cavities to increase vocabulary size (or working to decrease vocabulary size to protect against cavities). Number of cavities and vocabulary size are both strongly related to age, so older children tend to have higher values of both variables than do younger ones. In the ABCNews.com series "Who's Counting?" (February 1, 2001), John Paulos reminded readers that correlation does not imply causation and gave the following example: Consumption of hot chocolate is negatively correlated with crime rate (high values of hot chocolate consumption tend to be paired with lower crime rates), but both are responses to cold weather.

Scientific experiments can frequently make a strong case for causality by carefully controlling the values of all variables that might be related to the ones under study. Then, if $y$ is observed to change in a "smooth" way as the experimenter changes the value of $x$, a most plausible explanation would be that there is a causal relationship between $x$ and $y$. In the absence of such control and ability to manipulate values of one variable, we must admit the possibility that an unidentified underlying third variable is influencing both the variables under investigation. A high correlation in many uncontrolled studies carried out in different settings can also marshal support for causality—as in the case of cigarette smoking and cancer—but proving causality is an elusive task.

## ■ Exercises 5.1–5.16

**5.1** For each of the following pairs of variables, indicate whether you would expect a positive correlation, a negative correlation, or a correlation close to 0. Explain your choice.
**a.** Maximum daily temperature and cooling costs
**b.** Interest rate and number of loan applications
**c.** Incomes of husbands and wives when both have full-time jobs
**d.** Height and IQ
**e.** Height and shoe size
**f.** Score on the math section of the SAT exam and score on the verbal section of the same test

**Bold** exercises answered in back　　❖ Data set available online but not required　　▼ Video solution available

**g.** Time spent on homework and time spent watching television during the same day by elementary school children
**h.** Amount of fertilizer used per acre and crop yield (Hint: As the amount of fertilizer is increased, yield tends to increase for a while but then tends to start decreasing.)

**5.2** Is the following statement correct? Explain why or why not.

A correlation coefficient of 0 implies that no relationship exists between the two variables under study.

**5.3** Draw two scatterplots, one for which $r = 1$ and a second for which $r = -1$.

**5.4** The article "That's Rich: More You Drink, More You Earn" (*Calgary Herald*, April 16, 2002) reported that there was a positive correlation between alcohol consumption and income. Is it reasonable to conclude that increasing alcohol consumption will increase income? Give at least two reasons or examples to support your answer.

**5.5** ◉ The paper "A Cross-National Relationship Between Sugar Consumption and Major Depression?" (*Depression and Anxiety* [2002]: 118–120) concluded that there was a correlation between refined sugar consumption (calories per person per day) and annual rate of major depression (cases per 100 people) based on data from 6 countries. The following data were read from a graph that appeared in the paper:

| Country | Sugar Consumption | Depression Rate |
|---|---|---|
| Korea | 150 | 2.3 |
| United States | 300 | 3.0 |
| France | 350 | 4.4 |
| Germany | 375 | 5.0 |
| Canada | 390 | 5.2 |
| New Zealand | 480 | 5.7 |

**a.** Compute and interpret the correlation coefficient for this data set.
**b.** Is it reasonable to conclude that increasing sugar consumption leads to higher rates of depression? Explain.
**c.** Do you have any concerns about this study that would make you hesitant to generalize these conclusions to other countries?

**5.6** ◉ Cost-to-charge ratios (the percentage of the amount billed that represents the actual cost) for 11 Oregon hospi-

tals of similar size were reported separately for inpatient and outpatient services. The data are

| Hospital | Cost-to-Charge Ratio Inpatient | Outpatient |
|---|---|---|
| Blue Mountain | 80 | 62 |
| Curry General | 76 | 66 |
| Good Shepherd | 75 | 63 |
| Grande Ronde | 62 | 51 |
| Harney District | 100 | 54 |
| Lake District | 100 | 75 |
| Pioneer | 88 | 65 |
| St. Anthony | 64 | 56 |
| St. Elizabeth | 50 | 45 |
| Tillamook | 54 | 48 |
| Wallowa Memorial | 83 | 71 |

**a.** Does there appear to be a strong linear relationship between the cost-to-charge ratio for inpatient and outpatient services? Justify your answer based on the value of the correlation coefficient and examination of a scatterplot of the data.
**b.** Are any unusual features of the data evident in the scatterplot?
**c.** Suppose that the observation for Harney District was removed from the data set. Would the correlation coefficient for the new data set be greater than or less than the one computed in Part (a)? Explain.

**5.7** The following time-series plot is based on data from the article "Bubble Talk Expands: Corporate Debt Is Latest Concern Turning Heads" (*San Luis Obispo Tribune*, September 13, 2002) and shows how household debt and corporate debt have changed over the time period from 1991 (year 1 in the graph) to 2002:

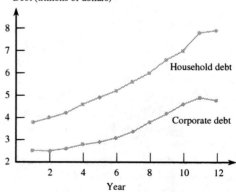

Based on the time-series plot, would the correlation co-efficient between household debt and corporate debt be positive or negative? Weak or strong? What aspect of the time-series plot supports your answer?

**5.8** ● Data from the U.S. Federal Reserve Board (Household Debt Service Burden, 2002) on the percentage of disposable personal income required to meet consumer loan payments and mortgage payments for selected years are shown in the following table:

| Consumer Debt | Household Debt | Consumer Debt | Household Debt |
|---|---|---|---|
| 7.88 | 6.22 | 6.24 | 5.73 |
| 7.91 | 6.14 | 6.09 | 5.95 |
| 7.65 | 5.95 | 6.32 | 6.09 |
| 7.61 | 5.83 | 6.97 | 6.28 |
| 7.48 | 5.83 | 7.38 | 6.08 |
| 7.49 | 5.85 | 7.52 | 5.79 |
| 7.37 | 5.81 | 7.84 | 5.81 |
| 6.57 | 5.79 | | |

a. What is the value of the correlation coefficient for this data set?
b. Is it reasonable to conclude in this case that there is no strong relationship between the variables (linear or otherwise)? Use a graphical display to support your answer.

**5.9** ● ▼ The accompanying data were read from graphs that appeared in the article "Bush Timber Proposal Runs Counter to the Record" (*San Luis Obispo Tribune*, September 22, 2002). The variables shown are the number of acres burned in forest fires in the western United States and timber sales.

| Year | Number of Acres Burned (thousands) | Timber Sales (billions of board feet) |
|---|---|---|
| 1945 | 200 | 2.0 |
| 1950 | 250 | 3.7 |
| 1955 | 260 | 4.4 |
| 1960 | 380 | 6.8 |
| 1965 | 80 | 9.7 |
| 1970 | 450 | 11.0 |
| 1975 | 180 | 11.0 |
| 1980 | 240 | 10.2 |
| 1985 | 440 | 10.0 |
| 1990 | 400 | 11.0 |
| 1995 | 180 | 3.8 |

**a.** Is there a correlation between timber sales and acres burned in forest fires? Compute and interpret the value of the correlation coefficient.
**b.** The article concludes that "heavier logging led to large forest fires." Do you think this conclusion is justified based on the given data? Explain.

**5.10** ● Peak heart rate (beats per minute) was determined both during a shuttle run and during a 300-yard run for a sample of $n = 10$ individuals with Down syndrome ("Heart Rate Responses to Two Field Exercise Tests by Adolescents and Young Adults with Down Syndrome," *Adapted Physical Activity Quarterly* [1995]: 43–51), resulting in the following data:

| Shuttle | 168 | 168 | 188 | 172 | 184 | 176 | 192 |
|---|---|---|---|---|---|---|---|
| 300-yd | 184 | 192 | 200 | 192 | 188 | 180 | 182 |
| Shuttle | 172 | 188 | 180 | | | | |
| 300-yd | 188 | 196 | 196 | | | | |

a. Construct a scatterplot of the data. What does the scatterplot suggest about the nature of the relationship between the two variables?
b. With $x$ = shuttle run peak rate and $y$ = 300-yd run peak rate, calculate $r$. Is the value of $r$ consistent with your answer in Part (a)?
c. With $x$ = 300-yd peak rate and $y$ = shuttle run peak rate, how does the value of $r$ compare to what you calculated in Part (b)?

**5.11** The accompanying scatterplot shows observations on hemoglobin level, determined both by the standard spectrophotometric method ($y$) and by a new, simpler method based on a color scale ($x$) ("A Simple and Reliable Method for Estimating Hemoglobin," *Bulletin of the World Health Organization* [1995]: 369–373):

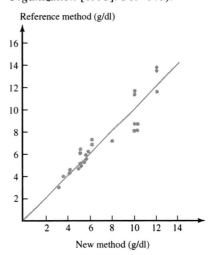

**a.** Does it appear that $x$ and $y$ are highly correlated?

**b.** The paper reported that $r = .9366$. How would you describe the relationship between the two variables?

**c.** The line pictured in the scatterplot has a slope of 1 and passes through (0, 0). If $x$ and $y$ were always identical, all points would lie exactly on this line. The authors of the paper claimed that perfect correlation ($r = 1$) would result in this line. Do you agree? Explain your reasoning.

**5.12** ● The following data on $x =$ score on a measure of test anxiety and $y =$ exam score for a sample of $n = 9$ students are consistent with summary quantities given in the paper "Effects of Humor on Test Anxiety and Performance" (*Psychological Reports* [1999]: 1203–1212):

| $x$ | 23 | 14 | 14 | 0 | 17 | 20 | 20 | 15 | 21 |
|-----|----|----|----|---|----|----|----|----|----|
| $y$ | 43 | 59 | 48 | 77 | 50 | 52 | 46 | 51 | 51 |

Higher values for $x$ indicate higher levels of anxiety.

a. Construct a scatterplot, and comment on the features of the plot.

b. Does there appear to be a linear relationship between the two variables? How would you characterize the relationship?

c. Compute the value of the correlation coefficient. Is the value of $r$ consistent with your answer to Part (b)?

d. Is it reasonable to conclude that test anxiety caused poor exam performance? Explain.

**5.13** According to the article "First-Year Academic Success: A Prediction Combining Cognitive and Psychosocial Variables for Caucasian and African American Students" (*Journal of College Student Development* [1999]: 599–605), there is a mild correlation between high school GPA ($x$) and first-year college GPA ($y$). The data can be summarized as follows:

$$n = 2600 \qquad \sum x = 9620 \qquad \sum y = 7436$$
$$\sum xy = 27{,}918 \qquad \sum x^2 = 36{,}168 \qquad \sum y^2 = 23{,}145$$

An alternative formula for computing the correlation coefficient that is based on raw data and is algebraically equivalent to the one given in the text is

$$r = \frac{\sum xy - \dfrac{(\sum x)(\sum y)}{n}}{\sqrt{\sum x^2 - \dfrac{(\sum x)^2}{n}}\sqrt{\sum y^2 - \dfrac{(\sum y)^2}{n}}}$$

Use this formula to compute the value of the correlation coefficient, and interpret this value.

**5.14** An auction house released a list of 25 recently sold paintings. Eight artists were represented in these sales. The sale price of each painting appears on the list. Would the correlation coefficient be an appropriate way to summarize the relationship between artist ($x$) and sale price ($y$)? Why or why not?

**5.15** Each individual in a sample was asked to indicate on a quantitative scale how willing he or she was to spend money on the environment and also how strongly he or she believed in God ("Religion and Attitudes Toward the Environment," *Journal for the Scientific Study of Religion* [1993]: 19–28). The resulting value of the sample correlation coefficient was $r = -.085$. Would you agree with the stated conclusion that stronger support for environmental spending is associated with a weaker degree of belief in God? Explain your reasoning.

**5.16** A sample of automobiles traversing a certain stretch of highway is selected. Each one travels at roughly a constant rate of speed, although speed does vary from auto to auto. Let $x =$ speed and $y =$ time needed to traverse this segment of highway. Would the sample correlation coefficient be closest to .9, .3, −.3, or −.9? Explain.

**Bold** exercises answered in back    ● Data set available online but not required    ▼ Video solution available

----

## 5.2  Linear Regression: Fitting a Line to Bivariate Data

The objective of *regression analysis* is to use information about one variable, $x$, to draw some sort of conclusion concerning a second variable, $y$. Often an investigator wants to predict the $y$ value that would result from making a single observation at a specified $x$ value—for example, to predict $y =$ product sales during a given period when amount spent on advertising is $x = \$10{,}000$. The two variables in a regression analysis play different roles: $y$ is called the **dependent** or **response variable**, and $x$ is referred to as the **independent**, **predictor**, or **explanatory variable**.

Scatterplots frequently exhibit a linear pattern. It is natural in such cases to summarize the relationship between the variables by finding a line that is as close as possible to the points in the plot. Before seeing how this might be done, let's review some elementary facts about lines and linear relationships.

The general form of a linear relation between $x$ and $y$ is $y = a + bx$. A particular relation is specified by choosing values of $a$ and $b$. Thus, one such relationship is $y = 10 + 2x$; another is $y = 100 - 5x$. If we choose some $x$ values and compute $y = a + bx$ for each value, the points in the plot of the resulting $(x, y)$ pairs will fall exactly on a straight line.

> **D E F I N I T I O N**
>
> The relationship
>
> $$\overset{\text{Intercept}}{\underset{\text{Slope}}{y = a + bx}}$$
>
> is the equation of a straight line. The value of $b$, called the **slope** of the line, is the amount by which $y$ increases when $x$ increases by 1 unit. The value of $a$, called the **intercept** (or sometimes the **y-intercept** or **vertical intercept**) of the line, is the height of the line above the value $x = 0$.

The equation $y = 10 + 2x$ has slope $b = 2$, so each 1-unit increase in $x$ is paired with an increase of 2 in $y$. When $x = 0$, $y = 10$, so the height at which the line crosses the vertical axis (where $x = 0$) is 10. This is illustrated in Figure 5.7(a). The slope of the line determined by $y = 100 - 5x$ is $-5$, so $y$ increases by $-5$ (i.e., decreases by 5) when $x$ increases by 1. The height of the line above $x = 0$ is $a = 100$. The resulting line is pictured in Figure 5.7(b).

**Figure 5.7** Graphs of two lines: (a) slope $b = 2$, intercept $a = 10$; (b) slope $b = -5$, intercept $a = 100$.

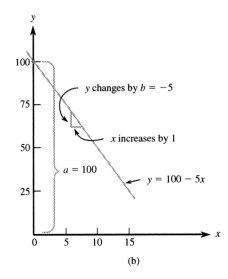

It is easy to draw the line corresponding to any particular linear equation. Choose any two $x$ values and substitute them into the equation to obtain the corresponding $y$ values. Then plot the resulting two $(x, y)$ pairs as two points. The desired line is the one passing through these points. For the equation $y = 10 + 2x$, substituting $x = 5$ yields $y = 20$, whereas using $x = 10$ gives $y = 30$. The resulting two points are then $(5, 20)$ and $(10, 30)$. The line in Figure 5.7(a) passes through these points.

## ■ Fitting a Straight Line: The Principle of Least Squares ...................................

**Figure 5.8** Line I gives a poor fit and Line II gives a good fit to the data.

Figure 5.8 shows a scatterplot with two lines superimposed on the plot. Line II clearly gives a better fit to the data than does Line I. In order to measure the extent to which a particular line provides a good fit, we focus on the vertical deviations from the line. For example, Line II in Figure 5.8 has equation $y = 10 + 2x$, and the third and fourth points from the left in the scatterplot are $(15, 44)$ and $(20, 45)$. For these two points, the vertical deviations from this line are

$$
\begin{aligned}
\text{3rd deviation} &= y_3 - \text{height of the line above } x_3 \\
&= 44 - [10 + 2(15)] \\
&= 4
\end{aligned}
$$

and

$$\text{4th deviation} = 45 - [10 + 2(20)] = -5$$

A positive vertical deviation results from a point that lies above the chosen line, and a negative deviation results from a point that lies below this line. A particular line is said to be a good fit to the data if the deviations from the line are small in magnitude. Line I in Figure 5.8 fits poorly, because all deviations from that line are larger in magnitude (some are much larger) than the corresponding deviations from Line II.

To assess the overall fit of a line, we need a way to combine the $n$ deviations into a single measure of fit. The standard approach is to square the deviations (to obtain nonnegative numbers) and then to sum these squared deviations.

**D e f i n i t i o n**

The most widely used criterion for measuring the goodness of fit of a line $y = a + bx$ to bivariate data $(x_1, y_1), \ldots, (x_n, y_n)$ is the **sum of the squared deviations** about the line

$$\sum [y - (a + bx)]^2 = [y_1 - (a + bx_1)]^2 + [y_2 - (a + bx_2)]^2 + \cdots + [y_n - (a + bx_n)]^2$$

The **least-squares line**, also called the **sample regression line**, is the line that minimizes this sum of squared deviations.

Fortunately, the equation of the least-squares line can be obtained without having to calculate deviations from any particular line. The accompanying box gives relatively simple formulas for the slope and intercept of the least-squares line.

The slope of the least-squares line is

$$b = \frac{\Sigma(x - \bar{x})(y - \bar{y})}{\Sigma(x - \bar{x})^2}$$

and the $y$ intercept is

$$a = \bar{y} - b\bar{x}$$

We write the equation of the least-squares line as

$$\hat{y} = a + bx$$

where the ^ above $y$ indicates that $\hat{y}$ (read as $y$-hat) is a prediction of $y$ resulting from the substitution of a particular $x$ value into the equation.

■

Statistical software packages and many calculators can compute the slope and intercept of the least-squares line. If the slope and intercept are to be computed by hand, the following computational formula can be used to reduce the amount of time required to perform the calculations.

### Calculating Formula for the Slope of the Least-Squares Line

$$b = \frac{\Sigma xy - \frac{(\Sigma x)(\Sigma y)}{n}}{\Sigma x^2 - \frac{(\Sigma x)^2}{n}}$$

■

## Example 5.5    Time to Defibrillator Shock and Heart Attack Survival Rate

● Studies have shown that people who suffer sudden cardiac arrest (SCA) have a better chance of survival if a defibrillator shock is administered very soon after cardiac arrest. How is survival rate related to the time between when cardiac arrest occurs and when the defibrillator shock is delivered? This question is addressed in the paper "Improving Survival from Sudden Cardiac Arrest: The Role of Home Defibrillators" (by J. K. Stross, University of Michigan, February 2002; available at www.heartstarthome.com). The accompanying data give $y$ = survival rate (percent) and $x$ = mean call-to-shock time (minutes) for a cardiac rehabilitation center (where cardiac arrests occurred while victims were hospitalized and so the call-to shock time tended to be short) and for four communities of different sizes:

| Mean call-to-shock time, $x$ | 2 | 6 | 7 | 9 | 12 |
| Survival rate, $y$ | 90 | 45 | 30 | 5 | 2 |

A scatterplot of these data (Figure 5.9) shows that the relationship between survival rate and mean call-to-shock time for times in the range 2–12 min could reasonably be summarized by a straight line.

The summary quantities necessary to compute the equation of the least-squares line are

$$\sum x = 36 \qquad \sum x^2 = 314 \qquad \sum xy = 729$$
$$\sum y = 172 \qquad \sum y^2 = 11{,}054$$

From these quantities, we compute

$$\bar{x} = 7.20 \qquad \bar{y} = 34.4$$

$$b = \dfrac{\sum xy - \dfrac{(\sum x)(\sum y)}{n}}{\sum x^2 - \dfrac{(\sum x)^2}{n}} = \dfrac{729 - \dfrac{(36)(172)}{5}}{314 - \dfrac{(36)^2}{5}} = \dfrac{-509.40}{54.80} = -9.30$$

and

$$a = \bar{y} - b\bar{x} = 34.4 - (-9.30)(7.20) = 34.4 + 66.96$$
$$= 101.36$$

The least-squares line is then

$$\hat{y} = 101.36 - 9.30x$$

This line is also shown on the scatterplot of Figure 5.9.

If we wanted to predict SCA survival rate for a community with a mean call-to-shock time of 5 minutes, we could use the point on the least-squares line above $x = 5$:

$$\hat{y} = 101.36 - 9.30(5) = 101.36 - 46.50 = 54.86$$

**Figure 5.9** MINITAB scatterplot for the data of Example 5.5.

Predicted survival rates for communities with different mean call-to-shock times could be obtained in a similar way.

But, be careful in making predictions—the least-squares line should not be used to predict survival rate for communities much outside the range 2–12 min (the range of x values in the data set) because we do not know whether the linear pattern observed in the scatterplot continues outside this range. This is sometimes referred to as the **danger of extrapolation**.

In this example, we can see that using the least-squares line to predict survival rate for communities with mean call-to-shock times much above 12 min leads to nonsensical predictions. For example, if the mean call-to-shock time is 15 min, the predicted survival rate is negative:

$$\hat{y} = 101.36 - 9.30(15) = -38.14$$

Because it is impossible for survival rate to be negative, this is a clear indication that the pattern observed for x values in the 2–12 range does not continue outside this range. Nonetheless, the least-squares line can be a useful tool for making predictions for x values within the 2- to 12-min range.

■

Calculations involving the least-squares line can obviously be tedious. This is where the computer comes to our rescue. All the standard statistical packages can fit a straight line to bivariate data.

## Example 5.6   Is Age Related to Recovery Time for Injured Athletes?

● How quickly can athletes return to their sport following injuries requiring surgery? The paper "Arthroscopic Distal Clavicle Resection for Isolated Atraumatic Osteolysis in Weight Lifters" (*American Journal of Sports Medicine* [1998]: 191–195) gave the following data on $x$ = age and $y$ = days after arthroscopic shoulder surgery before being able to return to their sport, for 10 weight lifters:

| $x$ | 33 | 31 | 32 | 28 | 33 | 26 | 34 | 32 | 28 | 27 |
|-----|----|----|----|----|----|----|----|----|----|----|
| $y$ | 6  | 4  | 4  | 1  | 3  | 3  | 4  | 2  | 3  | 2  |

Figure 5.10 is a scatterplot of the data. The predominant pattern is linear, although the points in the plot spread out quite a bit about *any* line (even the least-squares line).

**Figure 5.10** Scatterplot and least-squares line for the data of Example 5.6.

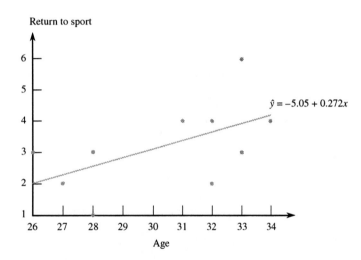

MINITAB was used to fit the least-squares line, and Figure 5.11 shows part of the resulting output. Instead of $x$ and $y$, the variable labels "Return to Sport" and "Age" are used. The equation at the top is that of the least-squares line. In the rectangular table just below the equation, the first row gives information about the intercept, $a$, and the second row gives information concerning the slope, $b$. In particular, the coefficient column labeled "Coef" contains the values of $a$ and $b$ using more digits than in the rounded values that appear in the equation.

**Figure 5.11** Partial MINITAB output for Example 5.6.

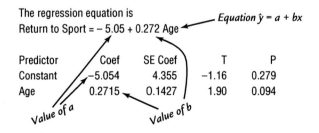

● Data set available online

The least-squares line should not be used to predict the number of days before returning to practice for weight lifters with ages such as $x = 21$ or $x = 48$. These $x$ values are well outside the range of the data, and there is no evidence to support extrapolation of the linear relationship.

■

# ■ Regression

The least-squares line is often called the **sample regression line**. This terminology comes from the relationship between the least-squares line and Pearson's correlation coefficient. To understand this relationship, we first need alternative expressions for the slope $b$ and the equation of the line itself. With $s_x$ and $s_y$ denoting the sample standard deviations of the $x$'s and $y$'s, respectively, a bit of algebraic manipulation gives

$$b = r\left(\frac{s_y}{s_x}\right)$$

$$\hat{y} = \bar{y} + r\left(\frac{s_y}{s_x}\right)(x - \bar{x})$$

You do not need to use these formulas in any computations, but several of their implications are important for appreciating what the least-squares line does.

1. When $x = \bar{x}$ is substituted in the equation of the line, $\hat{y} = \bar{y}$ results. That is, the least-squares line passes through the *point of averages* $(\bar{x}, \bar{y})$.
2. Suppose for the moment that $r = 1$, so that all points lie exactly on the line whose equation is

$$\hat{y} = \bar{y} + \frac{s_y}{s_x}(x - \bar{x})$$

Now substitute $x = \bar{x} + s_x$, which is 1 standard deviation above $\bar{x}$:

$$\hat{y} = \bar{y} + \frac{s_y}{s_x}(\bar{x} + s_x - \bar{x}) = \bar{y} + s_y$$

That is, with $r = 1$, when $x$ is 1 standard deviation above its mean, we predict that the associated $y$ value will be 1 standard deviation above its mean. Similarly, if $x = \bar{x} - 2s_x$ (2 standard deviations below its mean), then

$$\hat{y} = \bar{y} + \frac{s_y}{s_x}(\bar{x} - 2s_x - \bar{x}) = \bar{y} - 2s_y$$

which is also 2 standard deviations below the mean. If $r = -1$, then $x = \bar{x} + s_x$ results in $\hat{y} = \bar{y} - s_y$, so the predicted $y$ is also 1 standard deviation from its mean but on the opposite side of $\bar{y}$ from where $x$ is relative to $\bar{x}$. In general, if $x$ and $y$ are perfectly correlated, the predicted $y$ value associated with a given $x$ value will be the same number of standard deviations (of $y$) from its mean $\bar{y}$ as $x$ is from its mean, $\bar{x}$.
3. Now suppose that $x$ and $y$ are not perfectly correlated. For example, suppose $r = .5$, so the least-squares line has the equation

$$\hat{y} = \bar{y} + .5\left(\frac{s_y}{s_x}\right)(x - \bar{x})$$

Then substituting $x = \bar{x} + s_x$ gives

$$\hat{y} = \bar{y} + .5\left(\frac{s_y}{s_x}\right)(\bar{x} + s_x - \bar{x}) = \bar{y} + .5s_y$$

That is, for $r = .5$, when $x$ lies 1 standard deviation above its mean, we predict that $y$ will be only 0.5 standard deviation above its mean. Similarly, we can predict $y$ when $r$ is negative. If $r = -.5$, then the predicted $y$ value will be only half the number of standard deviations from $\bar{y}$ that it is from $\bar{x}$ but $x$ and the predicted $y$ will now be on opposite sides of their respective means.

Consider using the least-squares line to predict the value of $y$ associated with an $x$ value some specified number of standard deviations away from $\bar{x}$. Then the predicted $y$ value will be only $r$ times this number of standard deviations from $\bar{y}$. In terms of standard deviations, except when $r = 1$ or $-1$, the predicted $y$ will always be closer to $\bar{y}$ than $x$ is to $\bar{x}$.  ■

Using the least-squares line for prediction results in a predicted $y$ that is pulled back in, or regressed, toward the mean of $y$ compared to where $x$ is relative to the mean of $x$. This regression effect was first noticed by Sir Francis Galton (1822–1911), a famous biologist, when he was studying the relationship between the heights of fathers and their sons. He found that predicted heights of sons whose fathers were above average in height were also above average (because $r$ is positive here) but not by as much as the father's height; he found a similar relationship for fathers whose heights were below average. This regression effect has led to the term **regression analysis** for the collection of methods involving the fitting of lines, curves, and more complicated functions to bivariate and multivariate data.

The alternative form of the regression (least-squares) line emphasizes that predicting $y$ from knowledge of $x$ is not the same problem as predicting $x$ from knowledge of $y$. The slope of the least-squares line for predicting $x$ is $r(s_x/s_y)$ rather than $r(s_y/s_x)$ and the intercepts of the lines are almost always different. For purposes of prediction, it makes a difference whether $y$ is regressed on $x$, as we have done, or $x$ is regressed on $y$. *The regression line of $y$ on $x$ should not be used to predict $x$, because it is not the line that minimizes the sum of squared deviations in the $x$ direction.*

■ Exercises 5.17–5.35 ..................................................................

**5.17** ● ▼ The article "Air Pollution and Medical Care Use by Older Americans" (*Health Affairs* [2002]: 207–214) gave data on a measure of pollution (in micrograms of particulate matter per cubic meter of air) and the cost of medical care per person over age 65 for six geographical regions of the United States:

| Region | Pollution | Cost of Medical Care |
|---|---|---|
| North | 30.0 | 915 |
| Upper South | 31.8 | 891 |
| Deep South | 32.1 | 968 |
| West South | 26.8 | 972 |
| Big Sky | 30.4 | 952 |
| West | 40.0 | 899 |

**Bold** exercises answered in back     ● Data set available online but not required     ▼ Video solution available

**a.** Construct a scatterplot of the data. Describe any interesting features of the scatterplot.
**b.** Find the equation of the least-squares line describing the relationship between $y$ = medical cost and $x$ = pollution.
**c.** Is the slope of the least-squares line positive or negative? Is this consistent with your description of the relationship in Part (a)?
**d.** Do the scatterplot and the equation of the least-squares line support the researchers' conclusion that elderly people who live in more polluted areas have higher medical costs? Explain.

5.18 ● Researchers asked each child in a sample of 411 school-age children if they were more or less likely to purchase a lottery ticket at a store if lottery tickets were visible on the counter. The percentage that said that they were *more* likely to purchase a ticket by grade level are as follows (R&J Child Development Consultants, Quebec, 2001):

| Grade | Percentage That Said They Were More Likely to Purchase |
|---|---|
| 6 | 32.7 |
| 8 | 46.1 |
| 10 | 75.0 |
| 12 | 83.6 |

a. Construct a scatterplot of $y$ = percentage who said they were more likely to purchase and $x$ = grade. Does there appear to be a linear relationship between $x$ and $y$?
b. Find the equation of the least-squares line.

**5.19** A sample of 548 ethnically diverse students from Massachusetts were followed over a 19-month period from 1995 and 1997 in a study of the relationship between TV viewing and eating habits (*Pediatrics* [2003]: 1321–1326). For each additional hour of television viewed per day, the number of fruit and vegetable servings per day was found to decrease on average by 0.14 serving.
**a.** For this study, what is the dependent variable? What is the predictor variable?
**b.** Would the least-squares line for predicting number of servings of fruits and vegetables using number of hours spent watching TV as a predictor have a positive or negative slope? Explain.

5.20 The relationship between hospital patient-to-nurse ratio and various characteristics of job satisfaction and patient care has been the focus of a number of research studies. Suppose $x$ = patient-to-nurse ratio is the predictor variable. For each of the following potential dependent variables, indicate whether you expect the slope of the least-squares line to be positive or negative and give a brief explanation for your choice.
a. $y$ = a measure of nurse's job satisfaction (higher values indicate higher satisfaction)
b. $y$ = a measure of patient satisfaction with hospital care (higher values indicate higher satisfaction)
c. $y$ = a measure of patient quality of care.

**5.21** ● ▼ The accompanying data on $x$ = head circumference $z$ score (a comparison score with peers of the same age—a positive score suggests a larger size than for peers) at age 6 to 14 months and $y$ = volume of cerebral grey matter (in ml) at age 2 to 5 years were read from a graph in the article described in the chapter introduction (*Journal of the American Medical Association* [2003]).

| Cerebral Grey Matter (ml) 2–5 yr | Head Circumference z Scores at 6–14 Months |
|---|---|
| 680 | −.75 |
| 690 | 1.2 |
| 700 | −.3 |
| 720 | .25 |
| 740 | .3 |
| 740 | 1.5 |
| 750 | 1.1 |
| 750 | 2.0 |
| 760 | 1.1 |
| 780 | 1.1 |
| 790 | 2.0 |
| 810 | 2.1 |
| 815 | 2.8 |
| 820 | 2.2 |
| 825 | .9 |
| 835 | 2.35 |
| 840 | 2.3 |
| 845 | 2.2 |

a. Construct a scatterplot for these data.
b. What is the value of the correlation coefficient?
c. Find the equation of the least-squares line.

**d.** Predict the volume of cerebral grey matter for a child whose head circumference $z$ score at age 12 months was 1.8.

**e.** Explain why it would not be a good idea to use the least-squares line to predict the volume of grey matter for a child whose head circumference $z$ score was 3.0.

**5.22** In the article "Reproductive Biology of the Aquatic Salamander *Amphiuma tridactylum* in Louisiana" (*Journal of Herpetology* [1999]: 100–105), 14 female salamanders were studied. Using regression, the researchers predicted $y$ = clutch size (number of salamander eggs) from $x$ = snout-vent length (in centimeters) as follows:

$$\hat{y} = -147 + 6.175x$$

For the salamanders in the study, the range of snout-vent lengths was approximately 30 to 70 cm.

**a.** What is the value of the $y$ intercept of the least-squares line? What is the value of the slope of the least-squares line? Interpret the slope in the context of this problem.

**b.** Would you be reluctant to predict the clutch size when snout-vent length is 22 cm? Explain.

**5.23** ● Percentages of public school students in fourth grade in 1996 and in eighth grade in 2000 who were at or above the proficient level in mathematics were given in the article "Mixed Progress in Math" (*USA Today*, August 3, 2001) for eight western states:

| State | 4th grade (1996) | 8th grade (2000) |
|---|---|---|
| Arizona | 15 | 21 |
| California | 11 | 18 |
| Hawaii | 16 | 16 |
| Montana | 22 | 37 |
| New Mexico | 13 | 13 |
| Oregon | 21 | 32 |
| Utah | 23 | 26 |
| Wyoming | 19 | 25 |

**a.** Construct a scatterplot, and comment on any interesting features.

**b.** Find the equation of the least-squares line that summarizes the relationship between $x$ = 1996 fourth-grade math proficiency percentage and $y$ = 2000 eighth-grade math proficiency percentage.

**c.** Nevada, a western state not included in the data set, had a 1996 fourth-grade math proficiency of 14%. What

would you predict for Nevada's 2000 eighth-grade math proficiency percentage? How does your prediction compare to the actual eighth-grade value of 20 for Nevada?

**5.24** Data on high school GPA ($x$) and first-year college GPA ($y$) collected from a southeastern public research university can be summarized as follows ("First-Year Academic Success: A Prediction Combining Cognitive and Psychosocial Variables for Caucasian and African American Students," *Journal of College Student Development* [1999]: 599–605):

$$n = 2600 \qquad \sum x = 9620 \qquad \sum y = 7436$$
$$\sum xy = 27{,}918 \qquad \sum x^2 = 36{,}168 \qquad \sum y^2 = 23{,}145$$

**a.** Find the equation of the least-squares regression line.

**b.** Interpret the value of $b$, the slope of the least-squares line, in the context of this problem.

**c.** What first-year GPA would you predict for a student with a 4.0 high school GPA?

**5.25** ● Representative data on $x$ = carbonation depth (in millimeters) and $y$ = strength (in megapascals) for a sample of concrete core specimens taken from a particular building were read from a plot in the article "The Carbonation of Concrete Structures in the Tropical Environment of Singapore" (*Magazine of Concrete Research* [1996]: 293–300):

| Depth, $x$ | 8.0 | 20.0 | 20.0 | 30.0 | 35.0 |
|---|---|---|---|---|---|
| Strength, $y$ | 22.8 | 17.1 | 21.1 | 16.1 | 13.4 |
| Depth, $x$ | 40.0 | 50.0 | 55.0 | 65.0 | |
| Strength, $y$ | 12.4 | 11.4 | 9.7 | 6.8 | |

**a.** Construct a scatterplot. Does the relationship between carbonation depth and strength appear to be linear?

**b.** Find the equation of the least-squares line.

**c.** What would you predict for strength when carbonation depth is 25 mm?

**d.** Explain why it would not be reasonable to use the least-squares line to predict strength when carbonation depth is 100 mm.

**5.26** The data given in Example 5.5 on $x$ = call-to-shock time (in minutes) and $y$ = survival rate (percent) were used to compute the equation of the least-squares line, which was

$$\hat{y} = 101.36 - 9.30x$$

The newspaper article "FDA OKs Use of Home Defibrillators" (*San Luis Obispo Tribune*, November 13, 2002)

---

**Bold** exercises answered in back      ● Data set available online but not required      ▼ Video solution available

reported that "every minute spent waiting for paramedics to arrive with a defibrillator lowers the chance of survival by 10 percent." Is this statement consistent with the given least-squares line? Explain.

**5.27** An article on the cost of housing in California that appeared in the *San Luis Obispo Tribune* (March 30, 2001) included the following statement: "In Northern California, people from the San Francisco Bay area pushed into the Central Valley, benefiting from home prices that dropped on average $4000 for every mile traveled east of the Bay area." If this statement is correct, what is the slope of the least-squares regression line, $\hat{y} = a + bx$, where $y$ = house price (in dollars) and $x$ = distance east of the Bay (in miles)? Explain.

**5.28** ● The following data on sale price, size, and land-to-building ratio for 10 large industrial properties appeared in the paper "Using Multiple Regression Analysis in Real Estate Appraisal" (*Appraisal Journal* [2002]: 424–430):

| Property | Sale Price (millions of dollars) | Size (thousands of sq. ft.) | Land-to-Building Ratio |
|---|---|---|---|
| 1 | 10.6 | 2166 | 2.0 |
| 2 | 2.6 | 751 | 3.5 |
| 3 | 30.5 | 2422 | 3.6 |
| 4 | 1.8 | 224 | 4.7 |
| 5 | 20.0 | 3917 | 1.7 |
| 6 | 8.0 | 2866 | 2.3 |
| 7 | 10.0 | 1698 | 3.1 |
| 8 | 6.7 | 1046 | 4.8 |
| 9 | 5.8 | 1108 | 7.6 |
| 10 | 4.5 | 405 | 17.2 |

a. Calculate and interpret the value of the correlation coefficient between sale price and size.
b. Calculate and interpret the value of the correlation coefficient between sale price and land-to-building ratio.
c. If you wanted to predict sale price and you could use either size or land-to-building ratio as the basis for making predictions, which would you use? Explain.
d. Based on your choice in Part (c), find the equation of the least-squares regression line you would use for predicting $y$ = sale price.

**5.29** ● Representative data read from a plot that appeared in the paper "Effect of Cattle Treading on Erosion from

Hill Pasture: Modeling Concepts and Analysis of Rainfall Simulator Data" (*Australian Journal of Soil Research* [2002]: 963–977) on runoff sediment concentration for plots with varying amounts of grazing damage, measured by the percentage of bare ground in the plot, are given for gradually sloped plots and for steeply sloped plots.

**Gradually Sloped Plots**

| Bare ground (%) | 5 | 10 | 15 | 25 |
|---|---|---|---|---|
| Concentration | 50 | 200 | 250 | 500 |
| Bare ground (%) | 30 | 40 | | |
| Concentration | 600 | 500 | | |

**Steeply Sloped Plots**

| Bare ground (%) | 5 | 5 | 10 | 15 |
|---|---|---|---|---|
| Concentration | 100 | 250 | 300 | 600 |
| Bare ground (%) | 20 | 25 | 20 | 30 |
| Concentration | 500 | 500 | 900 | 800 |
| Bare ground (%) | 35 | 40 | 35 | |
| Concentration | 1100 | 1200 | 1000 | |

**a.** Using the data for steeply sloped plots, find the equation of the least-squares line for predicting $y$ runoff sediment concentration using $x$ = percentage of bare ground.
**b.** What would you predict runoff sediment concentration to be for a steeply sloped plot with 18% bare ground?
**c.** Would you recommend using the least-squares equation from Part (a) to predict runoff sediment concentration for gradually sloped plots? If so, explain why it would be appropriate to do so. If not, provide an alternative way to make such predictions.

5.30 The paper "Postmortem Changes in Strength of Gastropod Shells" (*Paleobiology* [1992]: 367–377) included scatterplots of data on $x$ = shell height (in centimeters) and $y$ = breaking strength (in newtons) for a sample of $n$ = 38 hermit crab shells. The least-squares line was $\hat{y} = -275.1 + 244.9x$.
a. What are the slope and the intercept of this line?
b. When shell height increases by 1 cm, by how much does breaking strength tend to change?
c. What breaking strength would you predict when shell height is 2 cm?
d. Does this approximate linear relationship appear to hold for shell heights as small as 1 cm? Explain.

**5.31** ● The paper "Increased Vital and Total Lung Capacities in Tibetan Compared to Han Residents of Lhasa" (*American Journal of Physical Anthropology* [1991]: 341–351) included a scatterplot of vital capacity ($y$)

versus chest circumference ($x$) for a sample of 16 Tibetan natives, from which the following data were read:

| $x$ | 79.4 | 81.8 | 81.8 | 82.3 | 83.7 | 84.3 | 84.3 | 85.2 |
|---|---|---|---|---|---|---|---|---|
| $y$ | 4.3 | 4.6 | 4.8 | 4.7 | 5.0 | 4.9 | 4.4 | 5.0 |
| $x$ | 87.0 | 87.3 | 87.7 | 88.1 | 88.1 | 88.6 | 89.0 | 89.5 |
| $y$ | 6.1 | 4.7 | 5.7 | 5.7 | 5.2 | 5.5 | 5.0 | 5.3 |

**a.** Construct a scatterplot. What does it suggest about the nature of the relationship between $x$ and $y$?
**b.** The summary quantities are

$$\sum x = 1368.1 \quad \sum y = 80.9$$
$$\sum xy = 6933.48 \quad \sum x^2 = 117{,}123.85 \quad \sum y^2 = 412.81$$

Verify that the equation of the least-squares line is $\hat{y} = -4.54 + 0.1123x$, and draw this line on your scatterplot.
**c.** On average, roughly what change in vital capacity is associated with a 1-cm increase in chest circumference? with a 10-cm increase?
**d.** What vital capacity would you predict for a Tibetan native whose chest circumference is 85 cm?
**e.** Is vital capacity completely determined by chest circumference? Explain.

**5.32** Explain why it can be dangerous to use the least-squares line to obtain predictions for $x$ values that are substantially larger or smaller than those contained in the sample.

**5.33** The sales manager of a large company selected a random sample of $n = 10$ salespeople and determined for each one the values of $x =$ years of sales experience and $y =$ annual sales (in thousands of dollars). A scatterplot of the resulting $(x, y)$ pairs showed a marked linear pattern.
**a.** Suppose that the sample correlation coefficient is $r = .75$ and that the average annual sales is $\bar{y} = 100$. If a

particular salesperson is 2 standard deviations above the mean in terms of experience, what would you predict for that person's annual sales?
**b.** If a particular person whose sales experience is 1.5 standard deviations below the average experience is predicted to have an annual sales value that is 1 standard deviation below the average annual sales, what is the value of $r$?

**5.34** Explain why the slope $b$ of the least-squares line always has the same sign (positive or negative) as does the sample correlation coefficient $r$.

**5.35** ● The accompanying data resulted from an experiment in which weld diameter $x$ and shear strength $y$ (in pounds) were determined for five different spot welds on steel. A scatterplot shows a pronounced linear pattern. With $\sum(x - \bar{x}) = 1000$ and $\sum(x - \bar{x})(y - \bar{y}) = 8577$, the least-squares line is $\hat{y} = -936.22 + 8.577x$.

| $x$ | 200.1 | 210.1 | 220.1 | 230.1 | 240.0 |
|---|---|---|---|---|---|
| $y$ | 813.7 | 785.3 | 960.4 | 1118.0 | 1076.2 |

**a.** Because 1 lb = 0.4536 kg, strength observations can be re-expressed in kilograms through multiplication by this conversion factor: new $y = 0.4536$(old $y$). What is the equation of the least-squares line when $y$ is expressed in kilograms?
**b.** More generally, suppose that each $y$ value in a data set consisting of $n$ $(x, y)$ pairs is multiplied by a conversion factor $c$ (which changes the units of measurement for $y$). What effect does this have on the slope $b$ (i.e., how does the new value of $b$ compare to the value before conversion), on the intercept $a$, and on the equation of the least-squares line? Verify your conjectures by using the given formulas for $b$ and $a$. (Hint: Replace $y$ with $cy$, and see what happens —and remember, this conversion will affect $\bar{y}$.)

**Bold** exercises answered in back   ● Data set available online but not required   ▼ Video solution available

# 5.3  Assessing the Fit of a Line

Once the least-squares regression line has been obtained, it is natural to examine how effectively the line summarizes the relationship between $x$ and $y$. Important questions to consider are

1. Is a line an appropriate way to summarize the relationship between the two variables?
2. Are there any unusual aspects of the data set that we need to consider before proceeding to use the regression line to make predictions?
3. If we decide that it is reasonable to use the regression line as a basis for prediction, how accurate can we expect predictions based on the regression line to be?

In this section, we look at graphical and numerical methods that will allow us to answer these questions. Most of these methods are based on the vertical deviations of the data points from the regression line. These vertical deviations are called *residuals*, and each represents the difference between an actual $y$ value and the corresponding predicted value, $\hat{y}$, that would result from using the regression line to make a prediction.

## ▪ Predicted Values and Residuals ....................................................................

If the $x$ value for the first observation is substituted into the equation for the least-squares line, the result is $a + bx_1$, the height of the line above $x_1$. The point $(x_1, y_1)$ in the scatterplot also lies above $x_1$, so the difference

$$y_1 - (a + bx_1)$$

is the vertical deviation from this point to the line (see Figure 5.12). A point lying above the line gives a positive deviation, and a point lying below the line results in a negative deviation. The remaining vertical deviations come from repeating this process for $x = x_2$, then $x = x_3$, and so on.

**Figure 5.12** Positive and negative deviations (residuals) from the least-squares line.

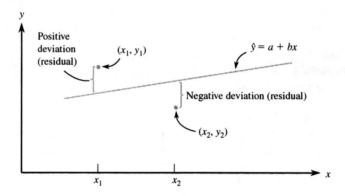

DEFINITION

The **predicted** or **fitted values** result from substituting each sample $x$ value in turn into the equation for the least-squares line. This gives

$$\hat{y}_1 = \text{first predicted value} = a + bx_1$$
$$\hat{y}_2 = \text{second predicted value} = a + bx_2$$
$$\vdots$$
$$\hat{y}_n = \text{nth predicted value} = a + bx_n$$

The **residuals** from the least-squares line are the $n$ quantities

$$y_1 - \hat{y}_1, y_2 - \hat{y}_2, \ldots, y_n - \hat{y}_n$$

Each residual is the difference between an observed $y$ value and the corresponding predicted $y$ value.

## Example 5.7

### How Does Range of Motion After Knee Surgery Change with Age?

● One measure of the success of knee surgery is postsurgical range of motion for the knee joint. Postsurgical range of motion was recorded for 12 patients who had surgery following a knee dislocation. The age of each patient was also recorded ("Reconstruction of the Anterior and Posterior Cruciate Ligaments After Knee Dislocation," *American Journal of Sports Medicine* [1999]: 189–194). The data are given in Table 5.1.

**Table 5.1**   Predicted Values and Residuals for the Data of Example 5.7

| Patient | Age (x) | Range of Motion (y) | Predicted Range of Motion (ŷ) | Residual y − ŷ |
|---|---|---|---|---|
| 1 | 35 | 154 | 138.07 | 15.93 |
| 2 | 24 | 142 | 128.49 | 13.51 |
| 3 | 40 | 137 | 142.42 | −5.42 |
| 4 | 31 | 133 | 134.58 | −1.58 |
| 5 | 28 | 122 | 131.97 | −9.97 |
| 6 | 25 | 126 | 129.36 | −3.36 |
| 7 | 26 | 135 | 130.23 | 4.77 |
| 8 | 16 | 135 | 121.52 | 13.48 |
| 9 | 14 | 108 | 119.78 | −11.78 |
| 10 | 20 | 120 | 125.00 | −5.00 |
| 11 | 21 | 127 | 125.87 | 1.13 |
| 12 | 30 | 122 | 133.71 | −11.71 |

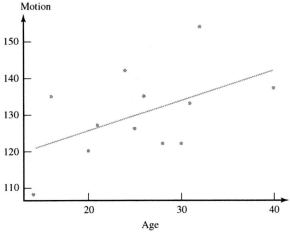

**Figure 5.13**   Scatterplot for the data of Example 5.7.

● Data set available online

MINITAB was used to fit the least-squares regression line. Partial computer output follows:

**Regression Analysis**

The regression equation is

Range of Motion = 108 + 0.871 Age

| Predictor | Coef | StDev | T | P |
|---|---|---|---|---|
| Constant | 107.58 | 11.12 | 9.67 | 0.000 |
| Age | 0.8710 | 0.4146 | 2.10 | 0.062 |

s = 10.42     R-Sq = 30.6%     R-Sq(adj) = 23.7%

The resulting least-squares regression line is $\hat{y} = 107.58 + 0.871x$. A scatterplot that also includes the regression line is shown in Figure 5.13. The residuals for this data set are the signed vertical distances from the points to the regression line.

For the youngest patient (patient 9 with $x_9 = 14$ and $y_9 = 108$), the corresponding predicted value and residual are

$$\text{predicted value} = \hat{y}_9 = 107.58 + .871 \text{ age} = 119.78$$
$$\text{residual} = y_9 - \hat{y}_9 = 108 - 119.78 = -11.78$$

The other predicted values and residuals are computed in a similar manner and are included in Table 5.1.

Computing the predicted values and residuals by hand can be tedious, but MINITAB and other statistical software packages, as well as many graphing calculators, include them as part of the output, as shown in Figure 5.14. The predicted values and residuals can be found in the table at the bottom of the MINITAB output in the columns labeled "Fit" and "Residual," respectively.

**FIGURE 5.14** MINITAB output for the data of Example 5.7.

The regression equation is
Range of Motion = 108 + 0.871 Age

| Predictor | Coef | StDev | T | P |
|---|---|---|---|---|
| Constant | 107.58 | 11.12 | 9.67 | 0.000 |
| Age | 0.8710 | 0.4146 | 2.10 | 0.062 |

s = 10.42    R-Sq = 30.6%    R-Sq(adj) = 23.7%

**Analysis of Variance**

| Source | DF | SS | MS | F | P |
|---|---|---|---|---|---|
| Regression | 1 | 479.2 | 479.2 | 4.41 | 0.062 |
| Residual Error | 10 | 1085.7 | 108.6 | | |
| Total | 11 | 1564.9 | | | |

| Obs | Age | Range | Fit | SE Fit | Residual | St Resid |
|---|---|---|---|---|---|---|
| 1 | 35.0 | 154.00 | 138.07 | 4.85 | 15.93 | 1.73 |
| 2 | 24.0 | 142.00 | 128.49 | 3.10 | 13.51 | 1.36 |
| 3 | 40.0 | 137.00 | 142.42 | 6.60 | −5.42 | −0.67 |
| 4 | 31.0 | 133.00 | 134.58 | 3.69 | −1.58 | −0.16 |
| 5 | 28.0 | 122.00 | 131.97 | 3.14 | −9.97 | −1.00 |
| 6 | 25.0 | 126.00 | 129.36 | 3.03 | −3.36 | −0.34 |
| 7 | 26.0 | 135.00 | 130.23 | 3.01 | 4.77 | 0.48 |
| 8 | 16.0 | 135.00 | 121.52 | 5.07 | 13.48 | 1.48 |
| 9 | 14.0 | 108.00 | 119.78 | 5.75 | −11.78 | −1.36 |
| 10 | 20.0 | 120.00 | 125.00 | 3.86 | −5.00 | −0.52 |
| 11 | 21.0 | 127.00 | 125.87 | 3.61 | 1.13 | 0.12 |
| 12 | 30.0 | 122.00 | 133.71 | 3.47 | −11.71 | −1.19 |

■

## Plotting the Residuals

A careful look at residuals can reveal many potential problems. A *residual plot* is a good place to start when assessing the appropriateness of the regression line.

> **DEFINITION**
>
> A **residual plot** is a scatterplot of the (x, residual) pairs. Isolated points or a pattern of points in the residual plot indicate potential problems.

A desirable plot is one that exhibits no particular pattern, such as curvature. Curvature in the residual plot is an indication that the relationship between *x* and *y* is not linear and that a curve would be a better choice than a line for describing the relationship between *x* and *y*. This is sometimes easier to see in a residual plot than in a scatterplot of *y* versus *x*, as illustrated in Example 5.8.

## Example 5.8   Heights and Weights of American Women

◉ Consider the accompanying data on *x* = height (in inches) and *y* = average weight (in pounds) for American females, age 30–39 (from *The World Almanac and Book of Facts*). The scatterplot displayed in Figure 5.15(a) appears rather straight. However, when the residuals from the least-squares line ($\hat{y} = 98.23 + 3.59x$) are plotted, substantial curvature is apparent (even though $r \approx .99$). It is not accurate to say that weight increases in direct proportion to height (linearly with height). Instead, average weight increases somewhat more rapidly for relatively large heights than it does for relatively small heights.

| *x* | 58 | 59 | 60 | 61 | 62 | 63 | 64 | 65 |
|-----|-----|-----|-----|-----|-----|-----|-----|-----|
| *y* | 113 | 115 | 118 | 121 | 124 | 128 | 131 | 134 |

| *x* | 66 | 67 | 68 | 69 | 70 | 71 | 72 |
|-----|-----|-----|-----|-----|-----|-----|-----|
| *y* | 137 | 141 | 145 | 150 | 153 | 159 | 164 |

**Figure 5.15** Plots for the data of Example 5.8: (a) scatterplot; (b) residual plot.

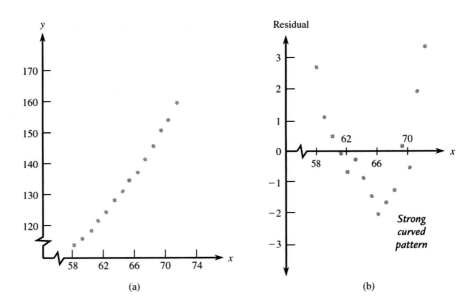

There is another common type of residual plot—one that plots the residuals versus the corresponding $\hat{y}$ values rather than versus the *x* values. Because $\hat{y} = a + bx$ is simply a linear function of *x*, the only real difference between the two types of residual plots is the scale on the horizontal axis. The pattern of points in the residual plots will be the same, and it is this pattern of points that is important, not the scale. Thus

**Figure 5.16** (a) Plot of residuals versus $x$; (b) plot of residuals versus $\hat{y}$.

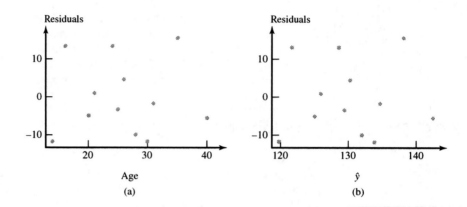

the two plots give equivalent information, as can be seen in Figure 5.16, which gives both plots for the data of Example 5.7.

It is also important to look for unusual values in the scatterplot or in the residual plot. A point falling far above or below the horizontal line at height 0 corresponds to a large residual, which may indicate some type of unusual behavior, such as a recording error, a nonstandard experimental condition, or an atypical experimental subject. A point whose $x$ value differs greatly from others in the data set may have exerted excessive influence in determining the fitted line. One method for assessing the impact of such an isolated point on the fit is to delete it from the data set, recompute the best-fit line, and evaluate the extent to which the equation of the line has changed.

# Example 5.9 Tennis Elbow

◉ One factor in the development of tennis elbow is the impact-induced vibration of the racket and arm at ball contact. Tennis elbow is thought to be related to various properties of the tennis racket used. The following data are a subset of those analyzed in the article "Transfer of Tennis Racket Vibrations into the Human Forearm" (*Medicine and Science in Sports and Exercise* [1992]: 1134–1140). Measurements on $x$ = racket resonance frequency (in hertz) and $y$ = sum of peak-to-peak accelerations (a characteristic of arm vibration in meters per second squared) are given for $n = 14$ different rackets:

| Racket | Resonance (x) | Acceleration (y) | Racket | Resonance (x) | Acceleration (y) |
|--------|---------------|------------------|--------|---------------|------------------|
| 1 | 105 | 36.0 | 8 | 114 | 33.8 |
| 2 | 106 | 35.0 | 9 | 114 | 35.0 |
| 3 | 110 | 34.5 | 10 | 119 | 35.0 |
| 4 | 111 | 36.8 | 11 | 120 | 33.6 |
| 5 | 112 | 37.0 | 12 | 121 | 34.2 |
| 6 | 113 | 34.0 | 13 | 126 | 36.2 |
| 7 | 113 | 34.2 | 14 | 189 | 30.0 |

♪♪ Step-by-step technology instructions available online ◉ Data set available online

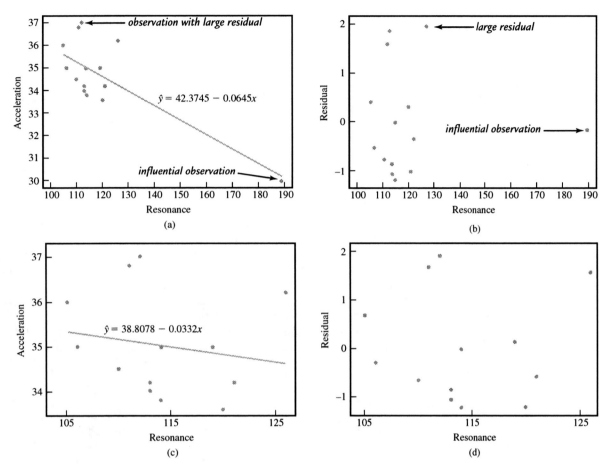

**Figure 5.17**   Plots from Example 5.9: (a) scatterplot for the full sample; (b) residual plot for the full sample; (c) scatterplot when the influential observation is deleted; (d) residual plot when the influential observation is deleted.

PhotoLink/Getty Images

A scatterplot and a residual plot are shown in Figures 5.17(a) and 5.17(b), respectively. One observation in the data set is far to the right of the other points in the scatterplot. Because the least-squares line minimizes the sum of squared residuals, the least-squares line is pulled down toward this discrepant point. This single observation plays a big role in determining the slope of the least-squares line, and it is therefore called an *influential observation*. Notice that an influential observation is not necessarily the one with the largest residual, because the least-squares line actually passes near this point.

Figures 5.17(c) and 5.17(d) show what happens when the influential observation is removed from the sample. Both the slope and the intercept of the least-squares line are quite different from the slope and intercept of the line with this observation included.

Deletion of the observation corresponding to the largest residual (1.955 for observation 13) also changes the values of the slope and intercept of the least-squares line, but these changes are not profound. For example, the least-squares line for the data set consisting of the 13 points that remain when observation 13 is deleted is $\hat{y} = 42.5 - .0670x$. This observation does not appear to be all that influential.

■

Careful examination of a scatterplot and a residual plot can help us determine the appropriateness of a line for summarizing a relationship. If we decide that a line is appropriate, the next step is to think about assessing the accuracy of predictions based on the least-squares line and whether these predictions (based on the value of $x$) are better in general than those made without knowledge of the value of $x$. Two numerical measures that are helpful in this assessment are the coefficient of determination and the standard deviation about the regression line.

## ■ Coefficient of Determination ...........................................................................

Suppose that we would like to predict the price of homes in a particular city. A random sample of 20 homes that are for sale is selected, and $y =$ price and $x =$ size (in square feet) are recorded for each house in the sample. Undoubtedly, there will be variability in house price (the houses will differ with respect to price), and it is this variability that makes accurate prediction of price a challenge. How much of the variability in house price can be explained by the fact that price is related to house size and that houses differ in size? If differences in size account for a large proportion of the variability in price, a price prediction that takes house size into account is a big improvement over a prediction that is not based on size.

The **coefficient of determination** is a measure of the proportion of variability in the $y$ variable that can be "explained" by a linear relationship between $x$ and $y$.

> **D E F I N I T I O N**
>
> The **coefficient of determination**, denoted by $r^2$, gives the proportion of variation in $y$ that can be attributed to an approximate linear relationship between $x$ and $y$; $100r^2$ is the percentage of variation in $y$ that can be attributed to an approximate linear relationship between $x$ and $y$.

Variation in $y$ can effectively be explained by an approximate straight-line relationship when the points in the scatterplot fall close to the least-squares line—that is, when the residuals are small in magnitude. A natural measure of variation about the least-squares line is the sum of the squared residuals. (Squaring before combining prevents negative and positive residuals from counteracting one another.) A second sum of squares assesses the total amount of variation in observed $y$ values.

> **D E F I N I T I O N**
>
> The **total sum of squares**, denoted by **SSTo**, is defined as
> $$\text{SSTo} = (y_1 - \bar{y})^2 + (y_2 - \bar{y})^2 + \cdots + (y_n - \bar{y})^2 = \sum(y - \bar{y})^2$$
> The **residual sum of squares** (sometimes referred to as the error sum of squares), denoted by **SSResid**, is defined as
> $$\text{SSResid} = (y_1 - \hat{y}_1)^2 + (y_2 - \hat{y}_2)^2 + \cdots + (y_n - \hat{y}_n)^2 = \sum(y - \hat{y})^2$$

These sums of squares can be found as part of the regression output from most standard statistical packages or can be obtained using the following computational formulas:

$$SSTo = \sum y^2 - \frac{(\sum y)^2}{n}$$
$$SSResid = \sum y^2 - a\sum y - b\sum xy$$

## Example 5.10  Range of Motion Revisited

Figure 5.18 displays part of the MINITAB output that results from fitting the least-squares line to the data on range of motion and age from Example 5.7. From the output,

$$SSTo = 1564.9 \text{ and } SSResid = 1085.7$$

**Figure 5.18**  MINITAB output for the data of Example 5.10.

**Regression Analysis**

The regression equation is
Range of Motion = 108 + 0.871 Age

| Predictor | Coef | StDev | T | P |
|---|---|---|---|---|
| Constant | 107.58 | 11.12 | 9.67 | 0.000 |
| Age | 0.8710 | 0.4146 | 2.10 | 0.062 |

S = 10.42   R-Sq = 30.6%   R-Sq(adj) = 23.7%

Analysis of Variance

| Source | DF | SS | MS | F | P |
|---|---|---|---|---|---|
| Regression | 1 | 479.2 | 479.2 | 4.41 | 0.062 |
| Residual Error | 10 | 1085.7 | 108.6 | | |
| Total | 11 | 1564.9 | | | |

Notice that SSResid is nearly as large as SSTo.  ■

The residual sum of squares is the sum of squared vertical deviations from the least-squares line. As Figure 5.19 illustrates, SSTo is also a sum of squared vertical deviations from a line—the horizontal line at height $\bar{y}$. The least-squares line is, by definition, the one having the smallest sum of squared deviations. It follows that SSResid ≤ SSTo. The two sums of squares are equal only when the least-squares line *is* the horizontal line.

**Figure 5.19** Interpreting sums of squares: (a) SSResid = sum of squared vertical deviations from the least-squares line; (b) SSTo = sum of squared vertical deviations from the horizontal line at height $\bar{y}$.

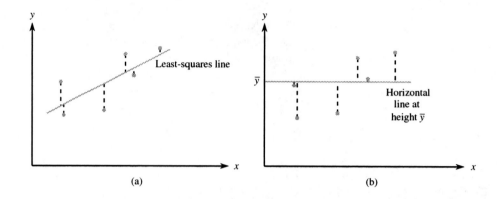

SSResid is often referred to as a measure of unexplained variation—the amount of variation in $y$ that cannot be attributed to the linear relationship between $x$ and $y$. The more the points in the scatterplot deviate from the least-squares line, the larger the value of SSResid and the greater the amount of $y$ variation that cannot be explained by the approximate linear relationship. Similarly, SSTo is interpreted as a measure of total variation. The larger the value of SSTo, the greater the amount of variability in $y_1, y_2, \ldots, y_n$. The ratio SSResid/SSTo is the fraction or proportion of total variation that is unexplained by a straight-line relation. Subtracting this ratio from 1 gives the proportion of total variation that *is* explained:

The coefficient of determination can be computed as

$$r^2 = 1 - \frac{\text{SSResid}}{\text{SSTo}}$$

Multiplying $r^2$ by 100 gives the percentage of $y$ variation attributable to the approximate linear relationship. The closer this percentage is to 100%, the more successful is the relationship in explaining variation in $y$.

## Example 5.11  $r^2$ for Age and Range of Motion Data

For the data on range of motion and age from Example 5.10, we found SSTo = 1564.9 and SSResid = 1085.7. Thus

$$r^2 = 1 - \frac{\text{SSResid}}{\text{SSTo}} = 1 - \frac{1085.7}{1564.9} = .306$$

This means that only 30.6% of the observed variability in postsurgical range of motion can be explained by an approximate linear relationship between range of motion and age. Note that the $r^2$ value can be found in the MINITAB output of Figure 5.18, labeled "R-Sq."

The symbol $r$ was used in Section 5.1 to denote Pearson's sample correlation coefficient. It is not coincidental that $r^2$ is used to represent the coefficient of determination. The notation suggests how these two quantities are related:

$$(\text{correlation coefficient})^2 = \text{coefficient of determination}$$

Thus, if $r = .8$ or $r = -.8$, then $r^2 = .64$, so 64% of the observed variation in the dependent variable can be explained by the linear relationship. Because the value of $r$ does not depend on which variable is labeled $x$, the same is true of $r^2$. The coefficient of determination is one of the few quantities computed in a regression analysis whose value remains the same when the roles of dependent and independent variables are interchanged. When $r = .5$, we get $r^2 = .25$, so only 25% of the observed variation is explained by a linear relation. This is why a value of $r$ between $-.5$ and $.5$ is not considered evidence of a strong linear relationship.

## ■ Standard Deviation About the Least-Squares Line ...........................................

The coefficient of determination measures the extent of variation about the best-fit line *relative* to overall variation in $y$. A high value of $r^2$ does not by itself promise that the deviations from the line are small in an absolute sense. A typical observation could deviate from the line by quite a bit, yet these deviations might still be small relative to overall $y$ variation.

Recall that in Chapter 4 the sample standard deviation

$$s = \sqrt{\frac{\sum(x - \bar{x})^2}{n - 1}}$$

was used as a measure of variability in a single sample; roughly speaking, $s$ is the typical amount by which a sample observation deviates from the mean. There is an analogous measure of variability when a least-squares line is fit.

---

**DEFINITION**

The **standard deviation about the least-squares line** is given by

$$s_e = \sqrt{\frac{\text{SSResid}}{n - 2}}$$

---

Roughly speaking, $s_e$ is the typical amount by which an observation deviates from the least-squares line. Justification for division by $(n - 2)$ and the use of the subscript $e$ is given in Chapter 13.

....................................................................................................................................

# Example 5.12 Predicting Graduation Rates

● Consider the accompanying data on six-year graduation rate (%), student-related expenditure per full-time student, and median SAT score for the 37 primarily undergraduate public universities and colleges in the United States with enrollments between 10,000 and 20,000 (Source: College Results Online, The Education Trust).

● Data set available online

| Graduation Rate | Expenditure | Median SAT |
|---|---|---|
| 80 | 6244 | 1165 |
| 65 | 6757 | 1045 |
| 65 | 8011 | 1195 |
| 62 | 7224 | 1120 |
| 61 | 7229 | 1110 |
| 57 | 6355 | 1090 |
| 55 | 7650 | 990 |
| 53 | 7323 | 1035 |
| 52 | 6382 | 1080 |
| 49 | 6792 | 990 |
| 49 | 7970 | 1065 |
| 49 | 7271 | 1065 |
| 48 | 6261 | 1085 |
| 46 | 5361 | 1080 |
| 46 | 8735 | 948 |
| 45 | 8553 | 990 |
| 45 | 7874 | 1005 |
| 43 | 5908 | 970 |
| 43 | 7548 | 890 |
| 41 | 6531 | 1010 |
| 39 | 7736 | 980 |
| 39 | 7209 | 970 |
| 39 | 7355 | 1050 |
| 39 | 7071 | 990 |
| 38 | 7186 | 970 |
| 38 | 6216 | 1010 |
| 37 | 6285 | 1045 |
| 37 | 7375 | 930 |
| 35 | 5435 | 1010 |
| 34 | 8248 | 860 |
| 33 | 6401 | 950 |
| 30 | 6169 | 1045 |
| 29 | 7126 | 1065 |
| 28 | 5604 | 1004 |
| 28 | 4327 | 990 |
| 26 | 6762 | 865 |
| 22 | 4541 | 950 |

Figure 5.20 displays scatterplots of graduation rate versus student-related expenditure and graduation rate versus median SAT score. The least-squares lines and the values of $r^2$ and $s_e$ are also shown.

Notice that while there is a positive linear relationship between student-related expenditure and graduation rate, the relationship is weak. The value of $r^2$ is only .095 (9.5%), indicating that only about 9.5% of the variability in graduation rate from university to university can be explained by student-related expenditures. The standard deviation about the regression line is $s_e = 12.0855$, which is larger than $s_e$ for the predictor median SAT, a reflection of the fact that the points in the scatterplot of graduation rate versus student-related expenditure tend to fall farther from the regression line than is the case for the line that describes graduation rate versus

**Figure 5.20** Scatterplots for the data of Example 5.12: (a) graduation rate versus student-related expenditure; (b) graduation rate versus median SAT.

median SAT. The value of $r^2$ for graduation rate versus median SAT is .447 (44.7%) and $s_e = 9.44933$, indicating that the predictor median SAT does a better job of explaining variability in graduation rates and the corresponding least-squares line would be expected to produce more accurate estimates of graduation rates than would be the case for the predictor student-related expenditure.

Based on the values of $r^2$ and $s_e$, median SAT would be a better choice for predicting graduation rates than student-related expenditures. It is also possible to develop a prediction equation that would incorporate both potential predictors—techniques for doing this are introduced in Chapter 14.

∎ Exercises 5.36–5.51 ····································································································································

**5.36** ● The following table gives the number of organ transplants performed in the United States each year from 1990 to 1999 (The Organ Procurement and Transplantation Network, 2003):

| Year | Number of Transplants (in thousands) |
|---|---|
| 1 (1990) | 15.0 |
| 2 | 15.7 |
| 3 | 16.1 |
| 4 | 17.6 |
| 5 | 18.3 |
| 6 | 19.4 |
| 7 | 20.0 |
| 8 | 20.3 |
| 9 | 21.4 |
| 10 (1999) | 21.8 |

a. Construct a scatterplot of these data, and then find the equation of the least-squares regression line that describes the relationship between $y$ = number of transplants performed and $x$ = year. Describe how the number of transplants performed has changed over time from 1990 to 1999.
b. Compute the 10 residuals, and construct a residual plot. Are there any features of the residual plot that indicate that the relationship between year and number of transplants performed would be better described by a curve rather than a line? Explain.

**5.37** ● The following data on $x$ = soil depth (in centimeters) and $y$ = percentage of montmorillonite in the soil were taken from a scatterplot in the paper "Ancient Maya Drained Field Agriculture: Its Possible Application Today in the New River Floodplain, Belize, C.A." (*Agricultural Ecosystems and Environment* [1984]: 67–84):

| $x$ | 40 | 50 | 60 | 70 | 80 | 90 | 100 |
|---|---|---|---|---|---|---|---|
| $y$ | 58 | 34 | 32 | 30 | 28 | 27 | 22 |

a. Draw a scatterplot of $y$ versus $x$.
**b.** The equation of the least-squares line is $\hat{y} = 64.50 - 0.45x$. Draw this line on your scatterplot. Do there appear to be any large residuals?
**c.** Compute the residuals, and construct a residual plot. Are there any unusual features in the plot?

**5.38** ● Data on pollution and cost of medical care for elderly people were given in Exercise 5.17 and are also shown here. The following data give a measure of pollution (micrograms of particulate matter per cubic meter of air) and the cost of medical care per person over age 65 for six geographic regions of the United States:

| Region | Pollution | Cost of Medical Care |
|---|---|---|
| North | 30.0 | 915 |
| Upper South | 31.8 | 891 |
| Deep South | 32.1 | 968 |
| West South | 26.8 | 972 |
| Big Sky | 30.4 | 952 |
| West | 40.0 | 899 |

The equation of the least-squares regression line for this data set is $\hat{y} = 1082.2 - 4.691x$, where $y$ = medical cost and $x$ = pollution.
a. Compute the six residuals.
b. What is the value of the correlation coefficient for this data set? Does the value of $r$ indicate that the linear relationship between pollution and medical cost is strong, moderate, or weak? Explain.
c. Construct a residual plot. Are there any unusual features of the plot?
d. The observation for the West, (40.0, 899), has an $x$ value that is far removed from the other $x$ values in the sample. Is this observation influential in determining the values of the slope and/or intercept of the least-squares line? Justify your answer.

**5.39** ● The following data on degree of exposure to $^{242}$Cm alpha particles ($x$) and the percentage of exposed cells without aberrations ($y$) appeared in the paper "Chromosome Aberrations Induced in Human Lymphocytes by D-T Neutrons" (*Radiation Research* [1984]: 561–573):

| $x$ | 0.106 | 0.193 | 0.511 | 0.527 |
|---|---|---|---|---|
| $y$ | 98 | 95 | 87 | 85 |
| $x$ | 1.08 | 1.62 | 1.73 | 2.36 |
| $y$ | 75 | 72 | 64 | 55 |
| $x$ | 2.72 | 3.12 | 3.88 | 4.18 |
| $y$ | 44 | 41 | 37 | 40 |

Summary quantities are

$$n = 12 \qquad \sum x = 22.027 \qquad \sum y = 793$$
$$\sum x^2 = 62.600235 \qquad \sum xy = 1114.5 \qquad \sum y^2 = 57{,}939$$

**a.** Obtain the equation of the least-squares line.
**b.** Construct a residual plot, and comment on any interesting features.

5.40 ◉ Cost-to-charge ratio (the percentage of the amount billed that represents the actual cost) for inpatient and outpatient services at 11 Oregon hospitals is shown in the following table (Oregon Department of Health Services, 2002). A scatterplot of the data is also shown.

### Cost-to-Charge Ratio

| Hospital | Outpatient Care | Inpatient Care |
|---|---|---|
| 1 | 62 | 80 |
| 2 | 66 | 76 |
| 3 | 63 | 75 |
| 4 | 51 | 62 |
| 5 | 75 | 100 |
| 6 | 65 | 88 |
| 7 | 56 | 64 |
| 8 | 45 | 50 |
| 9 | 48 | 54 |
| 10 | 71 | 83 |
| 11 | 54 | 100 |

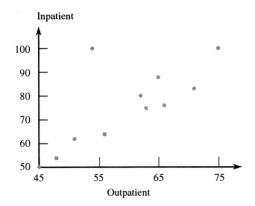

The least-squares regression line with $y$ = inpatient cost-to-charge ratio and $x$ = outpatient cost-to-charge ratio is $\hat{y} = -1.1 + 1.29x$.

**a.** Is the observation for Hospital 11 an influential observation? Justify your answer.
**b.** Is the observation for Hospital 11 an outlier? Explain.
**c.** Is the observation for Hospital 5 an influential observation? Justify your answer.
**d.** Is the observation for Hospital 5 an outlier? Explain.

**5.41** The article "Examined Life: What Stanley H. Kaplan Taught Us About the SAT" (*The New Yorker* [December 17, 2001]: 86–92) included a summary of findings regarding the use of SAT I scores, SAT II scores, and high school grade point average (GPA) to predict first-year college GPA. The article states that "among these, SAT II scores are the best predictor, explaining 16 percent of the variance in first-year college grades. GPA was second at 15.4 percent, and SAT I was last at 13.3 percent."
**a.** If the data from this study were used to fit a least-squares line with $y$ = first-year college GPA and $x$ = high school GPA, what would the value of $r^2$ have been?
**b.** The article stated that SAT II was the best predictor of first-year college grades. Do you think that predictions based on a least-squares line with $y$ = first-year college GPA and $x$ = SAT II score would have been very accurate? Explain why or why not.

5.42 Exercise 5.22 gave the least-squares regression line for predicting $y$ = clutch size from $x$ = snout-vent length ("Reproductive Biology of the Aquatic Salamander *Amphiuma tridactylum* in Louisiana," *Journal of Herpetology* [1999]: 100–105). The paper also reported $r^2 = .7664$ and SSTo = 43,951.
**a.** Interpret the value of $r^2$.
**b.** Find and interpret the value of $s_e$ (the sample size was $n = 14$).

**5.43** ◉ ▼ The article "Characterization of Highway Runoff in Austin, Texas, Area" (*Journal of Environmental Engineering* [1998]: 131–137) gave a scatterplot, along with the least-squares line for $x$ = rainfall volume (in cubic meters) and $y$ = runoff volume (in cubic meters), for a particular location. The following data were read from the plot in the paper:

| $x$ | 5 | 12 | 14 | 17 | 23 | 30 | 40 | 47 |
|---|---|---|---|---|---|---|---|---|
| $y$ | 4 | 10 | 13 | 15 | 15 | 25 | 27 | 46 |

| $x$ | 55 | 67 | 72 | 81 | 96 | 112 | 127 |
|---|---|---|---|---|---|---|---|
| $y$ | 38 | 46 | 53 | 70 | 82 | 99 | 100 |

**a.** Does a scatterplot of the data suggest a linear relationship between $x$ and $y$?

**b.** Calculate the slope and intercept of the least-squares line.

**c.** Compute an estimate of the average runoff volume when rainfall volume is 80.

**d.** Compute the residuals, and construct a residual plot. Are there any features of the plot that indicate that a line is not an appropriate description of the relationship between $x$ and $y$? Explain.

5.44 ● The paper "Accelerated Telomere Shortening in Response to Life Stress" (*Proceedings of the National Academy of Sciences* [2004]: 17312–17315) described a study that examined whether stress accelerates aging at a cellular level. The accompanying data on a measure of perceived stress ($x$) and telomere length ($y$) were read from a scatterplot that appeared in the paper. Telomere length is a measure of cell longevity.

| Perceived Stress | Telomere Length | Perceived Stress | Telomere Length |
|---|---|---|---|
| 5 | 1.25 | 20 | 1.22 |
| 6 | 1.32 | 20 | 1.3 |
| 6 | 1.5 | 20 | 1.32 |
| 7 | 1.35 | 21 | 1.24 |
| 10 | 1.3 | 21 | 1.26 |
| 11 | 1 | 21 | 1.3 |
| 12 | 1.18 | 22 | 1.18 |
| 13 | 1.1 | 22 | 1.22 |
| 14 | 1.08 | 22 | 1.24 |
| 14 | 1.3 | 23 | 1.18 |
| 15 | 0.92 | 24 | 1.12 |
| 15 | 1.22 | 24 | 1.5 |
| 15 | 1.24 | 25 | 0.94 |
| 17 | 1.12 | 26 | 0.84 |
| 17 | 1.32 | 27 | 1.02 |
| 17 | 1.4 | 27 | 1.12 |
| 18 | 1.12 | 28 | 1.22 |
| 18 | 1.46 | 29 | 1.3 |
| 19 | 0.84 | 33 | 0.94 |

**a.** Compute the equation of the least-squares line.
**b.** What is the value of $r^2$?
**c.** Does the linear relationship between perceived stress and telomere length account for a large or small proportion of the variability in telomere length? Justify your answer.

5.45 The article "Cost-Effectiveness in Public Education" (*Chance* [1995]: 38–41) reported that for a regression of $y$ = average SAT score on $x$ = expenditure per pupil, based on data from $n = 44$ New Jersey school districts, $a = 766$, $b = 0.015$, $r^2 = .160$, and $s_e = 53.7$.

**a.** One observation in the sample was (9900, 893). What average SAT score would you predict for this district, and what is the corresponding residual?
**b.** Interpret the value of $s_e$.
**c.** How effectively do you think the least-squares line summarizes the relationship between $x$ and $y$? Explain your reasoning.

5.46 ● The paper "Feeding of Predaceous Fishes on Out-Migrating Juvenile Salmonids in John Day Reservoir, Columbia River" (*Transactions of the American Fisheries Society* [1991]: 405–420) gave the following data on $y$ = maximum size of salmonids consumed by a northern squawfish (the most abundant salmonid predator) and $x$ = squawfish length, both in millimeters:

| $x$ | 218 | 246 | 270 | 287 | 318 | 344 |
|---|---|---|---|---|---|---|
| $y$ | 82 | 85 | 94 | 127 | 141 | 157 |

| $x$ | 375 | 386 | 414 | 450 | 468 |
|---|---|---|---|---|---|
| $y$ | 165 | 216 | 219 | 238 | 249 |

Use the accompanying output from MINITAB to answer the following questions.

The regression equation is size 89.1 + 0.729 length

| Predictor | Coef | Stdev | t ratio | p |
|---|---|---|---|---|
| Constant | 89.09 | 16.83 | 5.29 | 0.000 |
| length | 0.72907 | 0.04778 | 15.26 | 0.000 |

$s = 12.56$    R-sq = 96.3%    R-sq(adj) = 95.9%

**Analysis of Variance**

| Source | DF | SS | MS | F | p |
|---|---|---|---|---|---|
| Regression | 1 | 36736 | 36736 | 232.87 | 0.000 |
| Error | 9 | 1420 | 158 | | |
| Total | 10 | 38156 | | | |

**a.** What maximum salmonid size would you predict for a squawfish whose length is 375 mm, and what is the residual corresponding to the observation (375, 165)?

b. What proportion of observed variation in $y$ can be attributed to the approximate linear relationship between the two variables?

**5.47** ● The paper "Crop Improvement for Tropical and Subtropical Australia: Designing Plants for Difficult Climates" (*Field Crops Research* [1991]: 113–139) gave the following data on $x$ = crop duration (in days) for soybeans and $y$ = crop yield (in tons per hectare):

| $x$ | 92 | 92 | 96 | 100 | 102 |
|---|---|---|---|---|---|
| $y$ | 1.7 | 2.3 | 1.9 | 2.0 | 1.5 |

| $x$ | 102 | 106 | 106 | 121 | 143 |
|---|---|---|---|---|---|
| $y$ | 1.7 | 1.6 | 1.8 | 1.0 | 0.3 |

$$\sum x = 1060 \quad \sum y = 15.8 \quad \sum xy = 1601.1$$
$$a = 5.20683380 \quad b = -0.3421541$$

**a.** Construct a scatterplot of the data. Do you think the least-squares line will give accurate predictions? Explain.
**b.** Delete the observation with the largest $x$ value from the sample and recalculate the equation of the least-squares line. Does this observation greatly affect the equation of the line?
**c.** What effect does the deletion in Part (b) have on the value of $r^2$? Can you explain why this is so?

**5.48** A study was carried out to investigate the relationship between the hardness of molded plastic ($y$, in Brinell units) and the amount of time elapsed since termination of the molding process ($x$, in hours). Summary quantities include $n = 15$, SSResid = 1235.470, and SSTo = 25,321.368. Calculate and interpret the coefficient of determination.

**5.49** The paper "Effects of Canine Parvovirus (CPV) on Gray Wolves in Minnesota" (*Journal of Wildlife Management* [1995]: 565–570) summarized a regression of $y$ = percentage of pups in a capture on $x$ = percentage of CPV prevalence among adults and pups. The equation of the least-squares line, based on $n = 10$ observations, was $\hat{y} = 62.9476 - 0.54975x$, with $r^2 = .57$.
**a.** One observation was (25, 70). What is the corresponding residual?
**b.** What is the value of the sample correlation coefficient?

**c.** Suppose that SSTo = 2520.0 (this value was not given in the paper). What is the value of $s_e$?

**5.50** Both $r^2$ and $s_e$ are used to assess the fit of a line.
**a.** Is it possible that both $r^2$ and $s_e$ could be large for a bivariate data set? Explain. (A picture might be helpful.)
**b.** Is it possible that a bivariate data set could yield values of $r^2$ and $s_e$ that are both small? Explain. (Again, a picture might be helpful.)
**c.** Explain why it is desirable to have $r^2$ large and $s_e$ small if the relationship between two variables $x$ and $y$ is to be described using a straight line.

**5.51** Some straightforward but slightly tedious algebra shows that
$$\text{SSResid} = (1 - r^2)\sum(y - \bar{y})^2$$
from which it follows that
$$s_e = \sqrt{\frac{n-1}{n-2}}\sqrt{1 - r^2}\, s_y$$
Unless $n$ is quite small, $(n-1)/(n-2) \approx 1$, so
$$s_e \approx \sqrt{1 - r^2}\, s_y$$
**a.** For what value of $r$ is $s_e$ as large as $s_y$? What is the least-squares line in this case?
**b.** For what values of $r$ will $s_e$ be much smaller than $s_y$?
**c.** A study by the Berkeley Institute of Human Development (see the book *Statistics* by Freedman et al., listed in the back of the book) reported the following summary data for a sample of $n = 66$ California boys:

> $r \approx .80$
> At age 6, average height $\approx$ 46 in., standard deviation $\approx$ 1.7 in.
> At age 18, average height $\approx$ 70 in., standard deviation $\approx$ 2.5 in.

What would $s_e$ be for the least-squares line used to predict 18-year-old height from 6-year-old height?
**d.** Referring to Part (c), suppose that you wanted to predict the past value of 6-year-old height from knowledge of 18-year-old height. Find the equation for the appropriate least-squares line. What is the corresponding value of $s_e$?

# 5.4   Nonlinear Relationships and Transformations

As we have seen in previous sections, when the points in a scatterplot exhibit a linear pattern and the residual plot does not reveal any problems with the linear fit, the least-squares line is a sensible way to summarize the relationship between $x$ and $y$. A linear relationship is easy to interpret, departures from the line are easily detected, and using the line to predict $y$ from our knowledge of $x$ is straightforward. Often, though, a scatterplot or residual plot exhibits a curved pattern, indicating a more complicated relationship between $x$ and $y$. In this case, finding a curve that fits the observed data well is a more complex task. In this section, we consider two common approaches to fitting nonlinear relationships: polynomial regression and transformations.

## ■ Polynomial Regression

Let's reconsider the data first introduced in Example 5.4 on $x$ = age and $y$ = average marathon finish time:

| Age Group | $x$ = Representative Age | $y$ = Average Finish Time |
|---|---|---|
| 10–19 | 15 | 302.38 |
| 20–29 | 25 | 193.63 |
| 30–39 | 35 | 185.46 |
| 40–49 | 45 | 198.49 |
| 50–59 | 55 | 224.30 |
| 60–69 | 65 | 288.71 |

The scatterplot of these data is reproduced here as Figure 5.21. Because this plot shows a marked curved pattern, it is clear that no straight line can do a reasonable job of describing the relationship between $x$ and $y$. However, the relationship can be de-

**Figure 5.21** Scatterplot for the marathon data.

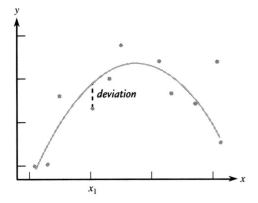

**Figure 5.22**   Deviation for a quadratic function.

scribed by a curve, and in this case the curved pattern in the scatterplot looks like a parabola (the graph of a quadratic function). This suggests trying to find a quadratic function of the form

$$\hat{y} = a + b_1 x + b_2 x^2$$

that would reasonably describe the relationship. That is, the values of the coefficients $a$, $b_1$, and $b_2$ in this equation must be selected to obtain a good fit to the data.

What are the best choices for the values of $a$, $b_1$, and $b_2$? In fitting a line to data, we used the principle of least squares to guide our choice of slope and intercept. Least squares can be used to fit a quadratic function as well. The deviations, $y - \hat{y}$, are still represented by vertical distances in the scatterplot, but now they are vertical distances from the points to a parabolic curve (the graph of a quadratic equation) rather than to a line, as shown in Figure 5.22. We then choose values for the coefficients in the quadratic equation so that the sum of squared deviations is as small as possible.

For a quadratic regression, the least squares estimates of $a$, $b_1$, and $b_2$ are those values that minimize the sum of squared deviations $\sum(y - \hat{y})^2$ where $\hat{y} = a + b_1 x + b_2 x^2$.

For quadratic regression, a measure that is useful for assessing fit is

$$R^2 = 1 - \frac{\text{SSResid}}{\text{SSTo}}$$

where **SSResid** $= \sum(y - \hat{y})^2$. The measure $R^2$ is defined in a way similar to $r^2$ for simple linear regression and is interpreted in a similar fashion. The notation $r^2$ is used only with linear regression to emphasize the relationship between $r^2$ and the correlation coefficient, $r$, in the linear case.

The general expressions for computing the least-squares estimates are somewhat complicated, so we rely on a statistical software package or graphing calculator to do the computations for us.

......................................................................................................

# Example 5.13   Marathon Data Revisited: Fitting a Quadratic Model

For the marathon data, the scatterplot (see Figure 5.21) showed a marked curved pattern. If the least-squares line is fit to these data, it is no surprise that the line does not do a good job of describing the relationship ($r^2 = .001$ or $.1\%$ and $s_e = 56.9439$), and the residual plot shows a distinct curved pattern as well (Figure 5.23).

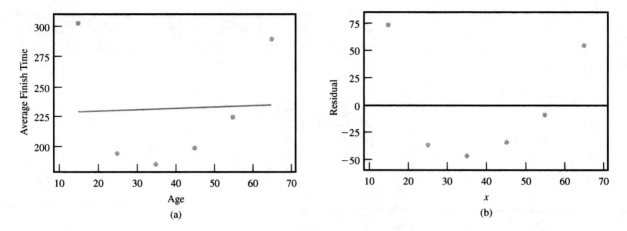

**Figure 5.23** Plots for the marathon data of Example 5.13: (a) fitted line plot; (b) residual plot.

Part of the MINITAB output from fitting a quadratic function to these data is as follows:

The regression equation is
$y = 462 - 14.2\ x + 0.179\ x\text{-squared}$

| Predictor | Coef | SE Coef | T | P |
|-----------|------|---------|------|-------|
| Constant | 462.00 | 43.99 | 10.50 | 0.002 |
| x | −14.205 | 2.460 | −5.78 | 0.010 |
| x-squared | 0.17888 | 0.03025 | 5.91 | 0.010 |

S = 18.4813    R-Sq = 92.1%    R-Sq(adj) = 86.9%

**Analysis of Variance**

| Source | DF | SS | MS | F | P |
|--------|----|--------|--------|-------|-------|
| Regression | 2 | 11965.0 | 5982.5 | 17.52 | 0.022 |
| Residual Error | 3 | 1024.7 | 341.6 | | |
| Total | 5 | 12989.7 | | | |

The least-squares coefficients are

$$a = 462.0 \qquad b_1 = -14.205 \qquad b_2 = 0.17888$$

and the least-squares quadratic is

$$\hat{y} = 462.0 - 14.205x + 0.17888x^2$$

A plot showing the curve and the corresponding residual plot for the quadratic regression are given in Figure 5.24. Notice that there is no strong pattern in the residual plot for the quadratic case, as there was in the linear case. For the quadratic regression, $R^2 = .921$ (as opposed to .001 for the least-squares line), which means that 92.1% of the variability in average marathon finish time can be explained by an approximate quadratic relationship between average finish time and age.

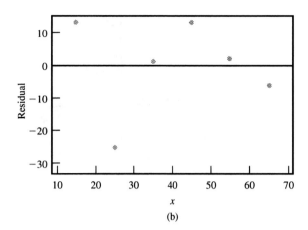

**Figure 5.24**   Quadratic regression of Example 5.13: (a) scatterplot; (b) residual plot.

■

Linear and quadratic regression are special cases of polynomial regression. A polynomial regression curve is described by a function of the form

$$\hat{y} = a + b_1x + b_2x^2 + b_3x^3 + \cdots + b_kx^k$$

which is called a $k$th-degree polynomial. The case of $k = 1$ results in linear regression ($\hat{y} = a + b_1x$) and $k = 2$ yields a quadratic regression ($\hat{y} = a + b_1x + b_2x^2$). A quadratic curve has only one bend (see Figure 5.25(a) and (b)). A less frequently encountered special case is for $k = 3$, where $\hat{y} = a + b_1x + b_2x^2 + b_3x^3$, which is called a cubic regression curve. Cubic curves have two bends, as shown in Figure 5.25(c).

**Figure 5.25**   Polynomial regression curves: (a) quadratic curve with $b_2 < 0$; (b) quadratic curve with $b_2 > 0$; (c) cubic curve.

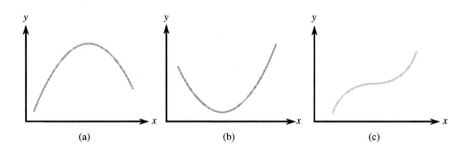

(a)                    (b)                    (c)

............................................................................................................

# Example 5.14   Nonlinear Relationship Between Cloud Cover Index and Sunshine Index

◉ Researchers have examined a number of climatic variables in an attempt to understand the mechanisms that govern rainfall runoff. The article "The Applicability of Morton's and Penman's Evapotranspiration Estimates in Rainfall-Runoff Modeling"

◉ Data set available online

(*Water Resources Bulletin* [1991]: 611–620) reported on a study that examined the relationship between $x$ = cloud cover index and $y$ = sunshine index. Suppose that the cloud cover index can have values between 0 and 1. Consider the accompanying data, which are consistent with summary quantities in the article:

| Cloud Cover Index (x) | Sunshine Index (y) |
|:---:|:---:|
| .2 | 10.98 |
| .5 | 10.94 |
| .3 | 10.91 |
| .1 | 10.94 |
| .2 | 10.97 |
| .4 | 10.89 |
| 0 | 10.88 |
| .4 | 10.92 |
| .3 | 10.86 |

The authors of the article used a cubic regression to describe the relationship between cloud cover and sunshine. Using the given data, MINITAB was instructed to fit a cubic regression, resulting in the following output:

The regression equation is
$y = 10.9 + 1.46\ x - 7.26\ x\text{-squared} + 9.23\ x\text{-cubed}$

| Predictor | Coef | SE Coef | T | P |
|---|---|---|---|---|
| Constant | 10.8768 | 0.0307 | 354.72 | 0.000 |
| x | 1.4604 | 0.5285 | 2.76 | 0.040 |
| x-squared | −7.259 | 2.550 | −2.85 | 0.036 |
| x-cubed | 9.234 | 3.346 | 2.76 | 0.040 |

$S = 0.0315265$     R-Sq = 62.0%     R-Sq(adj) = 39.3%

**Analysis of Variance**

| Source | DF | SS | MS | F | P |
|---|---|---|---|---|---|
| Regression | 3 | 0.0081193 | 0.0027064 | 2.72 | 0.154 |
| Residual Error | 5 | 0.0049696 | 0.0009939 | | |
| Total | 8 | 0.0130889 | | | |

The least-squares cubic regression is then

$$\hat{y} = 10.8768 + 1.4604x - 7.259x^2 + 9.234x^3$$

To predict the sunshine index for a day when the cloud cover index is .45, we use the regression equation to obtain

$$\hat{y} = 10.8768 + 1.4604(.45) - 7.259(.45)^2 + 9.234(.45)^3 = 10.91$$

The least-squares cubic regression and the corresponding residual plot are shown in Figure 5.26. The residual plot does not reveal any troublesome patterns that would suggest a choice other than the cubic regression.

**Figure 5.26** Plots for the data of Example 5.14: (a) least-squares cubic regression; (b) residual plot.

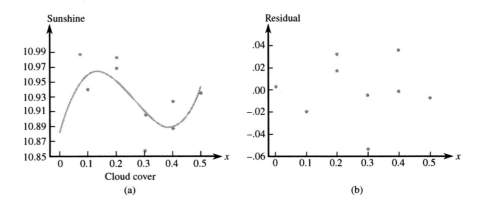

(a)  (b)

## ■ Transformations

An alternative to finding a curve to fit the data is to find a way to transform the $x$ values and/or $y$ values so that a scatterplot of the transformed data has a linear appearance. A **transformation** (sometimes called a reexpression) involves using a simple function of a variable in place of the variable itself. For example, instead of trying to describe the relationship between $x$ and $y$, it might be easier to describe the relationship between $\sqrt{x}$ and $y$ or between $x$ and $\log(y)$. And, if we can describe the relationship between, say, $\sqrt{x}$ and $y$, we will still be able to predict the value of $y$ for a given $x$ value. Common transformations involve taking square roots, logarithms, or reciprocals.

## Example 5.15  River Water Velocity and Distance from Shore

● As fans of white-water rafting know, a river flows more slowly close to its banks (because of friction between the river bank and the water). To study the nature of the relationship between water velocity and the distance from the shore, data were gathered on velocity (in centimeters per second) of a river at different distances (in meters) from the bank. Suppose that the resulting data were as follows:

| Distance | .5 | 1.5 | 2.5 | 3.5 | 4.5 | 5.5 | 6.5 | 7.5 | 8.5 | 9.5 |
|---|---|---|---|---|---|---|---|---|---|---|
| Velocity | 22.00 | 23.18 | 25.48 | 25.25 | 27.15 | 27.83 | 28.49 | 28.18 | 28.50 | 28.63 |

A graph of the data exhibits a curved pattern, as seen in both the scatterplot and the residual plot from a linear fit (see Figures 5.27(a) and 5.27(b)).

Let's try transforming the $x$ values by replacing each $x$ value by its square root. We define

$$x' = \sqrt{x}$$

The resulting transformed data are given in Table 5.2.

● Data set available online

**Figure 5.27** Plots for the data of Example 5.15: (a) scatterplot of the river data; (b) residual plot from linear fit.

Figure 5.28(a) shows a scatterplot of $y$ versus $x'$ (or equivalently $y$ versus $\sqrt{x}$). The pattern of points in this plot looks linear, and so we can fit a least-squares line using the transformed data. The MINITAB output from this regression appears below.

The residual plot in Figure 5.28(b) shows no indication of a pattern. The resulting regression equation is

$$\hat{y} = 20.1 + 3.01x'$$

**Table 5.2** Original and Transformed Data of Example 5.15

| Original Data | | Transformed Data | |
|---|---|---|---|
| $x$ | $y$ | $x'$ | $y$ |
| 0.5 | 22.00 | 0.7071 | 22.00 |
| 1.5 | 23.18 | 1.2247 | 23.18 |
| 2.5 | 25.48 | 1.5811 | 25.48 |
| 3.5 | 25.25 | 1.8708 | 25.25 |
| 4.5 | 27.15 | 2.1213 | 27.15 |
| 5.5 | 27.83 | 2.3452 | 27.83 |
| 6.5 | 28.49 | 2.5495 | 28.49 |
| 7.5 | 28.18 | 2.7386 | 28.18 |
| 8.5 | 28.50 | 2.9155 | 28.50 |
| 9.5 | 28.63 | 3.0822 | 28.63 |

**Regression Analysis**

The regression equation is
Velocity = 20.1 + 3.01 sqrt distance

| Predictor | Coef | StDev | T | P |
|---|---|---|---|---|
| Constant | 20.1102 | 0.6097 | 32.99 | 0.000 |
| Sqrt dis | 3.0085 | 0.2726 | 11.03 | 0.000 |

S = 0.6292    R-Sq = 93.8%     R-Sq(adj) = 93.1%

**Analysis of Variance**

| Source | DF | SS | MS | F | P |
|---|---|---|---|---|---|
| Regression | 1 | 48.209 | 48.209 | 121.76 | 0.000 |
| Residual Error | 8 | 3.168 | 0.396 | | |
| Total | 9 | 51.376 | | | |

**Figure 5.28** Plots for the transformed data of Example 5.15: (a) scatterplot of $y$ versus $x'$; (b) residual plot resulting from a linear fit to the transformed data.

An equivalent equation is:

$$\hat{y} = 20.1 + 3.01\sqrt{x}$$

The values of $r^2$ and $s_e$ (see the MINITAB output) indicate that a line is a reasonable way to describe the relationship between $y$ and $x'$. To predict velocity of the river at a distance of 9 meters from shore, we first compute $x' = \sqrt{x} = \sqrt{9} = 3$ and then use the sample regression line to obtain a prediction of $y$:

$$\hat{y} = 20.1 + 3.01x' = 20.1 + (3.01)(3) = 29.13$$

■

In Example 5.15, transforming the $x$ values using the square root function worked well. In general, how can we choose a transformation that will result in a linear pattern? Table 5.3 gives some guidance and summarizes some of the properties of the most commonly used transformations.

**Table 5.3**   Commonly Used Transformations

| Transformation | Mathematical Description | Try This Transformation When |
|---|---|---|
| No transformation | $\hat{y} = a + bx$ | The change in $y$ is constant as $x$ changes. A 1-unit increase in $x$ is associated with, on average, an increase of $b$ in the value of $y$. |
| Square root of $x$ | $\hat{y} = a + b\sqrt{x}$ | The change in $y$ is not constant. A 1-unit increase in $x$ is associated with smaller increases or decreases in $y$ for larger $x$ values. |
| Log of $x$* | $\hat{y} = a + b\log_{10}(x)$ or $\hat{y} = a + b\ln(x)$ | The change in $y$ is not constant. A 1-unit increase in $x$ is associated with smaller increases or decreases in the value of $y$ for larger $x$ values. |
| Reciprocal of $x$ | $\hat{y} = a + b\left(\dfrac{1}{x}\right)$ | The change in $y$ is not constant. A 1-unit increase in $x$ is associated with smaller increases or decreases in the value of $y$ for larger $x$ values. In addition, $y$ has a limiting value of $a$ as $x$ increases. |
| Log of $y$* (Exponential growth or decay) | $\log(\hat{y}) = a + bx$ or $\ln(\hat{y}) = a + bx$ | The change in $y$ associated with a 1-unit change in $x$ is proportional to $x$. |

*The values of $a$ and $b$ in the regression equation will depend on whether $\log_{10}$ or ln is used, but the $\hat{y}$'s and $r^2$ values will be identical.

## Example 5.16   Tortilla Chips: Relationship Between Frying Time and Moisture Content

● No tortilla chip lover likes soggy chips, so it is important to find characteristics of the production process that produce chips with an appealing texture. The following

● Data set available online

data on $x$ = frying time (in seconds) and $y$ = moisture content (%) appeared in the article "Thermal and Physical Properties of Tortilla Chips as a Function of Frying Time" (*Journal of Food Processing and Preservation* [1995]: 175–189):

| Frying time, $x$ | 5 | 10 | 15 | 20 | 25 | 30 | 45 | 60 |
|---|---|---|---|---|---|---|---|---|
| Moisture content, $y$ | 16.3 | 9.7 | 8.1 | 4.2 | 3.4 | 2.9 | 1.9 | 1.3 |

Figure 5.29(a) shows a scatterplot of the data. The pattern in this plot is typical of exponential decay, with the change in $y$ as $x$ increases much smaller for large $x$ values than for small $x$ values. You can see that a 5-sec change in frying time is associated with a much larger change in moisture content in the part of the plot where the $x$ values are small than in the part of the plot where the $x$ values are large. Table 5.3 suggests transforming the $y$ values (moisture content in this example) by taking their logarithms.

**Figure 5.29**   Plots for the data of Example 5.16: (a) scatterplot of the tortilla chip data; (b) scatterplot of transformed data with $y' = \log(y)$; (c) scatterplot of transformed data with $y' = \ln(y)$.

Two standard logarithmic functions are commonly used for such transformations —the common logarithm (log base 10, denoted by log or $\log_{10}$) and the natural logarithm (log base $e$, denoted ln). Either the common or the natural logarithm can be used; the only difference in the resulting scatterplots is the scale of the transformed $y$ variable. This can be seen in Figures 5.29(b) and 5.29(c). These two scatterplots show the same pattern, and it looks like a line would be appropriate to describe this relationship.

Table 5.4 displays the original data along with the transformed $y$ values using $y' = \log(y)$.

**Table 5.4**   Transformed Data from Example 5.16

| Frying Time $x$ | Moisture $y$ | Log(moisture) $y'$ |
|:---:|:---:|:---:|
| 5 | 16.3 | 1.21219 |
| 10 | 9.7 | .98677 |
| 15 | 8.1 | .90849 |
| 20 | 4.2 | .62325 |
| 25 | 3.4 | .53148 |
| 30 | 2.9 | .46240 |
| 45 | 1.9 | .27875 |
| 60 | 1.3 | .11394 |

The following MINITAB output shows the result of fitting the least-squares line to the transformed data:

### Regression Analysis

The regression equation is
log(moisture) = 1.14 − 0.0192 frying time

| Predictor | Coef | StDev | T | P |
|---|---|---|---|---|
| Constant | 1.14287 | 0.08016 | 14.26 | 0.000 |
| Frying t | −0.019170 | 0.002551 | −7.52 | 0.000 |

S = 0.1246    R-Sq = 90.4%    R-Sq(adj) = 88.8%

### Analysis of Variance

| Source | DF | SS | MS | F | P |
|---|---|---|---|---|---|
| Regression | 1 | 0.87736 | 0.87736 | 56.48 | 0.000 |
| Residual Error | 6 | 0.09320 | 0.01553 | | |
| Total | 7 | 0.97057 | | | |

The resulting regression equation is

$$y' = 1.14 - 0.0192x$$

or, equivalently,

$$\log(y) = 1.14 - 0.0192x$$

■

■ **Fitting a Curve Using Transformations**   The objective of a regression analysis is usually to describe the approximate relationship between $x$ and $y$ with an equation of the form $y = $ some function of $x$.

If we have transformed only $x$, fitting a least-squares line to the transformed data results in an equation of the desired form, for example,

$$\hat{y} = 5 + 3x' = 5 + 3\sqrt{x} \qquad where\ x' = \sqrt{x}$$

or

$$\hat{y} = 4 + .2x' = 4 + .2\frac{1}{x} \qquad where\ x' = \frac{1}{x}$$

These functions specify lines when graphed using $y$ and $x'$, and they specify curves when graphed using $y$ and $x$, as illustrated in Figure 5.30 for the square root transformation.

**Figure 5.30** (a) A plot of $\hat{y} = 5 + 3x'$ where $x' = \sqrt{x}$; (b) a plot of $\hat{y} = 5 + 3\sqrt{x}$.

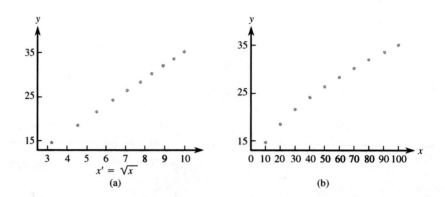

If the $y$ values have been transformed, after obtaining the least-squares line the transformation can be undone to yield an expression of the form $y =$ some function of $x$ (as opposed to $y' =$ some function of $x$). For example, to reverse a logarithmic transformation ($y' = \log(y)$), we can take the antilogarithm of each side of the equation. To reverse a square root transformation ($y' = \sqrt{y}$), we can square both sides of the equation, and to reverse a reciprocal transformation ($y' = 1/y$), we can take the reciprocal of each side of the equation. This is illustrated in Example 5.17.

........................................................................................................................

# Example 5.17 Revisiting the Tortilla Chip Data

For the tortilla chip data of Example 5.16, $y' = \log(y)$ and the least-squares line relating $y'$ and $x$ was

$$y' = 1.14 - .0192x$$

or, equivalently,

$$\log(y) = 1.14 - .0192x$$

To reverse this transformation, we take the antilog of both sides of the equation:

$$10^{\log(y)} = 10^{1.14 - .0192x}$$

Using the properties of logs and exponents

$$10^{\log(y)} = y$$
$$10^{1.14 - .0192x} = (10^{1.14})(10^{-.0192x})$$

We get

$$\hat{y} = (10^{1.14})(10^{-.0192x}) = (13.8038)(10^{-.0192x})$$

This equation can now be used to predict the $y$ value (moisture content) for a given $x$ (frying time). For example, the predicted moisture content when frying time is 35 sec is

$$\hat{y} = (13.8038)(10^{-.0192x}) = (13.8038)(.2128) = 2.9374$$

■

It should be noted that the process of transforming data, fitting a line to the transformed data, and then undoing the transformation to get an equation for a curved relationship between $x$ and $y$ usually results in a curve that provides a reasonable fit to the sample data, but it is not the least-squares curve for the data. For example, in Example 5.17, a transformation was used to fit the curve $\hat{y} = (13.8038)(10^{-.0192x})$. However, there may be another equation of the form $\hat{y} = a(10^{bx})$ that has a smaller sum of squared residuals for the *original* data than the one we obtained using transformations. Finding the least-squares estimates for $a$ and $b$ in an equation of this form is complicated. Fortunately, the curves found using transformations usually provide reasonable predictions of $y$.

■ **Power Transformations**   Frequently, an appropriate transformation is suggested by the data. One type of transformation that statisticians have found useful for straightening a plot is a **power transformation**. A power (exponent) is first selected, and each original value is raised to that power to obtain the corresponding transformed value. Table 5.5 displays a "ladder" of the most frequently used power transformations. The power 1 corresponds to no transformation at all. Using the power 0 would transform every value to 1, which is certainly not informative, so statisticians use the logarithmic transformation in its place in the ladder of transformations. Other powers intermediate to or more extreme than those listed can be used, of course, but they are less frequently needed than those on the ladder. Notice that all the transformations previously presented are included in this ladder.

**Table 5.5**  Power Transformation Ladder

| Power | Transformed Value | Name |
|---|---|---|
| 3 | (Original value)$^3$ | Cube |
| 2 | (Original value)$^2$ | Square |
| 1 | (Original value) | No transformation |
| $\frac{1}{2}$ | $\sqrt{\text{Original value}}$ | Square root |
| $\frac{1}{3}$ | $\sqrt[3]{\text{Original value}}$ | Cube root |
| 0 | Log(Original value) | Logarithm |
| $-1$ | $\dfrac{1}{\text{Original value}}$ | Reciprocal |

Figure 5.31 is designed to suggest where on the ladder we should go to find an appropriate transformation. The four curved segments, labeled 1, 2, 3, and 4, represent shapes of curved scatterplots that are commonly encountered. Suppose that a scatterplot

**Figure 5.31** Scatterplot shapes and where to go on the transformation ladder to straighten the plot.

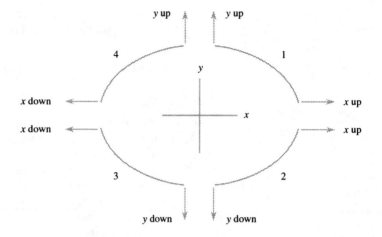

looks like the curve labeled 1. Then, to straighten the plot, we should use a power of $x$ that is up the ladder from the no-transformation row ($x^2$ or $x^3$) and/or a power on $y$ that is also up the ladder from the power 1. Thus, we might be led to squaring each $x$ value, cubing each $y$, and plotting the transformed pairs. If the curvature looks like curved segment 2, a power up the ladder from no transformation for $x$ and/or a power down the ladder for $y$ (e.g., $\sqrt{y}$ or $\log(y)$) should be used.

The scatterplot for the tortilla chip data (Figure 5.29(a)) has the pattern of segment 3 in Figure 5.31. This suggests going down the ladder of transformations for $x$ and/or for $y$. We found that transforming the $y$ values in this data set by taking logarithms worked well, and this is consistent with the suggestion of going down the ladder of transformations for $y$.

## Example 5.18 A Nonlinear Model: Iron Absorption and Polyphenol Content of Foods

● In many parts of the world, a typical diet consists mainly of cereals and grains, and many individuals suffer from a substantial iron deficiency. The article "The Effects of Organic Acids, Phytates, and Polyphenols on the Absorption of Iron from Vegetables" (*British Journal of Nutrition* [1983]: 331–342) reported the data in Table 5.6 on $x$ = proportion of iron absorbed and $y$ = polyphenol content (in milligrams per gram) when a particular food is consumed.

The scatterplot of the data in Figure 5.32(a) shows a clear curved pattern, which resembles the curved segment 3 in Figure 5.31. This suggests that $x$ and/or $y$ should be transformed by a power transformation down the ladder from 1. The authors of the article applied a square root transformation to both $x$ and $y$. The resulting scatterplot in Figure 5.32(b) is reasonably straight.

● Data set available online

**Table 5.6**   Original and Transformed Data for Example 5.18

| Vegetable | x | y | $\sqrt{x}$ | $\sqrt{y}$ |
|---|---|---|---|---|
| Wheat germ | .007 | 6.4 | .083666 | 2.52982 |
| Aubergine | .007 | 3.0 | .083666 | 1.73205 |
| Butter beans | .012 | 2.9 | .109545 | 1.70294 |
| Spinach | .014 | 5.8 | .118322 | 2.40832 |
| Brown lentils | .024 | 5.0 | .154919 | 2.23607 |
| Beetroot greens | .024 | 4.3 | .154919 | 2.07364 |
| Green lentils | .032 | 3.4 | .178885 | 1.84391 |
| Carrot | .096 | .7 | .309839 | .83666 |
| Potato | .115 | .2 | .339116 | .44721 |
| Beetroot | .185 | 1.5 | .430116 | 1.22474 |
| Pumpkin | .206 | .1 | .453872 | .31623 |
| Tomato | .224 | .3 | .473286 | .54772 |
| Broccoli | .260 | .4 | .509902 | .63246 |
| Cauliflower | .263 | .7 | .512835 | .83666 |
| Cabbage | .320 | .1 | .565685 | .31623 |
| Turnip | .327 | .3 | .571839 | .54772 |
| Sauerkraut | .327 | .2 | .571839 | .44721 |

**Figure 5.32**   Scatterplot of data of Example 5.18: (a) original data; (b) data transformed by taking square roots.

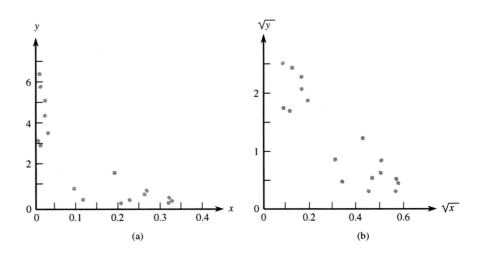

Using MINITAB to fit a least-squares line to the transformed data ($y' = \sqrt{y}$ and $x' = \sqrt{x}$) results in the following output:

**Regression Analysis**

The regression equation is
sqrt $y$ = 2.45 − 3.72 sqrt $x$

| Predictor | Coef | StDev | T | P |
|---|---|---|---|---|
| Constant | 2.4483 | 0.1833 | 13.35 | 0.000 |
| Sqrt $x$ | −3.7247 | 0.4836 | −7.70 | 0.000 |

S = 0.3695   R-Sq = 79.8%   R-Sq(adj) = 78.5%

The corresponding least-squares line is

$$\hat{y}' = 2.45 - 3.72x'$$

This transformation can be reversed by squaring both sides to obtain an equation of the form $y$ = some function of $x$:

$$\hat{y}'^2 = (2.45 - 3.72x')^2$$

Since $y'^2 = y$ and $x' = \sqrt{x}$ we get

$$\hat{y} = (2.45 - 3.72\sqrt{x})^2$$

■

■ **Exercises 5.52–5.60** ...................................................................

**5.52** ● The following data on $x$ = frying time (in seconds) and $y$ = moisture content (%) appeared in the paper "Thermal and Physical Properties of Tortilla Chips as a Function of Frying Time" (*Journal of Food Processing and Preservation* [1995]: 175–189):

| $x$ | 5 | 10 | 15 | 20 | 25 | 30 | 45 | 60 |
|---|---|---|---|---|---|---|---|---|
| $y$ | 16.3 | 9.7 | 8.1 | 4.2 | 3.4 | 2.9 | 1.9 | 1.3 |

a. Construct a scatterplot of the data. Would a straight line provide an effective summary of the relationship?
b. Here are the values of $x' = \log(x)$ and $y' = \log(y)$:

| $x'$ | 0.70 | 1.00 | 1.18 | 1.30 | 1.40 | 1.48 | 1.65 | 1.78 |
|---|---|---|---|---|---|---|---|---|
| $y'$ | 1.21 | 0.99 | 0.91 | 0.62 | 0.53 | 0.46 | 0.28 | 0.11 |

Construct a scatterplot of these transformed data, and comment on the pattern.
c. Based on the accompanying MINITAB output, does the least-squares line effectively summarize the relationship between $y'$ and $x'$?

The regression equation is
log(moisture) = 2.02 – 1.05 log(time)

| Predictor | Coef | SE Coef | T | P |
|---|---|---|---|---|
| Constant | 2.01780 | 0.09584 | 21.05 | 0.000 |
| log(time) | –1.05171 | 0.07091 | –14.83 | 0.000 |

S = 0.0657067    R-Sq = 97.3%    R-Sq(adj) = 96.9%

**Analysis of Variance**

| Source | DF | SS | MS | F | P |
|---|---|---|---|---|---|
| Regression | 1 | 0.94978 | 0.94978 | 219.99 | 0.000 |
| Residual Error | 6 | 0.02590 | 0.00432 | | |
| Total | 7 | 0.97569 | | | |

d. Use the MINITAB output to predict moisture content when frying time is 35 sec.
e. Do you think that predictions of moisture content using the model in Part (c) will be better than those using the model fit in Example 5.16, which used transformed $y$ values but did not transform $x$? Explain.

**5.53** ● ▼ The report "Older Driver Involvement in Injury Crashes in Texas" (Texas Transportation Institute, 2004) included a scatterplot of $y$ = fatality rate (percentage of drivers killed in injury crashes) versus $x$ = driver age. The accompanying data are approximate values read from the scatterplot.

| Age | Fatality Rate | Age | Fatality Rate |
|---|---|---|---|
| 40 | 0.75 | 80 | 2.20 |
| 45 | 0.75 | 85 | 3.00 |
| 50 | 0.95 | 90 | 3.20 |
| 55 | 1.05 | | |

a. Construct a scatterplot of these data.
b. Using Table 5.5 and the ladder of transformations in Figure 5.31, suggest a transformation that might result in variables for which the scatterplot would exhibit a pattern that was more nearly linear.
c. Reexpress $x$ and/or $y$ using the transformation you recommended in Part (b). Construct a scatterplot of the transformed data.

**Bold** exercises answered in back    ● Data set available online but not required    ▼ Video solution available

d. Does the scatterplot in Part (c) suggest that the transformation was successful in straightening the plot?
e. Using the transformed variables, fit the least-squares line and use it to predict the fatality rate for 78-year-old drivers.

5.54 ● The paper "Aspects of Food Finding by Wintering Bald Eagles" (*The Auk* [1983]: 477–484) examined the relationship between the time that eagles spend aerially searching for food (indicated by the percentage of eagles soaring) and relative food availability. The accompanying data were taken from a scatterplot that appeared in this paper. Let $x$ denote salmon availability and $y$ denote the percentage of eagles in the air.

| $x$ | 0 | 0 | 0.2 | 0.5 | 0.5 | 1.0 |
|-----|------|------|------|------|------|------|
| $y$ | 28.2 | 69.0 | 27.0 | 38.5 | 48.4 | 31.1 |
| $x$ | 1.2 | 1.9 | 2.6 | 3.3 | 4.7 | 6.5 |
| $y$ | 26.9 | 8.2 | 4.6 | 7.4 | 7.0 | 6.8 |

a. Draw a scatterplot for this data set. Would you describe the plot as linear or curved?
b. One possible transformation that might lead to a straighter plot involves taking the square root of both the $x$ and $y$ values. Use Figure 5.31 to explain why this might be a reasonable transformation.
c. Construct a scatterplot using the variables $\sqrt{x}$ and $\sqrt{y}$. Is this scatterplot straighter than the scatterplot in Part (a)?
d. Using Table 5.5, suggest another transformation that might be used to straighten the original plot.

5.55 Data on salmon availability ($x$) and the percentage of eagles in the air ($y$) were given in the previous exercise.
a. Calculate the correlation coefficient for these data.
b. Because the scatterplot of the original data appeared curved, transforming both the $x$ and $y$ values by taking square roots was suggested. Calculate the correlation coefficient for the variables $\sqrt{x}$ and $\sqrt{y}$. How does this value compare with that calculated in Part (a)? Does this indicate that the transformation was successful in straightening the plot?

5.56 ● The article "Organ Transplant Demand Rises Five Times as Fast as Existing Supply" (*San Luis Obispo Tribune*, February 23, 2001) included a graph that showed the number of people waiting for organ transplants each

year from 1990 to 1999. The following data are approximate values and were read from the graph in the article:

| Year | Number Waiting for Transplant (in thousands) |
|------|------|
| 1 (1990) | 22 |
| 2 | 25 |
| 3 | 29 |
| 4 | 33 |
| 5 | 38 |
| 6 | 44 |
| 7 | 50 |
| 8 | 57 |
| 9 | 64 |
| 10 (1999) | 72 |

a. Construct a scatterplot of the data with $y$ = number waiting for transplant and $x$ = year. Describe how the number of people waiting for transplants has changed over time from 1990 to 1999.
b. The scatterplot in Part (a) is shaped like segment 2 in Figure 5.31. Find a transformation of $x$ and/or $y$ that straightens the plot. Construct a scatterplot for your transformed variables.
c. Using the transformed variables from Part (b), fit a least-squares line and use it to predict the number waiting for an organ transplant in 2000 (Year 11).
d. The prediction made in Part (c) involves prediction for an $x$ value that is outside the range of the $x$ values in the sample. What assumption must you be willing to make for this to be reasonable? Do you think this assumption is reasonable in this case? Would your answer be the same if the prediction had been for the year 2010 rather than 2000? Explain.

5.57 ● A study, described in the paper "Prediction of Defibrillation Success from a Single Defibrillation Threshold Measurement" (*Circulation* [1988]: 1144–1149) investigated the relationship between defibrillation success and the energy of the defibrillation shock (expressed as a multiple of the defibrillation threshold) and presented the following data:

| Energy of Shock | Success (%) |
|-----------------|-------------|
| 0.5 | 33.3 |
| 1.0 | 58.3 |
| 1.5 | 81.8 |
| 2.0 | 96.7 |
| 2.5 | 100.0 |

**a.** Construct a scatterplot of $y$ = success and $x$ = energy of shock. Does the relationship appear to be linear or nonlinear?

**b.** Fit a least-squares line to the given data, and construct a residual plot. Does the residual plot support your conclusion in Part (a)? Explain.

**c.** Consider transforming the data by leaving $y$ unchanged and using either $x' = \sqrt{x}$ or $x'' = \log(x)$. Which of these transformations would you recommend? Justify your choice by appealing to appropriate graphical displays.

**d.** Using the transformation you recommended in Part (c), find the equation of the least-squares line that describes the relationship between $y$ and the transformed $x$.

**e.** What would you predict success to be when the energy of shock is 1.75 times the threshold level? When it is 0.8 times the threshold level?

**5.58** ◉ Penicillin was administered orally to five different horses, and concentration of penicillin in the blood was determined after five different lengths of time. The following data appeared in the paper "Absorption and Distribution Patterns of Oral Phenoxymethyl Penicillin in the Horse" (*Cornell Veterinarian* [1983]: 314–323):

**$x$ (time elapsed, hr)**

| 1 | 2 | 3 | 6 | 8 |
|---|---|---|---|---|

**$y$ (penicillin concentration, mg/ml)**

| 1.8 | 1.0 | 0.5 | 0.1 | 0.1 |
|-----|-----|-----|-----|-----|

Construct scatterplots using the following variables. Which transformation, if any, would you recommend?

a. $x$ and $y$      c. $x$ and $\sqrt{y}$
b. $\sqrt{x}$ and $y$      d. $\sqrt{x}$ and $\sqrt{y}$
e. $x$ and $\log(y)$ (values of $\log(y)$ are 0.26, 0, −0.30, −1, and −1)

**5.59** ◉ The paper "Population Pressure and Agricultural Intensity" (*Annals of the Association of American Geographers* [1977]: 384–396) reported a positive association between population density and agricultural intensity. The following data consist of measures of population density ($x$) and agricultural intensity ($y$) for 18 different subtropical locations:

| $x$ | 1.0 | 26.0 | 1.1 | 101.0 | 14.9 | 134.7 |
|-----|-----|------|-----|-------|------|-------|
| $y$ | 9 | 7 | 6 | 50 | 5 | 100 |
| $x$ | 3.0 | 5.7 | 7.6 | 25.0 | 143.0 | 27.5 |
| $y$ | 7 | 14 | 14 | 10 | 50 | 14 |
| $x$ | 103.0 | 180.0 | 49.6 | 140.6 | 140.0 | 233.0 |
| $y$ | 50 | 150 | 10 | 67 | 100 | 100 |

**a.** Construct a scatterplot of $y$ versus $x$. Is the scatterplot compatible with the statement of positive association made in the paper?

**b.** The scatterplot in Part (a) is curved upward like segment 2 in Figure 5.31, suggesting a transformation that is up the ladder for $x$ or down the ladder for $y$. Try a scatterplot that uses $y$ and $x^2$. Does this transformation straighten the plot?

**c.** Draw a scatterplot that uses $\log(y)$ and $x$. The $\log(y)$ values, given in order corresponding to the $y$ values, are 0.95, 0.85, 0.78, 1.70, 0.70, 2.00, 0.85, 1.15, 1.15, 1.00, 1.70, 1.15, 1.70, 2.18, 1.00, 1.83, 2.00, and 2.00. How does this scatterplot compare with that of Part (b)?

**d.** Now consider a scatterplot that uses transformations on both $x$ and $y$: $\log(y)$ and $x^2$. Is this effective in straightening the plot? Explain.

**5.60** ◉ Determining the age of an animal can sometimes be a difficult task. One method of estimating the age of harp seals is based on the width of the pulp canal in the seal's canine teeth. To investigate the relationship between age and the width of the pulp canal, researchers measured age and canal width in seals of known age. The following data on $x$ = age (in years) and $y$ = canal length (in millimeters) are a portion of a larger data set that appeared in the paper "Validation of Age Estimation in the Harp Seal Using Dentinal Annuli" (*Canadian Journal of Fisheries and Aquatic Science* [1983]: 1430–1441):

| $x$ | 0.25 | 0.25 | 0.50 | 0.50 | 0.50 | 0.75 | 0.75 | 1.00 |
|-----|------|------|------|------|------|------|------|------|
| $y$ | 700 | 675 | 525 | 500 | 400 | 350 | 300 | 300 |
| $x$ | 1.00 | 1.00 | 1.00 | 1.00 | 1.25 | 1.25 | 1.50 | 1.50 |
| $y$ | 250 | 230 | 150 | 100 | 200 | 100 | 100 | 125 |
| $x$ | 2.00 | 2.00 | 2.50 | 2.75 | 3.00 | 4.00 | 4.00 | 5.00 |
| $y$ | 60 | 140 | 60 | 50 | 10 | 10 | 10 | 10 |
| $x$ | 5.00 | 5.00 | 5.00 | 6.00 | 6.00 | | | |
| $y$ | 15 | 10 | 10 | 15 | 10 | | | |

Construct a scatterplot for this data set. Would you describe the relationship between age and canal length as linear? If not, suggest a transformation that might straighten the plot.

## 5.6 Interpreting and Communicating the Results of Statistical Analyses

Using either a least-squares line to summarize a linear relationship or a correlation coefficient to describe the strength of a linear relationship is common in investigations that focus on more than a single variable. In fact, the methods described in this chapter are among the most widely used of all statistical tools. When numerical bivariate data are analyzed in journal articles and other published sources, it is common to find a scatterplot of the data and a least-squares line or a correlation coefficient.

### ■ Communicating the Results of Statistical Analyses

When reporting the results of a data analysis involving bivariate numerical data, it is important to include graphical displays as well as numerical summaries. Including a scatterplot and providing a description of what the plot reveals about the form of the relationship between the two variables under study establish the context in which numerical summary measures, such as the correlation coefficient or the equation of the least-squares line, can be interpreted.

In general, the goal of an analysis of bivariate data is to give a quantitative description of the relationship, if any, between the two variables. If there is a relationship, you can describe how strong or weak the relationship is or model the relationship in a way that allows various conclusions to be drawn. If the goal of the study is to describe the strength of the relationship and the scatterplot shows a linear pattern, you can report the value of the correlation coefficient or the coefficient of determination as a measure of the strength of the linear relationship. When you interpret the value of the correlation coefficient, it is a good idea to relate the interpretation to the pattern observed in the scatterplot. This is especially important before making a statement of no relationship between two variables, because a correlation coefficient near 0 does not necessarily imply that there is no relationship of any form. Similarly, a correlation coefficient near 1 or $-1$, by itself, does not guarantee that the relationship is linear. A curved pattern, such as the one we saw in Figure 5.15, can produce a correlation coefficient that is near 1.

If the goal of a study is prediction, then, when you report the results of the study, you should not only give a scatterplot and the equation of the least-squares line but also address how well the linear prediction model fits the data. At a minimum, you should include both the values of $s_e$ (the standard deviation about the regression line) and $r^2$ (the coefficient of determination). Including a residual plot can also provide support for the appropriateness of the linear model for describing the relationship between the two variables.

### ■ What to Look for in Published Data

Here are a few things to consider when you read an article that includes an analysis of bivariate data:

- What two variables are being studied? Are they both numerical? Is a distinction made between a dependent variable and an independent variable?
- Does the article include a scatterplot of the data? If so, does there appear to be a relationship between the two variables? Can the relationship be described as linear, or is some type of nonlinear relationship a more appropriate description?

※ Does the relationship between the two variables appear to be weak or strong? Is the value of a correlation coefficient reported?

※ If the least-squares line is used to summarize the relationship between the dependent and independent variables, is any measure of goodness of fit reported, such as $r^2$ or $s_e$? How are these values interpreted, and what do they imply about the usefulness of the least-squares line?

※ If a correlation coefficient is reported, is it interpreted properly? Be cautious of interpretations that claim a causal relationship.

The article "Rubbish Regression and the Census Undercount" (*Chance* [1992]: 33) describes work done by the Garbage Project at the University of Arizona. Project researchers had analyzed different categories of garbage for a number of households. They were asked by the Census Bureau to see whether any of the garbage data variables were related to household size. They reported that "the weight data for different categories of garbage were plotted on graphs against data on household size, dwelling by dwelling, and the resulting scatterplots were analyzed to see in which categories the weight showed a steady, monotonic rise relative to household size."

The researchers determined that the strongest linear relationship appeared to be that between the amount of plastic discarded and household size. The line used to summarize this relationship was stated to be $\hat{y} = 0.2815x$, where $y$ = household size and $x$ = weight (in pounds) of plastic during a 5-week collection. Note that this line has an intercept of 0. Scientists at the Census Bureau believed that this relationship would extend to entire neighborhoods, and so the amount of plastic discarded by a neighborhood could be measured (rather than having to measure house to house) and then used to approximate the neighborhood size.

An example of the use of $r^2$ and the correlation coefficient is found in the article "Affective Variables Related to Mathematics Achievement Among High-Risk College Freshmen" (*Psychological Reports* [1991]: 399–403). The researchers wrote that "an examination of the Pearson correlations indicated that the two scales, Confidence in Learning Mathematics and Mathematics Anxiety, were highly related, with values ranging from .87 to .91 for the men, women, and for the total group. Such a high relationship indicates that the two scales are measuring essentially the same concept, so for further analysis, one of the two scales could be eliminated."

The reported correlation coefficients (from .87 to .91) indicate a strong positive linear relationship between scores on the two scales. Students who scored high on the Confidence in Learning Mathematics scale tended also to score high on the Mathematics Anxiety scale. (The researchers explain that a high score on the Mathematics Anxiety scale corresponds to low anxiety toward mathematics.) We should be cautious of the statement that the two scales are measuring essentially the same concept. Although that interpretation may make sense in this context, given what the researchers know about these two scales, it does not follow solely from the fact that the two are highly correlated. (For example, there might be a correlation between number of years of education and income, but it would be hard to argue that these two variables are measuring the same thing!)

The same article also states that Mathematics Anxiety score accounted for 27% of the variability in first-quarter math grades. The reported value of 27% is the value of $r^2$ converted to a percentage. Although a value of 27% ($r^2 = .27$) may not seem particularly large, it is in fact surprising that the variable *Math Anxiety score* would be able to explain more than one-fourth of the student-to-student variability in first-quarter math grades.

## ■ A Word to the Wise: Cautions and Limitations ..............................................

There are a number of ways to get into trouble when analyzing bivariate numerical data! Here are some of the things you need to keep in mind when conducting your own analyses or when reading reports of such analyses:

1. Correlation does not imply causation. A common media blunder is to infer a cause-and-effect relationship between two variables simply because there is a strong correlation between them. Don't fall into this trap! A strong correlation implies only that the two variables tend to vary together in a predictable way, but there are many possible explanations for why this is occurring besides one variable causing changes in the other.

   For example, the article "Ban Cell Phones? You May as Well Ban Talking Instead" (*USA Today*, April 27, 2000) gave data that showed a strong negative correlation between the number of cell phone subscribers and traffic fatality rates. During the years from 1985 to 1998, the number of cell phone subscribers increased from 200,000 to 60,800,000, and the number of traffic deaths per 100 million miles traveled decreased from 2.5 to 1.6 over the same period. However, based on this correlation alone, the conclusion that cell phone use improves road safety is not reasonable!

   Similarly, the *Calgary Herald* (April 16, 2002) reported that heavy and moderate drinkers earn more than light drinkers or those who do not drink. Based on the correlation between number of drinks consumed and income, the author of the study concluded that moderate drinking "causes" higher earnings. This is obviously a misleading statement, but at least the article goes on to state that "there are many possible reasons for the correlation. It could be because better-off men simply choose to buy more alcohol. Or it might have something to do with stress: Maybe those with stressful jobs tend to earn more after controlling for age, occupation, etc., and maybe they also drink more in order to deal with the stress."

2. A correlation coefficient near 0 does not necessarily imply that there is no relationship between two variables. Before such an interpretation can be given, it is important to examine a scatterplot of the data carefully. Although it may be true that the variables are unrelated, there may in fact be a strong but nonlinear relationship.

3. The least-squares line for predicting $y$ from $x$ is not the same line as the least-squares line for predicting $x$ from $y$. The least-squares line is, by definition, the line that has the smallest possible sum of squared deviations of points from the line *in the y direction* (it minimizes $\sum(y - \hat{y})^2$). The line that minimizes the sum of squared deviations in the $y$ direction is not generally the same as the line that minimizes the sum of the squared deviations in the $x$ direction. So, for example, it is not appropriate to fit a line to data using $y$ = house price and $x$ = house size and then use the resulting least-squares line Price = $a + b$(Size) to predict the size of a house by substituting in a price and then solving for size. Make sure that the dependent and independent variables are clearly identified and that the appropriate line is fit.

4. Beware of extrapolation. It is dangerous to assume that a linear model fit to data is valid over a wider range of $x$ values. Using the least-squares line to make predictions outside the range of $x$ values in the data set often leads to poor predictions.

5. Be careful in interpreting the value of the slope and intercept in the least-squares line. In particular, in many instances interpreting the intercept as the value of $y$ that would be predicted when $x = 0$ is equivalent to extrapolating way beyond the range of the $x$ values in the data set, and this should be avoided unless $x = 0$ is within the range of the data.

6. Remember that the least-squares line may be the "best" line (in that it has a smaller sum of squared deviations than any other line), but that doesn't necessarily mean that the line will produce good predictions. Be cautious of predictions based on a least-squares line without any information about the adequacy of the linear model, such as $s_e$ and $r^2$.

7. It is not enough to look at just $r^2$ or just $s_e$ when assessing a linear model. These two measures address different aspects of the fit of the line. In general, we would like to have a small value for $s_e$ (which indicates that deviations from the line tend to be small) and a large value for $r^2$ (which indicates that the linear relationship explains a large proportion of the variability in the $y$ values). It is possible to have a small $s_e$ combined with a small $r^2$ or a large $r^2$ combined with a large $s_e$. Remember to consider both values.

8. The value of the correlation coefficient as well as the values for the intercept and slope of the least-squares line can be sensitive to influential observations in the data set, particularly if the sample size is small. Because potentially influential observations are those whose $x$ values are far away from most of the $x$ values in the data set, it is important to look for such observations when examining the scatterplot. (Another good reason for *always* starting with a plot of the data!)

9. If the relationship between two variables is nonlinear, it is preferable to model the relationship using a nonlinear model rather than fitting a line to the data. A plot of the residuals from a linear fit is particularly useful in determining whether a nonlinear model would be a more appropriate choice.

## A c t i v i t y **5.1**  Exploring Correlation and Regression Technology Activity (Applets)

CENGAGENOW

Explore this applet activity

Open the applet (available in CengageNOW at www.cengage.com/login) called CorrelationPoints. You should see a screen like the one shown below.

1. Using the mouse, you can click to add points to form a scatterplot. The value of the correlation coefficient for the data in the plot at any given time (once you have two or more points in the plot) will be displayed at the top of the screen. Try to add points to obtain a correlation coefficient

that is close to −.8. Briefly describe the factors that influenced where you placed the points.

2. Reset the plot (by clicking on the Reset bar in the lower left corner of the screen) and add points trying to produce a data set with a correlation that is close to +.4. Briefly describe the factors that influenced where you placed the points.

Now open the applet called RegDecomp. You should see a screen that looks like the one shown here:

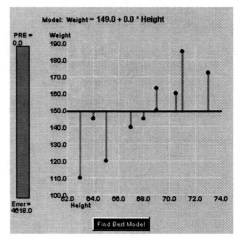

The black points in the plot represent the data set, and the blue line represents a possible line that might be used to describe the relationship between the two variables shown. The pink lines in the graph represent the deviations of points from the line, and the pink bar on the left-hand side of the display depicts the sum of squared errors for the line shown.

3. Using your mouse, you can move the line and see how the deviations from the line and the sum of squared errors change as the line changes. Try to move the line into a position that you think is close to the least-squares regression line. When you think you are close to the line that minimizes the sum of squared errors, you can click on the bar that says "Find Best Model" to see how close you were to the actual least-squares line.

## A c t i v i t y   **5.2**   Age and Flexibility

**Materials needed:** Yardsticks.

In this activity you will investigate the relationship between age and a measure of flexibility. Flexibility will be measured by asking a person to bend at the waist as far as possible, extending his or her arms toward the floor. Using a yardstick, measure the distance from the floor to the fingertip closest to the floor.

1. Age and the measure of flexibility just described will be measured for a group of individuals. Our goal is to determine whether there is a relationship between age and this measure of flexibility. What are two reasons why it would not be a good idea to use just the students in your class as the subjects for your study?

2. Working as a class, decide on a reasonable way to collect data on the two variables of interest.

3. After your class has collected appropriate data, use them to construct a scatterplot. Comment on the interesting features of the plot. Does it look like there is a relationship between age and flexibility?

4. If there appears to be a relationship between age and flexibility, fit a model that is appropriate for describing the relationship.

5. *In the context of this activity*, write a brief description of the danger of extrapolation.

# Summary of Key Concepts and Formulas

| Term or Formula | Comment |
|---|---|
| Scatterplot | A picture of bivariate numerical data in which each observation $(x, y)$ is represented as a point located with respect to a horizontal $x$ axis and a vertical $y$ axis. |
| Pearson's sample correlation coefficient $$r = \frac{\sum z_x z_y}{n - 1}$$ | A measure of the extent to which sample $x$ and $y$ values are linearly related; $-1 \leq r \leq 1$, so values close to 1 or $-1$ indicate a strong linear relationship. |
| Principle of least squares | The method used to select a line that summarizes an approximate linear relationship between $x$ and $y$. The least-squares line is the line that minimizes the sum of the squared vertical deviations for the points in the scatterplot. |

| Term or Formula | Comment |
|---|---|
| $b = \dfrac{\sum(x - \bar{x})(y - \bar{y})}{\sum(x - \bar{x})^2} = \dfrac{\sum xy - \dfrac{(\sum x)(\sum y)}{n}}{\sum x^2 - \dfrac{(\sum x)^2}{n}}$ | The slope of the least-squares line. |
| $a = \bar{y} - b\bar{x}$ | The intercept of the least-squares line. |
| Predicted (fitted) values $\hat{y}_1, \hat{y}_2, \ldots, \hat{y}_n$ | Obtained by substituting the $x$ value for each observation into the least-squares line; $\hat{y}_1 = a + bx_1, \ldots, \hat{y}_n = a + bx_n$ |
| Residuals | Obtained by subtracting each predicted value from the corresponding observed $y$ value: $y_1 - \hat{y}_1, \ldots, y_n - \hat{y}_n$. These are the vertical deviations from the least-squares line. |
| Residual plot | Scatterplot of the $(x, \text{residual})$ pairs. Isolated points or a pattern of points in a residual plot are indicative of potential problems. |
| Residual (error) sum of squares $\text{SSResid} = \sum(y - \hat{y})^2$ | The sum of the squared residuals is a measure of $y$ variation that cannot be attributed to an approximate linear relationship (unexplained variation). |
| Total sum of squares $\text{SSTo} = \sum(y - \bar{y})^2$ | The sum of squared deviations from the sample mean is a measure of total variation in the observed $y$ values. |
| Coefficient of determination $r^2 = 1 - \dfrac{\text{SSResid}}{\text{SSTo}}$ | The proportion of variation in observed $y$'s that can be attributed to an approximate linear relationship. |
| Standard deviation about the least-squares line $s_e = \sqrt{\dfrac{\text{SSResid}}{n - 2}}$ | The size of a "typical" deviation from the least-squares line. |
| Transformation | A simple function of the $x$ and/or $y$ variable, which is then used in a regression. |
| Power transformation | An exponent, or power, $p$, is first specified, and then new (transformed) data values are calculated as *transformed value* = (original value)$^p$. A logarithmic transformation is identified with $p = 0$. When the scatterplot of original data exhibits curvature, a power transformation of $x$ and/or $y$ will often result in a scatterplot that has a linear appearance. |
| Logistic regression equation $p = \dfrac{e^{a+bx}}{1 + e^{a+bx}}$ | The graph of this equation is an S-shaped curve. The logistic regression equation is used to describe the relationship between the probability of success and a numerical predictor variable. |

# Chapter Review Exercises 5.66–5.78

**5.66** ● The accompanying data represent $x$ = the amount of catalyst added to accelerate a chemical reaction and $y$ = the resulting reaction time:

| $x$ | 1 | 2 | 3 | 4 | 5 |
|---|---|---|---|---|---|
| $y$ | 49 | 46 | 41 | 34 | 25 |

a. Calculate $r$. Does the value of $r$ suggest a strong linear relationship?
b. Construct a scatterplot. From the plot, does the word *linear* really provide the most effective description of the relationship between $x$ and $y$? Explain.

**5.67** ● The article "The Epiphytic Lichen *Hypogymnia physodes* as a Bioindicator of Atmospheric Nitrogen and Sulphur Deposition in Norway" (*Environmental Monitoring and Assessment* [1993]: 27–47) gives the following data (read from a graph in the paper) on $x$ = $NO_3$ wet deposition (in grams per cubic meter) and $y$ = lichen (% dry weight):

| $x$ | 0.05 | 0.10 | 0.11 | 0.12 | 0.31 |
|---|---|---|---|---|---|
| $y$ | 0.48 | 0.55 | 0.48 | 0.50 | 0.58 |
| $x$ | 0.37 | 0.42 | 0.58 | 0.68 | 0.68 |
| $y$ | 0.52 | 1.02 | 0.86 | 0.86 | 1.00 |
| $x$ | 0.73 | 0.85 | 0.92 | | |
| $y$ | 0.88 | 1.04 | 1.70 | | |

**a.** What is the equation of the least-squares regression line?
**b.** Predict lichen dry weight percentage for an $NO_3$ deposition of 0.5 g/m$^3$.

**5.68** ● Athletes competing in a triathlon participated in a study described in the paper "Myoglobinemia and Endurance Exercise" (*American Journal of Sports Medicine* [1984]: 113–118). The following data on finishing time $x$ (in hours) and myoglobin level $y$ (in nanograms per milliliter) were read from a scatterplot in the paper:

| $x$ | 4.90 | 4.70 | 5.35 | 5.22 | 5.20 |
|---|---|---|---|---|---|
| $y$ | 1590 | 1550 | 1360 | 895 | 865 |
| $x$ | 5.40 | 5.70 | 6.00 | 6.20 | 6.10 |
| $y$ | 905 | 895 | 910 | 700 | 675 |
| $x$ | 5.60 | 5.35 | 5.75 | 5.35 | 6.00 |
| $y$ | 540 | 540 | 440 | 380 | 300 |

a. Obtain the equation of the least-squares line.
b. Interpret the value of $b$.
c. What happens if the line in Part (a) is used to predict the myoglobin level for a finishing time of 8 hr? Is this reasonable? Explain.

**5.69** The paper "Root Dentine Transparency: Age Determination of Human Teeth Using Computerized Densitometric Analysis" (*American Journal of Physical Anthropology* [1991]: 25–30) reported on an investigation of methods for age determination based on tooth characteristics. With $y$ = age (in years) and $x$ = percentage of root with transparent dentine, a regression analysis for premolars gave $n$ = 36, SSResid = 5987.16, and SSTo = 17,409.60. Calculate and interpret the values of $r^2$ and $s_e$.

**5.70** ● The paper cited in Exercise 5.69 gave a scatterplot in which $x$ values were for anterior teeth. Consider the following representative subset of the data:

| $x$ | 15 | 19 | 31 | 39 | 41 |
|---|---|---|---|---|---|
| $y$ | 23 | 52 | 65 | 55 | 32 |
| $x$ | 44 | 47 | 48 | 55 | 65 |
| $y$ | 60 | 78 | 59 | 61 | 60 |

$$\sum x = 404 \quad \sum xy = 18{,}448 \quad \sum y = 545$$
$$a = 32.080888 \quad b = 0.554929$$

a. Calculate the predicted values and residuals.
b. Use the results of Part (a) to obtain SSResid and $r^2$.
c. Does the least-squares line appear to give accurate predictions? Explain your reasoning.

**5.71** ● The following data on the relationship between degree of exposure to $^{242}$Cm alpha radiation particles ($x$) and the percentage of exposed cells without aberrations ($y$) appeared in the paper "Chromosome Aberrations Induced in Human Lymphocytes by DT Neutrons" (*Radiation Research* [1984]: 561–573):

| $x$ | 0.106 | 0.193 | 0.511 | 0.527 |
|---|---|---|---|---|
| $y$ | 98 | 95 | 87 | 85 |
| $x$ | 1.08 | 1.62 | 1.73 | 2.36 |
| $y$ | 75 | 72 | 64 | 55 |
| $x$ | 2.72 | 3.12 | 3.88 | 4.18 |
| $y$ | 44 | 41 | 37 | 40 |

**Bold** exercises answered in back    ● Data set available online but not required    ▼ Video solution available

Summary quantities are

$$n = 12 \qquad \sum x = 22.207 \qquad \sum y = 793$$
$$\sum x^2 = 62.600235 \qquad \sum xy = 1114.5 \qquad \sum y^2 = 57,939$$

a. Obtain the equation of the least-squares line.
b. Calculate SSResid and SSTo.
c. What percentage of observed variation in $y$ can be explained by the approximate linear relationship between the two variables?
d. Calculate and interpret the value of $s_e$.
e. Using just the results of Parts (a) and (c), what is the value of Pearson's sample correlation coefficient?

**5.72** ● The article "Reduction in Soluble Protein and Chlorophyll Contents in a Few Plants as Indicators of Automobile Exhaust Pollution" (*International Journal of Environmental Studies* [1983]: 239–244) reported the following data on $x$ = distance from a highway (in meters) and $y$ = lead content of soil at that distance (in parts per million):

| $x$ | 0.3 | 1 | 5 | 10 | 15 | 20 |
|-----|------|------|------|------|------|------|
| $y$ | 62.75 | 37.51 | 29.70 | 20.71 | 17.65 | 15.41 |

| $x$ | 25 | 30 | 40 | 50 | 75 | 100 |
|-----|------|------|------|------|------|------|
| $y$ | 14.15 | 13.50 | 12.11 | 11.40 | 10.85 | 10.85 |

a. Use a statistical computer package to construct scatterplots of $y$ versus $x$, $y$ versus $\log(x)$, $\log(y)$ versus $\log(x)$, and $\frac{1}{y}$ versus $\frac{1}{x}$.
b. Which transformation considered in Part (a) does the best job of producing an approximately linear relationship? Use the selected transformation to predict lead content when distance is 25 m.

**5.73** The sample correlation coefficient between annual raises and teaching evaluations for a sample of $n = 353$ college faculty was found to be $r = .11$ ("Determination of Faculty Pay: An Agency Theory Perspective," *Academy of Management Journal* [1992]: 921–955).
a. Interpret this value.
b. If a straight line were fit to the data using least squares, what proportion of variation in raises could be attributed to the approximate linear relationship between raises and evaluations?

**5.74** ● An accurate assessment of oxygen consumption provides important information for determining energy expenditure requirements for physically demanding tasks. The paper "Oxygen Consumption During Fire Suppression: Error of Heart Rate Estimation" (*Ergonomics* [1991]: 1469–1474) reported on a study in which $x$ = oxygen consumption (in milliliters per kilogram per minute) during a treadmill test was determined for a sample of 10 firefighters. Then $y$ = oxygen consumption at a comparable heart rate was measured for each of the 10 individuals while they performed a fire-suppression simulation. This resulted in the following data and scatterplot:

| Firefighter | 1 | 2 | 3 | 4 | 5 |
|-------------|------|------|------|------|------|
| $x$ | 51.3 | 34.1 | 41.1 | 36.3 | 36.5 |
| $y$ | 49.3 | 29.5 | 30.6 | 28.2 | 28.0 |

| Firefighter | 6 | 7 | 8 | 9 | 10 |
|-------------|------|------|------|------|------|
| $x$ | 35.4 | 35.4 | 38.6 | 40.6 | 39.5 |
| $y$ | 26.3 | 33.9 | 29.4 | 23.5 | 31.6 |

a. Does the scatterplot suggest an approximate linear relationship?
b. The investigators fit a least-squares line. The resulting MINITAB output is given in the following:

```
The regression equation is
firecon = +11.4 + 1.09 treadcon
```

| Predictor | Coef | Stdev | t-ratio | p |
|-----------|--------|-------|---------|-------|
| Constant | −11.37 | 12.46 | −0.91 | 0.388 |
| treadcon | 1.0906 | 0.3181 | 3.43 | 0.009 |

$s = 4.70$   R-sq = 59.5%   R-sq(adj) = 54.4%

Predict fire-simulation consumption when treadmill consumption is 40.
c. How effectively does a straight line summarize the relationship?
d. Delete the first observation, (51.3, 49.3), and calculate the new equation of the least-squares line and the value

of $r^2$. What do you conclude? (Hint: For the original data, $\sum x = 388.8$, $\sum y = 310.3$, $\sum x^2 = 15,338.54$, $\sum xy = 12,306.58$, and $\sum y^2 = 10,072.41$.)

**5.75** ● The relationship between the depth of flooding and the amount of flood damage was examined in the paper "Significance of Location in Computing Flood Damage" (*Journal of Water Resources Planning and Management* [1985]: 65–81). The following data on $x$ = depth of flooding (feet above first-floor level) and $y$ = flood damage (as a percentage of structure value) were obtained using a sample of flood insurance claims:

| $x$ | 1  | 2  | 3  | 4  | 5  | 6  | 7  |
|-----|----|----|----|----|----|----|----|
| $y$ | 10 | 14 | 26 | 28 | 29 | 41 | 43 |
| $x$ | 8  | 9  | 10 | 11 | 12 | 13 |    |
| $y$ | 44 | 45 | 46 | 47 | 48 | 49 |    |

**a.** Obtain the equation of the least-squares line.
**b.** Construct a scatterplot, and draw the least-squares line on the plot. Does it look as though a straight line provides an adequate description of the relationship between $y$ and $x$? Explain.
**c.** Predict flood damage for a structure subjected to 6.5 ft of flooding.
**d.** Would you use the least-squares line to predict flood damage when depth of flooding is 18 ft? Explain.

**5.76** Consider the four $(x, y)$ pairs $(0, 0)$, $(1, 1)$, $(1, -1)$, and $(2, 0)$.
**a.** What is the value of the sample correlation coefficient $r$?
**b.** If a fifth observation is made at the value $x = 6$, find a value of $y$ for which $r > .5$.
**c.** If a fifth observation is made at the value $x = 6$, find a value of $y$ for which $r < .5$.

**5.77** ● The paper "Biomechanical Characteristics of the Final Approach Step, Hurdle, and Take-Off of Elite American Springboard Divers" (*Journal of Human Movement Studies* [1984]: 189–212) gave the following data on $y$ = judge's score and $x$ = length of final step (in meters) for a sample of seven divers performing a forward pike with a single somersault:

| $y$ | 7.40 | 9.10 | 7.20 | 7.00 | 7.30 | 7.30 | 7.90 |
|-----|------|------|------|------|------|------|------|
| $x$ | 1.17 | 1.17 | 0.93 | 0.89 | 0.68 | 0.74 | 0.95 |

**a.** Construct a scatterplot.
**b.** Calculate the slope and intercept of the least-squares line. Draw this line on your scatterplot.
**c.** Calculate and interpret the value of Pearson's sample correlation coefficient.

**5.78** ● The following data on $y$ = concentration of penicillin-G in pig's blood plasma (units per milliliter) and $x$ = time (in minutes) from administration of a dose of penicillin (22 mg/kg body weight) appeared in the paper "Calculation of Dosage Regimens of Antimicrobial Drugs for Surgical Prophylaxis" (*Journal of the American Veterinary Medicine Association* [1984]: 1083–1087):

| $x$ | 5    | 15   | 45   | 90   | 180  |
|-----|------|------|------|------|------|
| $y$ | 32.6 | 43.3 | 23.1 | 16.7 | 5.7  |
| $x$ | 240  | 360  | 480  | 1440 |      |
| $y$ | 6.4  | 9.2  | 0.4  | 0.2  |      |

**a.** Construct a scatterplot for these data.
**b.** Using the ladder of transformations of Section 5.4 (see Figure 5.31 and Table 5.5), suggest a transformation that might straighten the plot. Give reasons for your choice of transformation.

Mentor

Do you need a live tutor for homework problems?

**Thomson** NOW
Are you ready? Take your exam-prep post-test now.

**Bold** exercises answered in back     ● Data set available online but not required     ▼ Video solution available

# Chapter 7

# Population Distributions

This chapter is the first of two that together link the basic ideas of probability explored in Chapter 6 with the techniques of statistical inference. Chapter 6 used probability to describe the long-run frequency of occurrence of various types of outcomes. Here, we introduce probability models that can be used to describe the distribution of characteristics of individuals in a population. In Chapter 8 we will see how such models help us reach conclusions based on a sample from the population.

In this chapter we begin by distinguishing between categorical and numerical variables and between discrete and continuous numerical variables. We show how a continuous numerical variable can be described by a probability distribution curve, which can also be used to make probability statements about values of the variable. Finally, one particular probability model, the normal distribution, is presented in detail.

## 7.1 Describing the Distribution of Values in a Population

In Chapter 1, we described statistical inference as the branch of statistics that involves generalizing from a sample to the population from which it was selected. A population is the entire collection of individuals or objects about which information is desired. Interest usually centers on the value of one or more variables. For example, if one wants to obtain information about the performance of a telephone registration system for selecting college courses, the population would consist of all students at the university who use the phone registration system. The variable of interest (a characteristic of each individual member of the population) might be *time to complete registration*.

A variable can be either categorical or numerical, depending on the possible values of the variable that occur in the population. The variable *time to complete registration* is numerical, because it associates a number with each individual in the population. If interest instead had centered on whether a student was able to complete registration for classes with a single phone call, rather than on the time required to complete registration, the variable of interest, which we might name *first call*, would be categorical. This variable associates a categorical response (successful completion or unsuccessful) with each individual in the population. The variable *class standing* is also categorical, with the four categories freshman, sophomore, junior, and senior.

> **DEFINITION**
>
> A **variable** associates a value with each individual or object in a population. A variable can be either **categorical** or **numerical**, depending on its possible values.

The distribution of categories or values in a population provides important information about the population. For example, if we knew something about the distribution of registration completion times for the population of all students, we might be able to give students an idea of how much time to allow (e.g., most students require 8 to 13 min to complete the registration process) or determine a reasonable amount of time after which a student should be automatically disconnected from the system. The distribution of all the values of a numerical variable or all the categories of a categorical variable is called a **population distribution**.

■ Categorical Variables .......................................................................................

Categorical variables are often dichotomous (having only two possible categories). For example, each individual in the population of students at a state university might be classified as a resident of the state or as a nonresident, or each owner of a Mazda automobile might be classified according to whether he or she would consider purchasing a Mazda the next time around. Each of these variables (*residence status* for the college population or *future purchase* for the population of Mazda owners) is a categorical variable with two possible categories.

...................................................................................................................

# Example 7.1    Residence Status

Consider the variable *residence status* for the population of students at a state university. This variable associates a category (resident or nonresident) with each individual in the population. The population distribution for this variable can be summarized in a bar chart, with a rectangle for each possible category. The height of each rectangle corresponds to the relative frequency (proportion) of the corresponding value in the population. Figure 7.1 shows a possible population distribution for the variable *residence status*. If an individual is randomly selected from this population, the two category relative frequencies can be interpreted as the probabilities of observing each of the two possible categories of residence status. Thus, in the long run, a resident will be selected about 73% of the time, and a nonresident will be selected about 27% of the time.

**Figure 7.1** Population distribution of the variable *residence status* for Example 7.1.

■

Example 7.2    Mode of Transportation

In a study of factors related to air quality, monitors were posted at every entrance to a California university campus on October 10, 2003. From 6 A.M. to 10 P.M., monitors recorded the mode of transportation for each person entering the campus. Based on the information collected, the population distribution of the variable

$$x = \text{mode of transportation}$$

was constructed; it is shown in Figure 7.2.

**Figure 7.2** Population distribution of the variable *mode of transportation* for Example 7.2.

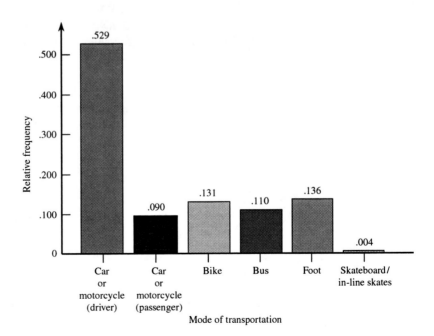

In this example, the population consists of all individuals entering campus on October 10, 2003. The variable $x$ is categorical, with the following possible categories: car or motorcycle (driver), car or motorcycle (passenger), bike, bus, foot, and skateboard or in-line skates. (This was in California!)

If an individual is selected at random from those who were on campus on October 10, 2003, the probability that the selected individual arrived as the driver of a car or motorcycle is .529. The probability that the selected individual arrived by car or motorcycle (either as the driver or as a passenger) is .529 + .090 = .619. The probability that the selected individual arrived on foot is .136.

It is common practice to use special notation when writing probability statements, such as those at the end of Example 7.2. The probability of an outcome is denoted by $P$(outcome). The outcome can be described with words or by using a variable name. Thus, continuing Example 7.2 where the outcome of interest is mode of transportation, we write

$$P(\text{selected individual arrives by bus}) = .110 \quad \text{or} \quad P(x = \text{bus}) = .110$$
$$P(\text{selected individual arrives by bike}) = .131 \quad \text{or} \quad P(x = \text{bike}) = .131$$

## ▪ Numerical Variables

Before considering examples of numerical variables, we must distinguish between two types of such variables.

> **DEFINITION**
>
> Numerical variables can be either discrete or continuous.
>
> A **discrete numerical variable** is one whose possible values are isolated points along the number line.
>
> A **continuous numerical variable** is one whose possible values form an interval along the number line.

The population distribution for a discrete numerical variable can be summarized by a relative frequency histogram, whereas a density histogram is used to summarize the distribution of a continuous numerical variable. The examples that follow demonstrate how this is done.*

## Example 7.3  Pet Ownership

The Department of Animal Regulation released information on pet ownership for the population of all households in a particular county. The variable considered was

$$x = \text{number of licensed dogs or cats for a household}$$

---

*One frequently encountered discrete distribution, the **binomial distribution**, is discussed in the Appendix at the end of this textbook.

**Figure 7.3**  Population distribution of the variable *number of licensed dogs or cats* for Example 7.3.

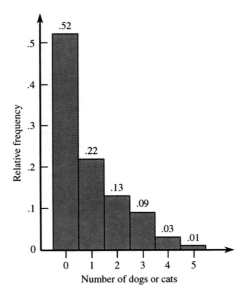

This variable associates a numerical value with each household in the population; possible $x$ values are 0, 1, 2, 3, 4, and 5 (county regulations prohibit more than 5 dogs or cats per household). Because possible values of $x$ are isolated points along the number line, $x$ is a discrete numerical variable.

One way to summarize the population distribution for a discrete numerical variable is to use a relative frequency histogram. The population distribution for the variable $x$ = number of licensed dogs or cats is shown in Figure 7.3.

The most common value of $x$ in the population (from Figure 7.3) is $x = 0$, and $P(x = 0) = .52$. Only 1% of all households have five licensed dogs or cats. Therefore if a household was selected at random from this population, it would be unusual to observe five licensed dogs or cats. The probability of observing a household with three or more licensed dogs or cats is

$$P(3 \text{ or more licensed dogs or cats}) = P(x \geq 3) = .09 + .03 + .01 = .13 \qquad ■$$

....................................................................................

# Example 7.4   Birth Weights

Birth weight was recorded for all full-term babies born during 2002 in a semirural county. The variable

$$x = \text{birth weight for a full-term baby}$$

for the population of all full-term babies in this county is an example of a continuous numerical variable. One way to describe the population distribution of $x$ values for this population is to construct a density histogram. Recall from Chapter 3 that, in a density histogram, the measurement scale (here, the range that includes all possible birth weights) is divided into class intervals. Each value in the data set (here, each birth weight) is classified into one of the intervals. For each interval, the resulting relative frequency is used to compute

$$\text{density} = \frac{\text{relative frequency}}{\text{interval width}}$$

**Figure 7.4** Population distribution of birth-weight values for Example 7.4.

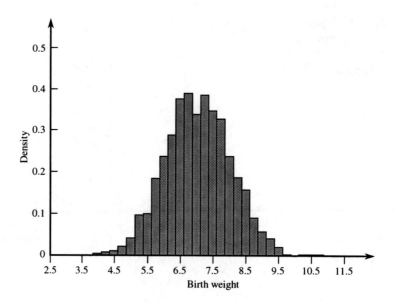

The density histogram has a rectangle for each interval; the height of the rectangle is determined by the corresponding density. (Review Section 3.3 of Chapter 3 for a more detailed description of density histograms.)

Figure 7.4 is a density histogram of the birth-weight values. This density histogram shows the distribution of birth weights for all full-term babies in this county, and so it can be viewed as the population distribution of the variable $x =$ birth weight.

From Figure 7.4, we can see that most birth weights are between 5 and 9 lb and that it would be unusual for a full-term baby born in this county to have a birth weight over 10 lb. In the next section, we will see how this distribution can be used to calculate various probabilities regarding the birth weight of a randomly selected child.

■

The population distribution for a numerical variable is useful for describing the distribution of its values in the population. Such a population distribution can also be summarized by a mean and a standard deviation. The mean describes where the distribution of values is centered, and the standard deviation describes how much the distribution spreads out about this central value.

## DEFINITION

The **mean value of a numerical variable** $x$, denoted by $\mu$, describes where the population distribution of $x$ is centered.

The **standard deviation of a numerical variable** $x$, denoted by $\sigma$, describes variability in the population distribution. When $\sigma$ is close to 0, the values of $x$ in the population tend to be close to the mean value (little variability). When the value of $\sigma$ is large, there is more variability in the population of $x$ values.

Figure 7.5(a) shows two discrete distributions with the same standard deviation (spread) but different means (center). One distribution has a mean of $\mu = 6$; the other has $\mu = 11$. Which is which? Figure 7.5(b) shows two continuous distributions that have the same mean but different standard deviations. Smooth curves have been used to approximate the shape of the underlying density histograms. Which distribution, (i) or (ii), has the larger standard deviation? Finally, Figure 7.5(c) shows three continuous distributions with different means and standard deviations. Which of the three distributions has the largest mean? Which has a mean of about 5? Which distribution has the smallest standard deviation? (Check your answers to the previous questions: Figure 7.5(a)(ii) has a mean of 6, and Figure 7.5(a)(i) has a mean of 11; Figure 7.5(b)(ii)

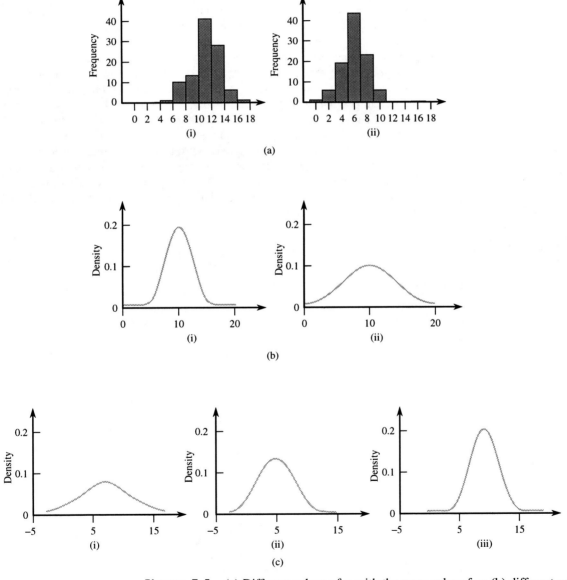

**Figure 7.5**   (a) Different values of $\mu$ with the same value of $\sigma$; (b) different values of $\sigma$ with the same value of $\mu$; (c) different values of $\mu$ and $\sigma$.

has the larger standard deviation; Figure 7.5(c)(iii) has the largest mean, Figure 7.5(c)(ii) has a mean of about 5, and Figure 7.5(c)(iii) has the smallest standard deviation.)

We will not concern ourselves with how to compute the values of $\mu$ and $\sigma$ (it is handled differently for discrete and for continuous variables), but we will look at how these values are interpreted. For the population distribution of Example 7.3, the mean value of $x$ turns out to be $\mu = .92$. This value is interpreted as the average number of licensed dogs or cats for the population of households in the county considered. Notice that $\mu$ is not a possible value of $x$. If another county (another population) had a mean of $\mu = .5$, we would know that the average number of licensed pets per household was smaller for the second county than for the first county, and so the distribution for the second county would be centered to the left of the first county's distribution.

For the population distribution in Example 7.4, $\mu = 7$ and $\sigma = 1$. The value of $\mu$ tells us that the average (mean) birth weight of full-term babies in the population is 7 lb. The value of the standard deviation provides information on the extent to which individual birth weights vary in the population. Because the population distribution is roughly bell shaped and symmetric, the Empirical Rule tells us that about 68% of the birth weights fall between 6 and 8 lb and that it would be extremely rare for a full-term baby to have a birth weight under 4 lb (or over 10 lb). If the birth-weight distribution for a different population (e.g., an urban county) had $\mu = 7.4$ and $\sigma = 1.3$, we would know that the average birth weight for the urban population was higher and that individual birth weights varied more than for the semirural area considered in Example 7.4 (i.e., the urban distribution is more spread out than the semirural distribution).

If the population distribution for a variable is known, it is possible to determine the values of $\mu$ and $\sigma$. Most often, however, the population distribution is not fully known, and the mean and standard deviation are estimated using sample data. In Chapter 9 we will use $\bar{x}$ and $s$ for this purpose.

## ■ Exercises 7.1–7.10 ..............................................................................................................

**7.1** State whether each of the following numerical variables is discrete or continuous:
**a.** The number of defective tires on a car
**b.** The body temperature of a hospital patient
**c.** The number of pages in a book
**d.** The number of checkout lines operating at a large grocery store
**e.** The lifetime of a light bulb

7.2 Classify each of the following numerical variables as either discrete or continuous:
a. The fuel efficiency (in miles per gallon) of an automobile
b. The amount of rainfall at a particular location during the next year
c. The distance that a person throws a baseball
d. The number of questions asked during a 1-hr lecture

e. The tension (in pounds per square inch) at which a tennis racket is strung
f. The amount of water used by a household during a given month
g. The number of traffic citations issued by the highway patrol in a particular county on a given day

**7.3** Consider the variable $x =$ earthquake insurance status for the population of homeowners in an earthquake-prone California county. This variable associates a category (insured or not insured) with each individual in the population.
**a.** Construct a relative frequency bar chart that represents the population distribution for $x$ for the case where 60% of the county homeowners have earthquake insurance.
**b.** If an individual is randomly selected from this population, what is the probability that the selected homeowner does not have earthquake insurance?

**Bold** exercises answered in back        ● Data set available online but not required        ▼ Video solution available

**7.4** Based on past history, a fire station reports that 25% of the calls to the station are false alarms, 60% are for small fires that can be handled by station personnel without outside assistance, and 15% are for major fires that require outside help.

a. Construct a relative frequency bar chart that represents the distribution of the variable $x$ = type of call, where *type of call* has three categories: false alarm, small fire, and major fire. What is the underlying population for this variable?

b. Based on the given information, we can write $P(x$ = false alarm) = .25. Use the other two relative frequencies shown in the bar chart from Part (a) to write two other probability statements.

**7.5** Suppose that fund-raisers at a university call recent graduates to request donations for campus outreach programs. They report the following information for last year's graduates:

| Size of donation | $0 | $10 | $25 | $50 |
|---|---|---|---|---|
| Proportion of calls | .45 | .30 | .20 | .05 |

Three attempts were made to contact each graduate; a donation of $0 was recorded both for those who were contacted but who declined to make a donation and for those who were not reached in three attempts. Consider the variable $x$ = amount of donation for the population of last year's graduates of this university.

a. Construct a relative frequency histogram to represent the population distribution of this variable.

b. What is the most common value of $x$ in this population?

c. What is $P(x \geq 25)$?    d. What is $P(x > 0)$?

**7.6** A pizza shop sells pizzas in four different sizes. The 1000 most recent orders for a single pizza gave the following proportions for the various sizes:

| Size | 12 in. | 14 in. | 16 in. | 18 in. |
|---|---|---|---|---|
| Proportion | .20 | .25 | .50 | .05 |

With $x$ denoting the size of a pizza in a single-pizza order, the given table is an approximation to the population distribution of $x$.

a. Construct a relative frequency histogram to represent the approximate distribution of this variable.

b. Approximate $P(x < 16)$.

c. Approximate $P(x \leq 16)$.

d. It can be shown that the mean value of $x$ is approximately 14.8 in. What is the approximate probability that $x$ is within 2 in. of this mean value?

**7.7** Airlines sometimes overbook flights. Suppose that for a plane with 100 seats, an airline takes 110 reservations.

Define the variable $x$ as the number of people who actually show up for a sold-out flight. From past experience, the population distribution of $x$ is given in the following table:

| x | Proportion | x | Proportion |
|---|---|---|---|
| 95 | .05 | 103 | .03 |
| 96 | .10 | 104 | .02 |
| 97 | .12 | 105 | .01 |
| 98 | .14 | 106 | .005 |
| 99 | .24 | 107 | .005 |
| 100 | .17 | 108 | .005 |
| 101 | .06 | 109 | .0037 |
| 102 | .04 | 110 | .0013 |

a. What is the probability that the airline can accommodate everyone who shows up for the flight?

b. What is the probability that not all passengers can be accommodated?

c. If you are trying to get a seat on such a flight and you are number 1 on the standby list, what is the probability that you will be able to take the flight? What if you are number 3?

**7.8** Homicide rate (homicides per 100,000 population) for each of the 50 states appeared in the *San Luis Obispo Telegram-Tribune* (February 2, 1995). A frequency distribution constructed from the 50 observations is shown in the following table:

| Homicide Rate | Frequency |
|---|---|
| 0 to <3 | 5 |
| 3 to <6 | 16 |
| 6 to <9 | 9 |
| 9 to <12 | 9 |
| 12 to <15 | 9 |
| 15 to <18 | 1 |
| 18 to <21 | 1 |

a. Calculate the relative frequency and density for each of the seven intervals in the frequency distribution. Use the computed densities to construct a density histogram for the variable $x$ = homicide rate for the population consisting of the 50 states.

b. Is the population distribution symmetric or skewed?

**Bold** exercises answered in back    ● Data set available online but not required    ▼ Video solution available

**Figure for Exercise 7.9**

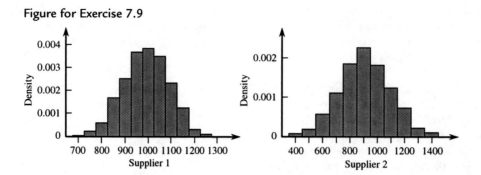

c. Use the population distribution to determine the following probabilities.

i. $P(x \geq 15)$      ii. $P(x < 9)$      iii. $P(12 \leq x < 18)$

**7.9** A company receives light bulbs from two different suppliers. Define the variables $x$ and $y$ by

$x$ = lifetime of a bulb from Supplier 1
$y$ = lifetime of a bulb from Supplier 2

Five hundred bulbs from each supplier are tested, and the lifetime of each bulb is recorded. The density histograms above are constructed from these two sets of observations. Although these histograms are constructed using data from only 500 bulbs, they can be considered approximations to the corresponding population distributions.

**a.** Which population distribution has the larger mean?
**b.** Which population distribution has the larger standard deviation?
**c.** Assuming that the cost of the light bulbs is the same for both suppliers, which supplier would you recommend? Explain.

**d.** One of the two distributions pictured has a mean of approximately 1000, and the other has a mean of about 900. What is the mean of the distribution for the variable $x$ (lifetime for a bulb made by Supplier 1)?
**e.** One of the two distributions pictured has a standard deviation of approximately 100, and the other has a standard deviation of about 175. What is the standard deviation of the distribution for the variable $x$ (lifetime for a bulb made by Supplier 1)?

7.10 A certain basketball player makes 70% of his free throws. Assume that results of successive free throws are independent of one another. At the end of a particular practice, the coach tells the player to begin shooting free throws and to stop only when he has made two consecutive shots. Let $x$ denote the number of shots until the player can stop. Describe how you would carry out a simulation experiment to approximate the distribution of $x$.

**Bold** exercises answered in back      ● Data set available online but not required      ▼ Video solution available

---

## 7.2 Population Models for Continuous Numerical Variables

In Example 7.4 of Section 7.1, we saw how a density histogram could be used to summarize a population distribution when the variable of interest is numerical and continuous. When this is done, the exact shape of the histogram and any approximate probability statements that we may make based on the population distribution depend somewhat on the number and location of intervals used in constructing the density histogram.

For example, let's look again at the distribution of birth weights for the population of all full-term babies born in 2002 in a particular county (see Example 7.4). Suppose that 2000 full-term babies were born. Then the population consists of 2000 individuals, and each individual has an associated value of the variable $x$ = birth weight.

**Figure 7.6** Density histograms for birth weight.

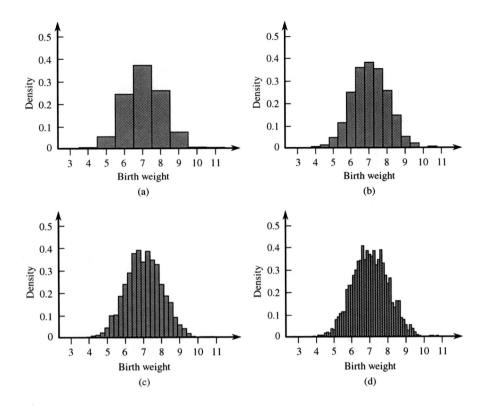

Figure 7.6(a) shows a density histogram for the population distribution of $x$ based on 7 intervals: 3.5 to <4.5, 4.5 to <5.5, and so on.

The area of any rectangle in a density histogram such as Figure 7.6(a) can be interpreted as the probability of observing a variable value in the corresponding interval, if an individual is selected at random from the population. This follows from the fact that, for any interval,

$$\text{density} = \frac{\text{relative frequency}}{\text{interval width}}$$

By construction, the corresponding rectangle has height equal to density, so the area of the rectangle is

$$\begin{aligned}
\text{area} &= (\text{height})(\text{interval width}) \\
&= (\text{density})(\text{interval width}) \\
&= \left(\frac{\text{relative frequency}}{\text{interval width}}\right)(\text{interval width}) \\
&= \text{relative frequency}
\end{aligned}$$

Thus, the area of the rectangle above each interval is equal to the relative frequency of values that fall in the interval. Because the area of a rectangle in the density histogram specifies the proportion of the population values that fall in the corresponding interval, it can be interpreted as the long-run proportion of time that a value in the interval would occur if individual after individual were randomly selected from the population.

Thus, for the interval 4.5 to <5.5 in Figure 7.6(a), the approximate probability that the weight of a randomly selected individual falls in the interval is

$$
\begin{aligned}
P(4.5 < x < 5.5) &= \text{area of rectangle above the interval from 4.5 to 5.5} \\
&= (\text{density})(1) \\
&= (.05)(1) \\
&= .05
\end{aligned}
$$

Similarly,

$$
P(7.5 < x < 8.5) = .25
$$

The probability of observing a value in an interval other than those used to construct the density histogram can be approximated. For example, to approximate the probability of observing a birth weight between 7 and 8 lb, we could add half the area of the rectangle for the 6.5–7.5 interval and half the area for the 7.5–8.5 interval. This gives only an approximate probability, because the area of each rectangle in the density histogram is equal to the proportion of the population falling in the corresponding interval. So

$$
\begin{aligned}
P(7 < x < 8) &\approx \frac{1}{2}(\text{area of rectangle for } 6.5-7.5) \\
&\quad + \frac{1}{2}(\text{area of rectangle for } 7.5-8.5) \\
&= \frac{1}{2}(.37)(1) + \frac{1}{2}(.25)(1) \\
&= .31
\end{aligned}
$$

The approximation of probabilities can be improved by increasing the number of intervals on which the density histogram is based. As Figure 7.6(a) shows, a density histogram based on a small number of intervals can be quite jagged. Figures 7.6(b)–(d) show density histograms based on 14, 28, and 56 intervals, respectively. As the number of intervals increases, the rectangles in the density histogram become much narrower and the histogram appears smoother.

Two important ideas were presented in the foregoing discussion. First, when summarizing a population distribution with a density histogram, the area of any rectangle in the histogram can be interpreted as the probability of observing a variable value in the corresponding interval when an individual is selected at random from the population. The second important idea is that when a density histogram based on a small number of intervals is used to summarize a population distribution for a continuous numerical variable, the histogram can be quite jagged. However, when the number of intervals is increased, the resulting histograms become much smoother in appearance. (You can see this in the histograms of Figure 7.6.)

It is often useful to represent a population distribution for a continuous variable by using a simple smooth curve that approximates the actual population distribution. For example, Figure 7.7 shows a smooth curve superimposed over the density histogram of Figure 7.6(d). Such a curve is called a **continuous probability distribution**. Because the total area of the rectangles in a density histogram is equal to 1, we consider only smooth curves for which the total area under the curve is equal to 1.

A continuous probability distribution is an abstract but simplified description of the population distribution that preserves important population

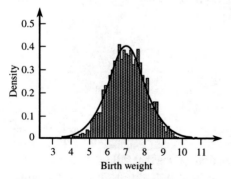

**Figure 7.7** A smooth curve specifies a continuous distribution for birth weight.

characteristics (general shape, center, spread, etc.). Thus, it can serve as a model for the distribution of values in the population. Because the area under the curve approximates the areas of rectangles in the density histogram, the area under the curve and above any particular interval can be interpreted as the approximate probability of observing a value in that interval when an individual is selected at random from the population.

A **continuous probability distribution** is a smooth curve, called a **density curve**, that serves as a model for the population distribution of a continuous variable.

Properties of continuous probability distributions are:

1. The total area under the curve is equal to 1.
2. The area under the curve and above any particular interval is interpreted as the (approximate) probability of observing a value in the corresponding interval when an individual or object is selected at random from the population.

Examples 7.5–7.7 show how a continuous probability distribution can be used to make probability statements about a variable.

# Example 7.5   Departure Delays

A morning commuter train never leaves before its scheduled departure time. The length of time that elapses between the scheduled departure time and the actual departure time is recorded on 200 occasions. The resulting observations are summarized in the density histogram shown in Figure 7.8(a). This histogram can serve as an approximation to the population distribution of the variable $x$ = elapsed time (in minutes).

Because the histogram in Figure 7.8(a) is fairly flat, a reasonable model (smooth curve) for the population distribution is the probability distribution "curve" shown in Figure 7.8(b). This model is sometimes referred to as a *uniform distribution*. The height of the curve (density = 0.1) is chosen so that the total area under the density curve is equal to 1.

The model can be used to approximate probabilities involving the variable $x$. For example, the probability that between 5 and 7 min elapse between scheduled and

**Figure 7.8**  Graphs for Example 7.5: (a) histogram of elapsed time values; (b) continuous probability distribution for elapsed time.

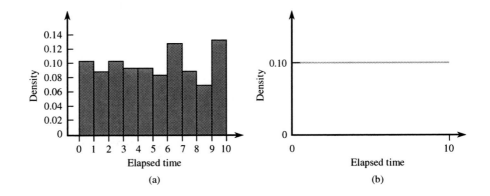

actual departure time is the area under the density curve and above the interval from 5 to 7, as shown in the accompanying illustration:

So

$$P(\text{elapsed time is between 5 and 7}) = P(5 < x < 7) = (2)(.1) = .2$$

Other probabilities are determined in a similar fashion. For example,

$$P(\text{elapsed time is less than 2.5})$$
$$= P(x < 2.5)$$
$$= \text{area under curve and above interval from 0 to 2.5}$$
$$= .25$$

For continuous numerical variables, probabilities are represented by an area under a probability distribution curve and above an interval. The area above an interval is not changed by including the interval endpoints, because there is no area above a single point. In Example 7.5, we found that $P(x < 2.5) = .25$. It is also true that $P(x \leq 2.5) = .25$.

For continuous numerical variables and any particular numbers $a$ and $b$,

$$P(x \leq a) = P(x < a)$$
$$P(x \geq b) = P(x > b)$$
$$P(a < x < b) = P(a \leq x \leq b)$$

## Example 7.6 Priority Mail Package Weights

Two hundred packages shipped using the Priority Mail rate for packages under 2 lb were weighed, resulting in a sample of 200 observations of the variable

$$x = \text{package weight (in pounds)}$$

from the population of all Priority Mail packages under 2 lb. A density histogram constructed from the 200 weights is shown in Figure 7.9(a). Because the histogram is based on a sample of 200 packages, it provides only an approximation to the population histogram. However, the shape of the sample density histogram does suggest that a reasonable model for the population might be the triangular distribution shown in Figure 7.9(b).

**Figure 7.9** Graphs for Example 7.6: (a) histogram of package weight values; (b) continuous probability distribution for package weight.

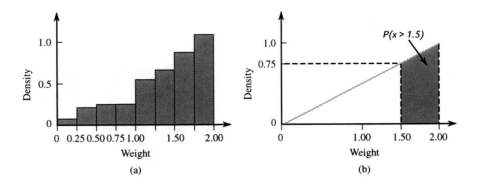

Note that the total area under the probability distribution curve (the density curve) is equal to

$$\text{total area of triangle } = \frac{1}{2}(\text{base})(\text{height}) = \frac{1}{2}(2)(1) = 1$$

The probability model can be used to compute the proportion of packages over 1.5 lb, $P(x > 1.5)$. This corresponds to the area of the shaded trapezoid in Figure 7.9(b). In this case, it is easier to compute the area of the unshaded region (which corresponds to $P(x \le 1.5)$), because this is just the area of a triangle:

$$P(x \le 1.5) = \frac{1}{2}(1.5)(.75) = .5625$$

Because the total area under a probability density curve is 1,

$$P(x > 1.5) = 1 - .5625 = .4375$$

It is also the case that

$$P(x \ge 1.5) = .4375$$

and that

$$P(x = 1.5) = 0$$

The last probability is a consequence of the fact that there is 0 area under the density curve above a single $x$ value.

■

.................................................................................................................

# Example 7.7   Service Times

An airline's toll-free reservation number recorded the length of time required to provide service to each of 500 callers. This resulted in 500 observations of the continuous numerical variable

$$x = \text{service time}$$

A density histogram is shown in Figure 7.10(a).

The population of interest is all callers to the reservation line. After studying the density histogram, we might think that a model for the population distribution would

**Figure 7.10** Graphs for Example 7.7: (a) histogram of service times; (b) continuous distribution of service times.

be flat over the interval from 0 to 3 and higher but also flat over the interval from 3 to 10. This type of model was thought to be reasonable, because service requests were usually one of two types: (1) requests to make a flight reservation and (2) requests to cancel a reservation. Canceling a reservation, which accounted for about one-eighth of the calls to the reservation line, could usually be accomplished fairly quickly, whereas making a reservation (seven-eighths of the calls) required more time.

Figure 7.10(b) shows the probability distribution curve proposed as a model for the variable $x$ = service time. The height of the curve for each of the two segments was chosen so that the total area under the curve would be 1 and so that $P(x \leq 3) = 1/8$ (these were thought to be cancellation calls) and $P(x > 3) = 7/8$.

Once the model has been developed, it can be used to compute probabilities. For example,

$$P(x > 8) = \text{area under curve and above interval from 8 to 10}$$

$$= 2\left(\frac{1}{8}\right) = \frac{2}{8} = \frac{1}{4}$$

In the long run, one-fourth of all service requests will require more than 8 min. Similarly,

$$P(2 < x < 4) = \text{area under curve and above interval from 2 to 4}$$
$$= (\text{area under curve and above interval from 2 to 3})$$
$$\quad + (\text{area under curve and above interval from 3 to 4})$$
$$= 1\left(\frac{1}{24}\right) + 1\left(\frac{1}{8}\right)$$
$$= \frac{1}{24} + \frac{3}{24}$$
$$= \frac{4}{24}$$
$$= \frac{1}{6}$$

■

In each of the previous examples, the continuous probability distribution used as a model for the population distribution was simple enough that we were able to calculate probabilities (evaluate areas under the curve) using simple geometry. Example 7.8 shows that this is not always the case.

# Example 7.8   Telephone Registration Times

Students at a university use a telephone registration system to register for courses. The variable

$$x = \text{length of time required for a student to register}$$

was recorded for a large number of students using the system, and the resulting values were used to construct the density histogram of Figure 7.11. The general form of the density histogram can be described as bell shaped and symmetric, and a smooth curve has been superimposed. This smooth curve serves as a reasonable model for the population distribution represented by the density histogram. Although this is a common population model (there are many variables whose distributions are described by curves of this sort), it is not obvious how we could use such a model to calculate probabilities, because at this point it is not clear how to find areas under such a curve.

**Figure 7.11**   Histogram and continuous probability distribution for time to register for Example 7.8.

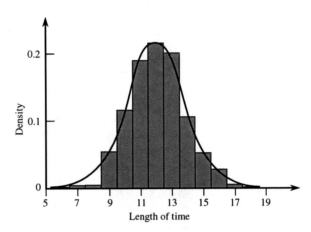

The probability model of Example 7.8 is an example of a type of symmetric bell-shaped distribution known as a *normal probability distribution*. Normal distributions have many and varied applications, and they are investigated in more detail in the next section.

## ■ Exercises 7.11–7.15

7.11 Consider the population of batteries made by a particular manufacturer. The following density curve represents the probability distribution for the variable $x =$ lifetime (in hours):

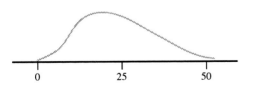

Shade the region under the curve corresponding to each of the following probabilities (draw a new curve for each part):
a.  $P(10 < x < 25)$
b.  $P(10 \leq x \leq 25)$
c.  $P(x < 30)$
d.  The probability that the lifetime is at least 25 hr
e.  The probability that the lifetime exceeds 30 hr

7.12  A particular professor never dismisses class early. Let $x$ denote the amount of time past the hour (in minutes) that elapses before the professor dismisses class. Suppose that the density curve shown in the following figure is an appropriate model for the probability distribution of $x$:

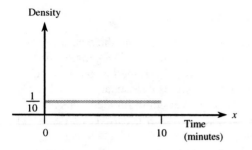

a. What is the probability that at most 5 min elapse before dismissal?
b. What is the probability that between 3 and 5 min elapse before dismissal?
c. What do you think is the value of the mean of this distribution?

**7.13** Consider the population that consists of all soft contact lenses made by a particular manufacturer, and define the variable $x$ = thickness (in millimeters). Suppose that a reasonable model for the population distribution is the one shown in the following figure:

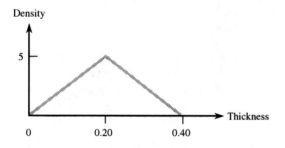

a. Verify that the total area under the density curve is equal to 1. (Hint: The area of a triangle is equal to 0.5(base)(height).)
**b.** What is the probability that $x$ is less than .20? less than .10? more than .30?
**c.** What is the probability that $x$ is between .10 and .20? (Hint: First find the probability that $x$ is *not* between .10 and .20.)
**d.** Because the density curve is symmetric, the mean of the distribution is .20. What is the probability that thickness is within 0.05 mm of the mean thickness?

**7.14** A delivery service charges a special rate for any package that weighs less than 1 lb. Let $x$ denote the weight of a randomly selected parcel that qualifies for this special rate. The probability distribution of $x$ is specified by the following density curve:

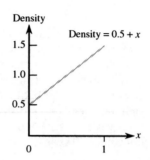

Use the fact that the area of a trapezoid = (base)(average of two side lengths) to answer each of the following questions.
a. What is the probability that a randomly selected package of this type weighs at most 0.5 lb?
b. What is the probability that a randomly selected package of this type weighs between 0.25 lb and 0.5 lb?
c. What is the probability that a randomly selected package of this type weighs at least 0.75 lb?

**7.15** Let $x$ denote the time (in seconds) necessary for an individual to react to a certain stimulus. The probability distribution of $x$ is specified by the following density curve:

**a.** What is the height of the density curve above $x = 0$? (Hint: Total area = 1.)
**b.** What is the probability that reaction time exceeds 0.5 sec?
**c.** What is the probability that reaction time is at most 0.25 sec?

## 7.3  Normal Distributions

Normal distributions formalize the notion of mound-shaped histograms introduced in Chapter 4. Normal distributions are widely used for two reasons. First, they provide a reasonable approximation to the distribution of many different variables. They also play a central role in many of the inferential procedures that will be discussed in Chapters 9–11. Normal distributions are continuous probability distributions that are bell shaped and symmetric, as shown in Figure 7.12. Normal distributions are also referred to as *normal curves*.

**Figure 7.12**  A normal distribution.

There are many different normal distributions, and they are distinguished from one another by their mean $\mu$ and standard deviation $\sigma$. The mean $\mu$ of a normal distribution describes where the corresponding curve is centered, and the standard deviation $\sigma$ describes how much the curve spreads out around that center. As with all continuous probability distributions, the total area under any normal curve is equal to 1. Three normal distributions are shown in Figure 7.13. Notice that the smaller the standard deviation, the taller and narrower the corresponding curve. Recall that areas under a continuous probability distribution curve represent probabilities; therefore, when the standard deviation is small, a larger area is concentrated near the center of the curve, and the chance of observing a value near the mean is much greater (because $\mu$ is at the center).

The value of $\mu$ is the number on the measurement axis lying directly below the top of the bell. The value of $\sigma$ can also be ascertained from a picture of the curve. Consider the normal curve in Figure 7.14. Starting at the top of the bell (above $\mu = 100$) and moving to the right, the curve turns downward until it is above the value 110. After that point, it continues to decrease in height but is turning upward rather than downward. Similarly, to the left of $\mu = 100$, the curve turns downward until it reaches 90 and then begins to turn upward. The curve changes from turning downward to turning upward at a distance of 10 on either side of $\mu$, so $\sigma = 10$. In general, $\sigma$ is the distance to either side of $\mu$ at which a normal curve changes from turning downward to turning upward.

If a particular normal distribution is to be used as a population model, a mean and a standard deviation must be specified. For example, a normal distribution with mean

**Figure 7.13**  Three normal distributions.

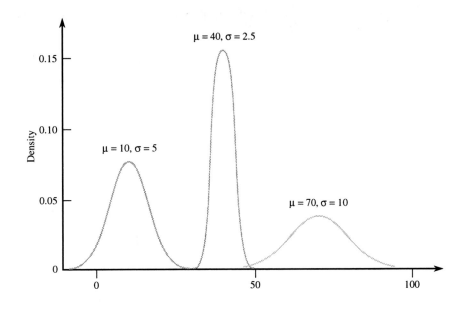

**Figure 7.14** $\mu$ and $\sigma$ for a normal curve.

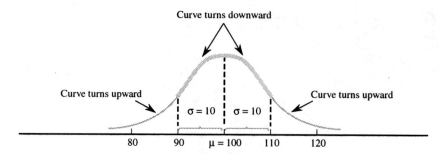

7 and standard deviation 1 might be used as a model for the distribution of $x =$ birth weight from Section 7.2. If this model is a reasonable description of the probability distribution, we could use areas under the normal curve with $\mu = 7$ and $\sigma = 1$ to approximate various probabilities related to birth weight. The probability that a birth weight is over 8 lb (expressed symbolically as $P(x > 8)$) corresponds to the shaded area in Figure 7.15(a). The shaded area in Figure 7.15(b) is the (approximate) probability $P(6.5 < x < 8)$ of a birth weight falling between 6.5 and 8 lb.

**Figure 7.15** Normal distribution for birth weight: (a) shaded area = $P(x > 8)$; (b) shaded area = $P(6.5 < x < 8)$.

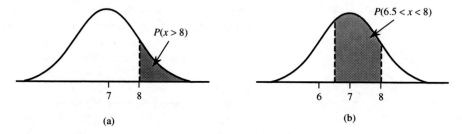

Unfortunately, direct computation of such probabilities (areas under a normal curve) is not simple. To overcome this difficulty, we rely on a table of areas for a reference normal distribution called the *standard normal distribution*.

### D E F I N I T I O N

The **standard normal distribution** is the normal distribution with $\mu = 0$ and $\sigma = 1$. The corresponding density curve is called the *standard normal curve*. It is customary to use the letter $z$ to represent a variable whose distribution is described by the standard normal curve. The term *z curve* is often used in place of standard normal curve.

Few naturally occurring variables have distributions that are well described by the standard normal distribution, but this distribution is important because it is also used in probability calculations for other normal distributions. When we are interested in finding a probability based on some other normal curve, we first translate the problem into an "equivalent" problem that involves finding an area under the standard normal curve. A table for the standard normal distribution is then used to find the desired area. To be able to do this, we must first learn to work with the standard normal distribution.

## ■ The Standard Normal Distribution

In working with normal distributions, we need two general skills:

1. We must be able to use the normal distribution to compute probabilities, which are areas under a normal curve and above given intervals.

2. We must be able to characterize extreme values in the distribution, such as the largest 5%, the smallest 1%, and the most extreme 5% (which would include the largest 2.5% and the smallest 2.5%).

Let's begin by looking at how to accomplish these tasks when the distribution of interest is the standard normal distribution.

The standard normal or $z$ curve is shown in Figure 7.16(a). It is centered at $\mu = 0$, and the standard deviation, $\sigma = 1$, is a measure of the extent to which it spreads out about its mean (in this case, 0). Note that this picture is consistent with the Empirical Rule of Chapter 4: About 95% of the area (probability) is associated with values that are within 2 standard deviations of the mean (between $-2$ and 2) and almost all of the area is associated with values that are within 3 standard deviations of the mean (between $-3$ and 3).

**Figure 7.16** (a) A standard normal ($z$) curve; (b) a cumulative area.

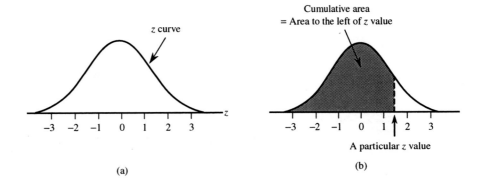

Appendix Table 2 tabulates cumulative $z$ curve areas of the sort shown in Figure 7.16(b) for many different values of $z$. The smallest value for which the cumulative area is given is $-3.89$, a value far out in the lower tail of the $z$ curve. The next smallest value for which the area appears is $-3.88$, then $-3.87$, then $-3.86$, and so on in increments of 0.01, terminating with the cumulative area to the left of 3.89.

## Using the Table of Standard Normal Curve Areas

For any number $z^*$ between $-3.89$ and 3.89 and rounded to two decimal places, Appendix Table 2 gives

(area under $z$ curve to the left of $z^*$) $= P(z < z^*) = P(z \leq z^*)$

where the letter $z$ is used to represent a variable whose distribution is the standard normal distribution.

To find this probability, locate the following:

1. The row labeled with the sign of $z^*$ and the digit to either side of the decimal point (e.g., $-1.7$ or 0.5)
2. The column identified with the second digit to the right of the decimal point in $z^*$ (e.g., .06 if $z^* = -1.76$)

The number at the intersection of this row and column is the desired probability, $P(z < z^*)$.

**Figure 7.17** Portion of Appendix Table 2 (standard normal curve areas).

| $z^*$ | .00 | .01 | .02 | .03 | .04 | .05 |
|------|------|------|------|------|------|------|
| 0.0 | .5000 | .5040 | .5080 | .5120 | .5160 | .5199 |
| 0.1 | .5398 | .5438 | .5478 | .5517 | .5557 | .5596 |
| 0.2 | .5793 | .5832 | .5871 | .5910 | .5948 | .5987 |
| 0.3 | .6179 | .6217 | .6255 | .6293 | .6331 | .6368 |
| 0.4 | .6554 | .6591 | .6628 | .6664 | .6700 | .6736 |
| 0.5 | .6915 | .6950 | .6985 | .7019 | .7054 | .7088 |
| 0.6 | .7257 | .7291 | .7324 | .7357 | .7389 | .7422 |
| 0.7 | .7580 | .7611 | .7642 | .7673 | .7704 | .7734 |
| 0.8 | .7881 | .7910 | .7939 | .7967 | .7995 | .8023 |
| 0.9 | .8159 | .8186 | .8212 | .8238 | .8264 | .8289 |
| 1.0 | .8413 | .8438 | .8461 | .8485 | .8508 | .8531 |
| 1.1 | .8643 | .8665 | .8686 | .8708 | .8729 | .8749 |
| 1.2 | .8849 | .8869 | .8888 | .8907 | .8925 | .8944 |
| 1.3 | .9032 | .9049 | .9066 | .9082 | .9099 | .9115 |
| 1.4 | .9192 | .9207 | .9222 | .9236 | .9251 | .9265 |
| 1.5 | .9332 | .9345 | .9357 | .9370 | .9382 | .9394 |
| 1.6 | .9452 | .9463 | .9474 | .9484 | .9495 | .9505 |
| 1.7 | .9554 | .9564 | .9573 | .9582 | .9591 | .9599 |
| 1.8 | .9641 | .9649 | .9656 | .9664 | .9671 | .9678 |

$P(z < 1.42)$

A portion of the table of standard normal curve areas appears in Figure 7.17. To find the area under the $z$ curve to the left of 1.42, look in the row labeled 1.4 and the column labeled .02 (the highlighted row and column in Figure 7.17). From the table, the corresponding cumulative area is .9222. So

$z$ curve area to the left of 1.42 = .9222

We can also use the table to find the area to the right of a particular value. Because the total area under the $z$ curve is 1, it follows that

$$z \text{ curve area to the right of } 1.42 = 1 - (z \text{ curve area to the left of } 1.42)$$
$$= 1 - .9222$$
$$= .0778$$

These probabilities can be interpreted to mean that in a long sequence of observations, roughly 92.22% of the observed $z$ values will be smaller than 1.42 and 7.78% will be larger than 1.42.

## Example 7.9   Finding Standard Normal Curve Areas

The probability $P(z < -1.76)$ is found at the intersection of the $-1.7$ row and the .06 column of the $z$ table. The result is

$$P(z < -1.76) = .0392$$

as shown in the following figure:

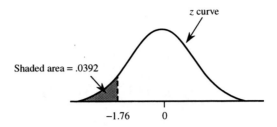

In other words, in a long sequence of observations, roughly 3.9% of the observed $z$ values will be smaller than $-1.76$. Similarly,

$P(z \leq 0.58)$ = entry in 0.5 row and .08 column of Appendix Table 2 = .7190

as shown in the following figure:

Now consider $P(z < -4.12)$. This probability does not appear in Appendix Table 2; there is no $-4.1$ row. However, it must be less than $P(z < -3.89)$, the smallest $z$ value in the table, because $-4.12$ is farther out in the lower tail of the $z$ curve. Because $P(z < -3.89) = .0000$ (i.e., 0 to four decimal places), it follows that

$$P(z < -4.12) \approx 0$$

Similarly,

$$P(z < 4.18) > P(z < 3.89) = 1.0000$$

from which we conclude that

$$P(z < 4.18) \approx 1$$

■

As illustrated in Example 7.9, we can use the cumulative areas tabulated in Appendix Table 2 to calculate other probabilities involving $z$. The probability that $z$ is larger than a value $c$ is

$P(z > c)$ = area under the $z$ curve to the right of $c = 1 - P(z \leq c)$

In other words, the area to the right of a value (a right-tail area) is 1 minus the corresponding cumulative area. This is illustrated in Figure 7.18.

**Figure 7.18** The relationship between an upper-tail area and a cumulative area.

Similarly, the probability that $z$ falls in the interval between a lower limit $a$ and an upper limit $b$ is

$$P(a < z < b) = \text{area under the } z \text{ curve and above the interval from } a \text{ to } b$$
$$= P(z < b) - P(z < a)$$

That is, $P(a < z < b)$ is the difference between two cumulative areas, as illustrated in Figure 7.19.

**Figure 7.19** $P(a < z < b)$ as a difference of two cumulative areas.

---

# Example 7.10 More About Standard Normal Curve Areas

The probability that $z$ is between $-1.76$ and $0.58$ is

$$P(-1.76 < z < 0.58) = P(z < 0.58) - P(z < -1.76)$$
$$= .7190 - .0392$$
$$= .6798$$

as shown in the following figure:

The probability that $z$ is between $-2$ and $+2$ (within 2 standard deviations of its mean, because $\mu = 0$ and $\sigma = 1$) is

$$P(-2.00 < z < 2.00) = P(z < 2.00) - P(z < -2.00)$$
$$= .9772 - .0228$$
$$= .9544$$
$$\approx .95$$

as shown in the following figure:

This last probability is the basis for one part of the Empiric[al] when a histogram is well approximated by a normal curve, [val]ues are within 2 standard deviations of the mean.

The probability that the value of $z$ exceeds 1.96 is

$$P(z > 1.96) = 1 - P(z \le 1.96)$$
$$= 1 - .9750$$
$$= .0250$$

as shown in the following figure:

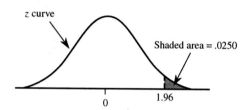

*z* curve

Shaded area = .0250

0    1.96

That is, 2.5% of the area under the $z$ curve lies to the right of 1.96 in the upper tail. Similarly,

$$P(z > -1.28) = \text{area to the right of} -1.28$$
$$= 1 - P(z \le -1.28)$$
$$= 1 - .1003$$
$$= .8997$$
$$\approx .90$$

■

■ **Identifying Extreme Values** Suppose that we want to describe the values included in the smallest 2% of a distribution or the values making up the most extreme 5% (which includes the largest 2.5% and the smallest 2.5%). Let's see how we can identify extreme values in the distribution by working through Examples 7.11 and 7.12.

## Example 7.11  Identifying Extreme Values

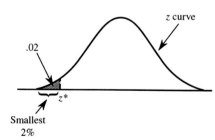

.02

*z* curve

$z^*$

Smallest 2%

**Figure 7.20**  The smallest 2% of the standard normal distribution.

Suppose that we want to describe the values that make up the smallest 2% of the standard normal distribution. Symbolically, we are trying to find a value (call it $z^*$) such that

$$P(z < z^*) = .02$$

This is illustrated in Figure 7.20, which shows that the cumulative area for $z^*$ is .02. Therefore we look for a cumulative area of .0200 in the body of Appendix Table 2. The closest cumulative area in the table is .0202, in the $-2.0$ row and .05 column; so we use $z^* = -2.05$, the best approximation from the table. Variable values less than $-2.05$ make up the smallest 2% of the standard normal distribution.

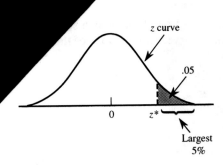

**Figure 7.21** The largest 5% of the standard normal distribution.

Now suppose that we had been interested in the largest 5% of all z values. We would then be trying to find a value of z* for which

$$P(z > z^*) = .05$$

as illustrated in Figure 7.21.

Because Appendix Table 2 always works with cumulative area (area to the left), the first step is to determine

$$\text{area to the left of } z^* = 1 - .05 = .95$$

Looking for the cumulative area closest to .95 in Appendix Table 2, we find that .95 falls exactly halfway between .9495 (corresponding to a z value of 1.64) and .9505 (corresponding to a z value of 1.65). Because .9500 is exactly halfway between the two areas, we use a z value that is halfway between 1.64 and 1.65. (If one value had been closer to .9500 than the other, we would just use the z value corresponding to the closest area). This gives

$$z^* = \frac{1.64 + 1.65}{2} = 1.645$$

Values greater than 1.645 make up the largest 5% of the standard normal distribution. By symmetry, −1.645 separates the smallest 5% of all z values from the others. ■

## Example 7.12 More Extremes

Sometimes we are interested in identifying the most extreme (unusually large *or* small) values in a distribution. Consider describing the values that make up the most extreme 5% of the standard normal distribution. That is, we want to separate the middle 95% from the extreme 5%. This is illustrated in Figure 7.22.

Because the standard normal distribution is symmetric, the most extreme 5% is equally divided between the high side and the low side of the distribution, resulting in an area of .025 for each of the tails of the z curve. Symmetry about 0 implies that if z* denotes the value that separates the largest 2.5%, the value that separates the smallest 2.5% is simply −z*.

To find z*, we must first determine the cumulative area for z*, which is

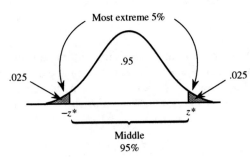

**Figure 7.22** The most extreme 5% of the standard normal distribution.

$$\text{area to the left of } z^* = .95 + .025 = .975$$

The cumulative area .9750 appears in the 1.9 row and .06 column of Appendix Table 2, so z* = 1.96. For the standard normal distribution, 95% of the variable values fall between −1.96 and 1.96; the most extreme 5% are those values that are either greater than 1.96 or less than −1.96. ■

### ■ Other Normal Distributions

We now show how z curve areas can be used to calculate probabilities and to describe extreme values for any normal distribution. Remember that the letter z is reserved for

those variables that have a standard normal distribution; the l
erally for any variable whose distribution is described by a no
and standard deviation $\sigma$.

Suppose that we want to compute $P(a < x < b)$, the proba
$x$ lies in a particular range. This probability corresponds to an
curve and above the interval from $a$ to $b$, as shown in Figure 7.2

**Figure 7.23** Equality
of nonstandard and standard
normal curve areas.

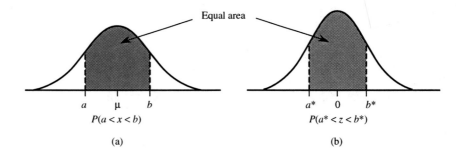

Our strategy for obtaining this probability is to find an "equivalent" problem involving the standard normal distribution. Finding an equivalent problem means determining an interval $(a^*, b^*)$ that has the same probability for $z$ (same area under
the $z$ curve) as does the interval $(a, b)$ in our original normal distribution (see Figure 7.23). The asterisk notation is used to distinguish $a$ and $b$, the values from the
original normal distribution with mean $\mu$ and standard deviation $\sigma$, from $a^*$ and $b^*$,
the corresponding values from the $z$ curve. To find $a^*$ and $b^*$, we simply calculate $z$
scores for the endpoints of the interval for which a probability is desired. This
process is called **standardizing** the endpoints. For example, suppose that the variable $x$ has a normal distribution with mean $\mu = 100$ and standard deviation $\sigma = 5$.
To calculate

$$P(98 < x < 107)$$

we first translate this problem into an equivalent problem for the standard normal distribution. Recall from Chapter 4 that a $z$ score, or standardized score, tells how many
standard deviations away from the mean a value lies; the $z$ score is calculated by first
subtracting the mean and then dividing by the standard deviation. Converting the
lower endpoint $a = 98$ to a $z$ score gives

$$a^* = \frac{98 - 100}{5} = \frac{-2}{5} = -0.40$$

and converting the upper endpoint yields

$$b^* = \frac{107 - 100}{5} = \frac{7}{5} = 1.40$$

Then

$$P(98 < x < 107) = P(-0.40 < z < 1.40)$$

The probability $P(-0.40 < z < 1.40)$ can now be evaluated using Appendix Table 2.

## Finding Probabilities

To calculate probabilities for any normal distribution, standardize the relevant values and then use the table of $z$ curve areas. More specifically, if $x$ is a variable whose behavior is described by a normal distribution with mean $\mu$ and standard deviation $\sigma$, then

$$P(x < b) = P(z < b^*)$$
$$P(a < x) = P(a^* < z) \quad \text{(equivalently, } P(x > a) = P(z > a^*))$$
$$P(a < x < b) = P(a^* < z < b^*)$$

where $z$ is a variable whose distribution is standard normal and

$$a^* = \frac{a - \mu}{\sigma} \qquad b^* = \frac{b - \mu}{\sigma}$$

........................................................................................................

# Example 7.13 Children's Heights

© Nicola Sutton/Life File/Getty Images

Data from the article "The Osteological Paradox: Problems in Inferring Prehistoric Health from Skeletal Samples" (*Current Anthropology* [1992]: 343–370) suggest that a reasonable model for the probability distribution of the continuous numerical variable $x$ = height of a randomly selected 5-year-old child is a normal distribution with a mean of $\mu = 100$ cm and standard deviation $\sigma = 6$ cm. What proportion of the heights is between 94 and 112 cm?

To answer this question, we must find

$$P(94 < x < 112)$$

First, we translate the endpoints to an equivalent problem for the standard normal distribution:

$$a^* = \frac{a - \mu}{\sigma} = \frac{94 - 100}{6} = -1.00$$
$$b^* = \frac{b - \mu}{\sigma} = \frac{112 - 100}{6} = 2.00$$

Then

$$
\begin{aligned}
P(94 < x < 112) &= P(-1.00 < z < 2.00) \\
&= (z \text{ curve area to the left of } 2.00) \\
&\quad - (z \text{ curve area to the left of } -1.00) \\
&= .9772 - .1587 \\
&= .8185
\end{aligned}
$$

The probabilities for $x$ and $z$ are shown in Figure 7.24. If heights were observed for many children from this population, about 82% of them would fall between 94 and 112 cm.

What is the probability that a randomly chosen child will be taller than 110 cm? To evaluate $P(x > 110)$, we first compute

$$a^* = \frac{a - \mu}{\sigma} = \frac{110 - 100}{6} = 1.67$$

**Figure 7.24**
$P(94 < x < 112)$ and corresponding $z$ curve area for Example 7.13.

Then (see Figure 7.25)

$$P(x > 110) = P(z > 1.67)$$
$$= z \text{ curve area to the right of } 1.67$$
$$= 1 - (z \text{ curve area to the left of } 1.67)$$
$$= 1 - .9525$$
$$= .0475$$

**Figure 7.25**  $P(x > 110)$
and corresponding $z$ curve area for Example 7.13.

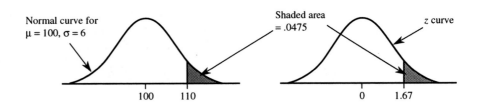

# Example 7.14  IQ Scores

Although there is some controversy regarding the appropriateness of IQ scores as a measure of intelligence, IQ scores are commonly used for a variety of purposes. One commonly used IQ scale has a mean of 100 and a standard deviation of 15, and scores are approximately normally distributed. (IQ score is actually a discrete variable [because it is based on the number of correct responses on a test], but its population distribution closely resembles a normal curve.) If we define

$$x = \text{IQ score of a randomly selected individual}$$

then $x$ has approximately a normal distribution with $\mu = 100$ and $\sigma = 15$.

One way to become eligible for membership in Mensa, an organization purportedly for those of high intelligence, is to have a Stanford–Binet IQ score above 130. What proportion of the population would qualify for Mensa membership? An answer to this question requires evaluating $P(x > 130)$. This probability is shown in Figure 7.26. With $a = 130$,

$$a^* = \frac{a - \mu}{\sigma} = \frac{130 - 100}{15} = 2.00$$

**Figure 7.26**  Normal distribution and desired proportion for Example 7.14.

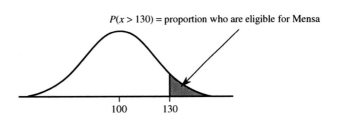

**Figure 7.27** $P(x > 130)$ and corresponding $z$ curve area for Example 7.14.

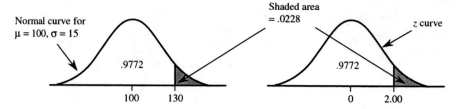

Therefore (see Figure 7.27)

$$P(x > 130) = P(z > 2.00)$$
$$= z \text{ curve area to the right of } 2.00$$
$$= 1 - (z \text{ curve area to the left of } 2.00)$$
$$= 1 - .9772$$
$$= .0228$$

Only 2.28% of the population would qualify for Mensa membership.

Suppose that we are interested in the proportion of the population with IQ scores below 80—that is, $P(x < 80)$. With $b = 80$,

$$b^* = \frac{b - \mu}{\sigma} = \frac{80 - 100}{15} = -1.33$$

Therefore

$$P(x < 80) = P(z < -1.33)$$
$$= z \text{ curve area to the left of } -1.33$$
$$= .0918$$

as shown in Figure 7.28. This probability (.0918) tells us that just a little over 9% of the population has an IQ score below 80.

**Figure 7.28** $P(x < 80)$ and corresponding $z$ curve area for Example 7.14.

Now consider the proportion of the population with IQs between 75 and 125. Using $a = 75$ and $b = 125$, we obtain

$$a^* = \frac{75 - 100}{15} = -1.67$$
$$b^* = \frac{125 - 100}{15} = 1.67$$

Therefore

$$P(75 < x < 125) = P(-1.67 < z < 1.67)$$
$$= z \text{ curve area between } -1.67 \text{ and } 1.67$$
$$= (z \text{ curve area to the left of } 1.67)$$
$$\quad - (z \text{ curve area to the left of } -1.67)$$
$$= .9525 - .0475$$
$$= .9050$$

**Figure 7.29**
$P(75 < x < 125)$ and corresponding $z$ curve area for Example 7.14.

This probability is illustrated in Figure 7.29. The calculation tells us that 90.5% of the population has an IQ score between 75 and 125. Of the 9.5% whose IQ score is not between 75 and 125, half of them (4.75%) have scores over 125, and the other half have scores below 75.

■

When we translate from a problem involving a normal distribution with mean $\mu$ and standard deviation $\sigma$ to a problem involving the standard normal distribution, we convert to $z$ scores:

$$z = \frac{x - \mu}{\sigma}$$

Because a $z$ score can be interpreted as giving the distance of an $x$ value from the mean in units of the standard deviation, a $z$ score of 1.4 corresponds to an $x$ value that is 1.4 standard deviations above the mean, and a $z$ score of $-2.1$ corresponds to an $x$ value that is 2.1 standard deviations below the mean.

Suppose that we are trying to evaluate $P(x < 60)$ for a variable whose distribution is normal with $\mu = 50$ and $\sigma = 5$. Converting the endpoint 60 to a $z$ score gives

$$z = \frac{60 - 50}{5} = 2$$

which tells us that the value 60 is 2 standard deviations above the mean. We then have

$$P(x < 60) = P(z < 2)$$

where $z$ is a standard normal variable. Notice that for the standard normal distribution, the value 2 is 2 standard deviations above the mean, because the mean is 0 and the standard deviation is 1. The value $z = 2$ is located the same distance (measured in standard deviations) from the mean of the standard normal distribution as the value $x = 60$ is from the mean in the normal distribution with $\mu = 50$ and $\sigma = 5$. This is why the translation using $z$ scores results in an "equivalent" problem involving the standard normal distribution.

## ■ Describing Extreme Values in a Normal Distribution .....................................

To describe the extreme values for a normal distribution with mean $\mu$ and standard deviation $\sigma$, we first solve the corresponding problem for the standard normal distribution and then translate our answer into one for the normal distribution of interest. This process is illustrated in Example 7.15.

## Example 7.15  Registration Times

Data on the length of time required to complete registration for classes using a telephone registration system suggests that the distribution of the variable

$$x = \text{time to register}$$

for students at a particular university can be well approximated by a normal distribution with mean $\mu = 12$ min and standard deviation $\sigma = 2$ min. (The normal distribution might not be an appropriate model for $x =$ time to register at another university. Many factors influence the shape, center, and spread of such a distribution.) Because some students do not sign off properly, the university would like to disconnect students automatically after some amount of time has elapsed. It is decided to choose this time such that only 1% of the students are disconnected while they are still attempting to register. To determine the amount of time that should be allowed before disconnecting a student, we need to describe the largest 1% of the distribution of time to register. These are the individuals who will be mistakenly disconnected. This is illustrated in Figure 7.30(a). To determine the value of $x^*$, we first solve the analogous problem for the standard normal distribution, as shown in Figure 7.30(b).

**Figure 7.30** Capturing the largest 1% in a normal distribution for Example 7.15.

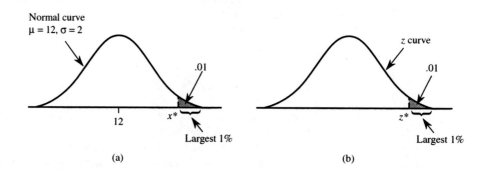

By looking in Appendix Table 2 for a cumulative area of .99, we find the closest entry (.9901) in the 2.3 row and the .03 column, from which $z^* = 2.33$. For the standard normal distribution, the largest 1% of the distribution is made up of those values greater than 2.33. An equivalent statement is that the largest 1% are those with $z$ scores greater than 2.33. This implies that in the distribution of time to register $x$ (or any other normal distribution), the largest 1% are those values with $z$ scores greater than 2.33 or, equivalently, those $x$ values that are more than 2.33 standard deviations above the mean. Here the standard deviation is 2, so 2.33 standard deviations is 2.33(2), and it follows that

$$x^* = 12 + 2.33(2) = 12 + 4.66 = 16.66$$

The largest 1% of the distribution for time to register is made up of values that are greater than 16.66 min. If the university system was set to disconnect students after 16.66 min, only 1% of the students registering would be disconnected before completing their registration.

■

A general formula for converting a $z$ score back to an $x$ value results from solving $z^* = \dfrac{x^* - \mu}{\sigma}$ for $x^*$, as shown in the accompanying box.

To convert a $z$ score $z^*$ back to an $x$ value, use

$$x^* = \mu + z^*\sigma$$

# Example 7.16  Motor Vehicle Emissions

© Hisham F. Ibrahim/Getty Images

The Environmental Protection Agency (EPA) has developed a testing program to monitor vehicle emission levels of several pollutants. The article "Determining Statistical Characteristics of a Vehicle Emissions Audit Procedure" (*Technometrics* [1980]: 483–493) described the program, which measures pollutants from various types of vehicles, all following a fixed driving schedule. Data from the article suggest that the emissions of nitrogen oxides, which are major constituents of smog, can be plausibly modeled using a normal distribution. Let $x$ denote the amount of this pollutant emitted by a randomly selected vehicle. The distribution of $x$ can be described by a normal distribution with $\mu = 1.6$ and $\sigma = 0.4$.

Suppose that the EPA wants to offer some sort of incentive to get the worst polluters off the road. What emission levels constitute the worst 10% of the vehicles? The worst 10% would be the 10% with the highest emissions level, as shown in the following illustration:

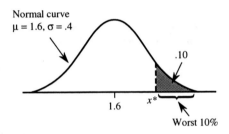

For the standard normal distribution, the largest 10% are those with $z$ values greater than $z^* = 1.28$ (from Appendix Table 2, based on a cumulative area of .90). Then

$$x^* = \mu + z^*\sigma$$
$$= 1.6 + 1.28(0.4)$$
$$= 1.6 + 0.512$$
$$= 2.112$$

In the population of vehicles of the type considered, about 10% would have oxide emission levels greater than 2.112.  ■

## Exercises 7.16–7.32

7.16 Determine the following standard normal ($z$) curve areas:
a. The area under the $z$ curve to the left of 1.75
b. The area under the $z$ curve to the left of $-0.68$
c. The area under the $z$ curve to the right of 1.20
d. The area under the $z$ curve to the right of $-2.82$
e. The area under the $z$ curve between $-2.22$ and 0.53
f. The area under the $z$ curve between $-1$ and 1
g. The area under the $z$ curve between $-4$ and 4

**7.17** Determine each of the areas under the standard normal ($z$) curve
**a.** To the left of $-1.28$       **b.** To the right of 1.28
**c.** Between $-1$ and 2       **d.** To the right of 0

**e.** To the right of $-5$    **f.** Between $-1.6$ and $2.5$
**g.** To the left of $0.23$

7.18 Let $z$ denote a variable that has a standard normal distribution. Determine each of the following probabilities:
a. $P(z < 2.36)$          b. $P(z \le 2.36)$
c. $P(z < -1.23)$          d. $P(1.14 < z < 3.35)$
e. $P(-0.77 \le z \le -0.55)$ f. $P(z > 2)$
g. $P(z \ge -3.38)$          h. $P(z < 4.98)$

**7.19** Let $z$ denote a variable having a normal distribution with $\mu = 0$ and $\sigma = 1$. Determine each of the following probabilities:
**a.** $P(z < 0.10)$          **b.** $P(z < -0.10)$
**c.** $P(0.40 < z < 0.85)$    **d.** $P(-0.85 < z < -0.40)$
**e.** $P(-0.40 < z < 0.85)$   **f.** $P(z > -1.25)$
**g.** $P(z < -1.50 \ or \ z > 2.50)$

7.20 Let $z$ denote a variable that has a standard normal distribution. Determine the value $z^*$ to satisfy the following conditions:
a. $P(z < z^*) = .025$      b. $P(z < z^*) = .01$
c. $P(z < z^*) = .05$        d. $P(z > z^*) = .02$
e. $P(z > z^*) = .01$
f. $P(z > z^* \ or \ z < -z^*) = .20$

**7.21** Determine the value $z^*$ that
**a.** Separates the largest 3% of all $z$ values from the others
**b.** Separates the largest 1% of all $z$ values from the others
**c.** Separates the smallest 4% of all $z$ values from the others
**d.** Separates the smallest 10% of all $z$ values from the others

7.22 Determine the value of $z^*$ such that
a. $z^*$ and $-z^*$ separate the middle 95% of all $z$ values from the most extreme 5%
b. $z^*$ and $-z^*$ separate the middle 90% of all $z$ values from the most extreme 10%
c. $z^*$ and $-z^*$ separate the middle 98% of all $z$ values from the most extreme 2%
d. $z^*$ and $-z^*$ separate the middle 92% of all $z$ values from the most extreme 8%

**7.23** Because $P(z < 0.44) = .67$, 67% of all $z$ values are less than 0.44, and 0.44 is the 67th percentile of the standard normal distribution. Determine the value of each of

the following percentiles for the standard normal distribution (Hint: If the cumulative area that you must look for does not appear in the $z$ table, use the closest entry):
**a.** The 91st percentile (Hint: Look for area .9100.)
**b.** The 77th percentile
**c.** The 50th percentile
**d.** The 9th percentile
**e.** What is the relationship between the 70th $z$ percentile and the 30th $z$ percentile?

7.24 Consider the population of all 1-gal cans of dusty rose paint manufactured by a particular paint company. Suppose that a normal distribution with mean $\mu = 5$ ml and standard deviation $\sigma = 0.2$ ml is a reasonable model for the distribution of the variable $x =$ amount of red dye in the paint mixture. Use the normal distribution model to calculate the following probabilities.
a. $P(x < 5.0)$          b. $P(x < 5.4)$
c. $P(x \le 5.4)$          d. $P(4.6 < x < 5.2)$
e. $P(x > 4.5)$          f. $P(x > 4.0)$

**7.25** Consider babies born in the "normal" range of 37–43 weeks gestational age. Extensive data support the assumption that for such babies born in the United States, birth weight is normally distributed with mean 3432 g and standard deviation 482 g ("Are Babies Normal," *The American Statistician* [1999]: 298–302). (The investigators who wrote the article analyzed data from a particular year. For a sensible choice of class intervals, the histogram did not look at all normal, but after further investigations the researchers determined that this was due to some hospitals measuring weight in grams and others measuring to the nearest ounce and then converting to grams. A modified choice of class intervals that allowed for this measurement difference gave a histogram that was well described by a normal distribution.)
**a.** What is the probability that the birth weight of a randomly selected baby of this type exceeds 4000 g? is between 3000 and 4000 g?
**b.** What is the probability that the birth weight of a randomly selected baby of this type is either less than 2000 g or greater than 5000 g?
**c.** What is the probability that the birth weight of a randomly selected baby of this type exceeds 7 lb? (Hint: 1 lb = 453.59 g.)
**d.** How would you characterize the most extreme 0.1% of all birth weights?

---

**Bold** exercises answered in back      ● Data set available online but not required      ▼ Video solution available

**e.** If x is a variable with a normal distribution and a is a numerical constant (a ≠ 0), then y = ax also has a normal distribution. Use this formula to determine the distribution of birth weight expressed in pounds (shape, mean, and standard deviation), and then recalculate the probability from Part (c). How does this compare to your previous answer?

7.26 A machine that cuts corks for wine bottles operates in such a way that the distribution of the diameter of the corks produced is well approximated by a normal distribution with mean 3 cm and standard deviation 0.1 cm. The specifications call for corks with diameters between 2.9 and 3.1 cm. A cork not meeting the specifications is considered defective. (A cork that is too small leaks and causes the wine to deteriorate; a cork that is too large doesn't fit in the bottle.) What proportion of corks produced by this machine are defective?

**7.27** Refer to Exercise 7.26. Suppose that there are two machines available for cutting corks. The machine described in the preceding problem produces corks with diameters that are approximately normally distributed with mean 3 cm and standard deviation 0.1 cm. The second machine produces corks with diameters that are approximately normally distributed with mean 3.05 cm and standard deviation 0.01 cm. Which machine would you recommend? (Hint: Which machine would produce the fewest defective corks?)

7.28 A gasoline tank for a certain car is designed to hold 15 gal of gas. Suppose that the variable x = actual capacity of a randomly selected tank has a distribution that is well approximated by a normal curve with mean 15.0 gal and standard deviation 0.1 gal.
a. What is the probability that a randomly selected tank will hold at most 14.8 gal?
b. What is the probability that a randomly selected tank will hold between 14.7 and 15.1 gal?
c. If two such tanks are independently selected, what is the probability that both tanks hold at most 15 gal?

**7.29** ▼ The time that it takes a randomly selected job applicant to perform a certain task has a distribution that can be approximated by a normal distribution with a mean value of 120 sec and a standard deviation of 20 sec. The

fastest 10% are to be given advanced training. What task times qualify individuals for such training?

7.30 A machine that produces ball bearings has initially been set so that the true average diameter of the bearings it produces is 0.500 in. A bearing is acceptable if its diameter is within 0.004 in. of this target value. Suppose, however, that the setting has changed during the course of production, so that the distribution of the diameters produced is well approximated by a normal distribution with mean 0.499 in. and standard deviation 0.002 in. What percentage of the bearings produced will not be acceptable?

**7.31** ▼ Suppose that the distribution of net typing rate in words per minute (wpm) for experienced typists can be approximated by a normal curve with mean 60 wpm and standard deviation 15 wpm. The paper "Effects of Age and Skill in Typing" (*Journal of Experimental Psychology* [1984]: 345–371) described how net rate is obtained from gross rate by using a correction for errors.
**a.** What is the probability that a randomly selected typist's net rate is at most 60 wpm? less than 60 wpm?
**b.** What is the probability that a randomly selected typist's net rate is between 45 and 90 wpm?
**c.** Would you be surprised to find a typist in this population whose net rate exceeded 105 wpm? (Note: The largest net rate in a sample described in the paper cited is 104 wpm.)
**d.** Suppose that two typists are independently selected. What is the probability that both their typing rates exceed 75 wpm?
**e.** Suppose that special training is to be made available to the slowest 20% of the typists. What typing speeds would qualify individuals for this training?

7.32 Consider the variable x = time required for a college student to complete a standardized exam. Suppose that for the population of students at a particular university, the distribution of x is well approximated by a normal curve with mean 45 min and standard deviation 5 min.
a. If 50 min is allowed for the exam, what proportion of students at this university would be unable to finish in the allotted time?
b. How much time should be allowed for the exam if we wanted 90% of the students taking the test to be able to finish in the allotted time?
c. How much time is required for the fastest 25% of all students to complete the exam?

**Bold** exercises answered in back  ● Data set available online but not required  ▼ Video solution available

## 7.4 Checking for Normality and Normalizing Transformations

Some of the most frequently used statistical methods are valid only when a sample $x_1, x_2, \ldots, x_n$, has come from a population distribution that is at least approximately normal. One way to see whether an assumption of population normality is plausible is to construct a **normal probability plot** of the data. One version of this plot uses certain quantities called **normal scores**. The values of the normal scores depend on the sample size $n$. For example, the normal scores when $n = 10$ are as follows:

$$
\begin{array}{ccccc}
-1.539 & -1.001 & -0.656 & -0.376 & -0.123 \\
0.123 & 0.376 & 0.656 & 1.001 & 1.539
\end{array}
$$

To interpret these numbers, think of selecting sample after sample from a standard normal distribution, each one consisting of $n = 10$ observations. Then $-1.539$ is the long-run average of the smallest observation from each sample, $-1.001$ is the long-run average of the second smallest observation from each sample, and so on. In other words, $-1.539$ is the mean value of the smallest observation in a sample of size 10 from the $z$ distribution, $-1.001$ is the mean value of the second smallest observation, and so on.

Extensive tabulations of normal scores for many different sample sizes are available. Alternatively, many software packages (such as MINITAB and SAS) and some graphing calculators can compute these scores on request and then construct a normal probability plot. Not all calculators and software packages use the same algorithm to compute normal scores. However, this does not change the overall character of a normal probability plot, so either the tabulated values or those given by the computer or calculator can be used.

After ordering the sample observations from smallest to largest, the smallest normal score is paired with the smallest observation, the second smallest normal score with the second smallest observation, and so on. The first number in a pair is the normal score, and the second number in the pair is the observed data value. A normal probability plot is just a scatterplot of the (normal score, observed value) pairs.

If the sample has been selected from a *standard* normal distribution, the second number in each pair should be reasonably close to the first number (ordered observation ≈ corresponding mean value). Then the $n$ plotted points fall near a line with slope equal to 1 (a 45° line) passing through $(0, 0)$. When the sample has been obtained from *some* normal population distribution, the plotted points should be close to *some* straight line.

### DEFINITION

A **normal probability plot** is a scatterplot of the (normal score, observed value) pairs.

A substantial linear pattern in a normal probability plot suggests that population normality is plausible. On the other hand, a systematic departure from a straight-line pattern (such as curvature in the plot) casts doubt on the legitimacy of assuming a normal population distribution.

# Example 7.17   Window Widths

The following 10 observations are widths of contact windows in integrated circuit chips:

  3.21    2.49    2.94    4.38    4.02    3.62    3.30    2.85    3.34    3.81

The 10 pairs for the normal probability plot are then

  (−1.539, 2.49)      (0.123, 3.34)
  (−1.001, 2.85)      (0.376, 3.62)
  (−0.656, 2.94)      (0.656, 3.81)
  (−0.376, 3.21)      (1.001, 4.02)
  (−0.123, 3.30)      (1.539, 4.38)

The normal probability plot is shown in Figure 7.31. The linearity of the plot supports the assumption that the window width distribution from which these observations were drawn is normal.

**Figure 7.31**   A normal probability plot for Example 7.17.

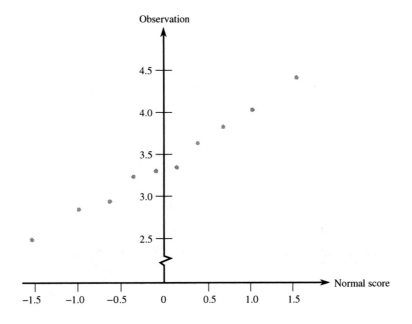

The decision as to whether or not a plot shows a substantial linear pattern is somewhat subjective. Particularly when $n$ is small, normality should not be ruled out unless the departure from linearity is clear-cut. Figure 7.32 displays several plots that suggest a nonnormal population distribution.

**Figure 7.32**   Plots suggesting nonnormality: (a) indication that the population distribution is skewed; (b) indication that the population distribution has heavier tails than a normal curve; (c) presence of an outlier.

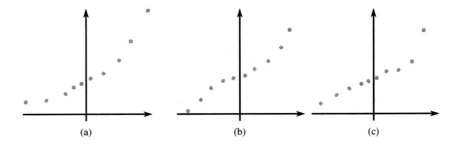

## ∎ Using the Correlation Coefficient to Check Normality ...............................

The correlation coefficient $r$ was introduced in Chapter 5 as a quantitative measure of the extent to which the points in a scatterplot fall close to a straight line. Let's denote the $n$ (normal score, observed value) pairs as follows:

(smallest normal score, smallest observation)

⋮

(largest normal score, largest observation)

Then the correlation coefficient can be computed as discussed in Chapter 5. The normal probability plot always slopes upward (because it is based on values ordered from smallest to largest), so $r$ is a positive number. A value of $r$ quite close to 1 indicates a very strong linear relationship in the normal probability plot. If $r$ is too much smaller than 1, normality of the underlying distribution is questionable.

How far below 1 does $r$ have to be before we begin to seriously doubt the plausibility of normality? The answer depends on the sample size $n$. If $n$ is small, an $r$ value somewhat below 1 is not surprising even when the distribution is normal, but if $n$ is large, only an $r$ value very close to 1 supports the assumption of normality. For selected values of $n$, Table 7.1 gives critical values to which $r$ can be compared in checking for normality. If your sample size is between two tabulated values of $n$, use the critical value for the larger sample size. (For example, if $n = 46$, use the value of .966 for sample size 50.)

**Table 7.1**   Values to Which $r$ Can Be Compared to Check for Normality

| $n$ | 5 | 10 | 15 | 20 | 25 | 30 | 40 | 50 | 60 | 75 |
|---|---|---|---|---|---|---|---|---|---|---|
| Critical $r$ | .832 | .880 | .911 | .929 | .941 | .949 | .960 | .966 | .971 | .976 |

*Source: MINITAB User's Manual.*

If

$r <$ critical $r$ for corresponding $n$

considerable doubt is cast on the assumption of population normality.

∎

How were the critical values in Table 7.1 obtained? Consider the critical value .941 for $n = 25$. Suppose that the underlying distribution is actually normal. Consider obtaining a large number of different samples, each one consisting of 25 observations, and computing the value of $r$ for each one. Then it can be shown that only 1% of the samples result in an $r$ value less than the critical value .941. That is, .941 was chosen to guarantee a 1% error rate: In only 1% of all cases will we judge normality implausible when the distribution is really normal. The other critical values are also chosen to yield a 1% error rate for the corresponding sample sizes. It might have occurred to you that another type of error is possible: obtaining a large value of $r$ and concluding that normality is a reasonable assumption when the distribution is actually nonnormal. This type of error is more difficult to control than the type mentioned previously, but the procedure we have described generally does a good job in both respects.

## Example 7.18   Window Widths Continued

The sample size for the contact window width data of Example 7.17 is $n = 10$. The critical $r$ from Table 7.1 is then .880. The correlation coefficient calculated using the (normal score, observed value) pairs is $r = .995$. Because $r$ is larger than the critical $r$ for a sample of size 10, it is plausible that the population distribution of window widths from which this sample was drawn is approximately normal.  ■

## ■ Transforming Data to Obtain a Distribution That Is Approximately Normal .................................................................

Many of the most frequently used statistical methods are valid only when the sample is selected at random from a population whose distribution is at least approximately normal. When a sample histogram shows a distinctly nonnormal shape, it is common to use a transformation or reexpression of the data. By *transforming* data, we mean applying some specified mathematical function (such as the square root, logarithm, or reciprocal) to each data value to produce a set of transformed data. We can then study and summarize the distribution of these transformed values using methods that require normality. We saw in Chapter 5 that, with bivariate data, one or both of the variables can be transformed in an attempt to find two variables that are linearly related. With univariate data, a transformation is usually chosen to yield a distribution of transformed values that is more symmetric and more closely approximated by a normal curve than was the original distribution.

## Example 7.19  Rainfall Data

Data that have been used by several investigators to introduce the concept of transformation (e.g., "Exploratory Methods for Choosing Power Transformations," *Journal of the American Statistical Association* [1982]: 103–108) consist of values of March precipitation for Minneapolis–St. Paul over a period of 30 years. These values are given in Table 7.2 along with the square root of each value. Histograms

**Table 7.2**  Original and Square-Root-Transformed Values of March Precipitation in Minneapolis–St. Paul over a 30-Year Period

| Year | Precipitation | $\sqrt{\text{Precipitation}}$ | Year | Precipitation | $\sqrt{\text{Precipitation}}$ |
|------|---------------|-------------------------------|------|---------------|-------------------------------|
| 1 | 0.77 | 0.88 | 16 | 1.62 | 1.27 |
| 2 | 1.74 | 1.32 | 17 | 1.31 | 1.14 |
| 3 | 0.81 | 0.90 | 18 | 0.32 | 0.57 |
| 4 | 1.20 | 1.10 | 19 | 0.59 | 0.77 |
| 5 | 1.95 | 1.40 | 20 | 0.81 | 0.90 |
| 6 | 1.20 | 1.10 | 21 | 2.81 | 1.68 |
| 7 | 0.47 | 0.69 | 22 | 1.87 | 1.37 |
| 8 | 1.43 | 1.20 | 23 | 1.18 | 1.09 |
| 9 | 3.37 | 1.84 | 24 | 1.35 | 1.16 |
| 10 | 2.20 | 1.48 | 25 | 4.75 | 2.18 |
| 11 | 3.00 | 1.73 | 26 | 2.48 | 1.57 |
| 12 | 3.09 | 1.76 | 27 | 0.96 | 0.98 |
| 13 | 1.51 | 1.23 | 28 | 1.89 | 1.37 |
| 14 | 2.10 | 1.45 | 29 | 0.90 | 0.95 |
| 15 | 0.52 | 0.72 | 30 | 2.05 | 1.43 |

**Figure 7.33** Histograms of precipitation data for Example 7.19: (a) untransformed data; (b) square-root-transformed data.

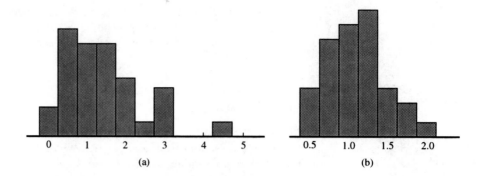

(a)  (b)

of both the original and the transformed data appear in Figure 7.33. The distribution of the original data is clearly skewed, with a long upper tail. The square-root transformation has resulted in a substantially more symmetric distribution, with a typical (i.e., central) value near the 1.25 boundary between the third and fourth class intervals.

■

Logarithmic transformations are also common and, as with bivariate data, either the natural logarithm or the base 10 logarithm can be used. A logarithmic transformation is usually applied to data that are positively skewed (a long upper tail). This affects values in the upper tail substantially more than values in the lower tail, yielding a more symmetric—and often more normal—distribution.

## Example 7.20 Beryllium Exposure

Exposure to beryllium is known to produce adverse effects on lungs as well as on other tissues and organs in both laboratory animals and humans. The article "Time Lapse Cinematographic Analysis of Beryllium: Lung Fibroblast Interactions" (*Environmental Research* [1983]: 34–43) reported the results of experiments designed to study the behavior of certain individual cells that had been exposed to beryllium. An important characteristic of such an individual cell is its interdivision time (IDT). IDTs were determined for a large number of cells under both exposed (treatment) and unexposed (control) conditions. The authors of the article state, "The IDT distributions are seen to be skewed, but the natural logs do have an approximate normal distribution." The same property holds for $\log_{10}$-transformed data. We give representative IDT data in Table 7.3 and the resulting histograms in Figure 7.34, which are in agreement with the authors' statement.

The sample size for the IDT data is $n = 40$. The correlation coefficient for the (normal score, untransformed data) pairs is .950, which is less than the critical $r$ for $n = 40$ (critical $r = .960$). The correlation coefficient using the transformed data is .998, which is much larger than the critical $r$, supporting the assertion that $\log_{10}(\text{IDT})$ has approximately a normal distribution. Figure 7.35 displays MINITAB normal probability plots for the original data and for the transformed data. The plot for the transformed data is clearly more linear in appearance than the plot for the original data.

**Table 7.3**   Original and log₁₀-Transformed IDT Values

| IDT | $\log_{10}$(IDT) | IDT | $\log_{10}$(IDT) | IDT | $\log_{10}$(IDT) | IDT | $\log_{10}$(IDT) |
|------|------|------|------|------|------|------|------|
| 28.1 | 1.45 | 15.5 | 1.19 | 26.2 | 1.42 | 21.1 | 1.32 |
| 46.0 | 1.66 | 38.4 | 1.58 | 17.4 | 1.24 | 60.1 | 1.78 |
| 34.8 | 1.54 | 21.4 | 1.33 | 55.6 | 1.75 | 21.4 | 1.33 |
| 17.9 | 1.25 | 40.9 | 1.61 | 21.0 | 1.32 | 32.0 | 1.51 |
| 31.9 | 1.50 | 31.2 | 1.49 | 36.3 | 1.56 | 38.8 | 1.59 |
| 23.7 | 1.37 | 25.8 | 1.41 | 72.8 | 1.86 | 25.5 | 1.41 |
| 26.6 | 1.42 | 62.3 | 1.79 | 20.7 | 1.32 | 22.3 | 1.35 |
| 43.5 | 1.64 | 19.5 | 1.29 | 13.7 | 1.14 | 19.1 | 1.28 |
| 30.6 | 1.49 | 28.9 | 1.46 | 16.8 | 1.23 | 48.9 | 1.69 |
| 52.1 | 1.72 | 18.6 | 1.27 | 28.0 | 1.45 | 57.3 | 1.76 |

**Figure 7.34**  Histograms of IDT data for Example 7.20: (a) untransformed data; (b) log₁₀-transformed data.

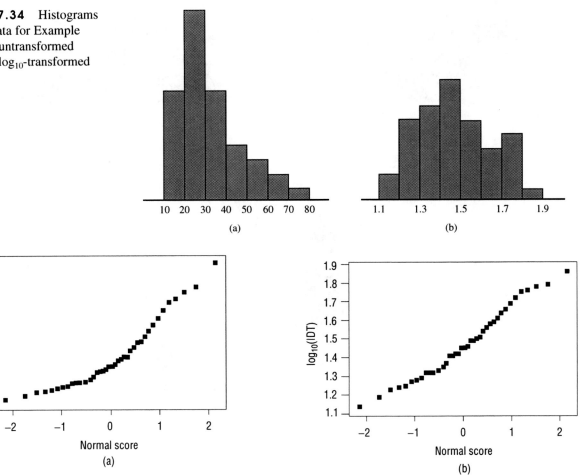

Figure 7.35   MINITAB-generated normal probability plots for Example 7.20: (a) original IDT data; (b) log-transformed IDT data.

## ■ Selecting a Transformation ...........................................................................

Occasionally, a particular transformation can be dictated by some theoretical argument, but often this is not the case and you may wish to try several different transformations to find one that is satisfactory. Figure 7.36, from the article "Distribution of Sperm Counts in Suspected Infertile Men" (*Journal of Reproduction and Fertility* [1983]: 91–96), shows what can result from such a search. Other investigators in this field had previously used all three of the transformations illustrated.

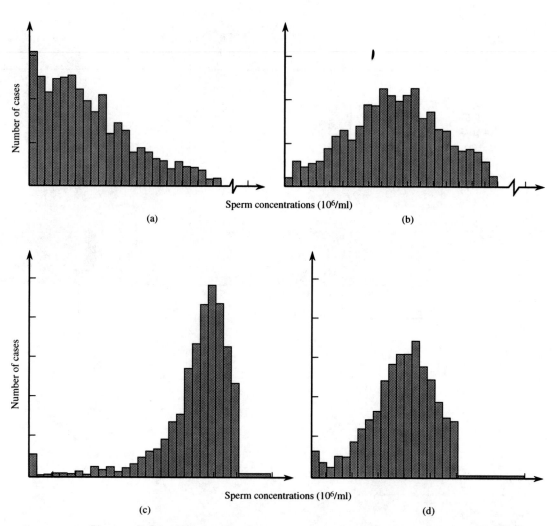

**Figure 7.36**  Histograms of sperm concentrations for 1711 suspected infertile men: (a) untransformed data (highly skewed); (b) log-transformed data (reasonably symmetric); (c) square-root-transformed data; (d) cube-root-transformed data.

## Exercises 7.33–7.44 ......................................................................

**7.33** Ten measurements of the steam rate (in pounds per hour) of a distillation tower were used to construct the following normal probability plot ("A Self-Descaling Distillation Tower," *Chemical Engineering Process* [1968]: 79–84):

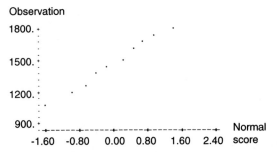

Observation

Based on the plot, do you think it is reasonable to assume that the normal distribution provides an adequate description of the steam rate distribution? Explain.

**7.34** The following normal probability plot was constructed using part of the data appearing in the paper "Trace Metals in Sea Scallops" (*Environmental Concentration and Toxicology* 19: 1326–1334):

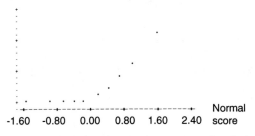

Observation

The variable under study was the amount of cadmium in North Atlantic scallops. Do the sample data suggest that the cadmium concentration distribution is not normal? Explain.

**7.35** ◉ Consider the following 10 observations on the lifetime (in hours) for a certain type of component:

| 152.7 | 172.0 | 172.5 | 173.3 | 193.0 |
| 204.7 | 216.5 | 234.9 | 262.6 | 422.6 |

Construct a normal probability plot, and comment on the plausibility of a normal distribution as a model for component lifetime.

**7.36** ◉ The paper "The Load-Life Relationship for M50 Bearings with Silicon Nitride Ceramic Balls" (*Lubrication*

*Engineering* [1984]: 153–159) reported the following data on bearing load life (in millions of revolutions); the corresponding normal scores are also given:

| $x$ | Normal Score | $x$ | Normal Score |
|---|---|---|---|
| 47.1 | −1.867 | 240.0 | 0.062 |
| 68.1 | −1.408 | 240.0 | 0.187 |
| 68.1 | −1.131 | 278.0 | 0.315 |
| 90.8 | −0.921 | 278.0 | 0.448 |
| 103.6 | −0.745 | 289.0 | 0.590 |
| 106.0 | −0.590 | 289.0 | 0.745 |
| 115.0 | −0.448 | 367.0 | 0.921 |
| 126.0 | −0.315 | 385.9 | 1.131 |
| 146.6 | −0.187 | 392.0 | 1.408 |
| 229.0 | −0.062 | 395.0 | 1.867 |

Construct a normal probability plot. Is normality plausible?

**7.37** ◉ The following observations are DDT concentrations in the blood of 20 people:

| 24 | 26 | 30 | 35 | 35 | 38 | 39 | 40 | 40 | 41 |
| 42 | 52 | 56 | 58 | 61 | 75 | 79 | 88 | 102 | 42 |

Use the normal scores from Exercise 7.36 to construct a normal probability plot, and comment on the appropriateness of a normal probability model.

**7.38** ◉ Consider the following sample of 25 observations on the diameter $x$ (in centimeters) of a disk used in a certain system.

| 16.01 | 16.08 | 16.13 | 15.94 | 16.05 | 16.27 | 15.89 |
| 15.84 | 15.95 | 16.10 | 15.92 | 16.04 | 15.82 | 16.15 |
| 16.06 | 15.66 | 15.78 | 15.99 | 16.29 | 16.15 | 16.19 |
| 16.22 | 16.07 | 16.13 | 16.11 |

The 13 largest normal scores for a sample of size 25 are 1.965, 1.524, 1.263, 1.067, 0.905, 0.764, 0.637, 0.519, 0.409, 0.303, 0.200, 0.100, and 0. The 12 smallest scores result from placing a negative sign in front of each of the given nonzero scores. Construct a normal probability plot. Does it appear plausible that disk diameter is normally distributed? Explain.

**7.39** ◉ Example 7.19 examined rainfall data for Minneapolis–St. Paul. The square-root transformation was used to obtain a distribution of values that was more symmetric than the distribution of the original data. Another transformation that has been suggested by meteorologists is the cube root: transformed value = (original value)$^{1/3}$. The original values and their cube roots (the transformed values) are given in the following table:

| Original | Transformed | Original | Transformed |
|----------|-------------|----------|-------------|
| 0.32 | 0.68 | 1.51 | 1.15 |
| 0.47 | 0.78 | 1.62 | 1.17 |
| 0.52 | 0.80 | 1.74 | 1.20 |
| 0.59 | 0.84 | 1.87 | 1.23 |
| 0.77 | 0.92 | 1.89 | 1.24 |
| 0.81 | 0.93 | 1.95 | 1.25 |
| 0.81 | 0.93 | 2.05 | 1.27 |
| 0.90 | 0.97 | 2.10 | 1.28 |
| 0.96 | 0.99 | 2.20 | 1.30 |
| 1.18 | 1.06 | 2.48 | 1.35 |
| 1.20 | 1.06 | 2.81 | 1.41 |
| 1.20 | 1.06 | 3.00 | 1.44 |
| 1.31 | 1.09 | 3.09 | 1.46 |
| 1.35 | 1.11 | 3.37 | 1.50 |
| 1.43 | 1.13 | 4.75 | 1.68 |

Construct a histogram of the transformed data. Compare your histogram to those given in Figure 7.33. Which of the cube-root and the square-root transformations appears to result in the more symmetric histogram(s)?

**7.40** ● The following data are a sample of survival times (in days from diagnosis) for patients suffering from chronic leukemia of a certain type (*Statistical Methodology for Survival Time Studies*, Bethesda, MD: National Cancer Institute, 1986):

| | | | | | | | |
|---|---|---|---|---|---|---|---|
| 7 | 47 | 58 | 74 | 177 | 232 | 273 | 285 |
| 317 | 429 | 440 | 445 | 455 | 468 | 495 | 497 |
| 532 | 571 | 579 | 581 | 650 | 702 | 715 | 779 |
| 881 | 900 | 930 | 968 | 1077 | 1109 | 1314 | 1334 |
| 1367 | 1534 | 1712 | 1784 | 1877 | 1886 | 2045 | 2056 |
| 2260 | 2429 | 2509 | 2045 | 2056 | | | |

a. Construct a relative frequency distribution for this data set, and draw the corresponding histogram.
b. Would you describe this histogram as having a positive or a negative skew?
c. Would you recommend transforming the data? Explain.

**7.41** ● In a study of warp breakage during the weaving of fabric (*Technometrics* [1982]: 59–65), 100 pieces of yarn were tested. The number of cycles of strain to breakage was recorded for each yarn sample. The resulting data are given in the following table:

| | | | | | | | | | |
|---|---|---|---|---|---|---|---|---|---|
| 86 | 146 | 251 | 653 | 98 | 249 | 400 | 292 | 131 | 176 |
| 76 | 264 | 15 | 364 | 195 | 262 | 88 | 264 | 42 | 321 |
| 180 | 198 | 38 | 20 | 61 | 121 | 282 | 180 | 325 | 250 |
| 196 | 90 | 229 | 166 | 38 | 337 | 341 | 40 | 40 | 135 |
| 597 | 246 | 211 | 180 | 93 | 571 | 124 | 279 | 81 | 186 |
| 497 | 182 | 423 | 185 | 338 | 290 | 398 | 71 | 246 | 185 |
| 188 | 568 | 55 | 244 | 20 | 284 | 93 | 396 | 203 | 829 |
| 239 | 236 | 277 | 143 | 198 | 264 | 105 | 203 | 124 | 137 |
| 135 | 169 | 157 | 224 | 65 | 315 | 229 | 55 | 286 | 350 |
| 193 | 175 | 220 | 149 | 151 | 353 | 400 | 61 | 194 | 188 |

a. Construct a frequency distribution using the class intervals 0 to <100, 100 to <200, and so on.
b. Draw the histogram corresponding to the frequency distribution in Part (a). How would you describe the shape of this histogram?
c. Find a transformation for these data that results in a more symmetric histogram than what you obtained in Part (b).

**7.42** ● The article "The Distribution of Buying Frequency Rates" (*Journal of Marketing Research* [1980]: 210–216) reported the results of a $3\frac{1}{2}$-yr study of dentifrice purchases. The investigators conducted their research using a national sample of 2071 households and recorded the number of toothpaste purchases for each household participating in the study. The results are given in the following frequency distribution:

| Number of Purchases | Number of Households (Frequency) | Number of Purchases | Number of Households (Frequency) |
|---------------------|----------------------------------|---------------------|----------------------------------|
| 10 to <20 | 904 | 90 to <100 | 13 |
| 20 to <30 | 500 | 100 to <110 | 9 |
| 30 to <40 | 258 | 110 to <120 | 7 |
| 40 to <50 | 167 | 120 to <130 | 6 |
| 50 to <60 | 94 | 130 to <140 | 6 |
| 60 to <70 | 56 | 140 to <150 | 3 |
| 70 to <80 | 26 | 150 to <160 | 0 |
| 80 to <90 | 20 | 160 to <170 | 2 |

a. Draw a histogram for this frequency distribution. Would you describe the histogram as positively or negatively skewed?
b. Does the square-root transformation result in a histogram that is more symmetric than that of the original data? (Be careful! This one is a bit tricky because you don't have the raw data; transforming the endpoints of the class intervals results in class intervals that are not

necessarily of equal widths, so the histogram of the transformed values has to be drawn with this in mind.)

7.43 ● Ecologists have long been interested in factors that might explain how far north or south particular animal species are found. As part of one such study, the paper "Temperature and the Northern Distributions of Wintering Birds" (*Ecology* [1991]: 2274–2285) gave the following body masses (in grams) for 50 different bird species that had previously been thought to have northern boundaries corresponding to a particular isotherm:

| | | | | | | | | |
|---|---|---|---|---|---|---|---|---|
| 7.7 | 10.1 | 21.6 | 8.6 | 12.0 | 11.4 | 16.6 | 9.4 | 11.5 |
| 9.0 | 8.2 | 20.2 | 48.5 | 21.6 | 26.1 | 6.2 | 19.1 | 21.0 |
| 28.1 | 10.6 | 31.6 | 6.7 | 5.0 | 68.8 | 23.9 | 19.8 | 20.1 |
| 6.0 | 99.6 | 19.8 | 16.5 | 9.0 | 448.0 | 21.3 | 17.4 | 36.9 |
| 34.0 | 41.0 | 15.9 | 12.5 | 10.2 | 31.0 | 21.5 | 11.9 | 32.5 |
| 9.8 | 93.9 | 10.9 | 19.6 | 14.5 | | | | |

a. Construct a stem-and-leaf display in which 448.0 is shown beside the display as an outlier value, the stem of an observation is the tens digit, the leaf is the ones digit, and the tenths digit is suppressed (e.g., 21.5 has stem 2 and leaf 1). What do you perceive as the most prominent feature of the display?

b. Draw a histogram based on the class intervals 5 to <10, 10 to <15, 15 to <20, 20 to <25, 25 to <30, 30 to <40, 40 to <50, 50 to <100, and 100 to <500. Is a transformation of the data desirable? Explain.

c. Use a calculator or statistical computer package to calculate logarithms of these observations and construct a histogram. Is the logarithmic transformation satisfactory?

d. Consider transformed value = $\dfrac{1}{\sqrt{\text{original value}}}$ and construct a histogram of the transformed data. Does it appear to resemble a normal curve?

7.44 The following figure appeared in the paper "EDTA-Extractable Copper, Zinc, and Manganese in Soils of the Canterbury Plains" (*New Zealand Journal of Agricultural Research* [1984]: 207–217):

**Figure for Exercise 7.44**

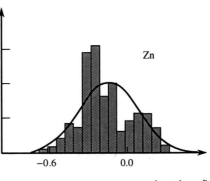

(*continued*)

**Figure for Exercise 7.44 (*continued*)**

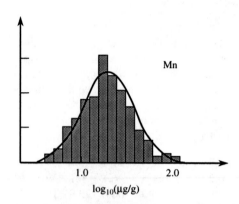

A large number of topsoil samples were analyzed for manganese (Mn), zinc (Zn), and copper (Cu), and the resulting data were summarized using histograms. The investigators

transformed each data set using logarithms in an effort to obtain more symmetric distributions of values. Do you think the transformations were successful? Explain.

**Bold** exercises answered in back    ● Data set available online but not required    ▼ Video solution available

# Activity **7.1** Rotten Eggs?

**Background:** The Salt Lake Tribune (October 11, 2002) printed the following account of an exchange between a restaurant manager and a health inspector:

> The recipe calls for four fresh eggs for each quiche. A Salt Lake County Health Department inspector paid a visit recently and pointed out that research by the Food and Drug Administration indicates that one in four eggs carries salmonella bacterium, so restaurants should never use more than three eggs when preparing quiche. The manager on duty wondered aloud if simply throwing out three eggs from each dozen and using the remaining nine in four-egg quiches would serve the same purpose.

1. Working in a group or as a class, discuss the folly of the above statement!

2. Suppose the following argument is made for three-egg quiches rather than four-egg quiches: Let $x$ = number of eggs that carry salmonella. Then

$$p(0) = P(x = 0) = (.75)^3 = .422$$

for three-egg quiches and

$$p(0) = P(x = 0) = (.75)^4 = .316$$

for four-egg quiches. What assumption must be made to justify these probability calculations? Do you think this is reasonable or not? Explain.

3. Suppose that a carton of one dozen eggs does happen to have exactly three eggs that carry salmonella and that

the manager does as he proposes: selects three eggs at random and throws them out, then uses the remaining nine eggs in four-egg quiches. Let $x$ = number of eggs that carry salmonella among four eggs selected at random from the remaining nine.

Working with a partner, conduct a simulation to approximate the distribution of $x$ by carrying out the following sequence of steps:

a. Take 12 identical slips of paper and write "Good" on 9 of them and "Bad" on the remaining 3. Place the slips of paper in a paper bag or some other container.

b. Mix the slips and then select three at random and remove them from the bag.

c. Mix the remaining slips and select four "eggs" from the bag.

d. Note the number of bad eggs among the four selected. (This is an observed $x$ value.)

e. Replace all slips, so that the bag now contains all 12 "eggs."

f. Repeat Steps (b)–(d) at least 10 times, each time recording the observed $x$ value.

4. Combine the observations from your group with those from the other groups. Use the resulting data to approximate the distribution of $x$. Comment on the resulting distribution in the context of the risk of salmonella exposure if the manager's proposed procedure is used.

# Summary of Key Concepts and Formulas

| Term or Formula | Comment |
|---|---|
| Population distribution | The distribution of all the values of a numerical variable or categories of a categorical variable. |
| Discrete numerical variable | A numerical variable whose possible values are isolated points along the number line. |
| Continuous numerical variable | A numerical variable whose possible values form an interval along the number line. |
| Continuous probability distribution (density curve) | A smooth curve that serves as a model for the population distribution of a continuous numerical variable. Areas under this curve are interpreted as probabilities. |
| $\mu, \sigma$ | The mean and standard deviation, respectively, of a probability distribution. The mean describes the center, and the standard deviation describes the spread of the probability distribution. |
| Normal distribution | A continuous probability distribution that is specified by a particular bell-shaped density curve. |
| Standard normal distribution (z curve) | The normal distribution with $\mu = 0$ and $\sigma = 1$. |
| $z = \dfrac{x - \mu}{\sigma}$ | The formula for a z score. When x has a normal distribution, z has a standard normal distribution. |
| Normal probability plot | A scatterplot of the (normal score, observed value) pairs. A linear pattern in the plot suggests that it is plausible that the data are from a normal population distribution. Curvature in the plot suggests that the population distribution is not normal. |

# Chapter Review Exercises 7.45–7.52

**7.45** A machine producing vitamin E capsules operates in such a way that the distribution of x = actual amount of vitamin E in a capsule can be modeled by a normal curve with mean 5 mg and standard deviation 0.05 mg. What is the probability that a randomly selected capsule contains less than 4.9 mg of vitamin E? at least 5.2 mg?

7.46 Accurate labeling of packaged meat is difficult because of weight decrease resulting from moisture loss (defined as a percentage of the package's original net weight). Suppose that the normal distribution with mean value 4.0% and standard deviation 1.0% is a reasonable model for the variable x = moisture loss for a package of chicken breasts. (This model is suggested in the paper "Drained Weight Labeling for Meat and Poultry: An Economic Analysis of a Regulatory Proposal," *Journal of Consumer Affairs* [1980]: 307–325.)

a. What is the probability that x is between 3.0% and 5.0%?
b. What is the probability that x is at most 4.0%?
c. What is the probability that x is at least 7%?
d. Describe the largest 10% of the moisture loss distribution.

**e.** Describe the most extreme 10% of the moisture loss distribution. (Hint: The most extreme 10% consists of the largest 5% and the smallest 5%.)

**7.47** The *Wall Street Journal* (February 15, 1972) reported that General Electric was being sued in Texas for sex discrimination because of a minimum height requirement of 5 ft 7 in. The suit claimed that this restriction eliminated more than 94% of adult females from consideration. Let $x$ represent the height of a randomly selected adult woman. Suppose that the probability distribution of $x$ is approximately normal with mean 66 in. and standard deviation 2 in.
**a.** Is the claim that 94% of all women are shorter than 5 ft 7 in. correct?
**b.** What proportion of adult women would be excluded from employment because of the height restriction?

**7.48** Your statistics professor tells you that the distribution of scores on a midterm exam was approximately normal with a mean of 78 and a standard deviation of 7. The top 15% of all scores have been designated A's. Your score was 89. Did you receive an A? Explain.

**7.49** Suppose that the distribution of pH readings for soil samples taken in a certain geographic region can be approximated by a normal distribution with mean 6.00 and standard deviation 0.10. The pH of a randomly selected soil sample from this region is to be determined.
**a.** What is the probability that the resulting pH is between 5.90 and 6.15?
**b.** What is the probability that the resulting pH exceeds 6.10?
**c.** What is the probability that the resulting pH is at most 5.95?
**d.** Describe the largest 5% of the pH distribution.

**7.50** The light bulbs used to provide exterior lighting for a large office building have an average lifetime of 700 hr. If the distribution of the variable $x$ = length of bulb life can be modeled as a normal distribution with a standard deviation of 50 hr, how often should all the bulbs be replaced so that only 20% of the bulbs will have already burned out?

**7.51** Let $x$ denote the duration of a randomly selected pregnancy (the time elapsed between conception and birth). Accepted values for the mean value and standard deviation of $x$ are 266 days and 16 days, respectively. Suppose that a normal distribution is an appropriate model for the probability distribution of $x$.
**a.** What is the probability that the duration of pregnancy is between 250 and 300 days?
**b.** What is the probability that the duration of pregnancy is at most 240 days?
**c.** What is the probability that the duration of pregnancy is within 16 days of the mean duration?
**d.** A *Dear Abby* column dated January 20, 1973, contained a letter from a woman who stated that the duration of her pregnancy was exactly 310 days. (She wrote that the last visit with her husband, who was in the navy, occurred 310 days before the birth.) What is the probability that the duration of a pregnancy is at least 310 days? Does this probability make you a bit skeptical of the claim?
**e.** Some insurance companies will pay the medical expenses associated with childbirth only if the insurance has been in effect for more than 9 months (275 days). This restriction is designed to ensure that the insurance company has to pay benefits only for those pregnancies for which conception occurred during coverage. Suppose that conception occurred 2 weeks after coverage began. What is the probability that the insurance company will refuse to pay benefits because of the 275-day insurance requirement?

**7.52** Let $x$ denote the systolic blood pressure of an individual selected at random from a certain population. Suppose that the normal distribution with mean $\mu = 120$ mm Hg and standard deviation $\sigma = 10$ mm Hg is a reasonable model for describing the population distribution of $x$. (The article "Oral Contraceptives, Pregnancy, and Blood Pressure," *Journal of the American Medical Association* [1972]: 1507–1510, reported on the results of a large study in which a sample histogram of blood pressures among women of similar ages was found to be well approximated by a normal curve.)
**a.** Calculate $P(110 < x < 140)$. How does this compare to $P(110 \le x \le 140)$, and why?
**b.** Calculate $P(x < 75)$.
**c.** Calculate $P(x < 95 \text{ or } x > 145)$, the probability that $x$ is more than 2.5 standard deviations from its mean value.

Mentor
Do you need a live tutor for homework problems?

**Thomson**NOW
Are you ready? Take your exam-prep post-test now.

## Chapter 7

# Hypothesis Testing Using a Single Sample

© Royalty-Free/Corbis

In Chapter 9, we considered situations in which the primary goal was to estimate the unknown value of some population characteristic. Sample data can also be used to decide whether some claim or *hypothesis* about a population characteristic is plausible. For example, cross-border purchasing of prescription drugs is a controversial topic of current interest, and there has been a great deal of media coverage on the practice of importing prescription medications from Canada or Mexico. But is this really a common practice? The article "Much Ado About Cross-Border Prescription Purchasing" (Ipsos, February 19, 2004) summarized the results of a poll of 1000 randomly selected adult Americans and reported that only 15 of the 750 adults in the sample who had purchased prescription drugs in the past year had made a purchase from a pharmacy in Canada or Mexico. Let $\pi$ denote the proportion of all American adults who have made a prescription drug purchase in the last year from a Canadian or Mexican pharmacy. The hypothesis testing methods presented in this chapter can be used to decide whether the sample data from this survey provide strong support for the hypothesis that this proportion is small, for example $\pi < .05$.

As another example, a report released by the National Association of Colleges and Employers stated that the average starting salary for students graduating in 2006 with a degree in accounting was \$45,656 ("Starting Salary Offers to New College Grads Continue to Climb," July 12, 2006, available at www.naceweb.org/press). Suppose that you are interested in investigating whether the mean starting salary for students graduating with an accounting degree from your university this year is greater than the 2006 average of \$45,656. You select a random sample of $n = 40$ accounting graduates from the current graduating class of your university and determine the starting salary of each one. If this sample produced a mean starting salary of $45,958 and a standard deviation of $1214, is it reasonable to conclude that $\mu$ the current mean starting salary for all accounting graduates in the current graduating class at your university, is greater than $45,656 (i.e., $\mu = 45,656$)? We will see in this chapter how these sample data can be analyzed to decide whether $\mu > 45,656$ is a reasonable conclusion.

# 10.1 Hypotheses and Test Procedures

A hypothesis is a claim or statement about the value of a single population characteristic or the values of several population characteristics. The following are examples of legitimate hypotheses:

$\mu = 1000$, where $\mu$ is the mean number of characters in an email message
$\pi < .01$, where $\pi$ is the proportion of email messages that are undeliverable

In contrast, the statements $\bar{x} = 1000$ and $p = .01$ are *not* hypotheses, because $\bar{x}$ and $p$ are *sample* characteristics.

A **test of hypotheses** or **test procedure** is a method that uses sample data to decide between two competing claims (hypotheses) about a population characteristic. One hypothesis might be $\mu = 1000$ and the other $\mu \neq 1000$ or one hypothesis might be $\pi = .01$ and the other $\pi < .01$. If it were possible to carry out a census of the entire population, we would know which of the two hypotheses is correct, but usually we must decide between them using information from a sample.

A criminal trial is a familiar situation in which a choice between two contradictory claims must be made. The person accused of the crime must be judged either guilty or not guilty. Under the U.S. system of justice, the individual on trial is initially presumed not guilty. Only strong evidence to the contrary causes the not guilty claim to be rejected in favor of a guilty verdict. The burden is thus put on the prosecution to prove the guilty claim. The French perspective in criminal proceedings is the opposite of ours. There, once enough evidence has been presented to justify bringing an individual to trial, the initial assumption is that the accused is guilty. The burden of proof then falls on the accused to establish otherwise.

As in a judicial proceeding, we initially assume that a particular hypothesis, called the *null hypothesis,* is the correct one. We then consider the evidence (the sample data) and reject the null hypothesis in favor of the competing hypothesis, called the *alternative hypothesis,* only if there is *convincing* evidence against the null hypothesis.

---

**DEFINITION**

The **null hypothesis,** denoted by $H_0$, is a claim about a population characteristic that is initially assumed to be true.

The **alternative hypothesis,** denoted by $H_a$, is the competing claim.

In carrying out a test of $H_0$ versus $H_a$, the hypothesis $H_0$ will be rejected in favor of $H_a$ only if sample evidence strongly suggests that $H_0$ is false. If the sample does not provide such evidence, $H_0$ will not be rejected. The two possible conclusions are then *reject $H_0$* or *fail to reject $H_0$*.

# Example 10.1 Tennis Ball Diameters

Because of variation in the manufacturing process, tennis balls produced by a particular machine do not have identical diameters. Let $\mu$ denote the true average diameter for tennis balls currently being produced. Suppose that the machine was initially calibrated to achieve the design specification $\mu = 3$ in. However, the manufacturer is now concerned that the diameters no longer conform to this specification. That is, $\mu \neq 3$ in. must now be considered a possibility. If sample evidence suggests that $\mu \neq 3$ in., the production process will have to be halted while the machine is recalibrated. Because stopping production is costly, the manufacturer wants to be quite sure that $\mu \neq 3$ in. before undertaking recalibration. Under these circumstances, a sensible choice of hypotheses is

$H_0$: $\mu = 3$ (the specification is being met, so recalibration is unnecessary)
$H_a$: $\mu \neq 3$ (the specification is not being met, so recalibration is necessary)

Only compelling sample evidence would then result in $H_0$ being rejected in favor of $H_a$.

■

# Example 10.2 Lightbulb Lifetimes

Kmart brand 60W lightbulbs state on the package "Avg. Life 1000 Hr." Let $\mu$ denote the true mean life of Kmart 60-W lightbulbs. Then the advertised claim is $\mu = 1000$ hr. People who purchase this brand would be unhappy if $\mu$ is actually less than the advertised value. Suppose that a sample of Kmart lightbulbs is selected and the lifetime for each bulb in the sample is recorded. The sample results can then be used to test the hypothesis $\mu = 1000$ hr against the hypothesis $\mu < 1000$ hr. The accusation that the company is overstating the mean lifetime is a serious one, and it is reasonable to require compelling evidence from the sample before concluding that $\mu < 1000$. This suggests that the claim $\mu = 1000$ should be selected as the null hypothesis and that $\mu < 1000$ should be selected as the alternative hypothesis. Then

$$H_0: \mu = 1000$$

would be rejected in favor of

$$H_a: \mu < 1000$$

only if sample evidence strongly suggests that the initial assumption, $\mu = 1000$ hr, is not plausible.

■

Because the alternative hypothesis in Example 10.2 asserted that $\mu < 1000$ (true average lifetime is less than the advertised value), it might have seemed sensible to state $H_0$ as the inequality $\mu \geq 1000$. The assertion $\mu \geq 1000$ is in fact the *implicit* null hypothesis, but we will state $H_0$ explicitly as a claim of equality. There are several reasons for this. First of all, the development of a decision rule is most easily understood if there is only a single hypothesized value of $\mu$ (or $\pi$ or whatever other population characteristic is under consideration). Second, suppose that the sample data provided compelling evidence that $H_0$: $\mu = 1000$ should be rejected in favor of $H_a$: $\mu < 1000$. This means that we were convinced by the sample data that the true mean was smaller than 1000. It follows that we would have also been convinced that the true mean could not have been 1001 or 1010 or any other value that was larger than 1000. As a consequence, the conclusion when testing $H_0$: $\mu = 1000$ versus $H_a$: $\mu < 1000$ is always the same as the conclusion for a test where the null hypothesis is $H_0$: $\mu \geq 1000$. For these reasons it is customary to state the null hypothesis $H_0$ as a claim of equality.

The form of a null hypothesis is

$H_0$: population characteristic = hypothesized value

where the hypothesized value is a specific number determined by the problem context.

The alternative hypothesis will have one of the following three forms:

$H_a$: population characteristic > hypothesized value
$H_a$: population characteristic < hypothesized value
$H_a$: population characteristic ≠ hypothesized value

Thus, we might test $H_0$: $\pi = .1$ versus $H_a$: $\pi < .1$; but we won't test $H_0$: $\mu = 50$ versus $H_a$: $\mu > 100$. The number appearing in the alternative hypothesis must be identical to the hypothesized value in $H_0$.

Example 10.3 illustrates how the selection of $H_0$ (the claim initially believed true) and $H_a$ depend on the objectives of a study.

# Example 10.3 Evaluating a New Medical Treatment

A medical research team has been given the task of evaluating a new laser treatment for certain types of tumors. Consider the following two scenarios:

Scenario 1: The current standard treatment is considered reasonable and safe by the medical community, has no major side effects, and has a known success rate of 0.85 (85%).

Scenario 2: The current standard treatment sometimes has serious side effects, is costly, and has a known success rate of 0.30 (30%).

In the first scenario, research efforts would probably be directed toward determining whether the new treatment has a higher success rate than the standard treatment. Unless convincing evidence of this is presented, it is unlikely that current medical practice would be changed. With $\pi$ representing the true proportion of successes for the laser treatment, the following hypotheses would be tested:

$$H_0: \ \pi = .85 \text{ versus } H_a: \ \pi > .85$$

In this case, rejection of the null hypothesis is indicative of compelling evidence that the success rate is higher for the new treatment.

In the second scenario, the current standard treatment does not have much to recommend it. The new laser treatment may be considered preferable because of cost or because it has fewer or less serious side effects, as long as the success rate for the new procedure is no worse than that of the standard treatment. Here, researchers might decide to test the hypothesis

$$H_0: \pi = .30 \text{ versus } H_a: \pi < .30$$

If the null hypothesis is rejected, the new treatment will not be put forward as an alternative to the standard treatment, because there is strong evidence that the laser method has a lower success rate.

If the null hypothesis is not rejected, we are able to conclude only that there is not convincing evidence that the success rate for the laser treatment is lower than that for the standard. This is *not* the same as saying that we have evidence that the laser treatment is as good as the standard treatment. If medical practice were to embrace the new procedure, it would not be because it has a higher success rate but rather because it costs less or has fewer side effects, and there is not strong evidence that it has a lower success rate than the standard treatment.

■

You should be careful in setting up the hypotheses for a test. *Remember that a statistical hypothesis test is only capable of demonstrating strong support for the alternative hypothesis (by rejection of the null hypothesis). When the null hypothesis is not rejected, it does not mean strong support for $H_0$—only lack of strong evidence against it.* In the lightbulb scenario of Example 10.2, if $H_0: \mu = 1000$ is rejected in favor of $H_a: \mu < 1000$, it is because we have strong evidence for believing that true average lifetime is less than the advertised value. However, nonrejection of $H_0$ does not necessarily provide strong support for the advertised claim. If the objective is to demonstrate that the average lifetime is greater than 1000 hr, the hypotheses to be tested are $H_0: \mu = 1000$ versus $H_a: \mu > 1000$. Now rejection of $H_0$ indicates strong evidence that $\mu > 1000$. When deciding which alternative hypothesis to use, *keep the research objectives in mind.*

■ **Exercises 10.1–10.11** .............................................................................

**10.1** Explain why the statement $\bar{x} = 50$ is not a legitimate hypothesis.

10.2 For the following pairs, indicate which do not comply with the rules for setting up hypotheses, and explain why:
a. $H_0: \mu = 15, H_a: \mu = 15$
b. $H_0: \pi = .4, H_a: \pi > .6$
c. $H_0: \mu = 123, H_a: \mu < 123$
d. $H_0: \mu = 123, H_a: \mu = 125$
e. $H_0: p = .1, H_a: p \neq .1$

**10.3** To determine whether the pipe welds in a nuclear power plant meet specifications, a random sample of welds is selected and tests are conducted on each weld in the sample. Weld strength is measured as the force required to break the weld. Suppose that the specifications state that the mean strength of welds should exceed 100 lb/in.$^2$. The inspection team decides to test $H_0: \mu = 100$ versus $H_a: \mu > 100$. Explain why this alternative hypothesis was chosen rather than $\mu < 100$.

10.4 Do state laws that allow private citizens to carry concealed weapons result in a reduced crime rate? The author of a study carried out by the Brookings Institution is reported as saying, "The strongest thing I could say is that I don't see any strong evidence that they are reducing crime" (*San Luis Obispo Tribune,* January 23, 2003).

a. Is this conclusion consistent with testing

$H_0$: concealed weapons laws reduce crime

versus

$H_a$: concealed weapons laws do not reduce crime

or with testing

$H_0$: concealed weapons laws do not reduce crime

versus

$H_a$: concealed weapons laws reduce crime

Explain.

b. Does the stated conclusion indicate that the null hypothesis was rejected or not rejected? Explain.

**10.5** Consider the following quote from the article "Review Finds No Link Between Vaccine and Autism" (*San Luis Obispo Tribune,* October 19, 2005): "'We found no evidence that giving MMR causes Crohn's disease and/or autism in the children that get the MMR,' said Tom Jefferson, one of the authors of *The Cochrane Review.* 'That does not mean it doesn't cause it. It means we could find no evidence of it.'" (MMR is a measles-mumps-rubella vaccine.) In the context of a hypothesis test with the null hypothesis being that MMR does not cause autism, explain why the author could not just conclude that the MMR vaccine does not cause autism.

**10.6** A certain university has decided to introduce the use of plus and minus with letter grades, as long as there is evidence that more than 60% of the faculty favor the change. A random sample of faculty will be selected, and the resulting data will be used to test the relevant hypotheses. If $\pi$ represents the true proportion of all faculty that favor a change to plus–minus grading, which of the following pair of hypotheses should the administration test:

$H_0$: $\pi = .6$ versus $H_a$: $\pi < .6$

or

$H_0$: $\pi = .6$ versus $H_a$: $\pi > .6$

Explain your choice.

**10.7** ▼ A certain television station has been providing live coverage of a particularly sensational criminal trial. The station's program director wishes to know whether more than half the potential viewers prefer a return to regular daytime programming. A survey of randomly selected viewers is conducted. Let $\pi$ represent the true proportion of viewers who prefer regular daytime programming. What hypotheses should the program director test to answer the question of interest?

**10.8** Researchers have postulated that because of differences in diet, Japanese children have a lower mean blood cholesterol level than U.S. children do. Suppose that the mean level for U.S. children is known to be 170. Let $\mu$ represent the true mean blood cholesterol level for Japanese children. What hypotheses should the researchers test?

**10.9** A county commissioner must vote on a resolution that would commit substantial resources to the construction of a sewer in an outlying residential area. Her fiscal decisions have been criticized in the past, so she decides to take a survey of constituents to find out whether they favor spending money for a sewer system. She will vote to appropriate funds only if she can be fairly certain that a majority of the people in her district favor the measure. What hypotheses should she test?

**10.10** The mean length of long-distance telephone calls placed with a particular phone company was known to be 7.3 min under an old rate structure. In an attempt to be more competitive with other long-distance carriers, the phone company lowered long-distance rates, thinking that its customers would be encouraged to make longer calls and thus that there would not be a big loss in revenue. Let $\mu$ denote the true mean length of long-distance calls after the rate reduction. What hypotheses should the phone company test to determine whether the mean length of long-distance calls increased with the lower rates?

**10.11** ▼ Many older homes have electrical systems that use fuses rather than circuit breakers. A manufacturer of 40-amp fuses wants to make sure that the mean amperage at which its fuses burn out is in fact 40. If the mean amperage is lower than 40, customers will complain because the fuses require replacement too often. If the mean amperage is higher than 40, the manufacturer might be liable for damage to an electrical system as a result of fuse malfunction. To verify the mean amperage of the fuses, a sample of fuses is selected and tested. If a hypothesis test is performed using the resulting data, what null and alternative hypotheses would be of interest to the manufacturer?

## 10.2 Errors in Hypothesis Testing

Once hypotheses have been formulated, we employ a method called a **test procedure** to use sample data to determine whether $H_0$ should be rejected. Just as a jury may reach the wrong verdict in a trial, there is some chance that using a test procedure with sample data may lead us to the wrong conclusion about a population characteristic. In this section, we discuss the kinds of errors that can occur and consider how the choice of a test procedure influences the chances of these errors.

One erroneous conclusion in a criminal trial is for a jury to convict an innocent person, and another is for a guilty person to be set free. Similarly, there are two different types of errors that might be made when making a decision in a hypothesis testing problem. One type of error involves rejecting $H_0$ even though the null hypothesis is true. The second type of error results from failing to reject $H_0$ when it is false. These errors are known as Type I and Type II errors, respectively.

> **DEFINITION**
>
> **Type I error:**  the error of rejecting $H_0$ when $H_0$ is true
> **Type II error:**  the error of failing to reject $H_0$ when $H_0$ is false

The only way to guarantee that neither type of error occurs is to base the decision on a census of the entire population. The risk of error is the price researchers pay for basing an inference on a sample. With any reasonable sample-based procedure, there is some chance that a Type I error will be made and some chance that a Type II error will result.

## Example 10.4 On-Time Arrivals

The U.S. Bureau of Transportation Statistics reports that for 2005, 78.6% of all domestic passenger flights arrived on time (meaning within 15 min of the scheduled arrival). Suppose that an airline with a poor on-time record decides to offer its employees a bonus if, in an upcoming month, the airline's proportion of on-time flights exceeds the overall industry rate of 0.786. Let $\pi$ be the true proportion of the airline's flights that are on time during the month of interest. A random sample of flights might be selected and used as a basis for choosing between

$$H_0: \pi = .786 \text{ and } H_a: \pi > .786$$

In this context, a Type I error (rejecting a true $H_0$) results in the airline rewarding its employees when in fact their true proportion of on-time flights did not exceed .786. A Type II error (not rejecting a false $H_0$) results in the airline employees *not* receiving a reward that in fact they deserved.

■

## Example 10.5 Slowing the Growth of Tumors

In 2004, Vertex Pharmaceuticals, a biotechnology company, issued a press release announcing that it had filed an application with the Food and Drug Administration to begin clinical trials of an experimental drug VX-680 that had been found to reduce the growth rate of pancreatic and colon cancer tumors in animal studies (*New York Times,* February 24, 2004).

Let $\mu$ denote the true mean growth rate of tumors for patients receiving the experimental drug. Data resulting from the planned clinical trials can be used to test

$H_0$: $\mu$ = mean growth rate of tumors for patients not taking the experimental drug

versus

$H_a$: $\mu$ < mean growth rate of tumors for patients not taking the experimental drug

The null hypothesis states that the experimental drug is not effective—that the mean growth rate of tumors for patients receiving the experimental drug is the same as for patients who do not take the experimental drug. The alternative hypothesis states that the experimental drug is effective in reducing the mean growth rate of tumors. In this context, a Type I error consists of incorrectly concluding that the experimental drug is effective in slowing the growth rate of tumors. A Type II error consists of concluding that the experimental drug is ineffective when in fact the mean growth rate of tumors is reduced.

■

Examples 10.4 and 10.5 illustrate the two different types of error that might occur when testing hypotheses. Type I and Type II errors—and the associated consequences of making such errors—are quite different. The accompanying box introduces the terminology and notation used to describe error probabilities.

> ### Definition
>
> The **probability of a Type I error** is denoted by $\alpha$ and is called the **level of significance** of the test. Thus, a test with $\alpha = .01$ is said to have a level of significance of .01 or to be a level .01 test.
>
> The **probability of a Type II error** is denoted by $\beta$.

## Example 10.6 Blood Test for Ovarian Cancer

Women with ovarian cancer usually are not diagnosed until the disease is in an advanced stage, when it is most difficult to treat. A blood test has been developed that appears to be able to identify ovarian cancer at its earliest stages. In a report issued by the National Cancer Institute and the Food and Drug Administration (February 8, 2002), the following information from a preliminary evaluation of the blood test was given:

* The test was given to 50 women known to have ovarian cancer, and it correctly identified all of them as having cancer.

※ The test was given to 66 women known not to have ovarian cancer, and it correctly identified 63 of these 66 as being cancer free.

We can think of using this blood test to choose between two hypotheses:

$H_0$: woman has ovarian cancer
$H_a$: woman does not have ovarian cancer

Note that although these are not "statistical hypotheses" (statements about a population characteristic), the possible decision errors are analogous to Type I and Type II errors.

In this situation, believing that a woman with ovarian cancer is cancer free would be a Type I error—rejecting the hypothesis of ovarian cancer when it is in fact true. Believing that a woman who is actually cancer free does have ovarian cancer is a Type II error—not rejecting the null hypothesis when it is in fact false. Based on the preliminary study results, we can estimate the error probabilities. The probability of a Type I error, $\alpha$, is approximately $0/50 = 0$. The probability of a Type II error, $\beta$, is approximately $3/66 = .046$.

■

The ideal test procedure would result in both $\alpha = 0$ and $\beta = 0$. However, if we must base our decision on incomplete information—a sample rather than a census —it is impossible to achieve this ideal. The standard test procedures allow us to control $\alpha$, but they provide no direct control over $\beta$. Because $\alpha$ represents the probability of rejecting a true null hypothesis, selecting a significance level $\alpha = .05$ results in a test procedure that, used over and over with different samples, rejects a *true* $H_0$ about 5 times in 100. Selecting $\alpha = .01$ results in a test procedure with a Type I error rate of 1% in long-term repeated use. Choosing a small value for $\alpha$ implies that the user wants to use a procedure for which the risk of a Type I error is quite small.

One question arises naturally at this point: If we can select $\alpha$, the probability of making a Type I error, why would we ever select $\alpha = .05$ rather than $\alpha = .01$? Why not always select a very small value for $\alpha$? To achieve a small probability of making a Type I error, we would need the corresponding test procedure to require the evidence against $H_0$ to be very strong before the null hypothesis can be rejected. Although this makes a Type I error unlikely, it increases the risk of a Type II error (*not* rejecting $H_0$ when it should have been rejected). Frequently the investigator must balance the consequences of Type I and Type II errors. If a Type II error has serious consequences, it may be a good idea to select a somewhat larger value for $\alpha$.

In general, there is a compromise between small $\alpha$ and small $\beta$, leading to the following widely accepted principle for specifying a test procedure.

After assessing the consequences of Type I and Type II errors, identify the largest $\alpha$ that is tolerable for the problem. Then employ a test procedure that uses this maximum acceptable value —rather than anything smaller—as the level of significance (because using a smaller $\alpha$ increases $\beta$). In other words, don't make $\alpha$ smaller than it needs to be.

■

..................................................................................................................................................

# Example 10.7 Lead in Tap Water

In 1991, the Environmental Protection Agency (EPA) adopted what is known as the Lead and Copper Rule, which defines drinking water as unsafe if the concentration of lead is 15 parts per billion (ppb) or greater or if the concentration of copper is 1.3 parts per million (ppm) or greater. The "2003 National Public Water Systems Compliance Report" (EPA, September 2005) indicates that 6% of public water systems reported violation of a health-based drinking water standard in 2003 and that 5% of these were violation of the Lead and Copper Rule. With $\mu$ denoting the mean concentration of lead, a water system monitoring lead levels might use lead level measurements from a sample of water specimens to test

$$H_0: \mu = 15 \text{ versus } H_a: \mu < 15$$

The null hypothesis (which is equivalent to the assertion $\mu \geq 15$) states that the mean lead concentration is excessive by EPA standards. The alternative hypothesis states that the mean lead concentration is at an acceptable level and that the water system meets EPA standards for lead.

In this context, a Type I error leads to the conclusion that a water source meets EPA standards for lead when in fact it does not. Possible consequences of this type of error include health risks associated with excessive lead consumption (e.g., increased blood pressure, hearing loss, and, in severe cases, anemia and kidney damage). A Type II error is to conclude that the water does not meet EPA standards for lead when in fact it actually does. Possible consequences of a Type II error include elimination of a community water source. Because a Type I error might result in potentially serious public health risks, a small value of $\alpha$ (Type I error probability), such as $\alpha = .01$, could be selected. Of course, selecting a small value for $\alpha$ increases the risk of a Type II error. If the community has only one water source, a Type II error could also have very serious consequences for the community, and we might want to rethink our choice of $\alpha$.

■

■ Exercises 10.12–10.22 ....................................................................................................................

10.12 Researchers at the University of Washington and Harvard University analyzed records of breast cancer screening and diagnostic evaluations ("Mammogram Cancer Scares More Frequent than Thought," *USA Today*, April 16, 1998). Discussing the benefits and downsides of the screening process, the article states that, although the rate of false-positives is higher than previously thought, if radiologists were less aggressive in following up on suspicious tests, the rate of false-positives would fall but the rate of missed cancers would rise. Suppose that such a screening test is used to decide between a null hypothesis of $H_0$: no cancer is present and an alternative hypothesis

of $H_a$: cancer is present. (Although these are not hypotheses about a population characteristic, this exercise illustrates the definitions of Type I and Type II errors.)
a. Would a false-positive (thinking that cancer is present when in fact it is not) be a Type I error or a Type II error?
b. Describe a Type I error in the context of this problem, and discuss the consequences of making a Type I error.
c. Describe a Type II error in the context of this problem, and discuss the consequences of making a Type II error.
d. What aspect of the relationship between the probability of Type I and Type II errors is being described by the statement in the article that if radiologists were less

aggressive in following up on suspicious tests, the rate of false-positives would fall but the rate of missed cancers would rise?

**10.13** Medical personnel are required to report suspected cases of child abuse. Because some diseases have symptoms that mimic those of child abuse, doctors who see a child with these symptoms must decide between two competing hypotheses:

$H_0$: symptoms are due to child abuse
$H_a$: symptoms are due to disease

(Although these are not hypotheses about a population characteristic, this exercise illustrates the definitions of Type I and Type II errors.) The article "Blurred Line Between Illness, Abuse Creates Problem for Authorities" (*Macon Telegraph*, February 28, 2000) included the following quote from a doctor in Atlanta regarding the consequences of making an incorrect decision: "If it's disease, the worst you have is an angry family. If it is abuse, the other kids (in the family) are in deadly danger."
**a.** For the given hypotheses, describe Type I and Type II errors.
**b.** Based on the quote regarding consequences of the two kinds of error, which type of error does the doctor quoted consider more serious? Explain.

10.14 Ann Landers, in her advice column of October 24, 1994 (*San Luis Obispo Telegram-Tribune*), described the reliability of DNA paternity testing as follows: "To get a completely accurate result, you would have to be tested, and so would (the man) and your mother. The test is 100 percent accurate if the man is *not* the father and 99.9 percent accurate if he is."
a. Consider using the results of DNA paternity testing to decide between the following two hypotheses:

$H_0$: a particular man is the father
$H_a$: a particular man is not the father

In the context of this problem, describe Type I and Type II errors. (Although these are not hypotheses about a population characteristic, this exercise illustrates the definitions of Type I and Type II errors.)
b. Based on the information given, what are the values of $\alpha$, the probability of Type I error, and $\beta$, the probability of Type II error?
c. Ann Landers also stated, "If the mother is not tested, there is a 0.8 percent chance of a false positive." For the hypotheses given in Part (a), what are the values of $\alpha$ and

$\beta$ if the decision is based on DNA testing in which the mother is not tested?

**10.15** ▼ Pizza Hut, after test-marketing a new product called the Bigfoot Pizza, concluded that introduction of the Bigfoot nationwide would increase its sales by more than 14% (*USA Today*, April 2, 1993). This conclusion was based on recording sales information for a random sample of Pizza Hut restaurants selected for the marketing trial. With $\mu$ denoting the mean percentage increase in sales for all Pizza Hut restaurants, consider using the sample data to decide between $H_0$: $\mu = 14$ and $H_a$: $\mu > 14$.
**a.** Is Pizza Hut's conclusion consistent with a decision to reject $H_0$ or to fail to reject $H_0$?
**b.** If Pizza Hut is incorrect in its conclusion, is the company making a Type I or a Type II error?

10.16 A television manufacturer claims that (at least) 90% of its TV sets will need no service during the first 3 years of operation. A consumer agency wishes to check this claim, so it obtains a random sample of $n = 100$ purchasers and asks each whether the set purchased needed repair during the first 3 years after purchase. Let $p$ be the sample proportion of responses indicating no repair (so that no repair is identified with a success). Let $\pi$ denote the true proportion of successes for all sets made by this manufacturer. The agency does not want to claim false advertising unless sample evidence strongly suggests that $\pi < .9$. The appropriate hypotheses are then $H_0$: $\pi = .9$ versus $H_a$: $\pi < .9$.
a. In the context of this problem, describe Type I and Type II errors, and discuss the possible consequences of each.
b. Would you recommend a test procedure that uses $\alpha = .10$ or one that uses $\alpha = .01$? Explain.

**10.17** A manufacturer of hand-held calculators receives large shipments of printed circuits from a supplier. It is too costly and time-consuming to inspect all incoming circuits, so when each shipment arrives, a sample is selected for inspection. Information from the sample is then used to test $H_0$: $\pi = .05$ versus $H_a$: $\pi > .05$, where $\pi$ is the true proportion of defective circuits in the shipment. If the null hypothesis is not rejected, the shipment is accepted, and the circuits are used in the production of calculators. If the null hypothesis is rejected, the entire shipment is returned to the supplier because of inferior quality. (A shipment is defined to be of inferior quality if it contains more than 5% defective circuits.)

**a.** In this context, define Type I and Type II errors.
**b.** From the calculator manufacturer's point of view, which type of error is considered more serious?
**c.** From the printed circuit supplier's point of view, which type of error is considered more serious?

**10.18** Water samples are taken from water used for cooling as it is being discharged from a power plant into a river. It has been determined that as long as the mean temperature of the discharged water is at most 150°F, there will be no negative effects on the river's ecosystem. To investigate whether the plant is in compliance with regulations that prohibit a mean discharge water temperature above 150°F, researchers will take 50 water samples at randomly selected times and record the temperature of each sample. The resulting data will be used to test the hypotheses $H_0$: $\mu = 150°F$ versus $H_a$: $\mu > 150°F$. In the context of this example, describe Type I and Type II errors. Which type of error would you consider more serious? Explain.

**10.19** ▼ Occasionally, warning flares of the type contained in most automobile emergency kits fail to ignite. A consumer advocacy group wants to investigate a claim against a manufacturer of flares brought by a person who claims that the proportion of defective flares is much higher than the value of .1 claimed by the manufacturer. A large number of flares will be tested, and the results will be used to decide between $H_0$: $\pi = .1$ and $H_a$: $\pi > .1$, where $\pi$ represents the true proportion of defective flares made by this manufacturer. If $H_0$ is rejected, charges of false advertising will be filed against the manufacturer.
**a.** Explain why the alternative hypothesis was chosen to be $H_a$: $\pi > .1$.
**b.** In this context, describe Type I and Type II errors, and discuss the consequences of each.

**10.20** Suppose that you are an inspector for the Fish and Game Department and that you are given the task of determining whether to prohibit fishing along part of the Oregon coast. You will close an area to fishing if it is determined that fish in that region have an unacceptably high mercury content.
a. Assuming that a mercury concentration of 5 ppm is considered the maximum safe concentration, which of the following pairs of hypotheses would you test:

$H_0$: $\mu = 5$ versus $H_a$: $\mu > 5$

or

$H_0$: $\mu = 5$ versus $H_a$: $\mu < 5$

Give the reasons for your choice.
b. Would you prefer a significance level of .1 or .01 for your test? Explain.

**10.21** The National Cancer Institute conducted a 2-year study to determine whether cancer death rates for areas near nuclear power plants are higher than for areas without nuclear facilities (*San Luis Obispo Telegram-Tribune*, September 17, 1990). A spokesperson for the Cancer Institute said, "From the data at hand, there was no convincing evidence of any increased risk of death from any of the cancers surveyed due to living near nuclear facilities. However, no study can prove the absence of an effect."
**a.** Let $\pi$ denote the true proportion of the population in areas near nuclear power plants who die of cancer during a given year. The researchers at the Cancer Institute might have considered the two rival hypotheses of the form

$H_0$: $\pi$ = value for areas without nuclear facilities
$H_a$: $\pi$ > value for areas without nuclear facilities

Did the researchers reject $H_0$ or fail to reject $H_0$?
**b.** If the Cancer Institute researchers were incorrect in their conclusion that there is no increased cancer risk associated with living near a nuclear power plant, are they making a Type I or a Type II error? Explain.
**c.** Comment on the spokesperson's last statement that no study can *prove* the absence of an effect. Do you agree with this statement?

**10.22** An automobile manufacturer is considering using robots for part of its assembly process. Converting to robots is an expensive process, so it will be undertaken only if there is strong evidence that the proportion of defective installations is lower for the robots than for human assemblers. Let $\pi$ denote the true proportion of defective installations for the robots. It is known that human assemblers have a defect proportion of .02.
a. Which of the following pairs of hypotheses should the manufacturer test:

$H_0$: $\pi = .02$ versus $H_a$: $\pi < .02$

or

$H_0$: $\pi = .02$ versus $H_a$: $\pi > .02$

Explain your answer.

b. In the context of this exercise, describe Type I and Type II errors.

c. Would you prefer a test with $\alpha = .01$ or $\alpha = .1$? Explain your reasoning.

**Bold** exercises answered in back     ● Data set available online but not required     ▼ Video solution available

# 10.3  Large-Sample Hypothesis Tests for a Population Proportion

Now that some general concepts of hypothesis testing have been introduced, we are ready to turn our attention to the development of procedures for using sample information to decide between a null and an alternative hypothesis. There are two possible conclusions: We either reject $H_0$ or else fail to reject $H_0$. The fundamental idea behind hypothesis-testing procedures is this: *We reject the null hypothesis if the observed sample is very unlikely to have occurred when $H_0$ is true.* In this section, we consider testing hypotheses about a population proportion when the sample size $n$ is large.

Let $\pi$ denote the proportion of individuals or objects in a specified population that possess a certain property. A random sample of $n$ individuals or objects is selected from the population. The sample proportion

$$p = \frac{\text{number in the sample that possess property}}{n}$$

is the natural statistic for making inferences about $\pi$.

The large-sample test procedure is based on the same properties of the sampling distribution of $p$ that were used previously to obtain a confidence interval for $\pi$, namely:

1. $\mu_p = \pi$

2. $\sigma_p = \sqrt{\dfrac{\pi(1 - \pi)}{n}}$

3. When $n$ is large, the sampling distribution of $p$ is approximately normal.

These three results imply that the standardized variable

$$z = \frac{p - \pi}{\sqrt{\dfrac{\pi(1 - \pi)}{n}}}$$

has approximately a standard normal distribution when $n$ is large. Example 10.8 shows how this information allows us to make a decision.

## Example 10.8  Impact of Food Labels

In June of 2006, an Associated Press survey was conducted to investigate how people use the nutritional information provided on food package labels. Interviews were conducted with 1003 randomly selected adult Americans, and each participant was asked a series of questions, including the following two:

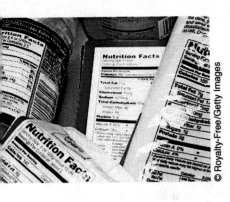

© Royalty-Free/Getty Images

Question 1: When purchasing packaged food, how often to you check the nutrition labeling on the package?

Question 2: How often do you purchase foods that are bad for you, even after you've checked the nutrition labels?

It was reported that 582 responded "frequently" to the question about checking labels and 441 responded very often or somewhat often to the question about purchasing "bad" foods even after checking the label.

Let's start by looking at the responses to the first question. Based on these data, is it reasonable to conclude that a majority of adult Americans frequently check the nutritional labels when purchasing packaged foods? We can answer this question by testing hypotheses, where

$\pi$ = true proportion of adult Americans who frequently check nutritional labels

$H_0$: $\pi = .5$

$H_a$: $\pi > .5$ (The proportion of adult Americans who frequently check nutritional labels is greater than .5. That is, more than half (a majority) frequently check nutritional labels.)

Recall that in a hypothesis test, the null hypothesis is rejected only if there is convincing evidence against it—in this case, convincing evidence that $\pi > .5$. If $H_0$ is rejected, there is strong support for the claim that a majority of adult Americans frequently check nutritional labels when purchasing packaged foods.

For this sample,

$$p = \frac{582}{1003} = .58$$

The observed sample proportion is certainly greater than .5, but this could just be due to sampling variability. That is, when $\pi = .5$ (meaning $H_0$ is true), the sample proportion $p$ usually differs somewhat from .5 simply because of chance variation from one sample to another. Is it plausible that a sample proportion of $p = .58$ occurred as a result of this chance variation, or is it unusual to observe a sample proportion this large when $\pi = .5$?

To answer this question, we form a *test statistic,* the quantity used as a basis for making a decision between $H_0$ and $H_a$. Creating a test statistic involves replacing $\pi$ with the hypothesized value in the $z$ variable $z = \dfrac{p - \pi}{\sqrt{\pi(1 - \pi)/n}}$ to obtain

$$z = \frac{p - .5}{\sqrt{\dfrac{(.5)(.5)}{n}}}$$

If the null hypothesis is true, this statistic should have approximately a standard normal distribution, because when the sample size is large and $H_0$ is true,

1. $\pi_p = .5,$

2. $\sigma_p = \sqrt{\dfrac{(.5)(.5)}{n}}$

3. $p$ has approximately a normal distribution.

The calculated value of $z$ expresses the distance between $p$ and the hypothesized value as a number of standard deviations. If, for example, $z = 3$, then the value of

$p$ that came from the sample is 3 standard deviations (of $p$) greater than what we would have expected if the null hypothesis were true. How likely is it that a $z$ value at least this contradictory to $H_0$ would be observed if in fact $H_0$ is true? The test statistic $z$ is constructed using the hypothesized value from the null hypothesis; if $H_0$ is true, the test statistic has (approximately) a standard normal distribution. Therefore

$$P(z \geq 3 \text{ when } H_0 \text{ is true}) = \text{area under the } z \text{ curve to the right of } 3.00 = .0013$$

That is, if $H_0$ is true, very few samples (much less than 1% of all samples) produce a value of $z$ at least as contradictory to $H_0$ as $z = 3$. Because this $z$ value is in the most extreme 1%, it is sensible to reject $H_0$.

For our data,

$$z = \frac{p - .5}{\sqrt{\dfrac{(.5)(.5)}{n}}} = \frac{.58 - .5}{\sqrt{\dfrac{(.5)(.5)}{1003}}} = \frac{.08}{.016} = 5.00$$

That is, $p = .58$ is 5 standard deviations greater than what we would expect it to be if the null hypothesis $H_0$: $\pi = .5$ were true. The sample data appear to be much more consistent with the alternative hypothesis, $H_a$: $\pi > .5$. In particular,

$$P(\text{value of } z \text{ is at least as contradictory to } H_0 \text{ as } 5.00 \text{ when } H_0 \text{ is true})$$
$$= P(z \geq 5.00 \text{ when } H_0 \text{ is true})$$
$$= \text{area under the } z \text{ curve to the right of } 5.00$$
$$\approx 0$$

There is virtually no chance of seeing a sample proportion and corresponding $z$ value this extreme as a result of chance variation alone when $H_0$ is true. If $p$ is 5 standard deviations or more away from .5, how can we believe that $\pi = .5$? The evidence for rejecting $H_0$ in favor of $H_a$ is very compelling.

Interestingly, in spite of the fact that there is strong evidence that a majority of adult Americans frequently check nutritional labels, the data on responses to the second question suggest that the percentage of people who then ignore the information on the label and purchase "bad" foods anyway is not small—the sample proportion who responded very often or somewhat often was .44.

■

The preceding example illustrates the rationale behind large-sample procedures for testing hypotheses about $\pi$ (and other test procedures as well). We begin by assuming that the null hypothesis is correct. The sample is then examined in light of this assumption. If the observed sample proportion would not be unusual when $H_0$ is true, then chance variability from one sample to another is a plausible explanation for what has been observed, and $H_0$ should not be rejected. On the other hand, if the observed sample proportion would have been quite unlikely when $H_0$ is true, then we would take the sample as convincing evidence against the null hypothesis and we should reject $H_0$. We base a decision to reject or to fail to reject the null hypothesis on an assessment of how extreme or unlikely the observed sample is if $H_0$ is true.

The assessment of how contradictory the observed data are to $H_0$ is based on first computing the value of the test statistic

$$z = \frac{p - \text{hypothesized value}}{\sqrt{\dfrac{(\text{hypothesized value})(1 - \text{hypothesized value})}{n}}}$$

We then calculate the *P-value,* the probability, assuming that $H_0$ is true, of obtaining a $z$ value at least as contradictory to $H_0$ as what was actually observed.

> **DEFINITION**
>
> A **test statistic** is the function of sample data on which a conclusion to reject or fail to reject $H_0$ is based.
>
> The **P-value** (also sometimes called the **observed significance level**) is a measure of inconsistency between the hypothesized value for a population characteristic and the observed sample. It is the probability, assuming that $H_0$ is true, of obtaining a test statistic value at least as inconsistent with $H_0$ as what actually resulted.

## Example 10.9 Detecting Plagiarism

Plagiarism is a growing concern among college and university faculty members, and many universities are now using software tools to detect student work that is not original. Researchers at the University of Luton conducted a survey of 321 faculty members at a variety of academic institutions ("Technical Review of Plagiarism Detection Software," University of Luton, 2001). Included in the survey were questions about strategies used to uncover instances of plagiarism. It was reported that 36% of those surveyed said they occasionally used online searches with key words from student work to check for plagiarism.

Assuming it is reasonable to regard this sample as representative of university faculty members, does the sample provide convincing evidence that more than one-third of faculty members occasionally use key word searches to check student work? With

$\pi$ = true proportion faculty members who use key word searches to check student work

the relevant hypotheses are

$$H_0: \pi = \frac{1}{3} = .33$$
$$H_a: \pi > .33$$

The sample proportion was reported to be $p = .36$. Does the value of $p$ exceed one-third by enough to cast substantial doubt on $H_0$?

Because the sample size is large, the statistic

$$z = \frac{p - .33}{\sqrt{\dfrac{(.33)(1 - .33)}{n}}}$$

has approximately a standard normal distribution when $H_0$ is true. The calculated value of the test statistic is

$$z = \frac{.36 - .33}{\sqrt{\dfrac{(.33)(1 - .33)}{321}}} = \frac{.03}{.026} = 1.15$$

The probability that a $z$ value at least this inconsistent with $H_0$ would be observed if in fact $H_0$ is true is

$$P\text{-value} = P(z \geq 1.15 \text{ when } H_0 \text{ is true})$$
$$= \text{area under the } z \text{ curve to the right of } 1.15$$
$$= 1 - .8749$$
$$= .1251$$

This probability indicates that when $\pi = .33$, it would not be all that unusual to observe a sample proportion as large as .36. When $H_0$ is true, roughly 12.5% of all samples would have a sample proportion larger than .36, so a sample proportion of .36 is reasonably consistent with the null hypothesis. Although .36 is larger than the hypothesized value of $\pi = .33$, chance variation from sample to sample is a plausible explanation for what was observed. There is not strong evidence that the proportion of faculty members who use key word searches to check student work for plagiarism is greater than one-third.

■

As illustrated by Examples 10.8 and 10.9, small $P$-values indicate that sample results are inconsistent with $H_0$, whereas larger $P$-values are interpreted as meaning that the data are consistent with $H_0$ and that sampling variability alone is a plausible explanation for what was observed in the sample. As you probably noticed, the two cases examined ($P$-value $\approx 0$ and $P$-value $= .1251$) were such that a decision between rejecting or not rejecting $H_0$ was clear-cut. A decision in other cases might not be so obvious. For example, what if the sample had resulted in a $P$-value of .04? Is this unusual enough to warrant rejection of $H_0$? How small must the $P$-value be before $H_0$ should be rejected?

The answer depends on the significance level $\alpha$ (the probability of a Type I error) selected for the test. For example, suppose that we set $\alpha = .05$. This implies that the probability of rejecting a true null hypothesis is .05. To obtain a test procedure with this probability of Type I error, we would reject the null hypothesis if the sample result is among the most unusual 5% of all samples when $H_0$ is true. That is, $H_0$ is rejected if the computed $P$-value $\leq .05$. If we had selected $\alpha = .01$, $H_0$ would be rejected only if we observed a sample result so extreme that it would be among the most unusual 1% if $H_0$ is true (i.e., if $P$-value $\leq .01$).

A decision as to whether $H_0$ should be rejected results from comparing the $P$-value to the chosen $\alpha$:

$H_0$ should be rejected if $P$-value $\leq \alpha$.
$H_0$ should not be rejected if $P$-value $> \alpha$.

■

Suppose, for example, that the $P$-value $= .0352$ and that a significance level of .05 is chosen. Then, because

$$P\text{-value} = .0352 \leq .05 = \alpha$$

$H_0$ would be rejected. This would not be the case, though, for $\alpha = .01$, because then $P$-value $> \alpha$.

## ▪ Computing a *P*-Value for a Large-Sample Test Concerning $\pi$ ...................

The computation of the *P*-value depends on the form of the inequality in the alternative hypothesis, $H_a$. Suppose, for example, that we wish to test

$$H_0: \pi = .6 \quad \text{versus} \quad H_a: \pi > .6$$

based on a large sample. The appropriate test statistic is

$$z = \frac{p - .6}{\sqrt{\dfrac{(.6)(1 - .6)}{n}}}$$

Values of $p$ contradictory to $H_0$ and much more consistent with $H_a$ are those much *larger* than .6 (because $\pi = .6$ when $H_0$ is true and $\pi > .6$ when $H_0$ is false and $H_a$ is true). Such values of $p$ correspond to $z$ values considerably greater than 0. If $n = 400$ and $p = .679$, then

$$z = \frac{.679 - .6}{\sqrt{\dfrac{(.6)(1 - .6)}{400}}} = \frac{.079}{.025} = 3.16$$

The value $p = .679$ is more than 3 standard deviations larger than what we would have expected if $H_0$ were true. Thus

*P*-value = *P*(z at least as contradictory to $H_0$ as 3.16 when $H_0$ is true)
= $P(z \geq 3.16$ when $H_0$ is true)
= area under the $z$ curve to the right of 3.16
= $1 - .9992$
= .0008

This *P*-value is illustrated in Figure 10.1. If $H_0$ is true, in the long run only 8 out of 10,000 samples would result in a $z$ value as or more extreme than what actually resulted; most of us would consider such a $z$ quite unusual. Using a significance level of .01, we reject the null hypothesis because *P*-value = .0008 ≤ .01 = $\alpha$.

Now consider testing $H_0: \pi = .3$ versus $H_a: \pi \neq .3$. A value of $p$ either much greater than .3 *or* much less than .3 is inconsistent with $H_0$ and provides support for $H_a$. Such a $p$ corresponds to a $z$ value far out in *either* tail of the $z$ curve. If

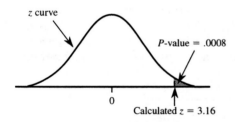

$z$ curve

*P*-value = .0008

0

Calculated $z$ = 3.16

**Figure 10.1** Calculating a *P*-value.

$$z = \frac{p - .3}{\sqrt{\dfrac{(.3)(1 - .3)}{n}}} = 1.75$$

then (as shown in Figure 10.2)

*P*-value = *P*(z value at least as inconsistent with $H_0$ as 1.75 when $H_0$ is true)
= $P(z \geq 1.75$ or $z \leq -1.75$ when $H_0$ is true)
= ($z$ curve area to the right of 1.75) + ($z$ curve area to the left of –1.75)
= $(1 - .9599) + .0401$
= .0802

The *P*-value in this situation is also .0802 if $z = -1.75$, because 1.75 and $-1.75$ are equally inconsistent with $H_0$.

**Figure 10.2** *P*-value as the sum of two tail areas.

Determination of the *P*-Value When the Test Statistic Is *z*

1. **Upper-tailed test:**

   $H_a$: $\pi >$ hypothesized value

   *P*-value computed as illustrated:

2. **Lower-tailed test:**

   $H_a$: $\pi <$ hypothesized value

   *P*-value computed as illustrated:

3. **Two-tailed test:**

   $H_a$: $\pi \neq$ hypothesized value

   *P*-value computed as illustrated:

The symmetry of the *z* curve implies that when the test is two-tailed (the "not equal" alternative), it is not necessary to add two curve areas. Instead,

If *z* is positive, *P*-value = 2(area to the right of *z*).
If *z* is negative, *P*-value = 2(area to the left of *z*).

# Example 10.10 Water Conservation

In December 2005 a countywide water conservation campaign was conducted in a particular county. In January 2006 a random sample of 500 homes was selected, and water usage was recorded for each home in the sample. The county supervisors wanted to know whether their data supported the claim that fewer than half the households in the county reduced water consumption. The relevant hypotheses are

$$H_0: \pi = .5 \quad \text{versus} \quad H_a: \pi < .5$$

where $\pi$ is the true proportion of households in the county with reduced water usage.

Suppose that the sample results were $n = 500$ and $p = .440$. Because the sample size is large and this is a lower-tailed test, we can compute the $P$-value by first calculating the value of the $z$ test statistic

$$z = \frac{p - .5}{\sqrt{\dfrac{(.5)(1 - .5)}{n}}}$$

and then finding the area under the $z$ curve to the left of this $z$.

Based on the observed sample data,

$$z = \frac{.440 - .5}{\sqrt{\dfrac{(.5)(1 - .5)}{500}}} = \frac{-.060}{.0224} = -2.68$$

The $P$-value is then equal to the area under the $z$ curve and to the left of $-2.68$. From the entry in the $-2.6$ row and .08 column of Appendix Table 2, we find that

$$P\text{-value} = .0037$$

Using a .01 significance level, we reject $H_0$ (because $.0037 \leq .01$), suggesting that the proportion with reduced water usage was less than .5. Notice that rejection of $H_0$ would not be justified if a *very* small significance level, such as .001, had been selected.

■

Example 10.10 illustrates the calculation of a $P$-value for a lower-tailed test. The use of $P$-values in upper-tailed and two-tailed tests is illustrated in Examples 10.11 and 10.12. But first we summarize large-sample tests of hypotheses about a population proportion and introduce a step-by-step procedure for carrying out a hypothesis test.

## Summary of Large-Sample z Test for π

**Null hypothesis:** $H_0: \pi =$ hypothesized value

**Test statistic:** $z = \dfrac{p - \text{hypothesized value}}{\sqrt{\dfrac{(\text{hypothesized value})(1 - \text{hypothesized})}{n}}}$

*(continued)*

**Alternative Hypothesis:**
$H_a$: $\pi$ > hypothesized value
$H_a$: $\pi$ < hypothesized value
$H_a$: $\pi$ ≠ hypothesized value

***P*-Value:**
Area under $z$ curve to right of calculated $z$
Area under $z$ curve to left of calculated $z$
(1) 2(area to right of $z$) if $z$ is positive, or
(2) 2(area to left of $z$) if $z$ is negative

**Assumptions:**

1. $p$ is the sample proportion from a *random sample*.
2. The *sample size is large*. This test can be used if $n$ satisfies both $n$(hypothesized value) ≥ 10 and $n$(1 − hypothesized value) ≥ 10.
3. If sampling is without replacement, the sample size is no more than 10% of the population size.  ■

We recommend that the following sequence of steps be used when carrying out a hypothesis test.

## Steps in a Hypothesis-Testing Analysis

1. Describe the population characteristic about which hypotheses are to be tested.
2. State the null hypothesis $H_0$.
3. State the alternative hypothesis $H_a$.
4. Select the significance level $\alpha$ for the test.
5. Display the test statistic to be used, with substitution of the hypothesized value identified in Step 2 but without any computation at this point.
6. Check to make sure that any assumptions required for the test are reasonable.
7. Compute all quantities appearing in the test statistic and then the value of the test statistic itself.
8. Determine the *P*-value associated with the observed value of the test statistic.
9. State the conclusion (which is to reject $H_0$ if *P*-value ≤ $\alpha$ and not to reject $H_0$ otherwise). The conclusion should then be stated in the context of the problem, and the level of significance should be included.

Steps 1–4 constitute a statement of the problem, Steps 5–8 give the analysis that leads to a decision, and Step 9 provides the conclusion.  ■

......................................................................................................................

# Example 10.11 Unfit Teens

The article "7 Million U.S. Teens Would Flunk Treadmill Tests" (Associated Press, December 11, 2005) summarized the results of a study in which 2205 adolescents aged 12 to 19 took a cardiovascular treadmill test. The researchers conducting the study indicated that the sample was selected in such a way that it could be regarded as representative of adolescents nationwide. Of the 2205 adolescents tested, 750 showed a poor level of cardiovascular fitness. Does this sample provide support for the claim that more than 30% of adolescents have a low level of cardiovascular fitness? We answer this question by carrying out a hypothesis test using a .05 significance level.

1. Population characteristic of interest:

$\pi$ = true proportion of adolescents who have a low level of cardiovascular fitness

2. Null hypothesis: $H_0$: $\pi = .3$
3. Alternative hypothesis: $H_a$: $\pi > .3$ (the percentage of adolescents with a low fitness level is greater than 30%)
4. Significance level: $\alpha = .05$
5. Test statistic:

$$z = \frac{p - \text{hypothesized value}}{\sqrt{\dfrac{(\text{hypothesized value})(1 - \text{hypothesized value})}{n}}} = \frac{p - .3}{\sqrt{\dfrac{(.3)(1 - .3)}{n}}}$$

6. Assumptions: This test requires a random sample and a large sample size. The given sample was considered to be representative of adolescents nationwide, and if this is the case it is reasonable to regard the sample as if it were a random sample. The sample size was $n = 2205$. Since $2205(.3) \geq 10$ and $2205(1 - .3) \geq 10$, the large-sample test is appropriate. The sample size is small compared to the population (adolescents) size.

7. Computations: $n = 2205$ and $p = 750/2205 = .34$, so

$$z = \frac{.34 - .3}{\sqrt{\dfrac{(.3)(1 - .3)}{2205}}} = \frac{.04}{.010} = 4.00$$

8. P-value: This is an upper-tailed test (the inequality in $H_a$ is >), so the P-value is the area to the right of the computed $z$ value. Since $z = 4.00$ is so far out in the upper tail of the standard normal distribution, the area to its right is negligible. Thus,

$$P\text{-value} \approx 0$$

9. Conclusion: Since $P$-value $\leq \alpha$ ($0 \leq .05$), $H_0$ is rejected at the .05 level of significance. We conclude that the proportion of adolescents who have a low level of cardiovascular fitness is greater than .3. That is, the sample provides convincing evidence to support the claim that more than 30% of adolescents have a low fitness level.

■

# Example 10.12 Single-Family Homes

The Public Policy Institute of California reported that 71% of people nationwide prefer to live in a single-family home. To determine whether the preferences of Californians are consistent with this nationwide figure, a random sample of 2002 Californians were interviewed. Of those interviewed, 1682 said that they consider a single-family home the ideal (Associated Press, November 13, 2001). Can we reasonably conclude that the proportion of Californians who prefer a single-family home is different from the national figure? We answer this question by carrying out a hypothesis test with $\alpha = .01$.

© Royalty-Free/Getty Images

1. $\pi$ = proportion of all Californians who prefer a single-family home.
2. $H_0$: $\pi = .71$.
3. $H_a$: $\pi \neq .71$ (differs from the national proportion).
4. Significance level: $\alpha = .01$.
5. Test statistic:

$$z = \frac{p - \text{hypothesized value}}{\sqrt{\dfrac{(\text{hypothesized value})(1 - \text{hypothesized value})}{n}}} = \frac{p - .71}{\sqrt{\dfrac{(.71)(.29)}{n}}}$$

6. Assumptions: This test requires a random sample and a large sample size. The given sample was a random sample, the population size is much larger than the sample size, and the sample size was $n = 2002$. Because $2002(.71) \geq 10$ and $2002(.29) \geq 10$, the large-sample test is appropriate.
7. Computations: $p = 1682/2002 = .84$, from which

$$z = \frac{.84 - .71}{\sqrt{\dfrac{(.71)(.29)}{2002}}} = \frac{.13}{.0101} = 12.87$$

8. P-value: The area under the $z$ curve to the right of 12.87 is approximately 0, so P-value $\approx 2(0) = 0$.
9. Conclusion: At significance level .01, we reject $H_0$ because P-value $\approx 0 < .01 = \alpha$. The data provide convincing evidence that the proportion in California who prefer a single-family home differs from the nationwide proportion.

■

Most statistical computer packages and graphing calculators can calculate and report P-values for a variety of hypothesis-testing situations, including the large sample test for a proportion. MINITAB was used to carry out the test of Example 10.10, and the resulting computer output follows (MINITAB uses $p$ instead of $\pi$ to denote the population proportion):

**Test and Confidence Interval for One Proportion**
Test of p = 0.5 vs p < 0.5

| Sample | X | N | Sample p | 95.0 % CI | Z-Value | P-Value |
|--------|-----|-----|----------|------------------------|---------|---------|
| 1 | 220 | 500 | 0.440000 | (0.396491, 0.483509) | −2.68 | 0.004 |

From the MINITAB output, $z = -2.68$, and the associated P-value is .004. The small difference in the P-value is the result of rounding.

It is also possible to compute the value of the $z$ test statistic and then use a statistical computer package or graphing calculator to determine the corresponding P-value as an area under the standard normal curve. For example, the user can specify a value and MINITAB will determine the area to the left of this value for any particular normal distribution. Because of this, the computer can be used in place of Appendix Table 2. In Example 10.10 the computed $z$ was −2.68. Using MINITAB gives the following output:

Normal with mean = 0 and standard deviation = 1.00000

| x | P(X ≤ x) |
|---------|----------|
| −2.6800 | 0.0037 |

Thus we learn that the area to the left of $-2.68 = .0037$, which agrees with the value obtained by using the tables.

## ■ Exercises 10.23–10.44 ......................................................

**10.23** Use the definition of the *P*-value to explain the following:
**a.** Why $H_0$ would certainly be rejected if *P*-value $= .0003$
**b.** Why $H_0$ would definitely not be rejected if *P*-value $= .350$

**10.24** For which of the following *P*-values will the null hypothesis be rejected when performing a level .05 test:
a. .001          d. .047
b. .021          e. .148
c. .078

**10.25** Pairs of *P*-values and significance levels, $\alpha$, are given. For each pair, state whether the observed *P*-value leads to rejection of $H_0$ at the given significance level.
**a.** *P*-value $= .084$, $\alpha = .05$
**b.** *P*-value $= .003$, $\alpha = .001$
**c.** *P*-value $= .498$, $\alpha = .05$
**d.** *P*-value $= .084$, $\alpha = .10$
**e.** *P*-value $= .039$, $\alpha = .01$
**f.** *P*-value $= .218$, $\alpha = .10$

**10.26** Let $\pi$ denote the proportion of grocery store customers that use the store's club card. For a large sample *z* test of $H_0: \pi = .5$ versus $H_a: \pi > .5$, find the *P*-value associated with each of the given values of the test statistic:
a. 1.40          d. 2.45
b. 0.93          e. $-0.17$
c. 1.96

**10.27** Assuming a random sample from a large population, for which of the following null hypotheses and sample sizes *n* is the large-sample *z* test appropriate:
**a.** $H_0: \pi = .2, n = 25$
**b.** $H_0: \pi = .6, n = 210$
**c.** $H_0: \pi = .9, n = 100$
**d.** $H_0: \pi = .05, n = 75$

10.28 The article "Poll Finds Most Oppose Return to Draft, Wouldn't Encourage Children to Enlist" (Associated Press, December 18, 2005) reports that in a random sample of 1000 American adults, 700 indicated that they oppose the reinstatement of a military draft. Is there convincing evidence that the proportion of American adults who oppose reinstatement of the draft is greater than two-thirds? Use a significance level of .05.

**10.29** The poll referenced in the previous exercise ("Military Draft Study," AP-Ipsos, June 2005) also included the following question: "If the military draft were reinstated, would you favor or oppose drafting women as well as men?" Forty-three percent of the 1000 people responding said that they would favor drafting women if the draft were reinstated. Using a .05 significance level, carry out a test to determine if there is convincing evidence that fewer than half of adult Americans would favor the drafting of women.

10.30 The article "Irritated by Spam? Get Ready for Spit" (*USA Today,* November 10, 2004) predicts that "spit," spam that is delivered via Internet phone lines and cell phones, will be a growing problem as more people turn to web-based phone services. In a 2004 poll of 5500 cell phone users conducted by the Yankee Group, 20% indicated that they had received commercial messages and ads on their cell phones. Is there sufficient evidence that the proportion of cell phone users who have received commercial messages or ads in 2004 was greater than the proportion of .13 reported for the previous year?

**10.31** In a survey conducted by Yahoo Small Business, 1432 of 1813 adults surveyed said that they would alter their shopping habits if gas prices remain high (Associated Press, November 30, 2005). The article did not say how the sample was selected, but for purposes of this exercise, assume that it is reasonable to regard this sample as representative of adult Americans. Based on these survey data, is it reasonable to conclude that more than three-quarters of adult Americans plan to alter their shopping habits if gas prices remain high?

**10.32** According to a *Washington Post-ABC News* poll, 331 of 502 randomly selected U.S. adults interviewed said they would not be bothered if the National Security

Agency collected records of personal telephone calls they had made. Is there sufficient evidence to conclude that a majority of U.S. adults feel this way? Test the appropriate hypotheses using a .01 significance level.

**10.33** According to a survey of 1000 adult Americans conducted by Opinion Research Corporation, 210 of those surveyed said playing the lottery would be the most practical way for them to accumulate $200,000 in net wealth in their lifetime ("One in Five Believe Path to Riches Is the Lottery," *San Luis Obispo Tribune,* January 11, 2006). Although the article does not describe how the sample was selected, for purposes of this exercise, assume that the sample can be regarded as a random sample of adult Americans. Is there convincing evidence that more than 20% of adult Americans believe that playing the lottery is the best strategy for accumulating $200,000 in net wealth?

10.34 The article "Theaters Losing Out to Living Rooms" (*San Luis Obispo Tribune,* June 17, 2005) states that movie attendance declined in 2005. The Associated Press found that 730 of 1000 randomly selected adult Americans preferred to watch movies at home rather than at a movie theater. Is there convincing evidence that the majority of adult Americans prefer to watch movies at home? Test the relevant hypotheses using a .05 significance level.

**10.35** The article referenced in Exercise 10.34 also reported that 470 of 1000 randomly selected adult Americans thought that the quality of movies being produced was getting worse.
**a.** Is there convincing evidence that fewer than half of adult Americans believe that movie quality is getting worse? Use a significance level of .05.
**b.** Suppose that the sample size had been 100 instead of 1000, and that 47 thought that the movie quality was getting worse (so that the sample proportion is still .47). Based on this sample of 100, is there convincing evidence that fewer than half of adult Americans believe that movie quality is getting worse? Use a significance level of .05.
**c.** Write a few sentences explaining why different conclusions were reached in the hypothesis tests of Parts (a) and (b).

10.36 The report "2005 Electronic Monitoring & Surveillance Survey: Many Companies Monitoring, Recording, Videotaping—and Firing—Employees" (American Management Association, 2005) summarized the results of a survey of 526 U.S. businesses. Four hundred of these companies indicated that they monitor employees' web site visits. For purposes of this exercise, assume that it is reasonable to regard this sample as representative of businesses in the United States.
a. Is there sufficient evidence to conclude that more than 75% of U.S. businesses monitor employees' web site visits? Test the appropriate hypotheses using a significance level of .01.
b. Is there sufficient evidence to conclude that a majority of U.S. businesses monitor employees' web site visits? Test the appropriate hypotheses using a significance level of .01.

**10.37** In an AP-AOL sports poll (Associated Press, December 18, 2005), 272 of 394 randomly selected baseball fans stated that they thought the designated hitter rule should either be expanded to both baseball leagues or eliminated. Based on the given information, is there sufficient evidence to conclude that a majority of baseball fans feel this way?

10.38 In a representative sample of 1000 adult Americans, only 430 could name at least one justice who is currently serving on the U.S. Supreme Court (Ipsos, January 10, 2006). Using a significance level of .01, carry out a hypothesis test to determine if there is convincing evidence to support the claim that fewer than half of adult Americans can name at least one justice currently serving on the Supreme Court.

**10.39** ▼ In a national survey of 2013 adults, 1590 responded that lack of respect and courtesy in American society is a serious problem, and 1283 indicated that they believe that rudeness is a more serious problem than in past years (Associated Press, April 3, 2002). Is there convincing evidence that more than three-quarters of U.S. adults believe that rudeness is a worsening problem? Test the relevant hypotheses using a significance level of .05.

10.40 The success of the U.S. census depends on people filling out and returning census forms. Despite extensive advertising, many Americans are skeptical about claims that the Census Bureau will guard the information it collects from other government agencies. In a *USA Today* poll (March 13, 2000), only 432 of 1004 adults surveyed said that they believe the Census Bureau when it says the information you give about yourself is kept confidential. Is there convincing evidence that, despite the advertising campaign, fewer than half of U.S. adults believe the

Census Bureau will keep information confidential? Use a significance level of .01.

**10.41** ▼ The article "Americans Seek Spiritual Guidance on Web" (*San Luis Obispo Tribune,* October 12, 2002) reported that 68% of the general population belong to a religious community. In a survey on Internet use, 84% of "religion surfers" (defined as those who seek spiritual help online or who have used the web to search for prayer and devotional resources) belong to a religious community. Suppose that this result was based on a sample of 512 religion surfers. Is there convincing evidence that the proportion of religion surfers who belong to a religious community is different from .68, the proportion for the general population? Use $\alpha = .05$.

10.42 Teenagers (age 15 to 20) make up 7% of the driving population. The article "More States Demand Teens Pass Rigorous Driving Tests" (*San Luis Obispo Tribune,* January 27, 2000) described a study of auto accidents conducted by the Insurance Institute for Highway Safety. The Institute found that 14% of the accidents studied involved teenage drivers. Suppose that this percentage was based on examining records from 500 randomly selected accidents. Does the study provide convincing evidence that the proportion of accidents involving teenage drivers differs from .07, the proportion of teens in the driving population?

**10.43** Students at the Akademia Podlaka conducted an experiment to determine whether the Belgium-minted Euro coin was equally likely to land heads up or tails up. Coins were spun on a smooth surface, and in 250 spins, 140 landed with the heads side up (*New Scientist,* January 4, 2002). Should the students interpret this result as convincing evidence that the proportion of the time the coin would land heads up is not .5? Test the relevant hypotheses using $\alpha = .01$. Would your conclusion be different if a significance level of .05 had been used? Explain.

10.44 The article "Fewer Parolees Land Back Behind Bars" (*Associated Press,* April 11, 2006) includes the following statement: "Just over 38 percent of all felons who were released from prison in 2003 landed back behind bars by the end of the following year, the lowest rate since 1979." Explain why it would not be necessary to carry out a hypothesis test to determine if the proportion of felons released in 2003 was less than .40.

---

**Bold** exercises answered in back ● Data set available online but not required ▼ Video solution available

---

## 10.4 Hypothesis Tests for a Population Mean

We now turn our attention to developing a method for testing hypotheses about a population mean. The test procedures in this case are based on the same two results that led to the $z$ and $t$ confidence intervals in Chapter 9. These results follow:

1. When either $n$ is large or the population distribution is approximately normal, then

$$z = \frac{\bar{x} - \mu}{\dfrac{\sigma}{\sqrt{n}}}$$

has approximately a standard normal distribution.

2. When either $n$ is large or the population distribution is approximately normal, then

$$t = \frac{\bar{x} - \mu}{\dfrac{s}{\sqrt{n}}}$$

has approximately a $t$ distribution with df $= n - 1$.

A consequence of these two results is that if we are interested in testing a null hypothesis of the form

$$H_0: \mu = \text{hypothesized value}$$

then, depending on whether $\sigma$ is known or unknown, we can use (as long as $n$ is large or the population distribution is approximately normal) either the accompanying $z$ or $t$ test statistic:

### Case 1: $\sigma$ known

Test statistic: $z = \dfrac{\bar{x} - \text{hypothesized value}}{\dfrac{\sigma}{\sqrt{n}}}$

$P$-value: Computed as an area under the $z$ curve

### Case 2: $\sigma$ unknown

Test statistic: $t = \dfrac{\bar{x} - \text{hypothesized value}}{\dfrac{s}{\sqrt{n}}}$

$P$-value: Computed as an area under the $t$ curve with df $= n - 1$

Because it is rarely the case that $\sigma$, the population standard deviation, is known, we focus our attention on the test procedure for the case in which $\sigma$ is unknown.

When testing a hypothesis about a population mean, the null hypothesis specifies a particular hypothesized value for $\mu$, specifically, $H_0\colon \mu = \text{hypothesized value}$. The alternative hypothesis has one of the following three forms, depending on the research question being addressed:

$H_a\colon \mu > \text{hypothesized value}$
$H_a\colon \mu < \text{hypothesized value}$
$H_a\colon \mu \neq \text{hypothesized value}$

If $n$ is large or if the population distribution is approximately normal, the test statistic

$$t = \dfrac{\bar{x} - \text{hypothesized value}}{\dfrac{s}{\sqrt{n}}}$$

can be used. For example, if the null hypothesis to be tested is $H_0\colon \mu = 100$, the test statistic becomes

$$t = \dfrac{\bar{x} - 100}{\dfrac{s}{\sqrt{n}}}$$

Consider the alternative hypothesis $H_a\colon \mu > 100$, and suppose that a sample of size $n = 24$ gives $\bar{x} = 104.20$ and $s = 8.23$. The resulting test statistic value is

$$t = \dfrac{104.20 - 100}{\dfrac{8.23}{\sqrt{24}}} = \dfrac{4.20}{1.6799} = 2.50$$

Because this is an upper-tailed test, if the test statistic had been $z$ rather than $t$, the $P$-value would be the area under the $z$ curve to the right of 2.50. With a $t$ statistic, the $P$-value is the area under an appropriate $t$ curve (here with df $= 24 - 1 = 23$) to the right of 2.50. Appendix Table 4 is a tabulation of $t$ curve tail areas. Each column of the table is for a different number of degrees of freedom: 1, 2, 3, . . . , 30, 35, 40, 60, 120, and a last column for df $= \infty$, which is the same as for the $z$ curve. The table

**Figure 10.3** Part of Appendix Table 4: $t$ curve tail areas.

| df $t$ | 1 | 2 | ... | 22 | 23 | 24 | ... | 60 | 120 |
|---|---|---|---|---|---|---|---|---|---|
| 0.0 | | | | | | | | | |
| 0.1 | | | | | | | | | |
| ⋮ | | | | ⋮ | ⋮ | ⋮ | | | |
| 2.5 | | | ... | .010 | .010 | .010 | ... | | |
| 2.6 | | | ... | .008 | .008 | .008 | ... | | |
| 2.7 | | | ... | .007 | .006 | .006 | ... | | |
| 2.8 | | | ... | .005 | .005 | .005 | ... | | |
| ⋮ | | | | ⋮ | ⋮ | ⋮ | | | |
| 4.0 | | | | | | | | | |

*Area under 23-df $t$ curve to right of 2.7*

gives the area under each $t$ curve to the right of values ranging from 0.0 to 4.0 in increments of 0.1. Part of this table appears in Figure 10.3. For example,

area under the 23-df $t$ curve to the right of $2.5 = .010$

$\qquad\qquad\qquad\qquad = P$-value for an upper-tailed $t$ test

Suppose that $t = -2.7$ for a lower-tailed test based on 23 df. Then, because any $t$ curve is symmetric about 0,

$P$-value = area to the left of $-2.7$ = area to the right of $2.7 = .006$

As is the case for $z$ tests, we double the captured tail area to obtain the $P$-value for two-tailed $t$ tests. Thus, if $t = 2.6$ or if $t = -2.6$ for a two-tailed test with 23 df, then

$P$-value = $2(.008) = .016$

Once past 30 df, the tail areas change very little, so the last column ($\infty$) in Appendix Table 4 provides a good approximation.

The following two boxes show how the $P$-value is obtained as a $t$ curve area and give a general description of the test procedure.

## Finding *P*-Values for a *t* Test

1. **Upper-tailed test:**

$H_a$: $\mu >$ hypothesized value

*(continued)*

2. **Lower-tailed test:**

$H_a$: $\mu <$ hypothesized value

3. **Two-tailed test:**

$H_a$: $\mu \neq$ hypothesized value

Appendix Table 4 gives upper-tail $t$ curve areas to the right of values 0.0, 0.1, . . . , 4.0. These areas are $P$-values for upper-tailed tests and, by symmetry, also for lower-tailed tests. Doubling an area gives the $P$-value for a two-tailed test. ■

## The One-Sample $t$ Test for a Population Mean

**Null hypothesis:** $H_0$: $\mu =$ hypothesized value

**Test statistic:** $t = \dfrac{\bar{x} - \text{hypothesized value}}{\dfrac{s}{\sqrt{n}}}$

| **Alternative Hypothesis:** | **P-Value:** |
|---|---|
| $H_a$: $\mu >$ hypothesized value | Area to right of calculated $t$ under $t$ curve with df $= n - 1$ |
| $H_a$: $\mu <$ hypothesized value | Area to the left of calculated $t$ under $t$ curve with df $= n - 1$ |
| $H_a$: $\mu \neq$ hypothesized value | (1) 2(area to right of $t$) if $t$ is positive, or |
|  | (2) 2(area to left of $t$) if $t$ is negative |

**Assumptions:** 1. $\bar{x}$ and $s$ are the sample mean and sample standard deviation from a *random sample*.

2. The *sample size is large* (generally $n \geq 30$) or *the population distribution is at least approximately normal*. ■

## Example 10.13 Time Stands Still (or So It Seems)

● A study conducted by researchers at Pennsylvania State University investigated whether time perception, a simple indication of a person's ability to concentrate, is impaired during nicotine withdrawal. The study results were presented in the paper

● Data set available online

"Smoking Abstinence Impairs Time Estimation Accuracy in Cigarette Smokers" (*Psychopharmacology Bulletin* [2003]: 90–95). After a 24-hr smoking abstinence, 20 smokers were asked to estimate how much time had passed during a 45-sec period. Suppose the resulting data on perceived elapsed time (in seconds) were as shown (these data are artificial but are consistent with summary quantities given in the paper):

| 69 | 65 | 72 | 73 | 59 | 55 | 39 | 52 | 67 | 57 |
| 56 | 50 | 70 | 47 | 56 | 45 | 70 | 64 | 67 | 53 |

From these data, we obtain

$$n = 20 \qquad \bar{x} = 59.30 \qquad s = 9.84$$

The researchers wanted to determine whether smoking abstinence had a negative impact on time perception, causing elapsed time to be overestimated. We can answer this question by testing

$H_0$: $\mu = 45$ (no consistent tendency to overestimate the time elapsed)

versus

$H_a$: $\mu > 45$ (tendency for elapsed time to be overestimated)

The null hypothesis is rejected only if there is convincing evidence that $\mu > 45$. The observed value, 59.30, is certainly larger than 45, but can a sample mean as large as this be plausibly explained by chance variation from one sample to another when $\mu = 45$? To answer this question, we carry out a hypothesis test with a significance level of .05 using the step-by-step procedure described in Section 10.3.

1. Population characteristic of interest:

   $\mu$ = mean perceived elapsed time for smokers who have abstained from smoking for 24 hours

2. Null hypothesis: $H_0$: $\mu = 45$
3. Alternative hypothesis: $H_a$: $\mu > 45$
4. Significance level: $\alpha = .05$
5. Test statistic: $t = \dfrac{\bar{x} - \text{hypothesized value}}{\dfrac{s}{\sqrt{n}}} = \dfrac{\bar{x} - 45}{\dfrac{s}{\sqrt{n}}}$

6. Assumptions: This test requires a random sample and either a large sample size or a normal population distribution. The authors of the paper believed that it was reasonable to consider this sample as representative of smokers in general, so we regard it as if it were a random sample. Because the sample size is only 20, for the *t* test to be appropriate, we must be willing to presume that the population distribution of perceived elapsed times is at least approximately normal. Is this reasonable? The following graph gives a boxplot of the data:

Perceived elapsed time

Although the boxplot is not perfectly symmetric, it is not too skewed and there are no outliers, so we judge the use of the $t$ test to be reasonable.

7. Computations: $n = 20$, $\bar{x} = 59.30$, and $s = 9.84$, so

$$t = \frac{59.30 - 45}{\dfrac{9.84}{\sqrt{20}}} = \frac{14.30}{2.20} = 6.50$$

8. $P$-value: This is an upper-tailed test (the inequality in $H_a$ is "greater than"), so the $P$-value is the area to the right of the computed $t$ value. Because df $= 20 - 1 = 19$, we can use the df $= 19$ column of Appendix Table 4 to find the $P$-value. With $t = 6.50$, we obtain $P$-value $=$ area to the right of $6.50 \approx 0$ (because $6.50$ is greater than $4.0$, the largest tabulated value).

9. Conclusion: Because $P$-value $\leq \alpha$, we reject $H_0$ at the .05 level of significance. There is virtually no chance of seeing a sample mean (and hence a $t$ value) this extreme as a result of just chance variation when $H_0$ is true. There is convincing evidence that the mean perceived time elapsed is greater than the actual time elapsed of 45 sec.

This paper also looked at perception of elapsed time for a sample of nonsmokers and for a sample of smokers who had not abstained from smoking. The investigators found that the null hypothesis of $\mu = 45$ could not be rejected for either of these groups.

■

# Example 10.14 Goofing Off at Work

● A growing concern of employers is time spent in activities like surfing the Internet and emailing friends during work hours. The *San Luis Obispo Tribune* summarized the findings from a survey of a large sample of workers in an article that ran under the headline "Who Goofs Off 2 Hours a Day? Most Workers, Survey Says" (August 3, 2006). Suppose that the CEO of a large company wants to determine whether the average amount of wasted time during an eight-hour work day for employees of her company is less than the reported 120 minutes. Each person in a random sample of 10 employees was contacted and asked about daily wasted time at work. (Participants would probably have to be guaranteed anonymity to obtain truthful responses!) The resulting data are the following:

| 108 | 112 | 117 | 130 | 111 | 131 | 113 | 113 | 105 | 128 |

Summary quantities are $n = 10$, $\bar{x} = 116.80$, and $s = 9.45$.

Do these data provide evidence that the mean wasted time for this company is less than 120 min? To answer this question, let's carry out a hypothesis test with $\alpha = .05$.

1. $\mu =$ mean daily wasted time for employees of this company
2. $H_0$: $\mu = 120$
3. $H_a$: $\mu < 120$
4. $\alpha = .05$

5. $t = \dfrac{\bar{x} - \text{hypothesized value}}{\dfrac{s}{\sqrt{n}}} = \dfrac{\bar{x} - 120}{\dfrac{s}{\sqrt{n}}}$

6. This test requires a random sample and either a large sample or a normal population distribution. The given sample was a random sample of employees. Because the sample size is small, we must be willing to assume that the population distribution of times is at least approximately normal. The following normal probability plot appears to be reasonably straight, and although the normal probability plot and the boxplot reveal some skewness in the sample, there are no outliers:

**Correlations (Pearson)**

Correlation of Time and Normal Score = 0.943

Also, the correlation between the expected normal scores and the observed data for this sample is .943, which is well above the critical $r$ value for $n = 10$ of .880 (see Chapter 5 for critical $r$ values). Based on these observations, it is plausible that the population distribution is approximately normal, so we proceed with the $t$ test.

7. Test statistic: $t = \dfrac{116.80 - 120}{\dfrac{9.45}{\sqrt{10}}} = -1.07$

8. From the df = 9 column of Appendix Table 4 and by rounding the test statistic value to $-1.1$, we get

$P$-value = area to the left of $-1.1$ = area to the right of $1.1$ = .150

as shown:

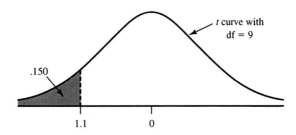

9. Because the $P$-value $> \alpha$, we fail to reject $H_0$. There is not sufficient evidence to conclude that the mean wasted time per eight-hour work day for employees at this company is less than 120 minutes.

MINITAB could also have been used to carry out the test, as shown in the accompanying output:

**One-Sample T: Wasted Time**
Test of mu = 120 vs < 120

| Variable | N | Mean | StDev | SE Mean | 95% Upper Bound | T | P |
|----------|---|------|-------|---------|-----------------|---|---|
| Wasted Time | 10 | 116.800 | 9.449 | 2.988 | 122.278 | −1.07 | 0.156 |

Although we had to round the computed $t$ value to $-1.1$ to use Appendix Table 4, MINITAB was able to compute the $P$-value corresponding to the actual value of the test statistic.

■

## Example 10.15 Cricket Love

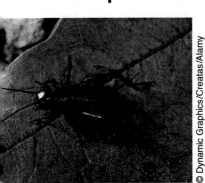

© Dynamic Graphics/Creatas/Alamy

The article "Well-Fed Crickets Bowl Maidens Over" (*Nature Science Update*, February 11, 1999) reported that female field crickets are attracted to males that have high chirp rates and hypothesized that chirp rate is related to nutritional status. The usual chirp rate for male field crickets was reported to vary around a mean of 60 chirps per second. To investigate whether chirp rate was related to nutritional status, investigators fed male crickets a high protein diet for 8 days, after which chirp rate was measured. The mean chirp rate for the crickets on the high protein diet was reported to be 109 chirps per second. Is this convincing evidence that the mean chirp rate for crickets on a high protein diet is greater than 60 (which would then imply an advantage in attracting the ladies)? Suppose that the sample size and sample standard deviation are $n = 32$ and $s = 40$. We test the relevant hypotheses with $\alpha = .01$.

1. $\mu$ = mean chirp rate for crickets on a high protein diet
2. $H_0$: $\mu = 60$
3. $H_a$: $\mu > 60$
4. $\alpha = .01$

5. $t = \dfrac{\bar{x} - \text{hypothesized value}}{\dfrac{s}{\sqrt{n}}} = \dfrac{\bar{x} - 60}{\dfrac{s}{\sqrt{n}}}$

6. This test requires a random sample and either a large sample or a normal population distribution. Because the sample size is large ($n = 32$), it is reasonable to proceed with the $t$ test as long as we are willing to consider the 32 male field crickets in this study as if they were a random sample from the population of male field crickets.

7. Test statistic: $t = \dfrac{109 - 60}{\dfrac{40}{\sqrt{32}}} = \dfrac{49}{7.07} = 6.93$

8. This is an upper-tailed test, so the $P$-value is the area under the $t$ curve with df $= 31$ and to the right of 6.93. From Appendix Table 4, $P$-value $\approx 0$.

9. Because $P$-value $\approx 0$, which is less than the significance level, $\alpha$, we reject $H_0$. There is convincing evidence that the mean chirp rate is higher for male field crickets that eat a high protein diet.

■

## ■ Statistical Versus Practical Significance .............................................................

Carrying out a hypothesis test amounts to deciding whether the value obtained for the test statistic could plausibly have resulted when $H_0$ is true. When the value of the test statistic leads to rejection of $H_0$, it is customary to say that the result is **statistically significant** at the chosen level $\alpha$. The finding of statistical significance means that, in the investigator's opinion, the observed deviation from what was expected under $H_0$ cannot plausibly be attributed only to chance variation. However, statistical significance cannot be equated with the conclusion that the true situation differs from what $H_0$ states in any practical sense. That is, even after $H_0$ has been rejected, the data may suggest that there is no *practical* difference between the true value of the population characteristic and what the null hypothesis states that value to be. This is illustrated in Example 10.16.

..............................................................................................................................................

# Example 10.16 "Significant" but Unimpressive Test Score Improvement

Let $\mu$ denote the true average score on a standardized test for children in a certain region of the United States. The average score for all children in the United States is 100. Regional education authorities are interested in testing $H_0$: $\mu = 100$ versus $H_a$: $\mu > 100$ using a significance level of .001. A sample of 2500 children resulted in the values $n = 2500$, $\bar{x} = 101.0$, and $s = 15.0$. Then

$$t = \dfrac{101.0 - 100}{\dfrac{15}{\sqrt{2500}}} = 3.3$$

This is an upper-tailed test, so (using the $z$ column of Appendix Table 4 because df $= 2499$) $P$-value $=$ area to the right of 3.33 $\approx$ .000. Because $P$-value $< .001$, we reject $H_0$. The true mean score for this region does appear to exceed 100.

However, with $n = 2500$, the point estimate $\bar{x} = 101.0$ is almost surely very close to the true value of $\mu$. Therefore it looks as though $H_0$ was rejected because $\mu \approx 101$ rather than 100. And, from a practical point of view, a 1-point difference is most likely of no practical importance. A statistically significant result does not necessarily mean that there are any practical consequences.

■

## ■ Exercises 10.45–10.64 ................................................

**10.45** Newly purchased automobile tires of a certain type are supposed to be filled to a pressure of 30 psi. Let $\mu$ denote the true average pressure. Find the $P$-value associated with each of the following given $z$ statistic values for testing $H_0$: $\mu = 30$ versus $H_a$: $\mu \neq 30$ when $\sigma$ is known:
**a.** 2.10    **d.** 1.44
**b.** −1.75    **e.** −5.00
**c.** 0.58

**10.46** The desired percentage of silicon dioxide in a certain type of cement is 5.0%. A random sample of $n = 36$ specimens gave a sample average percentage of $\bar{x} = 5.21$. Let $\mu$ be the true average percentage of silicon dioxide in this type of cement, and suppose that $\sigma$ is known to be 0.38. Test $H_0$: $\mu = 5$ versus $H_a$: $\mu \neq 5$ using a significance level of .01.

**10.47** Give as much information as you can about the $P$-value of a $t$ test in each of the following situations:
**a.** Upper-tailed test, df $= 8$, $t = 2.0$
**b.** Upper-tailed test, $n = 14$, $t = 3.2$
**c.** Lower-tailed test, df $= 10$, $t = -2.4$
**d.** Lower-tailed test, $n = 22$, $t = -4.2$
**e.** Two-tailed test, df $= 15$, $t = -1.6$
**f.** Two-tailed test, $n = 16$, $t = 1.6$
**g.** Two-tailed test, $n = 16$, $t = 6.3$

**10.48** Give as much information as you can about the $P$-value of a $t$ test in each of the following situations:
a. Two-tailed test, df $= 9$, $t = 0.73$
b. Upper-tailed test, df $= 10$, $t = -0.5$
c. Lower-tailed test, $n = 20$, $t = -2.1$
d. Lower-tailed test, $n = 20$, $t = -5.1$
e. Two-tailed test, $n = 40$, $t = 1.7$

**10.49** Paint used to paint lines on roads must reflect enough light to be clearly visible at night. Let $\mu$ denote the true average reflectometer reading for a new type of paint under consideration. A test of $H_0$: $\mu = 20$ versus $H_a$: $\mu > 20$ based on a sample of 15 observations gave $t = 3.2$. What conclusion is appropriate at each of the following significance levels?
**a.** $\alpha = .05$    **c.** $\alpha = .001$
**b.** $\alpha = .01$

**10.50** A certain pen has been designed so that true average writing lifetime under controlled conditions (involving the use of a writing machine) is at least 10 hr. A random sample of 18 pens is selected, the writing lifetime of each is determined, and a normal probability plot of the resulting data support the use of a one-sample $t$ test. The relevant hypotheses are $H_0$: $\mu = 10$ versus $H_a$: $\mu < 10$.
a. If $t = -2.3$ and $\alpha = .05$ is selected, what conclusion is appropriate?
b. If $t = -1.83$ and $\alpha = .01$ is selected, what conclusion is appropriate?
c. If $t = 0.47$, what conclusion is appropriate?

**10.51** The true average diameter of ball bearings of a certain type is supposed to be 0.5 in. What conclusion is appropriate when testing $H_0$: $\mu = 0.5$ versus $H_a$: $\mu \neq 0.5$ in each of the following situations:
**a.** $n = 13$, $t = 1.6$, $\alpha = .05$
**b.** $n = 13$, $t = -1.6$, $\alpha = .05$
**c.** $n = 25$, $t = -2.6$, $\alpha = .01$
**d.** $n = 25$, $t = -3.6$

**10.52** A credit bureau analysis of undergraduate students credit records found that the average number of credit cards in an undergraduate's wallet was 4.09 ("Undergraduate Students and Credit Cards in 2004," Nellie Mae, May 2005). It was also reported that in a random sample of 132 undergraduates, the sample mean number of credit cards carried was 2.6. The sample standard deviation was not reported, but for purposes of this exercise, suppose that it was 1.2. Is there convincing evidence that the mean number of credit cards that undergraduates report carrying is less than the credit bureau's figure of 4.09?

**10.53** ● Medical research has shown that repeated wrist extension beyond 20 degrees increases the risk of wrist and hand injuries. Each of 24 students at Cornell University used a proposed new mouse design, and while using the mouse their wrist extension was recorded for each one. Data consistent with summary values given in the paper "Comparative Study of Two Computer Mouse Designs" (Cornell Human Factors Laboratory Technical Report RP7992) are given. Use these data to test the hypothesis that the mean wrist extension for people using this new mouse design is greater than 20 degrees. Are any assumptions required in order for it to be appropriate to generalize the results of your test to the population of Cornell students? To the population of all university students? (data on next page)

**Bold** exercises answered in back    ● Data set available online but not required    ▼ Video solution available

| | | | | | | | | | | | |
|---|---|---|---|---|---|---|---|---|---|---|---|
| 27 | 28 | 24 | 26 | 27 | 25 | 25 | 24 | 24 | 24 | 25 | 28 |
| 22 | 25 | 24 | 28 | 27 | 26 | 31 | 25 | 28 | 27 | 27 | 25 |

**10.54** The international polling organization Ipsos reported data from a survey of 2000 randomly selected Canadians who carry debit cards (*Canadian Account Habits Survey*, July 24, 2006). Participants in this survey were asked what they considered the minimum purchase amount for which it would be acceptable to use a debit card. Suppose that the sample mean and standard deviation were $9.15 and $7.60 respectively. (These values are consistent with a histogram of the sample data that appears in the report.) Do these data provide convincing evidence that the mean minimum purchase amount for which Canadians consider the use of a debit card to be appropriate is less than $10? Carry out a hypothesis test with a significance level of .01.

**10.55** A comprehensive study conducted by the National Institute of Child Health and Human Development tracked more than 1000 children from an early age through elementary school (*New York Times*, November 1, 2005). The study concluded that children who spent more than 30 hours a week in child care before entering school tended to score higher in math and reading when they were in the third grade. The researchers cautioned that the findings should not be a cause for alarm because the effects of child care were found to be small. Explain how the difference between the mean math score for third graders who spent long hours in child care and the overall mean for third-graders could be small but the researchers could still reach the conclusion that the mean for the child care group is significantly higher than the overall mean for third-graders.

**10.56** In a study of computer use, 1000 randomly selected Canadian Internet users were asked how much time they spend using the Internet in a typical week (Ipsos Reid, August 9, 2005). The mean of the 1000 resulting observations was 12.7 hours.
**a.** The sample standard deviation was not reported, but suppose that it was 5 hours. Carry out a hypothesis test with a significance level of .05 to decide if there is convincing evidence that the mean time spent using the Internet by Canadians is greater than 12.5 hours.
**b.** Now suppose that the sample standard deviation was 2 hours. Carry out a hypothesis test with a significance level of .05 to decide if there is convincing evidence that the mean time spent using the Internet by Canadians is greater than 12.5 hours.

**c.** Explain why the null hypothesis was rejected in the test of Part (b) but not in the test of Part (a).

**10.57** A survey of teenagers and parents in Canada conducted by the polling organization Ipsos ("Untangling the Web: The Facts About Kids and the Internet," January 25, 2006) included questions about Internet use. It was reported that for a sample of 534 randomly selected teens, the mean number of hours per week spent online was 14.6 and the standard deviation was 11.6.
**a.** What does the large standard deviation, 11.6 hours, tell you about the distribution of online times for this sample of teens?
**b.** Do the sample data provide convincing evidence that the mean number of hours that teens spend online is greater than 10 hours per week?

**10.58** The same survey referenced in the previous exercise reported that for a random sample of 676 parents of Canadian teens, the mean number of hours parents thought their teens spent online was 6.5 and the sample standard deviation was 8.6.
**a.** Do the sample data provide convincing evidence that the mean number of hours that parents think their teens spend online is less than 10 hours per week?
**b.** Write a few sentences commenting on the results of the test in Part (a) and of the test in Part (b) of the previous exercise.

**10.59** The paper titled "Music for Pain Relief" (*The Cochrane Database of Systematic Reviews*, April 19, 2006) concluded, based on a review of 51 studies of the effect of music on pain intensity, that "Listening to music reduces pain intensity levels . . . However, the magnitude of these positive effects is small, the clinical relevance of music for pain relief in clinical practice is unclear." Are the authors of this paper claiming that the pain reduction attributable to listening to music is not statistically significant, not practically significant, or neither statistically nor practically significant? Explain.

**10.60** Typically, only very brave students are willing to speak out in a college classroom. Student participation may be especially difficult if the individual is from a different culture or country. The article "An Assessment of Class Participation by International Graduate Students" (*Journal of College Student Development* [1995]: 132–140) considered a numerical "speaking-up" scale, with possible values from 3 to 15 (a low value means that a student rarely speaks). For a random sample of 64 males from Asian countries where English is not the official language, the sample mean and sample standard deviation were 8.75 and 2.57, respectively. Suppose that the mean for the population of all males having English as their native language is 10.0 (suggested by data in the article). Does it appear that the population mean for males from non-English-speaking Asian countries is smaller than 10.0?

**10.61** ◉ ▼ A well-designed and safe workplace can contribute greatly to increasing productivity. It is especially important that workers not be asked to perform tasks, such as lifting, that exceed their capabilities. The following data on maximum weight of lift (MWOL, in kilograms) for a frequency of 4 lifts per minute were reported in the article "The Effects of Speed, Frequency, and Load on Measured Hand Forces for a Floor-to-Knuckle Lifting Task" (*Ergonomics* [1992]: 833–843):

| 25.8 | 36.6 | 26.3 | 21.8 | 27.2 |
|------|------|------|------|------|

Suppose that it is reasonable to regard the sample as a random sample from the population of healthy males, age 18–30. Do the data suggest that the population mean MWOL exceeds 25? Carry out a test of the relevant hypotheses using a .05 significance level.

**10.62** An article titled "Teen Boys Forget Whatever It Was" appeared in the Australian newspaper *The Mercury* (April 21, 1997). It described a study of academic performance and attention span and reported that the mean time to distraction for teenage boys working on an independent task was 4 min. Although the sample size was not given in the article, suppose that this mean was based on a random sample of 50 teenage Australian boys and that the sample standard deviation was 1.4 min. Is there convincing evidence that the average attention span for teenage boys is less than 5 min? Test the relevant hypotheses using $\alpha = .01$.

**10.63** ◉ ▼ Many consumers pay careful attention to stated nutritional contents on packaged foods when making purchases. It is therefore important that the information on packages be accurate. A random sample of $n = 12$ frozen dinners of a certain type was selected from production during a particular period, and the calorie content of each one was determined. (This determination entails destroying the product, so a census would certainly not be desirable!) Here are the resulting observations, along with a boxplot and normal probability plot:

| 255 | 244 | 239 | 242 | 265 | 245 | 259 | 248 |
|-----|-----|-----|-----|-----|-----|-----|-----|
| 225 | 226 | 251 | 233 |     |     |     |     |

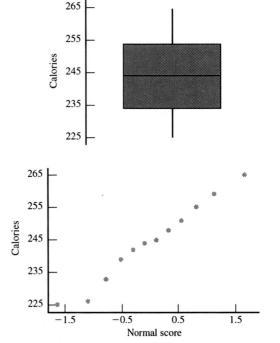

**a.** Is it reasonable to test hypotheses about true average calorie content $\mu$ by using a $t$ test?
**b.** The stated calorie content is 240. Does the boxplot suggest that true average content differs from the stated value? Explain your reasoning.
**c.** Carry out a formal test of the hypotheses suggested in Part (b).

**10.64** ◉ Much concern has been expressed in recent years regarding the practice of using nitrates as meat preservatives. In one study involving possible effects of these chemicals, bacteria cultures were grown in a medium containing nitrates. The rate of uptake of radio-labeled amino acid was then determined for each culture, yielding the following observations:

| 7251 | 6871 | 9632 | 6866 | 9094 | 5849 | 8957 | 7978 |
|------|------|------|------|------|------|------|------|
| 7064 | 7494 | 7883 | 8178 | 7523 | 8724 | 7468 |      |

Suppose that it is known that the true average uptake for cultures without nitrates is 8000. Do the data suggest that the addition of nitrates results in a decrease in the true average uptake? Test the appropriate hypotheses using a significance level of .10.

**Bold** exercises answered in back    ◉ Data set available online but not required    ▼ Video solution available

# 10.5 Power and Probability of Type II Error

In this chapter, we have introduced test procedures for testing hypotheses about population characteristics, such as $\mu$ and $\pi$. What characterizes a "good" test procedure? It makes sense to think that a good test procedure is one that has both a small probability of rejecting $H_0$ when it is true (a Type I error) and a high probability of rejecting $H_0$ when it is false. The test procedures presented in this chapter allow us to directly control the probability of rejecting a true $H_0$ by our choice of the significance level $\alpha$. But what about the probability of rejecting $H_0$ when it is false? As we will see, several factors influence this probability. Let's begin by considering an example.

Suppose that the student body president at a university is interested in studying the amount of money that students spend on textbooks each semester. The director of the financial aid office believes that the average amount spent on books is $300 per semester and uses this figure to determine the amount of financial aid for which a student is eligible. The student body president plans to ask each individual in a random sample of students how much he or she spent on books this semester and has decided to use the resulting data to test

$$H_0: \mu = 300 \quad \text{versus} \quad H_a: \mu > 300$$

using a significance level of .05. If the true mean is 300 (or less than 300), the correct decision is to fail to reject the null hypothesis (incorrectly rejecting the null hypothesis is a Type I error). On the other hand, if the true mean is 325 or 310 or even 301, the correct decision is to reject the null hypothesis (not rejecting the null hypothesis is a Type II error). How likely is it that the null hypothesis will in fact be rejected?

If the true mean is 301, the probability that we reject $H_0: \mu = 300$ is not very great. This is because when we carry out the test, we are essentially looking at the sample mean and asking, Does this look like what we would expect to see if the population mean were 300? As illustrated in Figure 10.4, if the true mean is greater than but very close to 300, chances are that the sample mean will look pretty much like what we would expect to see if the population mean were 300, and we will be unconvinced that the null hypothesis should be rejected. If the true mean is 325, it is less likely that the sample will be mistaken for a sample from a population with mean 300; sample means will tend to cluster around 325, and so it is more likely that we will correctly reject $H_0$. If the true mean is 350, rejection of $H_0$ is even more likely.

**Figure 10.4**
Sampling distribution of $\bar{x}$ when $\mu = 300, 305, 325$.

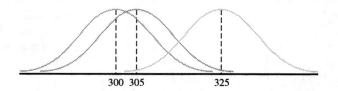

300 305         325

When we consider the probability of rejecting the null hypothesis, we are looking at what statisticians refer to as the **power** of the test.

The **power of a test** is the probability of rejecting the null hypothesis.

From the previous discussion, it should be apparent that the power of the test when a hypothesis about a population mean is being tested depends on the true value of the population mean, $\mu$. Because the true value of $\mu$ is unknown (if we knew the value of $\mu$ we wouldn't be doing the hypothesis test!), we cannot know what the power is for the actual true value of $\mu$. It is possible, however, to gain some insight into the power of a test by looking at a number of "what if" scenarios. For example, we might ask, What is the power if the true mean is 325? or What is the power if the true mean is 310? and so on. That is, we can determine the power at $\mu = 325$, the power at $\mu = 310$, and the power at any other value of interest. Although it is technically possible to consider power when the null hypothesis is true, an investigator is usually concerned about the power only at values for which the null hypothesis is false.

In general, when testing a hypothesis about a population characteristic, there are three factors that influence the power of the test:

1. The size of the difference between the true value of the population characteristic and the hypothesized value (the value that appears in the null hypothesis)
2. The choice of significance level, $\alpha$, for the test
3. The sample size

## Effect of Various Factors on the Power of a Test

1. The larger the size of the discrepancy between the hypothesized value and the true value of the population characteristic, the higher the power.
2. The larger the significance level, $\alpha$, the higher the power of the test.
3. The larger the sample size, the higher the power of the test.

Let's consider each of these three statements. The first statement has already been discussed in the context of the textbook example. Because power is the probability of rejecting the null hypothesis, it makes sense that the power will be higher when the true value of a population characteristic is quite different from the hypothesized value than when it is close to that value.

The effect of significance level on power is not quite as obvious. To understand the relationship between power and significance level, it helps to see the relationship between power and $\beta$, the probability of a Type II error.

When $H_0$ is false, power $= 1 - \beta$.

This relationship follows from the definitions of power and Type II error. A Type II error results from *not* rejecting a false $H_0$. Because power is the probability of rejecting $H_0$, it follows that *when $H_0$ is false*

$$\begin{aligned} \text{power} &= \text{probability of rejecting a false } H_0 \\ &= 1 - \text{probability of not rejecting a false } H_0 \\ &= 1 - \beta \end{aligned}$$

Recall from Section 10.2 that the choice of $\alpha$, the Type I error probability, affects the value of $\beta$, the Type II error probability. Choosing a larger value for $\alpha$ results in a smaller value for $\beta$ (and thus a larger value for $1 - \beta$). In terms of power, this means that choosing a larger value for $\alpha$ results in a larger value for the power of the test. That is, the larger the Type I error probability we are willing to tolerate, the more likely it is that the test will be able to detect any particular departure from $H_0$.

The third factor that affects the power of a test is the sample size. When $H_0$ is false, the power of a test is the probability that we will in fact "detect" that $H_0$ is false and, based on the observed sample, reject $H_0$. Intuition suggests that we will be more likely to detect a departure from $H_0$ with a large sample than with a small sample. This is in fact the case—the larger the sample size, the higher the power.

Consider testing the hypotheses presented previously:

$$H_0: \mu = 300 \text{ versus } H_a: \mu > 300$$

The observations about power imply the following, for example:

1. For any value of $\mu$ exceeding 300, the power of a test based on a sample of size 100 is higher than the power of a test based on a sample of size 75 (assuming the same significance level).
2. For any value of $\mu$ exceeding 300, the power of a test using a significance level of .05 is higher than the power of a test using a significance level of .01 (assuming the same sample size).
3. For any value of $\mu$ exceeding 300, the power of the test is greater if the true mean is 350 than if the true mean is 325 (assuming the same sample size and significance level).

As was mentioned previously in this section, it is impossible to calculate the *actual* power of a test because in practice we do not know the true value of population characteristics. However, we can evaluate the power at a selected alternative value if we want to know whether the power would be high or low if this alternative value is the true value.

The following optional subsection shows how Type II error probabilities and power can be evaluated for selected tests.

## ■ Calculating Power and Type II Error Probabilities for Selected Tests (Optional)

The test procedures presented in this chapter are designed to control the probability of a Type I error (rejecting $H_0$ when $H_0$ is true) at the desired level $\alpha$. However, little has been said so far about calculating the value of $\beta$, the probability of a Type II error (not rejecting $H_0$ when $H_0$ is false). Here we consider the determination of $\beta$ and power for the hypothesis tests previously introduced.

When we carry out a hypothesis test, we specify the desired value of $\alpha$, the probability of a Type I error. The probability of a Type II error, $\beta$, is the probability of not rejecting $H_0$ even though it is false. Suppose that we are testing

$$H_0: \mu = 1.5 \text{ versus } H_a: \mu > 1.5$$

Because we do not know the true value of $\mu$, we cannot calculate the actual value of $\beta$. However, the vulnerability of the test to Type II error can be investigated by calculating $\beta$ for several different potential values of $\mu$, such as $\mu = 1.55$, $\mu = 1.6$, and $\mu = 1.7$. Once the value of $\beta$ has been determined, the power of the test at the corresponding alternative value is just $1 - \beta$.

# Example 10.17  Calculating Power

A cigarette manufacturer claims that the mean nicotine content of its cigarettes is 1.5 mg. We might investigate this claim by testing

$$H_0: \mu = 1.5 \text{ versus } H_a: \mu > 1.5$$

where $\mu$ is the true mean nicotine content. A random sample of $n = 36$ cigarettes is to be selected, and the resulting data will be used to reach a conclusion. Suppose that the standard deviation of nicotine content ($\sigma$) is known to be 0.20 mg and that a significance level of .01 is to be used. Our test statistic (because $\sigma = 0.20$) is

$$z = \frac{\bar{x} - 1.5}{\dfrac{.20}{\sqrt{n}}} = \frac{\bar{x} - 75}{\dfrac{.20}{\sqrt{36}}} = \frac{\bar{x} - 1.5}{.0333}$$

The inequality in $H_a$ implies that

$$P\text{-value} = \text{area under } z \text{ curve to the right of calculated } z$$

From Appendix Table 2, it is easily verified that the $z$ critical value 2.33 captures an upper-tail $z$ curve area of .01. Thus, $P$-value $\leq$ .01 if and only if $z \geq 2.33$. This is equivalent to the decision rule

$$\text{reject } H_0 \text{ if calculated } z \geq 2.33$$

which becomes

$$\text{reject } H_0 \text{ if } \frac{\bar{x} - 1.5}{.0333} \geq 2.33$$

Solving this inequality for $\bar{x}$ we get

$$\bar{x} \geq 1.5 + 2.33(.0333)$$

or

$$\bar{x} \geq 1.578$$

So if $\bar{x} \geq 1.578$, we will reject $H_0$, and if $\bar{x} < 1.578$, we will fail to reject $H_0$. This decision rule corresponds to $\alpha = .01$.

Suppose now that $\mu = 1.6$ (so that $H_0$ is false). A Type II error will then occur if $\bar{x} < 1.578$. What is the probability that this occurs? If $\mu = 1.6$, the sampling distribution of $\bar{x}$ is approximately normal, centered at 1.6, and has a standard deviation of .0333. The probability of observing an $\bar{x}$ value less than 1.578 can then be determined by finding an area under a normal curve with mean 1.6 and standard deviation .0333, as illustrated in Figure 10.5.

**Figure 10.5**  $\beta$ when $\mu = 1.6$ in Example 10.17.

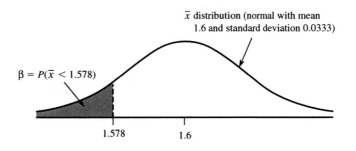

Because the curve in Figure 10.5 is not the standard normal ($z$) curve, we must first convert to a $z$ score before using Appendix Table 2 to find the area. Here,

$$z \text{ score for } 1.578 = \frac{1.578 - \mu_{\bar{x}}}{\sigma_{\bar{x}}} = \frac{1.578 - 1.6}{.0333} = -.66$$

and

$$\text{area under } z \text{ curve to left of } -0.66 = .2546$$

So, if $\mu = 1.6$, $\beta = .2546$. This means that if $\mu$ is 1.6, about 25% of all samples would still result in $\bar{x}$ values less than 1.578 and failure to reject $H_0$.

The power of the test at $\mu = 1.6$ is then

$$\begin{aligned}(\text{power at } \mu = 1.6) &= 1 - (\beta \text{ when } \mu \text{ is } 1.6) \\ &= 1 - .2546 \\ &= .7454\end{aligned}$$

Thus, if the true mean is 1.6, the probability of rejecting $H_0$: $\mu = 1.5$ in favor of $H_a$: $\mu > 1.5$ is .7454. That is, if $\mu$ is 1.6 and the test is used repeatedly with random samples selected from the population, in the long run about 75% of the samples will result in the correct conclusion to reject $H_0$.

Now consider $\beta$ and power when $\mu = 1.65$. The normal curve in Figure 10.5 would then be centered at 1.65. Because $\beta$ is the area to the left of 1.578 and the curve has shifted to the right, $\beta$ decreases. Converting 1.578 to a $z$ score and using Appendix Table 2 gives $\beta = .0154$. Also,

$$(\text{power at } \mu = 1.65) = 1 - .0154 = .9846$$

As expected, the power at $\mu = 1.65$ is higher than the power at $\mu = 1.6$ because 1.65 is farther from the hypothesized value of 1.

■

MINITAB can calculate the power for specified values of $\sigma$, $\alpha$, $n$, and the difference between the true and hypothesized values of $\mu$. The following output shows power calculations corresponding to those in Example 10.17:

1-Sample Z Test
Testing mean = null (versus > null)
Alpha = 0.01     Sigma = 0.2     Sample Size = 36

| Difference | Power |
|---|---|
| 0.10 | 0.7497 |
| 0.15 | 0.9851 |

The slight differences between the power values computed by MINITAB and those previously obtained are due to rounding in Example 10.17.

The probability of a Type II error and the power for $z$ tests concerning a population proportion are calculated in an analogous manner.

......................................................................................................................

# Example 10.18 Power for Testing Hypotheses About Proportions

A package delivery service advertises that at least 90% of all packages brought to its office by 9 A.M. for delivery in the same city are delivered by noon that day. Let $\pi$

denote the proportion of all such packages actually delivered by noon. The hypotheses of interest are

$$H_0: \pi = .9 \quad \text{versus} \quad H_a: \pi < .9$$

where the alternative hypothesis states that the company's claim is untrue. The value $\pi = .8$ represents a substantial departure from the company's claim. If the hypotheses are tested at level .01 using a sample of $n = 225$ packages, what is the probability that the departure from $H_0$ represented by this alternative value will go undetected?

At significance level .01, $H_0$ is rejected if $P$-value $\leq .01$. For the case of a lower-tailed test, this is the same as rejecting $H_0$ if

$$z = \frac{p - \mu_p}{\sigma_p} = \frac{p - .9}{\sqrt{\dfrac{(.9)(.1)}{225}}} = \frac{p - .9}{.02} \leq -2.33$$

(Because $-2.33$ captures a lower-tail $z$ curve area of .01, the smallest 1% of all $z$ values satisfy $z \leq -2.33$.) This inequality is equivalent to $p \leq .853$, so $H_0$ is *not* rejected if $p > .853$. When $\pi = .8$, $p$ has approximately a normal distribution with

$$\mu_p = .8 \qquad \sigma_p = \sqrt{\frac{(.8)(.2)}{225}} = .0267$$

Then $\beta$ is the probability of obtaining a sample proportion greater than .853, as illustrated in Figure 10.6.

**Figure 10.6** $\beta$ when $\pi = .8$ in Example 10.18.

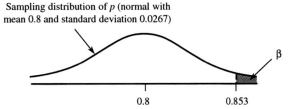

Sampling distribution of $p$ (normal with mean 0.8 and standard deviation 0.0267)

Converting to a $z$ score results in

$$z = \frac{.853 - .8}{.0267} = 1.99$$

and Appendix Table 2 gives

$$\beta = 1 - .9767 = .0233$$

When $\pi = .8$ and a level .01 test is used, less than 3% of all samples of size $n = 225$ will result in a Type II error. The power of the test at $\pi = .8$ is $1 - .0233 = .9767$. This means that the probability of rejecting $H_0: \pi = .9$ in favor of $H_a: \pi < .9$ when $\pi$ is really .8 is .9767, which is quite high.

■

## ■ $\beta$ and Power for the $t$ Test (Optional) .................................................

The power and $\beta$ values for $t$ tests can be determined by using a set of curves specially constructed for this purpose or by utilizing appropriate software. As with the $z$ test, the value of $\beta$ depends not only on the true value of $\mu$ but also on the selected significance level $\alpha$; $\beta$ increases as $\alpha$ is made smaller. In addition, $\beta$ depends on the number of degrees of freedom, $n - 1$. For any fixed level $\alpha$, it should be easier for the test to detect a specific departure from $H_0$ when $n$ is large than when $n$ is small. This is indeed the case; for a fixed alternative value, $\beta$ decreases as $n - 1$ increases.

Unfortunately, there is one other quantity on which $\beta$ depends: the population standard deviation $\sigma$. As $\sigma$ increases, so does $\sigma_{\bar{x}}$. This in turn makes it more likely that a value far from $\mu$ will be observed, resulting in an erroneous conclusion. Once $\alpha$ is specified and $n$ is fixed, the determination of $\beta$ at a particular alternative value of $\mu$ requires that a value of $\sigma$ be chosen, because each different value of $\sigma$ yields a different value of $\beta$. (This did not present a problem with the $z$ test because when using a $z$ test, the value of $\sigma$ is known.) If the investigator can specify a range of plausible values for $\sigma$, then using the largest such value will give a pessimistic $\beta$ (one on the high side) and a pessimistic value of power (one on the low side).

Figure 10.7 shows three different $\beta$ curves for a one-tailed $t$ test (appropriate for $H_a$: $\mu >$ hypothesized value or for $H_a$: $\mu <$ hypothesized value). A more complete set of curves for both one- and two-tailed tests when $\alpha = .05$ and when $\alpha = .01$ appears in Appendix Table 5. To determine $\beta$, first compute the quantity

$$d = \frac{|\text{alternative value} - \text{hypothesized value}|}{\sigma}$$

Then locate $d$ on the horizontal axis, move directly up to the curve for $n - 1$ df, and move over to the vertical axis to read $\beta$.

**Figure 10.7** $\beta$ curves for the one-tailed $t$ test.

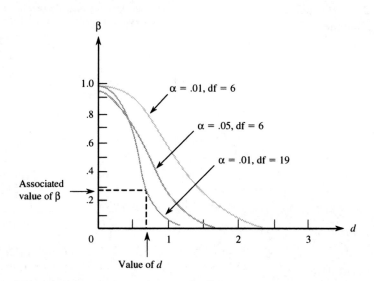

## Example 10.19 $\beta$ and Power for $t$ Tests

Consider testing

$$H_0\text{: } \mu = 100 \text{ versus } H_a\text{: } \mu > 100$$

and focus on the alternative value $\mu = 110$. Suppose that $\sigma = 10$, the sample size is $n = 7$, and a significance level of .01 has been selected. For $\sigma = 10$,

$$d = \frac{|110 - 100|}{10} = \frac{10}{10} = 1$$

Figure 10.7 (using df $= 7 - 1 = 6$) gives $\beta \approx .6$. The interpretation is that if $\sigma = 10$ and a level .01 test based on $n = 7$ is used when $\mu = 110$ (and thus $H_0$ is false), roughly 60% of all samples result in erroneously not rejecting $H_0$! Equivalently, the power of the test at $\mu = 110$ is only $1 - .6 = .4$. The probability of rejecting $H_0$ when $\mu = 110$ is not very large. If a level .05 test is used instead, then $\beta \approx .3$, which is still rather large. Using a level .01 test with $n = 20$ (df $= 19$) yields, from Figure 10.7, $\beta \approx .05$. At the alternative value $\mu = 110$, for $\sigma = 10$ the level .01 test based on $n = 20$ has smaller $\beta$ than the level .05 test with $n = 7$. Substantially increasing $n$ counterbalances using the smaller $\alpha$.

Now consider the alternative $\mu = 105$, again with $\sigma = 10$, so that

$$d = \frac{|105 - 100|}{10} = \frac{5}{10} = .5$$

Then, from Figure 10.7, $\beta = .95$ when $\alpha = .01$, $n = 7$; $\beta = .7$ when $\alpha = .05$, $n = 7$; and $\beta = .65$ when $\alpha = .01$, $n = 20$. These values of $\beta$ are all quite large; with $\sigma = 10$, $\mu = 105$ is too close to the hypothesized value of 100 for any of these three tests to have a good chance of detecting such a departure from $H_0$. A substantial decrease in $\beta$ necessitates using a much larger sample size. For example, from Appendix Table 5, $\beta = .08$ when $\alpha = .05$ and $n = 40$.

The curves in Figure 10.7 also give $\beta$ when testing $H_0: \mu = 100$ versus $H_a$: $\mu < 100$. If the alternative value $\mu = 90$ is of interest and $\sigma = 10$,

$$d = \frac{|90 - 100|}{10} = \frac{10}{10} = 1$$

and values of $\beta$ are the same as those given in the first paragraph of this example.

■

Because curves for only selected degrees of freedom appear in Appendix Table 5, other degrees of freedom require a visual approximation. For example, the 27-df curve (for $n = 28$) lies between the 19-df and 29-df curves, which do appear, and it is closer to the 29-df curve. This type of approximation is adequate because it is the general magnitude of $\beta$—large, small, or moderate—that is of primary concern.

MINITAB can also evaluate power for the $t$ test. For example, the following output shows MINITAB calculations for power at $\mu = 110$ for samples of size 7 and 20 when $\alpha = .01$. The corresponding approximate values from Appendix Table 5 found in Example 10.19 are fairly close to the MINITAB values.

```
1-Sample t Test
Testing mean = null (versus > null)
Calculating power for mean = null + 10
Alpha = 0.01    Sigma = 10
Sample Size      Power
          7     0.3968
         20     0.9653
```

The $\beta$ curves in Appendix Table 5 are those for $t$ tests. When the alternative value in $H_a$ corresponds to a value of $d$ relatively close to 0, $\beta$ for a $t$ test may be rather large. One might ask whether there is another type of test that has the same level of significance $\alpha$ as does the $t$ test and smaller values of $\beta$. The following result provides the answer to this question.

> When the population distribution is normal, the $t$ test for testing hypotheses about $\mu$ has smaller $\beta$ than does any other test procedure that has the same level of significance $\alpha$.

■

Stated another way, among all tests with level of significance $\alpha$, the $t$ test makes $\beta$ as small as it can possibly be when the population distribution is normal. In this sense, the $t$ test is a best test. Statisticians have also shown that when the population distribution is not too far from a normal distribution, no test procedure can improve on the $t$ test by very much (i.e., no test procedure can have the same $\alpha$ and substantially smaller $\beta$). However, when the population distribution is believed to be strongly non-normal (heavy-tailed, highly skewed, or multimodal), the $t$ test should not be used. Then it's time to consult your friendly neighborhood statistician, who can provide you with alternative methods of analysis.

## ■ Exercises 10.65–10.71 · · · · · · · · · · · · · · · · · · · · · · · · · · · · · · · · · · · · · · · · · · · · · · · · · · · · · · · · ·

**10.65** The power of a test is influenced by the sample size and the choice of significance level.
**a.** Explain how increasing the sample size affects the power (when significance level is held fixed).
**b.** Explain how increasing the significance level affects the power (when sample size is held fixed).

10.66 Water samples are taken from water used for cooling as it is being discharged from a power plant into a river. It has been determined that as long as the mean temperature of the discharged water is at most 150°F, there will be no negative effects on the river ecosystem. To investigate whether the plant is in compliance with regulations that prohibit a mean discharge water temperature above 150°F, a scientist will take 50 water samples at randomly selected times and will record the water temperature of each sample. She will then use a $z$ statistic

$$z = \frac{\bar{x} - 150}{\dfrac{\sigma}{\sqrt{n}}}$$

to decide between the hypotheses $H_0$: $\mu = 150$ and $H_a$: $\mu > 150$, where $\mu$ is the true mean temperature of discharged water. Assume that $\sigma$ is known to be 10.
a. Explain why use of the $z$ statistic is appropriate in this setting.
b. Describe Type I and Type II errors in this context.
c. The rejection of $H_0$ when $z \geq 1.8$ corresponds to what value of $\alpha$? (That is, what is the area under the $z$ curve to the right of 1.8?)
d. Suppose that the true value for $\mu$ is 153 and that $H_0$ is to be rejected if $z \geq 1.8$. Draw a sketch (similar to that of Figure 10.5) of the sampling distribution of $\bar{x}$, and shade the region that would represent $\beta$, the probability of making a Type II error.
e. For the hypotheses and test procedure described, compute the value of $\beta$ when $\mu = 153$.
f. For the hypotheses and test procedure described, what is the value of $\beta$ if $\mu = 160$?
g. If $H_0$ is rejected when $z \geq 1.8$ and $\bar{x} = 152.8$, what is the appropriate conclusion? What type of error might have been made in reaching this conclusion?

**Bold** exercises answered in back    ● Data set available online but not required    ▼ Video solution available

**10.67** ▼ Let $\mu$ denote the true average lifetime for a certain type of pen under controlled laboratory conditions. A test of $H_0$: $\mu = 10$ versus $H_a$: $\mu < 10$ will be based on a sample of size 36. Suppose that $\sigma$ is known to be 0.6, from which $\sigma_{\bar{x}} = 0.1$. The appropriate test statistic is then

$$z = \frac{\bar{x} - 10}{0.1}$$

**a.** What is $\alpha$ for the test procedure that rejects $H_0$ if $z \leq -1.28$?

**b.** If the test procedure of Part (a) is used, calculate $\beta$ when $\mu = 9.8$, and interpret this error probability.

**c.** Without doing any calculation, explain how $\beta$ when $\mu = 9.5$ compares to $\beta$ when $\mu = 9.8$. Then check your assertion by computing $\beta$ when $\mu = 9.5$.

**d.** What is the power of the test when $\mu = 9.8$? when $\mu = 9.5$?

**10.68** The city council in a large city has become concerned about the trend toward exclusion of renters with children in apartments within the city. The housing coordinator has decided to select a random sample of 125 apartments and determine for each whether children are permitted. Let $\pi$ be the true proportion of apartments that prohibit children. If $\pi$ exceeds .75, the city council will consider appropriate legislation.

a. If 102 of the 125 sampled apartments exclude renters with children, would a level .05 test lead you to the conclusion that more than 75% of all apartments exclude children?

b. What is the power of the test when $\pi = .8$ and $\alpha = .05$?

**10.69** The amount of shaft wear after a fixed mileage was determined for each of 7 randomly selected internal combustion engines, resulting in a mean of 0.0372 in. and a standard deviation of 0.0125 in.

**a.** Assuming that the distribution of shaft wear is normal, test at level .05 the hypotheses $H_0$: $\mu = .035$ versus $H_a$: $\mu > .035$.

**b.** Using $\sigma = 0.0125$, $\alpha = .05$, and Appendix Table 5, what is the approximate value of $\beta$, the probability of a Type II error, when $\mu = .04$?

**c.** What is the approximate power of the test when $\mu = .04$ and $\alpha = .05$?

**10.70** Optical fibers are used in telecommunications to transmit light. Current technology allows production of fibers that transmit light about 50 km (*Research at Rensselaer*, 1984). Researchers are trying to develop a new type of glass fiber that will increase this distance. In evaluating a new fiber, it is of interest to test $H_0$: $\mu = 50$ versus $H_a$: $\mu > 50$, with $\mu$ denoting the true average transmission distance for the new optical fiber.

a. Assuming $\sigma = 10$ and $n = 10$, use Appendix Table 5 to find $\beta$, the probability of a Type II error, for each of the given alternative values of $\mu$ when a level .05 test is employed:

i. 52  ii. 55  iii. 60  iv. 70

b. What happens to $\beta$ in each of the cases in Part (a) if $\sigma$ is actually larger than 10? Explain your reasoning.

**10.71** Let $\mu$ denote the true average diameter for bearings of a certain type. A test of $H_0$: $\mu = 0.5$ versus $H_a$: $\mu \neq 0.5$ will be based on a sample of $n$ bearings. The diameter distribution is believed to be normal. Determine the value of $\beta$ in each of the following cases:

**a.** $n = 15$, $\alpha = .05$, $\sigma = 0.02$, $\mu = 0.52$
**b.** $n = 15$, $\alpha = .05$, $\sigma = 0.02$, $\mu = 0.48$
**c.** $n = 15$, $\alpha = .01$, $\sigma = 0.02$, $\mu = 0.52$
**d.** $n = 15$, $\alpha = .05$, $\sigma = 0.02$, $\mu = 0.54$
**e.** $n = 15$, $\alpha = .05$, $\sigma = 0.04$, $\mu = 0.54$
**f.** $n = 20$, $\alpha = .05$, $\sigma = 0.04$, $\mu = 0.54$
**g.** Is the way in which $\beta$ changes as $n$, $\alpha$, $\sigma$, and $\mu$ vary consistent with your intuition? Explain.

**Bold** exercises answered in back  ● Data set available online but not required  ▼ Video solution available

# 10.6 Interpreting and Communicating the Results of Statistical Analyses

The step-by-step procedure that we have proposed for testing hypotheses provides a systematic approach for carrying out a complete test. However, you rarely see the results of a hypothesis test reported in publications in such a complete way.

## ■ Communicating the Results of Statistical Analyses ....................................

When summarizing the results of a hypothesis test, it is important that you include several things in the summary to have all the relevant information. These are

1. *Hypotheses*. Whether specified in symbols or described in words, it is important that both the null and the alternative hypotheses be clearly stated. If you are using symbols to define the hypotheses, be sure to describe them in the context of the problem at hand (e.g., $\mu$ = population mean calorie intake).
2. *Test procedure*. You should be clear about what test procedure was used (e.g., large-sample $z$ test for proportions) and why you think it was reasonable to use this procedure. The plausibility of any required assumptions should be satisfactorily addressed.
3. *Test statistic*. Be sure to include the value of the test statistic and the $P$-value. Including the $P$-value allows a reader who may have chosen a different significance level to see whether she would have reached the same or a different conclusion.
4. *Conclusion in context*. Never end the report of a hypothesis test with the statement "I rejected (or did not reject) $H_0$." Always provide a conclusion that is in the context of the problem and that answers the original research question which the hypothesis test was designed to answer. Be sure also to indicate the level of significance used as a basis for the decision.

## ■ Interpreting the Results of Statistical Analyses ...............................................

When the results of a hypothesis test are reported in a journal article or other published source, it is common to find only the value of the test statistic and the associated $P$-value accompanying the discussion of conclusions drawn from the data. Sometimes, even the exact $P$-value doesn't appear, but instead "coded" information is given. For example, * = significant ($P$-value < .05), ** = very significant ($P$-value < .01), and *** = highly significant ($P$-value < .001). Often, especially in newspaper articles, only sample summary statistics are given, with the conclusion immediately following. You may have to fill in some of the intermediate steps for yourself to see whether or not the conclusion is justified.

For example, the article "Physicians' Knowledge of Herbal Toxicities and Adverse Herb-Drug Interactions" (*European Journal of Emergency Medicine*, August 2004) summarizes the results of a study to assess doctors' familiarity with adverse effects of herbal remedies as follows: "A total of 142 surveys and quizzes were completed by 59 attending physicians, 57 resident physicians, and 26 medical students. The mean subject score on the quiz was only slightly higher than would have occurred from random guessing." The quiz consisted of 16 multiple-choice questions. If each question had four possible choices, the statement that the mean quiz score was only slightly higher than would have occurred from random guessing suggests that the researchers considered the hypotheses $H_0 : \mu = 4$ and $H_a : \mu > 4$, where $\mu$ represents the true mean score for the population of physicians and medical students and the null hypothesis corresponds to the expected number of correct choices for someone who is guessing. Assuming that it is reasonable to regard this sample as representative of the population of interest, the data from the sample could be used to carry out a test of these hypotheses.

## ■ What to Look For in Published Data ...............................................................

Here are some questions to consider when you are reading a report that contains the results of a hypothesis test:

* What hypotheses are being tested? Are the hypotheses about a population mean, a population proportion, or some other population characteristic?
* Was the appropriate test used? Does the validity of the test depend on any assumptions about the population from which the sample was selected? If so, are the assumptions reasonable?
* What is the *P*-value associated with the test? Was a significance level selected for the test (as opposed to simply reporting the *P*-value)? Is the chosen significance level reasonable?
* Are the conclusions drawn consistent with the results of the hypothesis test?

For example, consider the following statement from the paper "Didgeridoo Playing as Alternative Treatment for Obstructive Sleep Apnoea Syndrome" (*British Medical Journal* [2006]: 266–270): "We found that four months of training of the upper airways by didgeridoo playing reduces daytime sleepiness in people with snoring and obstructive apnoea syndrome." This statement was supported by data on a measure of daytime sleepiness called the Epworth scale. For the 14 participants in the study, the mean improvement in Epworth scale was 4.4 and the standard deviation was 3.7. The paper does not indicate what test was performed or what the value of the test statistic was. It appears that the hypotheses of interest are $H_0$: $\mu = 0$ (no improvement) versus $H_a$: $\mu > 0$, where $\mu$ represents the true mean improvement in Epworth score after four months of didgeridoo playing for people with snoring and obstructive sleep apnoea. Because the sample size is not large, the one-sample *t* test would be appropriate if the sample can be considered a random sample and the distribution of Epworth scale improvement scores is approximately normal. If these assumptions are reasonable (something that was not addressed in the paper), the *t* test results in $t = 4.45$ and an associated *P*-value of .000. Because the reported *P*-value is so small $H_0$ would be rejected, supporting the conclusion in the paper that didgeridoo playing is an effective treatment. (In case you are wondering, a didgeridoo is an Australian Aboriginal woodwind instrument.)

## ■ A Word to the Wise: Cautions and Limitations ............................................

There are several things you should watch for when conducting a hypothesis test or when evaluating a written summary of such a test.

1. The result of a hypothesis test can never show strong support for the null hypothesis. Make sure that you don't confuse "There is no reason to believe the null hypothesis is not true" with the statement "There is convincing evidence that the null hypothesis is true." These are very different statements!
2. If you have complete information for the population, don't carry out a hypothesis test! It should be obvious that no test is needed to answer questions about a population if you have complete information and don't need to generalize from a sample, but people sometimes forget this fact. For example, in an article on growth in the number of prisoners by state, the *San Luis Obispo Tribune* (August 13, 2001) reported "California's numbers showed a statistically insignificant change, with 66 fewer prisoners at the end of 2000." The use of the term "statistically insignificant" implies some sort of statistical inference, which is not appropriate when a complete accounting of the entire prison population is known. Perhaps the author confused statistical and practical significance. Which brings us to . . .
3. Don't confuse statistical significance with practical significance. When statistical significance has been declared, be sure to step back and evaluate the result in light of its practical importance. For example, we may be convinced that the proportion

who respond favorably to a proposed medical treatment is greater than .4, the known proportion that responds favorably for the currently recommended treatments. But if our estimate of this proportion for the proposed treatment is .405, is this of any practical interest? It might be if the proposed treatment is less costly or has fewer side effects, but in other cases it may not be of any real interest. Results must always be interpreted in context.

## A c t i v i t y  **10.1**  Comparing the *t* and *z* Distributions

**Technology Activity:** Requires use of a computer or a graphing calculator.

The instructions that follow assume the use of MINITAB. If you are using a different software package or a graphing calculator, your instructor will provide alternative instructions.

**Background:** Suppose a random sample will be selected from a population that is known to have a normal distribution. Then the statistic

$$z = \frac{\bar{x} - \mu}{\frac{\sigma}{\sqrt{n}}}$$

has a standard normal ($z$) distribution. Since it is rarely the case that $\sigma$ is known, inferences for population means are usually based on the statistic $t = \dfrac{\bar{x} - \mu}{(s/\sqrt{n})}$, which has a $t$ distribution rather than a $z$ distribution. The informal justification for this was that the use of $s$ to estimate $\sigma$ introduces additional variability, resulting in a statistic whose distribution is more spread out than is the $z$ distribution.

In this activity, you will use simulation to sample from a known normal population, and then investigate how the behavior of $t = \dfrac{\bar{x} - \mu}{s/\sqrt{n}}$ compares to $z = \dfrac{\bar{x} - \mu}{\sigma/(\sqrt{n})}$.

1. Generate 200 random samples of size 5 from a normal population with mean 100 and standard deviation 10.

Using MINTAB, go to the Calc Menu. Then

Calc → Random Data → Normal
In the "Generate" box, enter 200
In the "Store in columns" box, enter c1-c5
In the mean box, enter 100
In the standard deviation box, enter 10
Click on OK

You should now see 200 rows of data in each of the first 5 columns of the MINITAB worksheet.

2. Each row contains five values that have been randomly selected from a normal population with mean 100 and standard deviation 10. Viewing each row as a sample of size 5 from this population, calculate the mean and standard deviation for each of the 200 samples (the 200 rows) by using MINITAB's row statistics functions, which can also be found under the Calc menu:

Calc → Row statistics
Choose the "Mean" button
In the "Input Variables" box, enter c1-c5
In the "Store result in" box, enter c7
Click on OK

You should now see the 200 sample means in column 7 of the MINITAB worksheet. Name this column "x-bar", by typing the name in the gray box at the top of c7.

Now follow a similar process to compute the 200 sample standard deviations, and store them in c8. Name c8 "s."

3. Next, calculate the value of the $z$ statistic for each of the 200 samples. We can calculate $z$ in this example because we know that the samples were selected from a population for which $\sigma = 10$. Use the calculator function of MINITAB to compute $z = \dfrac{\bar{x} - \mu}{(\sigma/\sqrt{n})} = \dfrac{\bar{x} - 100}{(10/\sqrt{5})}$ as follows:

Calc → Calculator
In the "Store results in" box, enter c10
In the "Expression box" type in the following: (c7-100)/(10/sqrt(5))
Click on OK

You should now see the $z$ values for the 200 samples in c10. Name c10 "z".

4. Now calculate the value of the $t$ statistic for each of the 200 samples. Use the calculator function of MINITAB to compute $t = \dfrac{\bar{x} - \mu}{(s/\sqrt{n})} = \dfrac{\bar{x} - 100}{(s/\sqrt{5})}$ as follows:

Calc → Calculator
In the "Store results in" box, enter c11
In the "Expression box" type in the following: (c7-100)/(c8/sqrt(5))
Click on OK

You should now see the $t$ values for the 200 samples in c10. Name c10 "t."

5. Graphs, at last! Now construct histograms of the 200 $z$ values and the 200 $t$ values. These two graphical displays will provide insight about how each of these two statistics behaves in repeated sampling. Use the same scale for the two histograms so that it will be easier to compare the two distributions.

Graph → Histogram
In the "Graph variables" box, enter c10 for graph 1 and c11 for graph 2
Click the Frame dropdown menu and select multiple graphs.
Then under the scale choices, select "Same X and same Y."

6. Now use the histograms from Step 5 to answer the following questions:
a. Write a brief description of the shape, center and spread for the histogram of the $z$ values. Is what you see in the histogram consistent with what you would have expected to see? Explain. (Hint: In theory, what is the distribution of the $z$ statistic?)

b. How does the histogram of the $t$ values compare to the $z$ histogram? Be sure to comment on center, shape, and spread.
c. Is your answer to Part (b) consistent with what would be expected for a statistic that has a $t$ distribution? Explain.
d. The $z$ and $t$ histograms are based on only 200 samples, and they only approximate the corresponding sampling distributions. The 5th percentile for the standard normal distribution is $-1.645$ and the 95th percentile is $+1.645$. For a $t$ distribution with df $= 5 - 1 = 4$, the 5th and 95th percentiles are $-2.13$ and $+2.13$, respectively. How do these percentiles compare to those of the distributions displayed in the histograms? (Hint: Sort the 200 $z$ values— in MINITAB, choose "Sort" from the Manip menu. Once the values are sorted, percentiles from the histogram can be found by counting in 10 [which is 5% of 200] values from either end of the sorted list. Then repeat this with the $t$ values.)
e. Are the results of your simulation and analysis consistent with the statement that the statistic $z = \dfrac{\bar{x} - \mu}{(\sigma/\sqrt{n})}$ has a standard normal ($z$) distribution and the statistic $t = \dfrac{\bar{x} - \mu}{(s/\sqrt{n})}$ has a $t$ distribution? Explain.

## A c t i v i t y  10.2    A Meaningful Paragraph

Write a meaningful paragraph that includes the following six terms: **hypotheses, P-value, reject $H_0$, Type I error, statistical significance, practical significance**.

A "meaningful paragraph" is a coherent piece of writing in an appropriate context that uses all of the listed words. The paragraph should show that you understand the meaning of the terms and their relationship to one another. A sequence of sentences that just define the terms is *not* a meaningful paragraph. When choosing a context, think carefully about the terms you need to use. Choosing a good context will make writing a meaningful paragraph easier.

# Summary of Key Concepts and Formulas

| Term or Formula | Comment |
| --- | --- |
| Hypothesis | A claim about the value of a population characteristic. |
| Null hypothesis, $H_0$ | The hypothesis initially assumed to be true. It has the form $H_0$: population characteristic = hypothesized value. |
| Alternative hypothesis, $H_a$ | A hypothesis that specifies a claim that is contradictory to $H_0$ and is judged the more plausible claim when $H_0$ is rejected. |

| Term or Formula | Comment |
|---|---|
| Type I error | Rejection of $H_0$ when $H_0$ is true; the probability of a Type I error is denoted by $\alpha$ and is referred to as the significance level for the test. |
| Type II error | Nonrejection of $H_0$ when $H_0$ is false; the probability of a Type II error is denoted by $\beta$. |
| Test statistic | The quantity computed from sample data and used to make a decision between $H_0$ and $H_a$. |
| P-value | The probability, computed assuming $H_0$ to be true, of obtaining a value of the test statistic at least as contradictory to $H_0$ as what actually resulted. $H_0$ is rejected if P-value $\leq \alpha$ and not rejected if P-value $> \alpha$, where $\alpha$ is the chosen significance level. |
| $z = \dfrac{p - \text{hypothesized value}}{\sqrt{\dfrac{(\text{hyp. val})(1 - \text{hyp. val})}{n}}}$ | A test statistic for testing $H_0$: $\pi$ = hypothesized value when the sample size is large. The P-value is determined from the $z$ curve. |
| $z = \dfrac{\bar{x} - \text{hypothesized value}}{\dfrac{\sigma}{\sqrt{n}}}$ | A test statistic for testing $H_0$: $\mu$ = hypothesized value when $\sigma$ is known and either the population distribution is normal or the sample size is large. The P-value is determined from the $z$ curve. |
| $t = \dfrac{\bar{x} - \text{hypothesized value}}{\dfrac{s}{\sqrt{n}}}$ | A test statistic for testing $H_0$: $\mu$ = hypothesized value when $\sigma$ is unknown and either the population distribution is normal or the sample size is large. The P-value is determined from the $t$ curve with df $= n - 1$. |
| Power | The power of a test is the probability of rejecting the null hypothesis. Power is affected by the size of the difference between the hypothesized value and the true value, the sample size, and the significance level. |

# Chapter Review Exercises 10.72–10.95

**10.72** The authors of the article "Perceived Risks of Heart Disease and Cancer Among Cigarette Smokers" (*Journal of the American Medical Association* [1999]: 1019–1021) expressed the concern that a majority of smokers do not view themselves as being at increased risk of heart disease or cancer. A study of 737 current smokers selected at random from U.S. households with telephones found that of 737 smokers surveyed, 295 indicated that they believed they have a higher than average risk of cancer. Do these data suggest that $\pi$, the true proportion of smokers who view themselves as being at increased risk of cancer is in fact less than .5, as claimed by the authors of the paper? Test the relevant hypotheses using $\alpha = .05$.

**10.73** A number of initiatives on the topic of legalized gambling have appeared on state ballots. Suppose that a political candidate has decided to support legalization of casino gambling if he is convinced that more than two-thirds of U.S. adults approve of casino gambling. *USA Today* (June 17, 1999) reported the results of a Gallup poll in which 1523 adults (selected at random from households with telephones) were asked whether they approved of casino gambling. The number in the sample who approved was 1035. Does the sample provide convincing evidence that more than two-thirds approve?

10.74 The article "Credit Cards and College Students: Who Pays, Who Benefits?" (*Journal of College Student Development* [1998]: 50–56) described a study of credit card payment practices of college students. According to the authors of the article, the credit card industry asserts that at most 50% of college students carry a credit card balance from month to month. However, the authors of the article report that, in a random sample of 310 college students, 217 carried a balance each month. Does this sample provide sufficient evidence to reject the industry claim?

**10.75** Although arsenic is known to be a poison, it also has some beneficial medicinal uses. In one study of the use of arsenic to treat acute promyelocytic leukemia (APL), a rare type of blood cell cancer, APL patients were given an arsenic compound as part of their treatment. Of those receiving arsenic, 42% were in remission and showed no signs of leukemia in a subsequent examination (*Washington Post*, November 5, 1998). It is known that 15% of APL patients go into remission after the conventional treatment. Suppose that the study had included 100 randomly selected patients (the actual number in the study was much smaller). Is there sufficient evidence to conclude that the proportion in remission for the arsenic treatment is greater than .15, the remission proportion for the conventional treatment? Test the relevant hypotheses using a .01 significance level.

10.76 According to the article "Which Adults Do Under-age Youth Ask for Cigarettes?" (*American Journal of Public Health* [1999]: 1561–1564), 43.6% of the 149 18- to 19-year-olds in a random sample have been asked to buy cigarettes for an underage smoker.
a. Is there convincing evidence that fewer than half of 18- to 19-year-olds have been approached to buy cigarettes by an underage smoker?
b. The article went on to state that of the 110 nonsmoking 18- to 19-year-olds, only 38.2% had been approached to buy cigarettes for an underage smoker. Is there evidence that less than half of nonsmoking 18- to 19-year-olds have been approached to buy cigarettes?

**10.77** Many people have misconceptions about how profitable small, consistent investments can be. In a survey of 1010 randomly selected U.S. adults (Associated Press, October 29, 1999), only 374 responded that they thought that an investment of $25 per week over 40 years with a 7% annual return would result in a sum of over $100,000 (the correct amount is $286,640). Is there sufficient evidence to conclude that less than 40% of U.S. adults are aware that such an investment would result in a sum of over $100,000? Test the relevant hypotheses using $\alpha = .05$.

10.78 The same survey described in Exercise 10.77 also asked the individuals in the sample what they thought was their best chance to obtain more than $500,000 in their lifetime. Twenty-eight percent responded "win a lottery or sweepstakes." Does this provide convincing evidence that more than one-fourth of U.S. adults see a lottery or sweepstakes win as their best chance of accumulating $500,000? Carry out a test using a significance level of .01.

**10.79** The state of Georgia's HOPE scholarship program guarantees fully paid tuition to Georgia public universities for Georgia high school seniors who have a B average in academic requirements as long as they maintain a B average in college. Of 137 randomly selected students enrolling in the Ivan Allen College at the Georgia Institute of Technology (social science and humanities majors) in 1996 who had a B average going into college, 53.2% had a GPA below 3.0 at the end of their first year ("Who Loses HOPE? Attrition from Georgia's College Scholarship Program," *Southern Economic Journal* [1999]: 379–390). Do these data provide convincing evidence that a majority of students at Ivan Allen College who enroll with a HOPE scholarship lose their scholarship?

10.80 Speed, size, and strength are thought to be important factors in football performance. The article "Physical and Performance Characteristics of NCAA Division I Football Players" (*Research Quarterly for Exercise and Sport* [1990]: 395–401) reported on physical characteristics of Division I starting football players in the 1988 football season. Information for teams ranked in the top 20 was easily obtained, and it was reported that the mean weight of starters on top-20 teams was 105 kg. A random sample of 33 starting players (various positions were represented) from Division I teams that were not ranked in the top 20 resulted in a sample mean weight of 103.3 kg and a sample standard deviation of 16.3 kg. Is there sufficient evidence to conclude that the mean weight for non-top-20 starters is less than 105, the known value for top-20 teams?

**10.81** Are young women delaying marriage and marrying at a later age? This question was addressed in a report issued by the Census Bureau (Associated Press, June 8, 1991). The report stated that in 1970 (based on census results) the mean age of brides marrying for the first time was 20.8 years. In 1990 (based on a sample, because census results were not yet available), the mean was 23.9. Suppose that the 1990 sample mean had been based on a random sample of size 100 and that the sample standard deviation was 6.4. Is there sufficient evidence to support the claim that in 1990 women were marrying later in life than in 1970? Test the relevant hypotheses using $\alpha = .01$. (Note: It is probably not reasonable to think that the distribution of age at first marriage is normal in shape.)

**10.82** According to the article "Workaholism in Organizations: Gender Differences" (*Sex Roles* [1999]: 333–346), the following data were reported on 1996 income for random samples of male and female MBA graduates from a certain Canadian business school:

| | N | $\overline{x}$ | s |
|---|---|---|---|
| Males | 258 | $133,442 | $131,090 |
| Females | 233 | $105,156 | $98,525 |

Note: These salary figures are in Canadian dollars.

a. Test the hypothesis that the mean salary of male MBA graduates from this school was in excess of $100,000 in 1996.
b. Is there convincing evidence that the mean salary for all female MBA graduates is above $100,000? Test using $\alpha = .10$.
c. If a significance level of .05 or .01 were used instead of .10 in the test of Part (b), would you still reach the same conclusion? Explain.

**10.83** Duck hunting in populated areas faces opposition on the basis of safety and environmental issues. The *San Luis Obispo Telegram-Tribune* (June 18, 1991) reported the results of a survey to assess public opinion regarding duck hunting on Morro Bay (located along the central coast of California). A random sample of 750 local residents included 560 who strongly opposed hunting on the bay. Does this sample provide sufficient evidence to conclude that the majority of local residents oppose hunting on Morro Bay? Test the relevant hypotheses using $\alpha = .01$.

**10.84** Seat belts help prevent injuries in automobile accidents, but they certainly don't offer complete protection in extreme situations. A random sample of 319 front-seat occupants involved in head-on collisions in a certain region resulted in 95 people who sustained no injuries ("Influencing Factors on the Injury Severity of Restrained Front Seat Occupants in Car-to-Car Head-on Collisions," *Accident Analysis and Prevention* [1995]: 143–150). Does this suggest that the true (population) proportion of uninjured occupants exceeds .25? State and test the relevant hypotheses using a significance level of .05.

**10.85** White remains the most popular car color in the United States, but its popularity appears to be slipping. According to an annual survey by DuPont (*Los Angeles Times*, February 22, 1994), white was the color of 20% of the vehicles purchased during 1993, a decline of 4% from the previous year. (According to a DuPont spokesperson, white represents "innocence, purity, honesty, and cleanliness.") A random sample of 400 cars purchased during this period in a certain metropolitan area resulted in 100 cars that were white. Does the proportion of all cars purchased in this area that are white appear to differ from the national percentage? Test the relevant hypotheses using $\alpha = .05$. Does your conclusion change if $\alpha = .01$ is used?

**10.86** When a published article reports the results of many hypothesis tests, the $P$-values are not usually given. Instead, the following type of coding scheme is frequently used: $*p < .05$, $**p < .01$, $***p < .001$, $****p < .0001$. Which of the symbols would be used to code for each of the following $P$-values?
a. .037
b. .0026
c. .072
d. .0003

**10.87** A random sample of $n = 44$ individuals with a B.S. degree in accounting who started with a Big Eight accounting firm and subsequently changed jobs resulted in a sample mean time to change of 35.02 months and a sample standard deviation of 18.94 months ("The Debate over Post-Baccalaureate Education: One University's Experience," *Issues in Accounting Education* [1992]: 18–36). Can it be concluded that the true average time to change exceeds 2 years? Test the appropriate hypotheses using a significance level of .01.

**10.88** What motivates companies to offer stock ownership plans to their employees? In a random sample of 87 companies having such plans, 54 said that the primary rationale was tax related ("The Advantages and Disadvantages of ESOPs: A Long-Range Analysis," *Journal of Small Business Management* [1991]: 15–21). Does this information provide strong support for concluding that more than half of all such firms feel this way?

**10.89** The article "Caffeine Knowledge, Attitudes, and Consumption in Adult Women" (*Journal of Nutrition Education* [1992]: 179–184) reported the following summary statistics on daily caffeine consumption for a random sample of adult women: $n = 47$, $\bar{x} = 215$ mg, $s = 235$ mg, and the data values ranged from 5 to 1176.
**a.** Does it appear plausible that the population distribution of daily caffeine consumption is normal? Is it necessary to assume a normal population distribution to test hypotheses about the value of the population mean consumption? Explain your reasoning.
**b.** Suppose that it had previously been believed that mean consumption was at most 200 mg. Does the given information contradict this prior belief? Test the appropriate hypotheses at significance level .10.

**10.90** Past experience has indicated that the true response rate is 40% when individuals are approached with a request to fill out and return a particular questionnaire in a stamped and addressed envelope. An investigator believes that if the person distributing the questionnaire is stigmatized in some obvious way, potential respondents would feel sorry for the distributor and thus tend to respond at a rate higher than 40%. To investigate this theory, a distributor is fitted with an eye patch. Of the 200 questionnaires distributed by this individual, 109 were returned. Does this strongly suggest that the response rate in this situation exceeds the rate in the past? State and test the appropriate hypotheses at significance level .05.

**10.91** ● An automobile manufacturer who wishes to advertise that one of its models achieves 30 mpg (miles per gallon) decides to carry out a fuel efficiency test. Six nonprofessional drivers are selected, and each one drives a car from Phoenix to Los Angeles. The resulting fuel efficiencies (in miles per gallon) are:

27.2    29.3    31.2    28.4    30.3    29.6

Assuming that fuel efficiency is normally distributed under these circumstances, do the data contradict the claim that true average fuel efficiency is (at least) 30 mpg?

**10.92** A student organization uses the proceeds from a particular soft-drink dispensing machine to finance its activities. The price per can had been $0.75 for a long time, and the average daily revenue during that period had been $75.00. The price was recently increased to $1.00 per can. A random sample of $n = 20$ days after the price increase yielded a sample average daily revenue and sample standard deviation of $70.00 and $4.20, respectively. Does this information suggest that the true average daily revenue has decreased from its value before the price increase? Test the appropriate hypotheses using $\alpha = .05$.

**10.93** A hot tub manufacturer advertises that with its heating equipment, a temperature of 100°F can be achieved in at most 15 min. A random sample of 25 tubs is selected, and the time necessary to achieve a 100°F temperature is determined for each tub. The sample average time and sample standard deviation are 17.5 min and 2.2 min, respectively. Does this information cast doubt on the company's claim? Carry out a test of hypotheses using significance level .05.

**10.94** Let $\pi$ denote the proportion of voters in a certain state who favor a particular proposed constitutional amendment. Consider testing $H_0$: $\pi = .5$ versus $H_a$: $\pi > .5$ at significance level .05 based on a sample of size $n = 50$.
**a.** Suppose that $H_0$ is in fact true. Use Appendix Table 1 (our table of random numbers) to simulate selecting a sample, and use the resulting data to carry out the test.
**b.** If you repeated Part (a) a total of 100 times (a simulation consisting of 100 replications), how many times would you expect $H_0$ to be rejected?
**c.** Now suppose that $\pi = .6$, which implies that $H_0$ is false. Again, use Appendix Table 1 to simulate selecting a sample, and carry out the test. If you repeated this a total of 100 times, would you expect $H_0$ to be rejected more frequently than when $H_0$ is true?

**10.95** A type of lie detector that measures brain waves was developed by a professor of neurobiology at Northwestern University (Associated Press, July 7, 1988). He said, "It would probably not falsely accuse any innocent people and it would probably pick up 70% to 90% of guilty people." Suppose that the result of this lie detector test is allowed as evidence in a criminal trial as the sole basis of a decision between two rival hypotheses: accused is innocent versus accused is guilty. Although these are not "statistical hypotheses" (statements about a population characteristic), the possible decision errors are analogous to Type I and Type II errors.

In this situation, a Type I error is finding an innocent person guilty—rejecting the null hypothesis of innocence when it is in fact true. A Type II error is finding a guilty person innocent—not rejecting the null hypothesis of in-nocence when it is in fact false. If the developer of the lie detector is correct in his statements, what is the probability of a Type I error, $\alpha$? What can you say about the probability of a Type II error, $\beta$?

Mentor

Do you need a live tutor for homework problems?

**Thomson**NOW

Are you ready? Take your exam-prep post-test now.

# Chapter 12

## The Analysis of Categorical Data and Goodness-of-Fit Tests

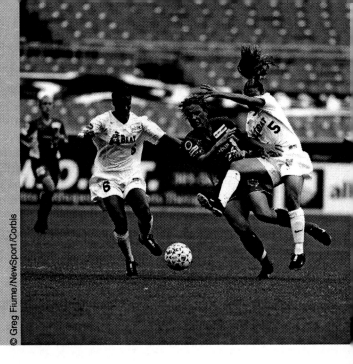

© Greg Fiume/NewSport/Corbis

I t is often the case that information is collected on categorical variables, such as political affiliation, gender, or college major. As with numerical data, categorical data sets can be univariate (consisting of observations on a single categorical variable), bivariate (observations on two categorical variables), or even multivariate. In this chapter, we will first consider inferential methods for analyzing univariate categorical data sets and then turn to techniques appropriate for use with bivariate categorical data.

## 12.1 Chi-Square Tests for Univariate Data

Univariate categorical data sets arise in a variety of settings. If each student in a sample of 100 is classified according to whether he or she is enrolled full-time or part-time, data on a categorical variable with two categories result. Each airline passenger in a sample of 50 might be classified into one of three categories based on type of ticket—coach, business class, or first class. Each registered voter in a sample of 100 selected from those registered in a particular city might be asked which of the five city council members he or she favors for mayor. This would yield observations on a categorical variable with five categories.

Univariate categorical data are most conveniently summarized in a **one-way frequency table**. For example, the article "Fees Keeping American Taxpayers From Using Credit Cards to Make Tax Payments" (*IPSOS Insight,* March 24, 2006) surveyed American taxpayers regarding their intent to pay taxes with a credit card. Suppose that 100 randomly selected taxpayers participated in such a survey, with possible responses being definitely will use a credit card to pay taxes next year, probably will use a credit card, probably won't use a credit card, and definitely won't use a credit card. The first few observations might be

| | | |
|---|---|---|
| Probably will | Definitely will not | Probably will not |
| Probably will not | Definitely will | Definitely will not |

Counting the number of observations of each type might then result in the following one-way table:

| | Outcome | | | |
|---|---|---|---|---|
| | Definitely Will | Probably Will | Probably Will Not | Definitely Will Not |
| Frequency | 14 | 12 | 24 | 50 |

For a categorical variable with $k$ possible values ($k$ different levels or categories), sample data are summarized in a one-way frequency table consisting of $k$ cells, which may be displayed either horizontally or vertically.

In this section, we consider testing hypotheses about the proportion of the population that falls into each of the possible categories. For example, the manager of a tax preparation company might be interested in determining whether the four possible responses to the tax credit card question occur equally often. If this is indeed the case, the long-run proportion of responses falling into each of the four categories is 1/4, or .25. The test procedure to be presented shortly would allow the manager to decide whether the hypothesis that all four category proportions are equal to .25 is plausible.

## Notation

$k$ = number of categories of a categorical variable
$\pi_1$ = true proportion for Category 1
$\pi_2$ = true proportion for Category 2
$\vdots$

$\pi_k$ = true proportion for Category $k$
  (Note: $\pi_1 + \pi_2 + \cdots + \pi_k = 1$)

The hypotheses to be tested have the form

$H_0$: $\pi_1$ = hypothesized proportion for Category 1
  $\pi_2$ = hypothesized proportion for Category 2
  $\vdots$

  $\pi_k$ = hypothesized proportion for Category $k$
$H_a$: $H_0$ is not true, so at least one of the true category proportions differs from the corresponding hypothesized value.

For the example involving responses to the tax survey, let

$\pi_1$ = the proportion of all taxpayers who will definitely pay by credit card
$\pi_2$ = the proportion of all taxpayers who will probably pay by credit card
$\pi_3$ = the proportion of all taxpayers who will probably not pay by credit card

and

$\pi_4$ = the proportion of all taxpayers who will definitely not pay by credit card

The null hypothesis of interest is then

$H_0$: $\pi_1 = .25$, $\pi_2 = .25$, $\pi_3 = .25$, $\pi_4 = .25$

A null hypothesis of the type just described can be tested by first selecting a random sample of size $n$ and then classifying each sample response into one of the $k$ possible categories. To decide whether the sample data are compatible with the null hypothesis, we compare the observed cell counts (frequencies) to the cell counts that would have been expected when the null hypothesis is true. The expected cell counts are

Expected cell count for Category 1 = $n\pi_1$
Expected cell count for Category 2 = $n\pi_2$

and so on. The expected cell counts when $H_0$ is true result from substituting the corresponding hypothesized proportion for each $\pi_i$.

..................................................................................................................

# Example 12.1   Births and the Lunar Cycle

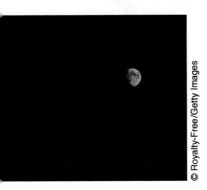

● A common urban legend is that more babies than expected are born during certain phases of the lunar cycle, especially near the full moon. The paper "The Effect of the Lunar Cycle on Frequency of Births and Birth Complications" (*American Journal of Obstetrics and Gynecology* [2005]: 1462–1464) classified births according to the lunar cycle. Data for a sample of randomly selected births occurring during 24 lunar cycles consistent with summary quantities appearing in the paper are given in the accompanying table.

| Lunar Phase | Number of Days | Number of Births |
|---|---|---|
| New moon | 24 | 7680 |
| Waxing crescent | 152 | 48442 |
| First quarter | 24 | 7579 |
| Waxing gibbous | 149 | 47814 |
| Full moon | 24 | 7711 |
| Waning gibbous | 150 | 47595 |
| Last quarter | 24 | 7733 |
| Waning crescent | 152 | 48230 |

● Data set available online

Let's define lunar phase category proportions as follows:

$\pi_1$ = proportion of births that occur during the new moon
$\pi_2$ = proportion of births that occur during the waxing crescent moon
$\pi_3$ = proportion of births that occur during the first quarter moon
$\pi_4$ = proportion of births that occur during the waxing gibbous moon
$\pi_5$ = proportion of births that occur during the full moon
$\pi_6$ = proportion of births that occur during the waning gibbous moon
$\pi_7$ = proportion of births that occur during the last quarter moon
$\pi_8$ = proportion of births that occur during the waning crescent moon

If there is no relationship between number of births and the lunar cycle, then the number of births in each lunar cycle category should be proportional to the number of days included in that category. Since there are a total of 699 days in the 24 lunar cycles considered and 24 of those days are in the new moon category, if there is no relationship between number of births and lunar cycle,

$$\pi_1 = \frac{24}{699} = .0343$$

Similarly, in the absence of any relationship,

$$\pi_2 = \frac{152}{699} = .2175 \qquad \pi_3 = \frac{24}{699} = .0343$$

$$\pi_4 = \frac{149}{699} = .2132 \qquad \pi_5 = \frac{24}{699} = .0343$$

$$\pi_6 = \frac{150}{699} = .2146 \qquad \pi_7 = \frac{24}{699} = .0343$$

$$\pi_8 = \frac{152}{699} = .2175$$

The hypotheses of interest are then

$H_0$: $\pi_1 = .0343$, $\pi_2 = .2175$, $\pi_3 = .0343$, $\pi_4 = .2132$, $\pi_5 = .0343$, $\pi_6 = .2146$, $\pi_7 = .0343$, $\pi_8 = .2175$
$H_a$: $H_0$ is not true.

There were a total of 222,784 births in the sample, so if $H_0$ is true, the expected counts for the first two categories are

$$\begin{pmatrix} \text{expected count} \\ \text{for new moon} \end{pmatrix} = n\begin{pmatrix} \text{hypothesized proportion} \\ \text{for new moon} \end{pmatrix}$$
$$= 222,784(.0343) = 7641.49$$
$$\begin{pmatrix} \text{expected count} \\ \text{for waxing crescent} \end{pmatrix} = n\begin{pmatrix} \text{hypothesized proportion} \\ \text{for waxing crescent} \end{pmatrix}$$
$$= 222,784(.2175) = 48,455.52$$

Expected counts for the other six categories are computed in a similar fashion, and observed and expected cell counts are given in the following table.

| Lunar Phase | Observed Number of Births | Expected Number of Births |
|---|---|---|
| New moon | 7680 | 7641.49 |
| Waxing crescent | 48442 | 48455.52 |
| First quarter | 7579 | 7641.49 |
| Waxing gibbous | 47814 | 47497.55 |
| Full moon | 7711 | 7641.49 |
| Waning gibbous | 47595 | 47809.45 |
| Last quarter | 7733 | 7641.49 |
| Waning crescent | 48230 | 48455.52 |

Because the observed counts are based on a *sample* of births, it would be somewhat surprising to see *exactly* 3.43% of the sample falling in the first category, exactly 21.75% in the second, and so on, even when $H_0$ is true. If the differences between the observed and expected cell counts can reasonably be attributed to sampling variation, the data are considered compatible with $H_0$. On the other hand, if the discrepancy between the observed and the expected cell counts is too large to be attributed solely to chance differences from one sample to another, $H_0$ should be rejected in favor of $H_a$. Thus, we need an assessment of how different the observed and expected counts are.

■

The goodness-of-fit statistic, denoted by $X^2$, is a quantitative measure of the extent to which the observed counts differ from those expected when $H_0$ is true. (The Greek letter $\chi$ is often used in place of $X$. The symbol $X^2$ is referred to as the chi-square [$\chi^2$] statistic. In using $X^2$ rather than $\chi^2$, we are adhering to the convention of denoting sample quantities by Roman letters.)

The **goodness-of-fit statistic**, $X^2$, results from first computing the quantity

$$\frac{(\text{observed cell count} - \text{expected cell count})^2}{\text{expected cell count}}$$

for each cell, where, for a sample of size $n$,

$$\left( \begin{array}{c} \text{expected cell} \\ \text{count} \end{array} \right) = n \left( \begin{array}{c} \text{hypothesized value of corresponding} \\ \text{population proportion} \end{array} \right)$$

The $X^2$ statistic is the sum of these quantities for all $k$ cells:

$$X^2 = \sum_{\text{all cells}} \frac{(\text{observed cell count} - \text{expected cell count})^2}{\text{expected cell count}}$$

The value of the $X^2$ statistic reflects the magnitude of the discrepancies between observed and expected cell counts. When the differences are sizable, the value of $X^2$ tends to be large. Therefore, large values of $X^2$ suggest rejection of $H_0$. A small value of $X^2$ (it can never be negative) occurs when the observed cell counts are quite similar to those expected when $H_0$ is true and so would be consistent with $H_0$.

As with previous test procedures, a conclusion is reached by comparing a $P$-value to the significance level for the test. The $P$-value is computed as the probability of observing a value of $X^2$ at least as large as the observed value when $H_0$ is true. This requires information about the sampling distribution of $X^2$ when $H_0$ is true.

When the null hypothesis is correct and the sample size is sufficiently large, the behavior of $X^2$ is described approximately by a **chi-square distribution**. A chi-square curve has no area associated with negative values and is asymmetric, with a longer tail on the right. There are actually many chi-square distributions, each one identified with a different number of degrees of freedom. Curves corresponding to several chi-square distributions are shown in Figure 12.1.

**Figure 12.1** Chi-square curves.

For a test procedure based on the $X^2$ statistic, the associated $P$-value is the area under the appropriate chi-square curve and to the right of the computed $X^2$ value. Appendix Table 8 gives upper-tail areas for chi-square distributions with up to 20 df. Our chi-square table has a different appearance from the $t$ table used in previous chapters. In the $t$ table, there is a single "value" column on the far left and then a column of $P$-values (tail areas) for each different number of degrees of freedom. A single column of $t$ values works for the $t$ table because all $t$ curves are centered at 0, and the $t$ curves approach the $z$ curve as the number of degrees of freedom increases. However, because the chi-square curves move farther and farther to the right and spread out more as the number of degrees of freedom increases, a single "value" column is impractical in this situation.

To find the area to the right for a particular $X^2$ value, locate the appropriate df column in Appendix Table 8. Determine which listed value is closest to the $X^2$ value of interest, and read the right-tail area corresponding to this value from the left-hand column of the table. For example, for a chi-square distribution with df = 4, the area to the right of $X^2 = 8.18$ is .085, as shown in Figure 12.2. For this same chi-square distribution (df = 4), the area to the right of 9.70 is approximately .045 (the area to the right of 9.74, the closest entry in the table for df = 4).

**Figure 12.2** A chi-square upper-tail area.

It is also possible to use computer software or a graphing calculator to compute areas under a chi-square curve.

## ■ Goodness-of-Fit Tests

When $H_0$ is true, the $X^2$ goodness-of-fit statistic has approximately a chi-square distribution with df $= (k - 1)$, as long as none of the expected cell counts are too small. *It is generally agreed that use of the chi-square distribution is appropriate when the sample size is large enough for every expected cell count to be at least 5.* If any of the expected cell frequencies are less than 5, categories can be combined in a sensible way to create acceptable expected cell counts. Just remember to compute the number of degrees of freedom based on the reduced number of categories.

### Goodness-of-Fit Test Procedure

**Hypotheses:**   $H_0$: $\pi_1$ = hypothesized proportion for Category 1

$\vdots$

$\pi_k$ = hypothesized proportion for Category $k$

$H_a$: $H_0$ is not true

**Test statistic:**   $X^2 = \sum_{\text{all cells}} \dfrac{(\text{observed cell count} - \text{expected cell count})^2}{\text{expected cell count}}$

**P-values:**   When $H_0$ is true and all expected counts are at least 5, $X^2$ has approximately a chi-square distribution with df $= k - 1$. Therefore, the $P$-value associated with the computed test statistic value is the area to the right of $X^2$ under the df $= k - 1$ chi-square curve. Upper-tail areas for chi-square distributions are found in Appendix Table 8.

**Assumptions:**   1. Observed cell counts are based on a *random sample*.
2. The *sample size is large*. The sample size is large enough for the chi-square test to be appropriate as long as every expected cell count is at least 5.

■

.....

# Example 12.2   Births and the Lunar Cycle Revisited

We use the births data of Example 12.1 to test the hypothesis that number of births is unrelated to lunar cycle. Let's use a .05 level of significance and the nine-step hypothesis-testing procedure illustrated in previous chapters.

1. Let $\pi_1$, $\pi_2$, $\pi_3$, $\pi_4$, $\pi_5$, $\pi_6$, $\pi_7$, and $\pi_8$ denote the proportions of all births falling in the eight lunar cycle categories as defined in Example 12.1.
2. $H_0$: $\pi_1 = .0343$, $\pi_2 = .2175$, $\pi_3 = .0343$, $\pi_4 = .2132$, $\pi_5 = .0343$, $\pi_6 = .2146$, $\pi_7 = .0343$, $\pi_8 = .2175$
3. $H_a$: $H_0$ is not true.
4. Significance level: $\alpha = .05$.
5. Test statistic: $X^2 = \sum_{\text{all cells}} \dfrac{(\text{observed cell count} - \text{expected cell count})^2}{\text{expected cell count}}$
6. Assumptions: The expected cell counts (from Example 12.1) are all greater than 5. The births represent a random sample of births occurring during the lunar cycles considered.
7. Calculation:

$$X^2 = \frac{(7680 - 7641.49)^2}{7641.49} + \frac{(48442 - 48455.52)^2}{48455.52} + \cdots + \frac{(48230 - 48455.52)^2}{48455.52}$$
$$= .194 + .004 + .511 + 2.108 + .632 + .962 + 1.096 + 1.050$$
$$= 6.557$$

8. $P$-value: The $P$-value is based on a chi-square distribution with df $= 8 - 1 = 7$. The computed value of $X^2$ is smaller than 12.01 (the smallest entry in the df $= 7$ column of Appendix Table 8), so $P$-value $> .10$.
9. Conclusion: Because $P$-value $> \alpha$, $H_0$ cannot be rejected. There is not sufficient evidence to conclude that number of births and lunar cycle are related. This is

consistent with the conclusion in the paper: "We found no statistical evidence that deliveries occurred in a predictable pattern across the phases of the lunar cycle."

MINITAB will perform a chi-square goodness-of-fit test. MINITAB output for the data and hypothesized proportions of this example is shown here.

**Chi-Square Goodness-of-Fit Test for Observed Counts in Variable: Number of Births**
Using category names in Lunar Phase

| Category | Observed | Test Proportion | Expected | Contribution to Chi-Sq |
|---|---|---|---|---|
| First Quarter | 7579 | 0.0343 | 7641.5 | 0.51105 |
| Full Moon | 7711 | 0.0343 | 7641.5 | 0.63227 |
| Last Quarter | 7733 | 0.0343 | 7641.5 | 1.09584 |
| New Moon | 7680 | 0.0343 | 7641.5 | 0.19406 |
| Waning Crescent | 48230 | 0.2175 | 48455.5 | 1.04961 |
| Waning Gibbous | 47595 | 0.2146 | 47809.4 | 0.96189 |
| Waxing Crescent | 48442 | 0.2175 | 48455.5 | 0.00377 |
| Waxing Gibbous | 47814 | 0.2132 | 47497.5 | 2.10835 |

| N | DF | Chi-Sq | P-Value |
|---|---|---|---|
| 222784 | 7 | 6.55683 | 0.476 |

Note that MINITAB has reordered the categories from smallest to largest based on the observed count. MINITAB also carried a bit more decimal accuracy in the computation of the chi-square statistic, reporting $X^2 = 6.55683$ and an associated $P$-value of .476. The computed $P$-value $= .476$ is consistent with the statement $P$-value $> .10$ from step 8 of the hypothesis test.

■

## Example 12.3 Hybrid Car Purchases

● *USA Today* ("Hybrid Car Sales Rose 81% Last Year," April 25, 2005) reported the top five states for sales of hybrid cars in 2004 as California, Virginia, Washington, Florida, and Maryland. Suppose that each car in a sample of 2004 hybrid car sales is classified by state where the sale took place. Sales from states other than the top five were excluded from the sample, resulting in the accompanying table.

| State | Observed Frequency |
|---|---|
| California | 250 |
| Virginia | 56 |
| Washington | 34 |
| Florida | 33 |
| Maryland | 33 |
| **Total** | **406** |

● Data set available online

(The given observed counts are artificial, but they are consistent with hybrid sales figures given in the article.)

We will use the $X^2$ goodness-of-fit test and a significance level of $\alpha = .01$ to test the hypothesis that hybrid sales for these five states are proportional to the 2004 population for these states. 2004 population estimates from the Census Bureau web site are given in the following table. The population proportion for each state was computed by dividing each state population by the total population for all five states.

| State | 2004 Population | Population Proportion |
|---|---|---|
| California | 35842038 | 0.495 |
| Virginia | 7481332 | 0.103 |
| Washington | 6207046 | 0.085 |
| Florida | 17385430 | 0.240 |
| Maryland | 5561332 | 0.077 |
| **Total** | **72477178** | |

If these same population proportions hold for hybrid car sales, the expected counts are

$$\text{Expected count for California} = 406(.495) = 200.970$$
$$\text{Expected count for Virginia} = 406(.103) = 41.818$$
$$\text{Expected count for Washington} = 406(.085) = 34.510$$
$$\text{Expected count for Florida} = 406(.240) = 97.440$$
$$\text{Expected count for Maryland} = 406(.077) = 31.362$$

These expected counts have been entered in Table 12.1.

**Table 12.1**   Observed and Expected Counts for Example 12.3

| State | Observed Counts | Expected Counts |
|---|---|---|
| California | 250 | 200.970 |
| Virginia | 56 | 41.818 |
| Washington | 34 | 34.510 |
| Florida | 33 | 97.440 |
| Maryland | 33 | 31.262 |

1. Let $\pi_1, \pi_2, \ldots, \pi_5$ denote the true proportion of hybrid car sales for the five states in the following order: California, Virginia, Washington, Florida, and Maryland.
2. $H_0$: $\pi_1 = .495$, $\pi_2 = .103$, $\pi_3 = .085$, $\pi_4 = .240$, $\pi_5 = .077$
3. $H_a$: $H_0$ is not true.
4. Significance level: $\alpha = .01$
5. Test statistic: $X^2 = \sum_{\text{all cells}} \dfrac{(\text{observed cell count} - \text{expected cell count})^2}{\text{expected cell count}}$

6. Assumptions: The sample was a random sample of hybrid car sales. All expected counts are greater than 5, so the sample size is large enough to use the chi-square test.

7. Calculation: From MINITAB

**Chi-Square Goodness-of-Fit Test for Observed Counts in Variable: Hybrid Sales**

Using category names in State

| Category | Observed | Test Proportion | Expected | Contribution to Chi-Sq |
|----------|----------|-----------------|----------|------------------------|
| California | 250 | 0.495 | 200.970 | 11.9617 |
| Florida | 33 | 0.240 | 97.440 | 42.6161 |
| Maryland | 33 | 0.077 | 31.262 | 0.0966 |
| Virginia | 56 | 0.103 | 41.818 | 4.8096 |
| Washington | 34 | 0.085 | 34.510 | 0.0075 |

| N | DF | Chi-Sq | P-Value |
|-----|----|--------|---------|
| 406 | 4 | 59.4916 | 0.000 |

8. $P$-value: All expected counts exceed 5, so the $P$-value can be based on a chi-square distribution with df $= 5 - 1 = 4$. From MINITAB, the $P$-value is 0.000.

9. Conclusion: Since $P$-value $\leq \alpha$, $H_0$ is rejected. There is convincing evidence that hybrid sales are not proportional to population size for at least one of the five states.

Based on the hybrid sales data, we have determined that there is convincing evidence that at least one of these five states has hybrid sales that are not proportional to population size. Looking back at the MINITAB output, notice that there is a column labeled "Contribution to Chi-Sq." This column shows the individual values of

$$\frac{(\text{observed cell count} - \text{expected cell count})^2}{\text{expected cell count}},$$ which are summed to produce the

value of the chi-square statistic. Notice that the two states with the largest contribution to the chi-square statistic are Florida and California. For Florida, observed hybrid sales were smaller than expected (observed $= 33$, expected $= 97.44$), whereas for California observed sales were higher than expected (observed $= 250$, expected $= 200.970$).

■

■ **Exercises 12.1–12.14** ...............................................................................................

**12.1** From the given information in each case below, state what you know about the $P$-value for a chi-square test and give the conclusion for a significance level of $\alpha = .01$.
**a.** $X^2 = 7.5$, df $= 2$  **d.** $X^2 = 21.3$, df $= 4$
**b.** $X^2 = 13.0$, df $= 6$  **e.** $X^2 = 5.0$, df $= 3$
**c.** $X^2 = 18.0$, df $= 9$

**12.2** A particular paperback book is published in a choice of four different covers. A certain bookstore keeps copies of each cover on its racks. To test the hypothesis that sales are equally divided among the four choices, a random sample of 100 purchases is identified.

a. If the resulting $X^2$ value were 6.4, what conclusion would you reach when using a test with significance level .05?
b. What conclusion would be appropriate at significance level .01 if $X^2 = 15.3$?
c. If there were six different covers rather than just four, what would you conclude if $X^2 = 13.7$ and a test with $\alpha = .05$ was used?

**12.3** Packages of mixed nuts made by a certain company contain four types of nuts. The percentages of nuts of Types 1, 2, 3, and 4 are supposed to be 40%, 30%, 20%, and 10%, respectively. A random sample of nuts is selected, and each one is categorized by type.
a. If the sample size is 200 and the resulting test statistic value is $X^2 = 19.0$, what conclusion would be appropriate for a significance level of .001?
b. If the random sample had consisted of only 40 nuts, would you use the chi-square test here? Explain your reasoning.

**12.4** ● The paper "Cigarette Tar Yields in Relation to Mortality from Lung Cancer in the Cancer Prevention Study II Prospective Cohort" (*British Medical Journal* [2004]: 72–79) included the accompanying data on the tar level of cigarettes smoked for a sample of male smokers who subsequently died of lung cancer.

| Tar Level | Frequency |
|---|---|
| 0–7 mg | 103 |
| 8–14 mg | 378 |
| 15–21 mg | 563 |
| ≥22 mg | 150 |

Assume it is reasonable to regard the sample as representative of male smokers who die of lung cancer. Is there convincing evidence that the proportion of male smoker lung cancer deaths is not the same for the four given tar level categories?

**12.5** ● The paper referenced in the previous exercise also gave the accompanying data on the age at which smoking started for a sample of 1031 men who smoked low-tar cigarettes.

| Age | Frequency |
|---|---|
| <16 | 237 |
| 16–17 | 258 |
| 18–20 | 320 |
| ≥21 | 216 |

a. Use a chi-square goodness-of-fit test to test the null hypothesis $H_0$: $\pi_1 = .25$, $\pi_2 = .2$, $\pi_3 = .3$, $\pi_4 = .25$, where $\pi_1$ = proportion of male low-tar cigarette smokers who started smoking before age 16, and $\pi_2$, $\pi_3$, and $\pi_4$ are defined in a similar way for the other three age groups.
b. The null hypothesis from Part (a) specifies that half of male smokers of low-tar cigarettes began smoking between the ages of 16 and 20. Explain why $\pi_2 = .2$ and $\pi_3 = .3$ is consistent with the ages between 16 and 20 being equally likely to be when smoking started.

**12.6** ● The report "Fatality Facts 2004: Bicycles" (Insurance Institute, 2004) included the following table classifying 715 fatal bicycle accidents according to time of day the accident occurred.

| Time of Day | Number of Accidents |
|---|---|
| Midnight to 3 A.M. | 38 |
| 3 A.M. to 6 A.M. | 29 |
| 6 A.M. to 9 A.M. | 66 |
| 9 A.M. to Noon | 77 |
| Noon to 3 P.M. | 99 |
| 3 P.M. to 6 P.M. | 127 |
| 6 P.M. to 9 P.M. | 166 |
| 9 P.M. to Midnight | 113 |

a. Assume it is reasonable to regard the 715 bicycle accidents summarized in the table as a random sample of fatal bicycle accidents in 2004. Do these data support the hypothesis that fatal bicycle accidents are not equally likely to occur in each of the 3-hour time periods used to construct the table? Test the relevant hypotheses using a significance level of .05.
b. Suppose a safety office proposes that bicycle fatalities are twice as likely to occur between noon and midnight as during midnight to noon and suggests the following

hypothesis: $H_0$: $\pi_1 = 1/3$, $\pi_2 = 2/3$, where $\pi_1$ is the proportion of accidents occurring between midnight and noon and $\pi_2$ is the proportion occurring between noon and midnight. Do the given data provide evidence against this hypothesis, or are the data consistent with it? Justify your answer with an appropriate test. (Hint: Use the data to construct a one-way table with just two time categories.)

**12.7** ● The report referenced in the previous exercise ("Fatality Facts 2004: Bicycles") also classified 719 fatal bicycle accidents according to the month in which the accident occurred, resulting in the accompanying table.

| Month | Number of Accidents |
|---|---|
| January | 38 |
| February | 32 |
| March | 43 |
| April | 59 |
| May | 78 |
| June | 74 |
| July | 98 |
| August | 85 |
| September | 64 |
| October | 66 |
| November | 42 |
| December | 40 |

**a.** Use the given data to test the null hypothesis $H_0$: $\pi_1 = 1/12$, $\pi_2 = 1/12$, . . . , $\pi_{12} = 1/12$, where $\pi_1$ is the proportion of fatal bicycle accidents that occur in January, $\pi_2$ is the proportion for February, and so on. Use a significance level of .01.
**b.** The null hypothesis in Part (a) specifies that fatal accidents were equally likely to occur in any of the 12 months. But not all months have the same number of days. What null and alternative hypotheses would you test to determine if some months are riskier than others if you wanted to take differing month lengths into account? (Hint: 2004 was a leap year, with 366 days.)
**c.** Test the hypotheses proposed in Part (b) using a .05 significance level.

**12.8** ● Each observation in a random sample of 100 bicycle accidents resulting in death was classified according to the day of the week on which the accident occurred. Data consistent with information given on the web site www.highwaysafety.com are given in the following table

| Day of Week | Frequency |
|---|---|
| Sunday | 14 |
| Monday | 13 |
| Tuesday | 12 |
| Wednesday | 15 |
| Thursday | 14 |
| Friday | 17 |
| Saturday | 15 |

Based on these data, is it reasonable to conclude that the proportion of accidents is not the same for all days of the week? Use $\alpha = .05$.

**12.9** ● ▼ The color vision of birds plays a role in their foraging behavior: Birds use color to select and avoid certain types of food. The authors of the article "Colour Avoidance in Northern Bobwhites: Effects of Age, Sex, and Previous Experience" (*Animal Behaviour* [1995]: 519–526) studied the pecking behavior of 1-day-old bobwhites. In an area painted white, they inserted four pins with different colored heads. The color of the pin chosen on the bird's first peck was noted for each of 33 bobwhites, resulting in the accompanying table.

| Color | First Peck Frequency |
|---|---|
| Blue | 16 |
| Green | 8 |
| Yellow | 6 |
| Red | 3 |

Do the data provide evidence of a color preference? Test using $\alpha = .01$.

**12.10** An article about the California lottery that appeared in the *San Luis Obispo Tribune* (Dec. 15, 1999) gave the following information on the age distribution of adults in California: 35% are between 18 and 34 years old, 51% are between 35 and 64 years old, and 14% are 65 years old or older. The article also gave information on the age distribution of those who purchase lottery tickets. The following table is consistent with the values given in the article:

| Age of Purchaser | Frequency |
| --- | --- |
| 18–34 | 36 |
| 35–64 | 130 |
| 65 and over | 34 |

Suppose that the data resulted from a random sample of 200 lottery ticket purchasers. Based on these sample data, is it reasonable to conclude that one or more of these three age groups buys a disproportionate share of lottery tickets? Use a chi-square goodness-of-fit test with $\alpha = .05$.

**12.11** When public opinion surveys are conducted by mail, a cover letter explaining the purpose of the survey is usually included. To determine whether the wording of the cover letter influences the response rate, three different cover letters were used in a survey of students at a Midwestern university ("The Effectiveness of Cover-Letter Appeals," *Journal of Social Psychology* [1984]: 85–91). Suppose that each of the three cover letters accompanied questionnaires sent to an equal number of randomly selected students. Returned questionnaires were then classified according to the type of cover letter (I, II, or III). Use the accompanying data to test the hypothesis that $\pi_1 = 1/3$, $\pi_2 = 1/3$, and $\pi_3 = 1/3$, where $\pi_1$, $\pi_2$, and $\pi_3$ are the true proportions of all returned questionnaires accompanied by cover letters I, II, and III, respectively. Use a .05 significance level.

| | Cover-letter Type | | |
| --- | --- | --- | --- |
| | I | II | III |
| Frequency | 48 | 44 | 39 |

**12.12** A certain genetic characteristic of a particular plant can appear in one of three forms (phenotypes). A researcher has developed a theory, according to which the hypothesized proportions are $\pi_1 = .25$, $\pi_2 = .50$, and $\pi_3 = .25$. A random sample of 200 plants yields $X^2 = 4.63$.

a. Carry out a test of the null hypothesis that the theory is correct, using level of significance $\alpha = .05$.
b. Suppose that a random sample of 300 plants had resulted in the same value of $X^2$. How would your analysis and conclusion differ from those in Part (a)?

**12.13** ▼ The article "Linkage Studies of the Tomato" (*Transactions of the Royal Canadian Institute* [1931]: 1–19) reported the accompanying data on phenotypes resulting from crossing tall cut-leaf tomatoes with dwarf potato-leaf tomatoes. There are four possible phenotypes: (1) tall cut-leaf, (2) tall potato-leaf, (3) dwarf cut-leaf, and (4) dwarf potato-leaf.

| | Phenotype | | | |
| --- | --- | --- | --- | --- |
| | 1 | 2 | 3 | 4 |
| Frequency | 926 | 288 | 293 | 104 |

Mendel's laws of inheritance imply that $\pi_1 = 9/16$, $\pi_2 = 3/16$, $\pi_3 = 3/16$, and $\pi_4 = 1/16$. Are the data from this experiment consistent with Mendel's laws? Use a .01 significance level.

12.14 ● It is hypothesized that when homing pigeons are disoriented in a certain manner, they will exhibit no preference for any direction of flight after takeoff. To test this, 120 pigeons are disoriented and released, and the direction of flight of each is recorded. The resulting data are given in the accompanying table.

| Direction | Frequency |
| --- | --- |
| 0° to < 45° | 12 |
| 45° to < 90° | 16 |
| 90° to < 135° | 17 |
| 135° to < 180° | 15 |
| 180° to < 225° | 13 |
| 225° to < 270° | 20 |
| 270° to < 315° | 17 |
| 315° to < 360° | 10 |

Use the goodness-of-fit test with significance level .10 to determine whether the data are consistent with this hypothesis.

**Bold** exercises answered in back  ● Data set available online but not required  ▼ Video solution available

## 12.2 Tests for Homogeneity and Independence in a Two-way Table

Data resulting from observations made on two different categorical variables can also be summarized using a tabular format. As an example, suppose that residents of a particular city can watch national news on affiliate stations of ABC, CBS, NBC, or PBS. A researcher wishes to know whether there is any relationship between political philosophy (liberal, moderate, or conservative) and preferred news program among those residents who regularly watch the national news. Let $x$ denote the variable *political philosophy* and $y$ the variable *preferred network*. A random sample of 300 regular watchers is selected, and each individual is asked for his or her $x$ and $y$ values. The data set is bivariate and might initially be displayed as follows:

| Observation | x Value | y Value |
|---|---|---|
| 1 | Liberal | CBS |
| 2 | Conservative | ABC |
| 3 | Conservative | PBS |
| ⋮ | ⋮ | ⋮ |
| 299 | Moderate | NBC |
| 300 | Liberal | PBS |

Bivariate categorical data of this sort can most easily be summarized by constructing a **two-way frequency table**, or **contingency table**. This is a rectangular table that consists of a row for each possible value of $x$ (each category specified by this variable) and a column for each possible value of $y$. There is then a cell in the table for each possible $(x, y)$ combination. Once such a table has been constructed, the number of times each particular $(x, y)$ combination occurs in the data set is determined, and these numbers (frequencies) are entered in the corresponding cells of the table. The resulting numbers are called **observed cell counts**. The table for the example relating political philosophy to preferred network contains 3 rows and 4 columns (because $x$ and $y$ have 3 and 4 possible values, respectively). Table 12.2 is one possible table.

**Table 12.2** An Example of a 3 × 4 Frequency Table

|  | ABC | CBS | NBC | PBS | Row Marginal Total |
|---|---|---|---|---|---|
| Liberal | 20 | 20 | 25 | 15 | **80** |
| Moderate | 45 | 35 | 50 | 20 | **150** |
| Conservative | 15 | 40 | 10 | 5 | **70** |
| Column Marginal Total | **80** | **95** | **85** | **40** | **300** |

**Marginal totals** are obtained by adding the observed cell counts in each row and also in each column of the table. The row and column marginal totals, along with the total of all observed cell counts in the table—the **grand total**—have been included in Table 12.2. The marginal totals provide information on the distribution of observed values for each variable separately. In this example, the row marginal totals reveal that the sample consisted of 80 liberals, 150 moderates, and 70 conservatives. Similarly, column marginal totals indicate how often each of the preferred program categories occurred: 80 preferred ABC news, 95 preferred CBS, and so on. The grand total, 300, is the number of observations in the bivariate data set.

Two-way frequency tables are often characterized by the number of rows and columns in the table (specified in that order: rows first, then columns). Table 12.2 is called a $3 \times 4$ table. The smallest two-way frequency table is a $2 \times 2$ table, which has only two rows and two columns and thus four cells.

Two-way tables arise naturally in two different types of investigations. A researcher may be interested in comparing two or more populations or treatments on the basis of a single categorical variable and so may obtain independent samples from each population or treatment. For example, data could be collected at a university to compare students, faculty, and staff on the basis of primary mode of transportation to campus (car, bicycle, motorcycle, bus, or on foot). One random sample of 200 students, another of 100 faculty members, and a third of 150 staff members might be chosen, and the selected individuals could be interviewed to obtain the necessary transportation information. Data from such a study could be summarized in a $3 \times 5$ two-way frequency table with row categories of student, faculty, and staff and column categories corresponding to the five possible modes of transportation. The observed cell counts could then be used to gain insight into differences and similarities among the three groups with respect to the means of transportation. This type of bivariate categorical data set is characterized by having one set of marginal totals predetermined (the sample sizes from the different groups). In the $3 \times 5$ situation just discussed, the row totals would be fixed at 200, 100, and 150.

A two-way table also arises when the values of two different categorical variables are observed for all individuals or items in a single sample. For example, a sample of 500 registered voters might be selected. Each voter could then be asked both if he or she favored a particular property tax initiative and if he or she was a registered Democrat, Republican, or Independent. This would result in a bivariate data set with $x$ representing the variable *political affiliation* (with categories Democrat, Republican, and Independent) and $y$ representing the variable *response* (favors initiative or opposes initiative). The corresponding $3 \times 2$ frequency table could then be used to investigate any association between position on the tax initiative and political affiliation. This type of bivariate categorical data set is characterized by having only the grand total predetermined (by the sample size).

## ■ Comparing Two or More Populations or Treatments: A Test of Homogeneity

When the value of a categorical variable is recorded for members of independent random samples obtained from each population or treatment under study, the central issue is whether the category proportions are the same for all the populations or treatments. As in Section 12.1, the test procedure uses a chi-square statistic that compares the observed counts to those that would be expected if there were no differences.

# Example 12.4 Risky Soccer??

● The paper "No Evidence of Impaired Neurocognitive Performance in Collegiate Soccer Players" (*American Journal of Sports Medicine* [2002]:157–162) compared collegiate soccer players, athletes in sports other than soccer, and a group of students who were not involved in collegiate sports with respect to history of head injuries. Table 12.3, a 3 × 4 two-way frequency table, is the result of classifying each student in independently selected random samples of 91 soccer players, 96 non-soccer athletes, and 53 non-athletes according to the number of previous concussions the student reported on a medical history questionnaire.

**Table 12.3** Observed Counts for Example 12.4

| | Number of Concussions | | | | |
|---|---|---|---|---|---|
| | 0 Concussions | 1 Concussion | 2 Concussions | 3 or More Concussions | Row Marginal Total |
| Soccer Players | 45 | 25 | 11 | 10 | **91** |
| Non-Soccer Athletes | 68 | 15 | 8 | 5 | **96** |
| Non-Athletes | 45 | 5 | 3 | 0 | **53** |
| Column Marginal Total | **158** | **45** | **22** | **15** | **240** |

Estimates of expected cell counts can be thought of in the following manner: There were 240 responses on number of concussions, of which 158 were "0 concussions." The proportion of the total responding "0 concussions" is then

$$\frac{158}{240} = .658$$

If there were no difference in response for the different groups, we would then expect about 65.8% of the soccer players to have responded "0 concussions," 65.8% of the non-soccer athletes to have responded "0 concussions," and so on. Therefore the estimated expected cell counts for the three cells in the "0 concussions" column are

Expected count for soccer player *and* 0 concussions cell = .658(91) = 59.9
Expected count for non-soccer athlete *and* 0 concussions cell = .658(96) = 63.2
Expected count for non-athlete *and* 0 concussions cell = .658(53) = 34.9

Note that the expected cell counts need not be whole numbers. The expected cell counts for the remaining cells can be computed in a similar manner. For example,

$$\frac{45}{240} = .188$$

of all responses were in the "1 concussion" category, so

Expected count for soccer player *and* 1 concussion cell = .188(91) = 17.1
Expected count for non-soccer athlete *and* 1 concussion cell = .188(96) = 18.0
Expected count for non-athlete *and* 1 concussion cell = .188(53) = 10.0

● Data set available online

It is common practice to display the observed cell counts and the corresponding expected cell counts in the same table, with the expected cell counts enclosed in parentheses. Expected cell counts for the remaining cells have been computed and entered into Table 12.4. Except for small differences resulting from rounding, each marginal total for the expected cell counts is identical to that of the corresponding observed counts.

**Table 12.4**   Observed and Expected Counts for Example 12.4

| | Number of Concussions | | | | |
|---|---|---|---|---|---|
| | 0 Concussions | 1 Concussion | 2 Concussions | 3 or More Concussions | Row Marginal Total |
| Soccer players | 45 (59.9) | 25 (17.1) | 11 (8.3) | 10 (5.7) | 91 |
| Non-Soccer Athletes | 68 (63.2) | 15 (18.0) | 8 (8.8) | 5 (6.0) | 96 |
| Non-Athletes | 45 (34.9) | 5 (10.0) | 3 (4.9) | 0 (3.3) | 53 |
| Column Marginal Total | 158 | 45 | 22 | 15 | 240 |

A quick comparison of the observed and expected cell counts in Table 12.4 reveals some large discrepancies, suggesting that the proportions falling into the concussion categories may not be the same for all three groups. This will be explored further in Example 12.5. ■

In Example 12.4, the expected count for a cell corresponding to a particular group–response combination was computed in two steps. First, the response *marginal proportion* was computed (e.g., 158/240 for the "0 concussions" response). Then this proportion was multiplied by a marginal group total (e.g., 91(158/240) for the soccer player group). Algebraically, this is equivalent to first multiplying the row and column marginal totals and then dividing by the grand total:

$$\frac{(91)(158)}{240}$$

To compare two or more populations or treatments on the basis of a categorical variable, calculate an **expected cell count** for each cell by selecting the corresponding row and column marginal totals and then computing

$$\text{expected cell count} = \frac{(\text{row marginal total})(\text{column marginal total})}{\text{grand total}}$$

These quantities represent what would be expected when there is no difference between the groups under study. ■

The $X^2$ statistic, introduced in Section 12.1, can now be used to compare the observed cell counts to the expected cell counts. A large value of $X^2$ results when there are substantial discrepancies between the observed and expected counts and suggests that the hypothesis of no differences between the populations should be rejected. A formal test procedure is described in the accompanying box.

## Comparing Two or More Populations or Treatments Using the $X^2$ Statistic

**Null hypothesis:** $H_0$: The true category proportions are the same for all the populations (homogeneity of populations).

**Alternative hypothesis:** $H_a$: The true category proportions are not all the same for all of the populations.

**Test Statistic:** $X^2 = \sum_{\text{all cells}} \dfrac{(\text{observed cell count} - \text{expected cell count})^2}{\text{expected cell count}}$

The expected cell counts are estimated from the sample data (assuming that $H_0$ is true) using the formula

$$\text{expected cell count} = \frac{(\text{row marginal total})(\text{column marginal total})}{\text{grand total}}$$

**P-values:** When $H_0$ is true, $X^2$ has approximately a chi-square distribution with df = (number of rows $-$ 1)(number of columns $-$ 1) The $P$-value associated with the computed test statistic value is the area to the right of $X^2$ under the chi-square curve with the appropriate df. Upper-tail areas for chi-square distributions are found in Appendix Table 8.

**Assumptions:**
1. The data consists of *independently chosen random samples or subjects were assigned at random to treatment groups.*
2. *The sample size is large:* all expected counts are at least 5. If some expected counts are less than 5, rows or columns of the table may be combined to achieve a table with satisfactory expected counts.

# Example 12.5 Risky Soccer Revisited

The following table of observed and expected cell counts appeared in Example 12.4:

| | Number of Concussions | | | | |
|---|---|---|---|---|---|
| | 0 Concussions | 1 Concussion | 2 Concussions | 3 or More Concussions | Row Marginal Total |
| Soccer Players | 45 (59.9) | 25 (17.1) | 11 (8.3) | 10 (5.7) | 91 |
| Non-Soccer Athletes | 68 (63.2) | 15 (18.0) | 8 (8.8) | 5 (6.0) | 96 |
| Non-Athletes | 45 (34.9) | 5 (10.0) | 3 (4.9) | 0 (3.3) | 53 |
| Column Marginal Total | 158 | 45 | 22 | 15 | 240 |

Hypotheses: $H_0$: Proportions in each response (number of concussions) category are the same for all three groups

$H_a$: $H_0$ is not true.

Significance level:  A significance level of $\alpha = .05$ will be used.

Test statistic:  $X^2 = \sum\limits_{\text{all cells}} \dfrac{(\text{observed cell count} - \text{expected cell count})^2}{\text{expected cell count}}$

Assumptions:  The random samples were independently chosen, so use of the test is appropriate if the sample size is large enough. One of the expected cell counts (in the 3 or more concussions column) is less than 5, so we will combine the last two columns of the table prior to carrying out the chi-square test. The table we will work with is then

| | Number of Concussions | | | |
| | 0 Concussions | 1 Concussion | 2 or More Concussions | Row Marginal Total |
|---|---|---|---|---|
| **Soccer Players** | 45 (59.9) | 25 (17.1) | 21 (14.0) | **91** |
| **Non-Soccer Athletes** | 68 (63.2) | 15 (18.0) | 13 (14.8) | **96** |
| **Non-Athletes** | 45 (34.9) | 5 (10.0) | 3 (8.2) | **53** |
| **Column Marginal Total** | **158** | **45** | **22** | **240** |

Calculation:

$$X^2 = \frac{(45 - 59.9)^2}{59.9} + \cdots + \frac{(3 - 8.2)^2}{8.2} = 20.6$$

P-value:  The two-way table for this example has 3 rows and 3 columns, so the appropriate df is $(3 - 1)(3 - 1) = 4$. Since 20.6 is greater than 18.46, the largest entry in the 4-df column of Appendix Table 8,

$$P\text{-value} < .001$$

Conclusion:  P-value $\leq \alpha$, so $H_0$ is rejected. There is strong evidence to support the claim that the proportions in the number of concussions categories are not the same for the three groups compared. The largest differences between the observed frequencies and those that would be expected if there were no group differences occur in the response categories for soccer players and for non-athletes, with soccer players having higher than expected proportions in the 1 and 2 or more concussion categories and non-athletes having a higher than expected proportion in the 0 concussion category.

■

Most statistical computer packages can calculate expected cell counts, the value of the $X^2$ statistic, and the associated P-value. This is illustrated in the following example.

## Example 12.6 Keeping the Weight Off

⬤ The article "Daily Weigh-ins Can Help You Keep Off Lost Pounds, Experts Say" (*Associated Press*, October 17, 2005) describes an experiment in which 291 people who had lost at least 10% of their body weight in a medical weight loss program

⬤ Data set available online

were assigned at random to one of three groups for follow-up. One group met monthly in person, one group "met" online monthly in a chat room, and one group received a monthly newsletter by mail. After 18 months, participants in each group were classified according to whether or not they had regained more than 5 pounds, resulting in the data given in Table 12.5.

**Table 12.5** Observed and Expected Counts for Example 12.6

| | Amount of Weight Gained | | |
| --- | --- | --- | --- |
| | Regained 5 Lb or Less | Regained More Than 5 Lb | Row Marginal Total |
| In-Person | 52 (41.0) | 45 (56.0) | 97 |
| Online | 44 (41.0) | 53 (56.0) | 97 |
| Newsletter | 27 (41.0) | 70 (56.0) | 97 |

Does there appear to be a difference in the weight regained proportions for the three follow-up methods? The relevant hypotheses are

$H_0$: True proportions for the two weight regained categories are the same for the three follow-up methods.

$H_a$: $H_0$ is not true.

Significance level: $\alpha = .01$

Test statistic: $X^2 = \sum_{\text{all cells}} \dfrac{(\text{observed cell count} - \text{expected cell count})^2}{\text{expected cell count}}$

Assumptions: Table 12.5 contains the computed expected counts, all of which are greater than 5. The subjects in this experiment were assigned at random to the treatment groups.

Calculation: MINITAB output follows. From the output, $X^2 = 13.773$.

**Chi-Square Test**
Expected counts are printed below observed counts
Chi-Square contributions are printed below expected counts

| | <=5 | >5 | Total |
| --- | --- | --- | --- |
| In-person | 52 | 45 | 97 |
| | 41.00 | 56.00 | |
| | 2.951 | 2.161 | |
| Online | 44 | 53 | 97 |
| | 41.00 | 56.00 | |
| | 0.220 | 0.161 | |
| Newsletter | 27 | 70 | 97 |
| | 41.00 | 56.00 | |
| | 4.780 | 3.500 | |
| Total | 123 | 168 | 291 |

Chi-Sq = 13.773, DF = 2, P-Value = 0.001

$P$-value: From the MINITAB output, $P$-value $= .001$.

Conclusion: Since $P$-value $\le \alpha$, $H_0$ is rejected. The data indicate that the proportions who have regained more than five pounds are not the same for the three follow-up methods. Comparing the observed and expected cell counts, we can see that the observed number in the newsletter group who had regained more than five pounds was higher than would have been expected and the observed number in the in-person group who had regained five or more pounds was lower than would have been expected if there were no difference in the three follow-up methods.

■

## ■ Testing for Independence of Two Categorical Variables ..........................

The $X^2$ test statistic and test procedure can also be used to investigate association between two categorical variables in a single population. As an example, television viewers in a particular city might be categorized with respect to both preferred network (ABC, CBS, NBC, or PBS) and favorite type of programming (comedy, drama, or information and news). The question of interest is often whether knowledge of one variable's value provides any information about the value of the other variable—that is, are the two variables independent?

Continuing the example, suppose that those who favor ABC prefer the three types of programming in proportions .4, .5, and .1 and that these proportions are also correct for individuals favoring any of the other three networks. Then, learning an individual's preferred network provides no added information about that individual's favorite type of programming. The categorical variables *preferred network* and *favorite program type* would be independent.

To see how expected counts are obtained in this situation, recall from Chapter 6 that if two outcomes $A$ and $B$ are independent, then

$$P(A \text{ and } B) = P(A)P(B)$$

so the proportion of time that the two outcomes occur together in the long run is the product of the two individual long-run relative frequencies. Similarly, two categorical variables are independent in a population if, for each particular category of the first variable and each particular category of the second variable,

$$\left(\begin{array}{c}\text{proportion of individuals}\\ \text{in a particular category}\\ \text{combination}\end{array}\right) = \left(\begin{array}{c}\text{proportion in}\\ \text{specified category}\\ \text{of first variable}\end{array}\right) \cdot \left(\begin{array}{c}\text{proportion in}\\ \text{specified category}\\ \text{of second variable}\end{array}\right)$$

Thus, if 30% of all viewers prefer ABC and the proportions of program type preferences are as previously given, then, assuming that the two variables are independent, the proportion of individuals who both favor ABC and prefer comedy is $(.3)(.4) = .12$ (or 12%).

Multiplying the right-hand side of this expression by the sample size gives us the expected number of individuals in the sample who are in both specified categories of the two variables when the variables are independent. However, these expected counts cannot be calculated, because the individual population proportions are not known.

The solution to this dilemma is to estimate each population proportion using the corresponding sample proportion:

$$\left(\begin{array}{c}\text{estimated expected number}\\\text{in specified categories}\\\text{of the two variables}\end{array}\right) = (\text{sample size}) \cdot \frac{\left(\begin{array}{c}\text{observed number}\\\text{in category of}\\\text{first variable}\end{array}\right)}{\text{sample size}} \cdot \frac{\left(\begin{array}{c}\text{observed number}\\\text{in category of}\\\text{second variable}\end{array}\right)}{\text{sample size}}$$

$$= \frac{\left(\begin{array}{c}\text{observed number in}\\\text{category of first variable}\end{array}\right) \cdot \left(\begin{array}{c}\text{observed number in}\\\text{category of second variable}\end{array}\right)}{\text{sample size}}$$

Suppose that the observed counts are displayed in a rectangular table in which rows correspond to the categories of the first variable and columns to the categories of the second variable. Then the numerator in the preceding expression for expected counts is just the product of the row and column marginal totals. This is exactly how expected counts were computed in the test for homogeneity of several populations, even though the reasoning used to arrive at the formula is different.

## $X^2$ Test for Independence

**Null hypothesis:**   $H_0$: The two variables are independent.

**Alternative hypothesis:**   $H_a$: The two variables are not independent.

**Test statistic:**   $X^2 = \sum_{\text{all cells}} \dfrac{(\text{observed cell count} - \text{expected cell count})^2}{\text{expected cell count}}$

The expected cell counts are estimated (assuming $H_0$ is true) by the formula

$$\text{expected cell count} = \frac{(\text{row marginal total})(\text{column marginal total})}{\text{grand total}}$$

**P-values:**   When $H_0$ is true and the assumptions of the $X^2$ test are satisfied, $X^2$ has approximately a chi-square distribution with

$$\text{df} = (\text{number of rows} - 1)(\text{number of columns} - 1)$$

The *P*-value associated with the computed test statistic value is the area to the right of $X^2$ under the chi-square curve with the appropriate df. Upper-tail areas for chi-square distributions are found in Appendix Table 8.

**Assumptions:**   1. The observed counts are from a *random sample*.
2. The *sample size is large*: All expected counts are at least 5. If some expected counts are less than 5, rows or columns of the table should be combined to achieve a table with satisfactory expected counts.

# Example 12.7   A Pained Expression

● The paper "Facial Expression of Pain in Elderly Adults with Dementia" (*Journal of Undergraduate Research* [2006]) examined the relationship between a nurse's assessment of a patient's facial expression and his or her self-reported level of pain. Data for 89 patients are summarized in Table 12.6.

The authors were interested in determining if there is evidence of a relationship between a facial expression that reflects pain and self-reported pain because patients with dementia do not always give a verbal indication that they are in pain.

Using a .05 significance level, we will test

$H_0$: Facial expression and self-reported pain are independent.
$H_a$: Facial expression and self-reported pain are not independent.

Significance level: $\alpha = .05$

**Table 12.6**   Observed Counts for Example 12.7

| Facial Expression | Self-Report | |
| --- | --- | --- |
| | No Pain | Pain |
| No Pain | 17 | 40 |
| Pain | 3 | 29 |

Test statistic: $X^2 = \displaystyle\sum_{\text{all cells}} \dfrac{(\text{observed cell count} - \text{expected cell count})^2}{\text{expected cell count}}$

Assumptions: Before we can check the assumptions we must first compute the expected cell counts.

| Cell | | Expected Cell Count |
| --- | --- | --- |
| Row | Column | |
| 1 | 1 | $\dfrac{(57)(20)}{89} = 12.81$ |
| 1 | 2 | $\dfrac{(57)(69)}{89} = 44.19$ |
| 2 | 1 | $\dfrac{(32)(20)}{89} = 7.19$ |
| 2 | 2 | $\dfrac{(32)(69)}{89} = 24.81$ |

All expected cell counts are greater than 5. Although the participants in the study were not randomly selected, they were thought to be representative of the population of nursing home patients with dementia. The observed and expected counts are given together in Table 12.7.

**Table 12.7**   Observed and Expected Counts for Example 12.7

| Facial Expression | Self-Report | |
| --- | --- | --- |
| | No Pain | Pain |
| No Pain | 17 (12.81) | 40 (44.19) |
| Pain | 3 (7.19) | 29 (24.81) |

Calculation: $X^2 = \dfrac{(17 - 12.81)^2}{12.81} + \cdots + \dfrac{(29 - 24.81)^2}{24.81} = 4.92$

*P*-value: The table has 2 rows and 2 columns, so df = $(2 - 1)(2 - 1) = 1$. The entry closest to 4.92 in the 1-df column of Appendix Table 8 is 5.02, so the approximate *P*-value for this test is

$$P\text{-value} \approx .025$$

Conclusion: Since *P*-value $\leq \alpha$, we reject $H_0$ and conclude that there is an association between a nurse's assessment of facial expression and self-reported pain.

■

## Example 12.8 Stroke Mortality and Education

● Table 12.8 was constructed using data from the article "Influence of Socioeconomic Status on Mortality After Stroke" (*Stroke* [2005]: 310–314). One of the questions of interest to the author was whether there was an association between survival after a stroke and level of education. Medical records for a sample of 2333 residents of Vienna, Austria who had suffered a stroke were used to classify each individual according to two variables—survival (survived, died) and level of education (no basic education, secondary school graduation, technical training/apprenticed, higher secondary school degree, university graduate). Expected cell counts (computed under the assumption of no association between survival and level of education) appear in parentheses in the table.

**Table 12.8**   Observed and Expected Counts for Example 12.8

|  | No Basic Education | Secondary School Graduation | Technical Training/ Apprenticed | Higher Secondary School Degree | University Graduate |
|---|---|---|---|---|---|
| **Died** | 13 (17.40) | 91 (77.18) | 196 (182.68) | 33 (41.91) | 36 (49.82) |
| **Survived** | 97 (92.60) | 397 (410.82) | 959 (972.32) | 232 (223.09) | 279 (265.18) |

The $X^2$ test with a significance level of .01 will be used to test the relevant hypotheses:

$H_0$: Survival and level of education are independent.
$H_a$: Survival and level of education are not independent.

Significance level: $\alpha = .01$

Test statistic: $X^2 = \displaystyle\sum_{\text{all cells}} \dfrac{(\text{observed cell count} - \text{expected cell count})^2}{\text{expected cell count}}$

Assumptions: All expected cell counts are at least 5. Assuming that the data can be viewed as a random sample of adults, the $X^2$ test can be used.

Calculation: MINITAB output is shown. From the MINITAB output, $X^2 = 12.219$.

**Chi-Square Test**
Expected counts are printed below observed counts
Chi-Square contributions are printed below expected counts

|   | 1 | 2 | 3 | 4 | 5 | Total |
|---|---|---|---|---|---|-------|
| 1 | 13 | 91 | 196 | 33 | 36 | 369 |
|   | 17.40 | 77.18 | 182.68 | 41.91 | 49.82 |   |
|   | 1.112 | 2.473 | 0.971 | 1.896 | 3.835 |   |
| 2 | 97 | 397 | 959 | 232 | 279 | 1964 |
|   | 92.60 | 410.82 | 972.32 | 223.09 | 265.18 |   |
|   | 0.209 | 0.465 | 0.182 | 0.356 | 0.720 |   |
| Total | 110 | 488 | 1155 | 265 | 315 | 2333 |

Chi-Sq = 12.219,   DF = 4,   P-Value = 0.016

$P$-value: From the MINITAB output, $P$-value $= .016$.

Conclusion: Since $P$-value $> \alpha$, $H_0$ is not rejected. There is not sufficient evidence to conclude that an association exists between level of education and survival.

■

In some investigations, values of more than two categorical variables are recorded for each individual in the sample. For example, in addition to the variable *survival* and *level of education*, the researchers in the study referenced in Example 12.8 also collected information on occupation. A number of interesting questions could then be explored: Are all three variables independent of one another? Is it possible that occupation and survival are dependent but that the relationship between them does not depend on level of education? For a particular education level group, is there an association between survival and occupation? The $X^2$ test procedure described in this section for analysis of bivariate categorical data can be extended for use with *multivariate categorical data*. Appropriate hypothesis tests can then be used to provide insight into the relationships between variables. However, the computations required to calculate expected cell counts and to compute the value of $X^2$ are quite tedious, so they are seldom done without the aid of a computer. Most statistical computer packages can perform this type of analysis. Consult the references by Agresti and Findlay, Everitt, or Mosteller and Rourke in the back of the book for further information on the analysis of categorical data.

■ Exercises 12.15–12.36 ........................................................................................................

**12.15** A particular state university system has six campuses. On each campus, a random sample of students will be selected, and each student will be categorized with respect to political philosophy as liberal, moderate, or conservative. The null hypothesis of interest is that the proportion of students falling in these three categories is the same at all six campuses.
**a.** On how many degrees of freedom will the resulting $X^2$ test be based?

**b.** How does your answer in Part (a) change if there are seven campuses rather than six?

**c.** How does your answer in Part (a) change if there are four rather than three categories for political philosophy?

**12.16** A random sample of 1000 registered voters in a certain county is selected, and each voter is categorized with respect to both educational level (four categories) and preferred candidate in an upcoming election for county supervisor (five possibilities). The hypothesis of interest is that educational level and preferred candidate are independent factors.

**a.** If $X^2 = 7.2$, what would you conclude at significance level .10?

**b.** If there were only four candidates vying for election, what would you conclude if $X^2 = 14.5$ and $\alpha = .05$?

**12.17** ● ▼ The polling organization Ipsos conducted telephone surveys in March of 2004, 2005, and 2006. In each year, 1001 people age 18 or older were asked about whether they planned to use a credit card to pay federal income taxes that year. The data given in the accompanying table are from the report "Fees Keeping Taxpayers from Using Credit Cards to Make Tax Payments" (*IPSOS Insight*, March 24, 2006). Is there evidence that the proportion falling in the three credit card response categories is not the same for all three years? Test the relevant hypotheses using a .05 significance level.

**Intent to Pay Taxes with a Credit Card**

|  | 2004 | 2005 | 2006 |
|---|---|---|---|
| Definitely/Probably Will | 40 | 50 | 40 |
| Might/Might Not/Probably Not | 180 | 190 | 160 |
| Definitely Will Not | 781 | 761 | 801 |

**12.18** ● In November 2005, an international study to assess public opinion on the treatment of suspected terrorists was conducted ("Most in U.S., Britain, S. Korea and France Say Torture Is OK in at Least Rare Instances," *Associated Press*, December 7, 2005). Each individual in random samples of 1000 adults from each of nine different countries was asked the following question: "Do you feel the use of torture against suspected terrorists to obtain information about terrorism activities is justified?"

Responses consistent with percentages given in the article for the samples from Italy, Spain, France, the United States, and South Korea are summarized in the accompanying table. Based on these data, is it reasonable to conclude that the response proportions are not the same for all five countries? Use a .01 significance level to test the appropriate hypotheses.

| Country | Response | | | | |
|---|---|---|---|---|---|
|  | Never | Rarely | Some-times | Often | Not Sure |
| Italy | 600 | 140 | 140 | 90 | 30 |
| Spain | 540 | 160 | 140 | 70 | 90 |
| France | 400 | 250 | 200 | 120 | 30 |
| United States | 360 | 230 | 270 | 110 | 30 |
| South Korea | 100 | 330 | 470 | 60 | 40 |

**12.19** ● In a study to determine if hormone therapy increases risk of venous thrombosis in menopausal women, each person in a sample of 579 women who had been diagnosed with venous thrombosis was classified according to hormone use. Each woman in a sample of 2243 women who had not been diagnosed with venous thrombosis was also classified according to hormone use. Data from the study are given in the accompanying table (*Journal of the American Medical Association* [2004]: 1581–1587). The women in each of the two samples were selected at random from the patients at a large HMO in the state of Washington.

**a.** Is there convincing evidence that the proportions falling in to each of the hormone use categories is not the same for women who have been diagnosed with venous thrombosis and those who have not?

**b.** To what population would it be reasonable to generalize the conclusions of Part (a)? Explain.

**Current Hormone Use**

|  | None | Esterified Estrogen | Conjugated Equine Estrogen |
|---|---|---|---|
| Venous Thrombosis | 372 | 86 | 121 |
| No Venous Thrombosis | 1439 | 515 | 289 |

12.20 ● The Harvard University Institute of Politics surveys undergraduates across the United States annually. Responses to the question "When it comes to voting, do you consider yourself to be affiliated with the Democratic Party, the Republican Party, or are you Independent or unaffiliated with a major party?" for the survey conducted in 2003, 2004, and 2005 are summarized in the given table. The samples for each year were independently selected and are considered to be representative of the population of undergraduate students in the year the survey was conducted. Is there evidence that the distribution of political affiliation is not the same for all three years for which data are given?

| | Year | | |
|---|---|---|---|
| Political Affiliation | 2005 | 2004 | 2003 |
| Democrat | 397 | 409 | 325 |
| Republican | 301 | 349 | 373 |
| Independent/unaffiliated | 458 | 397 | 457 |
| Other | 60 | 48 | 48 |

12.21 ● The survey described in the previous exercise also asked the following question: "Please tell me whether you trust the President to do the right thing all of the time, most of the time, some of the time, or never. Use the data in the given table and an appropriate hypothesis test to determine if there is evidence that trust in the President was not the same in 2005 as it was in 2002.

| | Year | |
|---|---|---|
| Response | 2005 | 2002 |
| All of the time | 132 | 180 |
| Most of the time | 337 | 528 |
| Some of the time | 554 | 396 |
| Never | 169 | 96 |

12.22 ● The report "Undergraduate Students and Credit Cards in 2004" (Nellie Mae, May 2005) included information collected from individuals in a random sample of undergraduate students in the United States. Students were classified according to region of residence and whether or not they have one or more credit cards, resulting in the accompanying two-way table. Carry out a test to determine if there is evidence that region of residence and having a credit card are not independent. Use $\alpha = .05$.

| | Credit Card? | |
|---|---|---|
| Region | At Least One Credit Card | No Credit Cards |
| Northeast | 401 | 164 |
| Midwest | 162 | 36 |
| South | 408 | 115 |
| West | 104 | 23 |

12.23 ● The report described in the previous exercise also classified students according to region of residence and whether or not they had a credit card with a balance of more than $7000. Do these data support the conclusion that there is an association between region of residence and whether or not the student has a balance exceeding $7000? Test the relevant hypotheses using a .01 significance level.

| | Balance Over $7000? | |
|---|---|---|
| Region | No | Yes |
| Northeast | 28 | 537 |
| Midwest | 162 | 182 |
| South | 42 | 481 |
| West | 9 | 118 |

12.24 ● The paper "Overweight Among Low-Income Preschool Children Associated with the Consumption of Sweet Drinks" (*Pediatrics* [2005]: 223–229) described a study of children who were underweight or normal weight at age 2. Children in the sample were classified according to the number of sweet drinks consumed per day and whether or not the child was overweight one year after the study began. Is there evidence of an association between whether or not children are overweight after one year and the number of sweet drinks consumed? Assume that it is reasonable to regard the sample of children in this study as representative of 2- to 3-year-old children and then test the appropriate hypotheses using a .05 significance level.

| Number of Sweet Drinks Consumed per Day | Overweight? | |
|---|---|---|
| | Yes | No |
| 0 | 22 | 930 |
| 1 | 73 | 2074 |
| 2 | 56 | 1681 |
| 3 or More | 102 | 3390 |

**12.25** ● Data consistent with summary quantities given in a paper that appeared in the *British Medical Journal* ("Cigarette Tar Yields in Relation to Mortality from Lung Cancer in the Cancer Prevention Study II Prospective Cohort" [2004]: 72–79) are shown in the accompanying table. Suppose that the table was constructed by classifying individuals in a random sample of smokers according to gender and the age at which they began smoking. Do these data support the hypothesis that there is an association between gender and the age at which smoking began?

| Age When Smoking Began | Gender | |
|---|---|---|
| | Male | Female |
| <16 | 25 | 10 |
| 16–17 | 24 | 17 |
| 18–20 | 28 | 32 |
| ≥21 | 19 | 34 |

**12.26** ● The 2006 Expedia Vacation Deprivation Survey (*Ipsos Insight*, May 18, 2006) described the results of a poll of working adults in Canada. Each person in a random sample was classified according to gender and the number of vacation days he or she usually took each year. The resulting data are summarized in the given table. Is it reasonable to conclude that there is an association between gender and the number of vacation days taken? To

what population would it be reasonable to generalize this conclusion?

| Days of Vacation | Gender | |
|---|---|---|
| | Male | Female |
| None | 51 | 42 |
| 1–5 | 21 | 25 |
| 6–10 | 67 | 79 |
| 11–15 | 111 | 94 |
| 16–20 | 71 | 70 |
| 21–25 | 82 | 58 |
| More than 25 | 118 | 79 |

**12.27** ● The report "Health Insurance Coverage of the Near Elderly" (Urban Institute, July 2000) includes information from a study of American adults. The sample used in the study was a random sample of those who participated in the National Survey of America's Families, a national survey of more than 100,000 people, and was considered to be representative of American adults. Using data consistent with summary quantities appearing in the report, the following table classifies individuals in the sample according to age group and whether or not the individual was considered to be in good health. Use the given data to test the hypothesis that age group and whether or not an individual is in good health are independent. Use $\alpha = .01$.

| | Health Status | |
|---|---|---|
| Age | Good Health | Poor Health |
| 18–34 | 920 | 80 |
| 35–54 | 860 | 140 |
| 55–64 | 790 | 210 |

12.28 ● A survey was conducted in the San Francisco Bay area in which each participating individual was classified according to the type of vehicle used most often and city of residence. A subset of the resulting data are given in the accompanying table (*The Relationship of Vehicle Type Choice to Personality, Lifestyle, Attitudinal and Demographic Variables*, Technical Report UCD-ITS-RR02-06, DaimlerCrysler Corp., 2002).

| Vehicle Type | City | | |
|---|---|---|---|
| | Concord | Pleasant Hill | North San Francisco |
| Small | 68 | 83 | 221 |
| Compact | 63 | 68 | 106 |
| Midsize | 88 | 123 | 142 |
| Large | 24 | 18 | 11 |

Do the data provide convincing evidence of an association between city of residence and vehicle type? Use a significance level of .05. You may assume that it is reasonable to regard the sample as a random sample of Bay area residents.

**12.29** ● ▼ Do women have different patterns of work behavior than men? The article "Workaholism in Organizations: Gender Differences" (*Sex Roles: A Journal of Research* [1999]: 333–346) attempts to answer this question. Each person in a random sample of 423 graduates of a business school in Canada were polled and classified by gender and workaholism type, resulting in the accompanying table:

| Workaholism Types | Gender | |
|---|---|---|
| | Female | Male |
| Work Enthusiasts | 20 | 41 |
| Workaholics | 32 | 37 |
| Enthusiastic Workaholics | 34 | 46 |
| Unengaged Workers | 43 | 52 |
| Relaxed Workers | 24 | 27 |
| Disenchanted Workers | 37 | 30 |

**a.** Test the hypothesis that gender and workaholism type are independent.
**b.** The author writes "women and men fell into each of the six workaholism types to a similar degree." Does the outcome of the test you performed in Part (a) support this conclusion? Explain.

**12.30** ● The article "Motion Sickness in Public Road Transport: The Effect of Driver, Route and Vehicle" (*Ergonomics* [1999]: 1646–1664) reported that seat position within a bus may have some effect on whether one experiences motion sickness. The accompanying table classifies each person in a random sample of bus riders by the location of his or her seat and whether nausea was reported.

| | Nausea | No Nausea |
|---|---|---|
| Front | 58 | 870 |
| Middle | 166 | 1163 |
| Rear | 193 | 806 |

Based on these data, can you conclude that there is an association between seat location and nausea? Test the relevant hypotheses using $\alpha = .05$.

**12.31** ● The article "Mortality Among Recent Purchasers of Handguns" (*New England Journal of Medicine* [1999]: 1583–1589) examined the relationship between handgun purchases and cause of death. Suppose that a random sample of 4000 death records was examined and cause of death was noted for each individual in the sample. Gun registration records were also examined to determine which of these 4000 individuals had purchased a handgun within the previous year. Data consistent with summary values given in the article are shown in the accompanying table.

| | Suicide | Not Suicide |
|---|---|---|
| Handgun Purchased | 4 | 12 |
| No Handgun Purchased | 63 | 3921 |

Is it reasonable to use the chi-square test to determine whether there is an association between handgun purchase within the year prior to death and whether the death was a suicide? Justify your answer.

**12.32** ● A story describing a date rape was read by 352 high school students. To investigate the effect of the victim's clothing on subject's judgment of the situation described, the story was accompanied by either a photograph of the victim dressed provocatively, a photo of the victim dressed conservatively, or no picture. Each student was asked whether the situation described in the story was one of rape. Data from the article "The Influence of

Victim's Attire on Adolescent Judgments of Date Rape" (*Adolescence* [1995]: 319–323) are given in the accompanying table. Is there evidence that the proportion who believe that the story described a rape differs for the three different photo groups? Test the relevant hypotheses using $\alpha = .01$.

| | Picture | | |
|---|---|---|---|
| Response | Provocative | Conservative | No Picture |
| Rape | 80 | 104 | 92 |
| Not Rape | 47 | 12 | 17 |

**12.33** ● Can people tell the difference between a female nose and a male nose? This important (?) research question was examined in the article "You Can Tell by the Nose: Judging Sex from an Isolated Facial Feature" (*Perception* [1995]: 969–973). Eight Caucasian males and eight Caucasian females posed for nose photos. The article states that none of the volunteers wore nose studs or had prominent nasal hair. Each person placed a black Lycra tube over his or her head in such a way that only the nose protruded through a hole in the material. Photos were then taken from three different angles: front view, three-quarter view, and profile. These photos were shown to a sample of undergraduate students. Each student in the sample was shown one of the nose photos and asked whether it was a photo of a male or a female; and the response was classified as either correct or incorrect. The accompanying table was constructed using summary values reported in the article. Is there evidence that the proportion of correct sex identifications differs for the three different nose views?

| | View | | |
|---|---|---|---|
| Sex ID | Front | Profile | Three-Quarter |
| Correct | 23 | 26 | 29 |
| Incorrect | 17 | 14 | 11 |

**12.34** ● The accompanying table appeared in the article "Europe's Receptivity to New Religious Movements: Round Two" (*Journal for the Scientific Study of Religion*

[1993]: 389–397). Suppose that the percentages in the table were based on random samples of size 200 from each of the six countries.

| Country | Percentage Who Believe in Fortune-Tellers |
|---|---|
| Great Britain | 42 |
| West Germany | 32 |
| East Germany | 22 |
| Slovenia | 55 |
| Ireland | 27 |
| Northern Ireland | 33 |

a. Use the given percentages to construct a two-way table with rows corresponding to the six countries and columns corresponding to the categories "believe in fortune-tellers" and "don't believe in fortune-tellers." Enter the observed counts in the table. (*Hint*: The observed counts for Great Britain are (.42)(200) = 84 for the "believe" column and (.58)(200) = 116 for the "don't believe" column.)
b. Is there evidence that the proportion who believe in fortune-tellers is not the same for all six countries? Test the relevant hypotheses using $\alpha = .01$.

**12.35** ● Job satisfaction of professionals was examined in the article "Psychology of the Scientist: Work-Related Attitudes of U.S. Scientists" (*Psychological Reports* [1991]: 443–450). Each person in a random sample of 778 teachers was classified according to a job satisfaction variable and also by teaching level, resulting in the accompanying two-way table. Can we conclude that there is an association between job satisfaction and teaching level? Test the relevant hypotheses using $\alpha = .05$.

| | Job Satisfaction | |
|---|---|---|
| Teaching Level | Satisfied | Unsatisfied |
| College | 74 | 43 |
| High School | 224 | 171 |
| Elementary | 126 | 140 |

**12.36** ● The article "Victim's Race Affects Killer's Sentence, Study Finds" (*New York Times*, April 20, 2001) included the following information:

| Defendant's Race | Victim's Race | Death Penalty | No Death Penalty |
|---|---|---|---|
| Not white | White | 33 | 251 |
| White | White | 33 | 508 |
| Not white | Not white | 29 | 587 |
| White | Not white | 4 | 76 |

The table was based on a study of *all* homicide cases in North Carolina for the period 1993 to 1997 where it was possible that the person convicted of murder could receive the death penalty. Explain why it would not be necessary (or appropriate) to use a chi-square test to determine if there was an association between the defendant–victim race combination and whether or not the convicted murderer receive a death sentence for convicted murders in North Carolina during 1993 to 1997.

**Bold** exercises answered in back     ● Data set available online but not required     ▼ Video solution available

## 12.3 Interpreting and Communicating the Results of Statistical Analyses

Many studies, particularly those in the social sciences, result in categorical data. The questions of interest in such studies often lead to an analysis that involves using a chi-square test.

### ■ Communicating the Results of Statistical Analyses

Three different chi-square tests were introduced in this chapter—the goodness-of-fit test, the test for homogeneity, and the test for independence. They are used in different settings and to answer different questions. When summarizing the results of a chi-square test, be sure to indicate which chi-square test was performed. One way to do this is to be clear about how the data were collected and the nature of the hypotheses being tested.

It is also a good idea to include a table of observed and expected counts in addition to reporting the computed value of the test statistic and the *P*-value. And finally, make sure to give a conclusion in context, and make sure that the conclusion is worded appropriately for the type of test conducted. For example, don't use terms such as *independence* and *association* to describe the conclusion if the test performed was a test for homogeneity.

### ■ Interpreting the Results of Statistical Analyses

As with the other hypothesis tests considered, it is common to find the result of a chi-square test summarized by giving the value of the chi-square test statistic and an associated *P*-value. Because categorical data can be summarized compactly in frequency tables, the data often are given in the article (unlike data for numerical variables, which are rarely given).

### ■ What to Look For in Published Data

Here are some questions to consider when you are reading an article that contains the results of a chi-square test:

* Are the variables of interest categorical rather than numerical?
* Are the data given in the article in the form of a frequency table?

» If a two-way frequency table is involved, is the question of interest one of homogeneity or one of independence?

» What null hypothesis is being tested? Are the results of the analysis reported in the correct context (homogeneity, etc.)?

» Is the sample size large enough to make use of a chi-square test reasonable? (Are all expected counts at least 5?)

» What is the value of the test statistic? Is the associated $P$-value given? Should the null hypothesis be rejected?

» Are the conclusions drawn by the authors consistent with the results of the test?

» How different are the observed and expected counts? Does the result have practical significance as well as statistical significance?

The authors of the article "Predicting Professional Sports Game Outcomes from Intermediate Game Scores" (*Chance* [1992]: 18–22) used a chi-square test to determine whether there was any merit to the idea that basketball games are not settled until the last quarter, whereas baseball games are over by the seventh inning. They also considered football and hockey. Data were collected for 189 basketball games, 92 baseball games, 80 hockey games, and 93 football games. The analyzed games were sampled randomly from all games played during the 1990 season for baseball and football and for the 1990–1991 season for basketball and hockey. For each game, the late-game leader was determined, and then it was noted whether the late-game leader actually ended up winning the game. The resulting data are summarized in the following table:

| Sport | Late-Game Leader Wins | Late-Game Leader Loses |
|---|---|---|
| Basketball | 150 | 39 |
| Baseball | 86 | 6 |
| Hockey | 65 | 15 |
| Football | 72 | 21 |

The authors stated that the "*late-game leader* is defined as the team that is ahead after three quarters in basketball and football, two periods in hockey, and seven innings in baseball. The chi-square value (with three degrees of freedom) is 10.52 ($P < .015$)." They also concluded that "the sports of basketball, hockey, and football have remarkably similar percentages of late-game reversals, ranging from 18.8% to 22.6%. The sport that is an anomaly is baseball. Only 6.5% of baseball games resulted in late reversals. . . . [The chi-square test] is statistically significant due almost entirely to baseball."

In this particular analysis, the authors are comparing four populations (games from each of the four sports) on the basis of a categorical variable with two categories (late-game leader wins and late-game leader loses). The appropriate null hypothesis is then

$H_0$: The true proportion in each category (leader wins, leader loses) is the same for all four sports.

Based on the reported value of the chi-square statistic and the associated $P$-value, this null hypothesis is rejected, leading to the conclusion that the category proportions are not the same for all four sports.

The validity of the chi-square test requires that the sample sizes be large enough so that no expected counts are less than 5. Is this reasonable here? The following MINITAB output shows the expected cell counts and the computation of the $X^2$ statistic:

**Chi-Square Test**

Expected counts are printed below observed counts

| | Leader W | Leader L | Total |
|---|---|---|---|
| 1 | 150 | 39 | 189 |
| | 155.28 | 33.72 | |
| 2 | 86 | 6 | 92 |
| | 75.59 | 16.41 | |
| 3 | 65 | 15 | 80 |
| | 65.73 | 14.27 | |
| 4 | 72 | 21 | 93 |
| | 76.41 | 16.59 | |
| Total | 373 | 81 | 454 |

Chi-Sq = 0.180 + 0.827 +
           1.435 + 6.607 +
           0.008 + 0.037 +
           0.254 + 1.171 = 10.518

DF = 3, P-Value = 0.015

The smallest expected count is 14.27, so the sample sizes are large enough to justify the use of the $X^2$ test. Note also that the two cells in the table that correspond to baseball contribute a total of $1.435 + 6.607 = 8.042$ to the value of the $X^2$ statistic of 10.518. This is due to the large discrepancies between the observed and expected counts for these two cells. There is reasonable agreement between the observed and the expected counts in the other cells. This is probably the basis for the authors' conclusion that baseball is the only anomaly and that the other sports were similar.

## ■ A Word to the Wise: Cautions and Limitations ............................................

Be sure to keep the following in mind when analyzing categorical data using one of the chi-square tests presented in this chapter:

1. Don't confuse tests for homogeneity with tests for independence. The hypotheses and conclusions are different for the two types of test. Tests for homogeneity are used when the individuals in each of two or more independent samples are classified according to a single categorical variable. Tests for independence are used when individuals in a *single* sample are classified according to two categorical variables.
2. As was the case for the hypothesis tests of earlier chapters, remember that we can never say we have strong support for the null hypothesis. For example, if we do not reject the null hypothesis in a chi-square test for independence, we cannot conclude that there is convincing evidence that the variables are independent. We can only say that we were not convinced that there is an association between the variables.
3. Be sure that the assumptions for the chi-square test are reasonable. *P*-values based on the chi-square distribution are only approximate, and if the large sample

conditions are not met, the true $P$-value may be quite different from the approximate one based on the chi-square distribution. This can sometimes lead to erroneous conclusions. Also, for the chi-square test of homogeneity, the assumption of *independent* samples is particularly important.

4. Don't jump to conclusions about causation. Just as a strong correlation between two numerical variables does not mean that there is a cause-and-effect relationship between them, an association between two categorical variables does not imply a causal relationship.

## A c t i v i t y  **12.1**  Pick a Number, Any Number . . .

**Background:** There is evidence to suggest that human beings are not very good random number generators. In this activity, you will investigate this phenomenon by collecting and analyzing a set of human-generated "random" digits.

For this activity, work in a group with four or five other students.

1. Each member of the group should complete this step individually. Ask 25 different people to pick a digit from 0 to 9 at random. Record the responses.
2. Combine the responses you collected with those of the other members of your group to form a single sample. Summarize the resulting data in a one-way frequency table.

3. If people are adept at picking digits at random, what would you expect for the proportion of the responses in the sample that were 0? that were 1?
4. State a null hypothesis and an alternative hypothesis that could be tested to determine whether there is evidence that the 10 digits from 0 to 9 are not selected an equal proportion of the time when people are asked to pick a digit at random.
5. Carry out the appropriate hypothesis test, and write a few sentences indicating whether or not the data support the theory that people are not good random number generators.

## A c t i v i t y  **12.2**  Color and Perceived Taste

**Background:** Does the color of a food or beverage affect the way people perceive its taste? In this activity you will conduct an experiment to investigate this question and analyze the resulting data using a chi-square test.

You will need to recruit at least 30 subjects for this experiment, so it is advisable to work in a large group (perhaps even the entire class) to complete this activity.

Subjects for the experiment will be assigned at random to one of two groups. Each subject will be asked to taste a sample of gelatin (e.g., Jell-O) and rate the taste as not very good, acceptable, or very good. Subjects assigned to the first group will be asked to taste and rate a cube of lemon-flavored gelatin. Subjects in the second group will be asked to taste and rate a cube of lemon-flavored gelatin that has been colored an unappealing color by adding food coloring to the gelatin mix before the gelatin sets.

Note: You may choose to use something other than gelatin, such as lemonade. Any food or beverage whose color can be altered using food coloring can be used. You

can experiment with the food colors to obtain a color that you think is particularly unappealing!

1. As a class, develop a plan for collecting the data. How will subjects be recruited? How will they be assigned to one of the two treatment groups (unaltered color, altered color)? What extraneous variables will be directly controlled, and how will you control them?
2. After the class is satisfied with the data collection plan, assign members of the class to prepare the gelatin to be used in the experiment.
3. Carry out the experiment, and summarize the resulting data in a two-way table like the one shown:

| | Taste Rating | | |
|---|---|---|---|
| Treatment | Not Very Good | Acceptable | Very Good |
| **Unaltered Color** | | | |
| **Altered Color** | | | |

4. The two-way table summarizes data from two independent samples (as long as subjects were assigned *at random* to the two treatments, the samples are independent). Carry out an appropriate test to determine whether the proportion for each of the three taste rating categories is the same when the color is altered as for when the color is not altered.

# Summary of Key Concepts and Formulas

| Term or Formula | Comment |
|---|---|
| One-way frequency table | A compact way of summarizing data on a categorical variable; it gives the number of times each of the possible categories in the data set occurs (the frequencies). |
| Goodness-of-fit statistic, $$X^2 = \sum_{\text{all cells}} \frac{(\text{observed cell count} - \text{expected cell count})^2}{\text{expected cell count}}$$ | A statistic used to provide a comparison between observed counts and those expected when a given hypothesis is true. When none of the expected counts are too small, $X^2$ has approximately a chi-square distribution. |
| $X^2$ goodness-of-fit test | A hypothesis test performed to determine whether the true category proportions are different from those specified by the given null hypothesis. |
| Two-way frequency table (contingency table) | A rectangular table used to summarize a bivariate categorical data set; two-way tables are used to compare several populations on the basis of a categorical variable or to identify whether an association exists between two categorical variables. |
| $X^2$ test for homogeneity | The hypothesis test performed to determine whether the true category proportions are the same for two or more populations or treatments. |
| $X^2$ test for independence | The hypothesis test performed to determine whether an association exists between two categorical variables. |

# Chapter Review Exercises 12.37–12.47

**Thomson**NOW Know exactly what to study! Take a pre-test and receive your Personalized Learning Plan.

**12.37** ● According to Census Bureau data, in 1998 the California population consisted of 50.7% whites, 6.6% blacks, 30.6% Hispanics, 10.8% Asians, and 1.3% other ethnic groups. Suppose that a random sample of 1000 students graduating from California colleges and universities in 1998 resulted in the accompanying data on ethnic group. These data are consistent with summary statistics contained in the article titled "Crumbling Public School System a Threat to California's Future (*Investor's Business Daily*, November 12, 1999).

**Bold** exercises answered in back   ● Data set available online but not required   ▼ Video solution available

| Ethnic Group | Number in Sample |
|---|---|
| White | 679 |
| Black | 51 |
| Hispanic | 77 |
| Asian | 190 |
| Other | 3 |

Do the data provide evidence that the proportion of students graduating from colleges and universities in California for these ethnic group categories differs from the respective proportions in the population for California? Test the appropriate hypotheses using $\alpha = .01$.

12.38  Criminologists have long debated whether there is a relationship between weather and violent crime. The author of the article "Is There a Season for Homicide?" (*Criminology* [1988]: 287–296) classified 1361 homicides according to season, resulting in the accompanying data. Do these data support the theory that the homicide rate is not the same over the four seasons? Test the relevant hypotheses using a significance level of .05.

**Season**

| Winter | Spring | Summer | Fall |
|---|---|---|---|
| 328 | 334 | 372 | 327 |

**12.39** ● The following table is based on data reported in "Light-to-Moderate Alcohol Consumption and Risk of Stroke Among U.S. Male Physicians" (*New England Journal of Medicine* [1999]: 1557–1564). The table is based on 21,870 male physicians age 40–84 who are participating in the Physician's Health Study.
**a.** Calculate row percentages by dividing each observed count by the corresponding row total. Are the proportions falling in each of the alcohol consumption categories similar for the three smoking categories?

**b.** Test the hypothesis that smoking status and alcohol consumption are independent.
**c.** Is the result of your test in Part (b) consistent with what you expected based on your answer to Part (a)? If not, explain why your initial impression based on the percentages may not have been accurate. What aspect of the data set factors into your explanation?

**12.40** ● Each boy in a sample of Mexican American males, age 10–18, was classified according to smoking status and response to a question asking whether he likes to do risky things. The following table is based on data given in the article "The Association Between Smoking and Unhealthy Behaviors Among a National Sample of Mexican-American Adolescents" (*Journal of School Health* [1998]: 376–379):

| | Smoking Status | |
|---|---|---|
| | Smoker | Nonsmoker |
| Likes Risky Things | 45 | 46 |
| Doesn't Like Risky Things | 36 | 153 |

Assume that it is reasonable to regard the sample as a random sample of Mexican-American male adolescents.
a. Is there sufficient evidence to conclude that there is an association between smoking status and desire to do risky things? Test the relevant hypotheses using $\alpha = .05$.
b. Based on your conclusion in Part (a), is it reasonable to conclude that smoking *causes* an increase in the desire to do risky things? Explain.

**12.41** ● The article "Cooperative Hunting in Lions: The Role of the Individual" (*Behavioral Ecology and Sociobiology* [1992]: 445–454) discusses the different roles taken by lionesses as they attack and capture prey. The authors were interested in the effect of the position in line as stalking occurs; an individual lioness may be in the center

Table for Exercise 12.39

| | Alcohol Consumption (No. of Drinks) | | | | |
|---|---|---|---|---|---|
| | <1/Wk | 1/Wk | 2–4/Wk | 5–6/Wk | 1/Day |
| Never Smoked | 3577 | 1711 | 2430 | 1211 | 1910 |
| Smoked in the Past | 1595 | 1068 | 1999 | 1264 | 2683 |
| Currently Smokes | 524 | 289 | 470 | 296 | 849 |

of the line or on the wing (end of the line) as they advance toward their prey. In addition to position, the role of the lioness was also considered. A lioness could initiate a chase (be the first one to charge the prey), or she could participate and join the chase after it has been initiated. Data from the article are summarized in the accompanying table.

| | Role | |
|---|---|---|
| Position | Initiate Chase | Participate in Chase |
| Center | 28 | 48 |
| Wing | 66 | 41 |

Is there evidence of an association between position and role? Test the relevant hypotheses using $\alpha = .01$. What assumptions about how the data were collected must be true for the chi-square test to be an appropriate way to analyze these data?

**12.42** ● The authors of the article "A Survey of Parent Attitudes and Practices Regarding Underage Drinking" (*Journal of Youth and Adolescence* [1995]: 315–334) conducted a telephone survey of parents with preteen and teenage children. One of the questions asked was "How effective do you think you are in talking to your children about drinking?" Responses are summarized in the accompanying $3 \times 2$ table. Using a significance level of .05, carry out a test to determine whether there is an association between age of children and parental response.

| | Age of Children | |
|---|---|---|
| Response | Preteen | Teen |
| Very Effective | 126 | 149 |
| Somewhat Effective | 44 | 41 |
| Not at All Effective or Don't Know | 51 | 26 |

**12.43** ● The article "Regional Differences in Attitudes Toward Corporal Punishment" (*Journal of Marriage and Family* [1994]: 314–324) presents data resulting from a random sample of 978 adults. Each individual in the

sample was asked whether he or she agreed with the following statement: "Sometimes it is necessary to discipline a child with a good, hard spanking." Respondents were also classified according to the region of the United States in which they lived. The resulting data are summarized in the accompanying table. Is there an association between response (agree, disagree) and region of residence? Use $\alpha = .01$.

| | Response | |
|---|---|---|
| Region | Agree | Disagree |
| Northeast | 130 | 59 |
| West | 146 | 42 |
| Midwest | 211 | 52 |
| South | 291 | 47 |

**12.44** When charities solicit donations, they must know what approach will encourage people to donate. Would a picture of a needy child tug at the heartstrings and convince someone to contribute to the charity? As reported in the article "The Effect of Photographs of the Handicapped on Donation" (*Journal of Applied Social Psychology* [1979]: 426–431), experimenters went door-to-door with four types of displays: a picture of a smiling child, a picture of an unsmiling child, a verbal message, and an identification of the charity only. At each door, they would randomly select which display to present. Suppose 18 of 30 subjects contributed when shown the picture of the smiling child, 14 of 30 contributed when shown the picture of an unsmiling child, 16 of 26 contributed when shown the verbal message, and 18 of 22 contributed when shown only the identification of the charity. What conclusions can be drawn from these data? Explain your procedure and reasoning.

**12.45** ● Jail inmates can be classified into one of the following four categories according to the type of crime committed: violent crime, crime against property, drug offenses, and public-order offenses. Suppose that random samples of 500 male inmates and 500 female inmates are selected, and each inmate is classified according to type of offense. The data in the accompanying table are based on summary values given in the article "Profile of Jail Inmates" (*USA Today*, April 25, 1991). We would like to know whether male and female inmates differ with respect to type of offense.

| | Gender | |
|---|---|---|
| Type of Crime | Male | Female |
| Violent | 117 | 66 |
| Property | 150 | 160 |
| Drug | 109 | 168 |
| Public-Order | 124 | 106 |

**a.** Is this a test of homogeneity or a test of independence?
**b.** Test the relevant hypotheses using a significance level of .05.

12.46 ● Drivers born under the astrological sign of Capricorn are the worst drivers in Australia, according to an article that appeared in the Australian newspaper *The Mercury* (October 26, 1998). This statement was based on a study of insurance claims that resulted in the following data for male policyholders of a large insurance company.

| Astrological Sign | Number of Policyholders |
|---|---|
| Aquarius | 35,666 |
| Aries | 37,926 |
| Cancer | 38,126 |
| Capricorn | 54,906 |
| Gemini | 37,179 |
| Leo | 37,354 |
| Libra | 37,910 |
| Pisces | 36,677 |
| Sagittarius | 34,175 |
| Scorpio | 35,352 |
| Taurus | 37,179 |
| Virgo | 37,718 |

**a.** Assuming that it is reasonable to treat the policyholders of this particular insurance company as a random sample of insured drivers in Australia, are the observed data consistent with the hypothesis that the proportion of policyholders is the same for each of the 12 astrological signs?
**b.** Why do you think that the proportion of Capricorn policyholders is so much higher than would be expected if the proportions are the same for all astrological signs?
**c.** Suppose that a random sample of 1000 accident claims submitted to this insurance company is selected and each claim classified according to the astrological sign of the driver. (The accompanying table is consistent with accident rates given in the article.)

| Astrological Sign | Observed Number in Sample |
|---|---|
| Aquarius | 85 |
| Aries | 83 |
| Cancer | 82 |
| Capricorn | 88 |
| Gemini | 83 |
| Leo | 83 |
| Libra | 83 |
| Pisces | 82 |
| Sagittarius | 81 |
| Scorpio | 85 |
| Taurus | 84 |
| Virgo | 81 |

Test the null hypothesis that the proportion of accident claims submitted by drivers of each astrological sign is consistent with the proportion of policyholders of each sign. Use the information on the distribution of policyholders from Part (a) to compute expected frequencies and then carry out an appropriate test.

12.47 ● The article "Identification of Cola Beverages" (*Journal of Applied Psychology* [1962]: 356–360) reported on an experiment in which each of 79 subjects was presented with glasses of cola in pairs and asked to identify which glass contained a specific brand of cola. The accompanying data appeared in the article. Do these data suggest that individuals' abilities to make correct identification differ for the different brands of cola?

| | Number of Correct Identifications | | | |
|---|---|---|---|---|
| Cola | 0 | 1 | 2 | 3 or 4 |
| Coca-Cola | 13 | 23 | 24 | 19 |
| Pepsi Cola | 12 | 20 | 26 | 21 |
| Royal Crown | 18 | 28 | 19 | 14 |

**Mentor**

Do you need a live tutor for homework problems?

**Thomson**NOW

Are you ready? Take your exam-prep post-test now.

# Appendix B: Statistical Tables

## Table 1 Random Numbers

| Row | | | | | | | | | | | | | | | | | | | | |
|-----|---|---|---|---|---|---|---|---|---|---|---|---|---|---|---|---|---|---|---|---|
| 1 | 4 | 5 | 1 | 8 | 5 | 0 | 3 | 3 | 7 | 1 | 2 | 8 | 4 | 5 | 1 | 1 | 0 | 9 | 5 | 7 |
| 2 | 4 | 2 | 5 | 5 | 8 | 0 | 4 | 5 | 7 | 0 | 7 | 0 | 3 | 6 | 6 | 1 | 3 | 1 | 3 | 1 |
| 3 | 8 | 9 | 9 | 3 | 4 | 3 | 5 | 0 | 6 | 3 | 9 | 1 | 1 | 8 | 2 | 6 | 9 | 2 | 0 | 9 |
| 4 | 8 | 9 | 0 | 7 | 2 | 9 | 9 | 0 | 4 | 7 | 6 | 7 | 4 | 7 | 1 | 3 | 4 | 3 | 5 | 3 |
| 5 | 5 | 7 | 3 | 1 | 0 | 3 | 7 | 4 | 7 | 8 | 5 | 2 | 0 | 1 | 3 | 7 | 7 | 6 | 3 | 6 |
| 6 | 0 | 9 | 3 | 8 | 7 | 6 | 7 | 9 | 9 | 5 | 6 | 2 | 5 | 6 | 5 | 8 | 4 | 2 | 6 | 4 |
| 7 | 4 | 1 | 0 | 1 | 0 | 2 | 2 | 0 | 4 | 7 | 5 | 1 | 1 | 9 | 4 | 7 | 9 | 7 | 5 | 1 |
| 8 | 6 | 4 | 7 | 3 | 6 | 3 | 4 | 5 | 1 | 2 | 3 | 1 | 1 | 8 | 0 | 0 | 4 | 8 | 2 | 0 |
| 9 | 8 | 0 | 2 | 8 | 7 | 9 | 3 | 8 | 4 | 0 | 4 | 2 | 0 | 8 | 9 | 1 | 2 | 3 | 3 | 2 |
| 10 | 9 | 4 | 6 | 0 | 6 | 9 | 7 | 8 | 8 | 2 | 5 | 2 | 9 | 6 | 0 | 1 | 4 | 6 | 0 | 5 |
| 11 | 6 | 6 | 9 | 5 | 7 | 4 | 4 | 6 | 3 | 2 | 0 | 6 | 0 | 8 | 9 | 1 | 3 | 6 | 1 | 8 |
| 12 | 0 | 7 | 1 | 7 | 7 | 7 | 2 | 9 | 7 | 8 | 7 | 5 | 8 | 8 | 6 | 9 | 8 | 4 | 1 | 0 |
| 13 | 6 | 1 | 3 | 0 | 9 | 7 | 3 | 3 | 6 | 6 | 0 | 4 | 1 | 8 | 3 | 2 | 6 | 7 | 6 | 8 |
| 14 | 2 | 2 | 3 | 6 | 2 | 1 | 3 | 0 | 2 | 2 | 6 | 6 | 9 | 7 | 0 | 2 | 1 | 2 | 5 | 8 |
| 15 | 0 | 7 | 1 | 7 | 4 | 2 | 0 | 0 | 0 | 1 | 3 | 1 | 2 | 0 | 4 | 7 | 8 | 4 | 1 | 0 |
| 16 | 6 | 6 | 5 | 1 | 6 | 1 | 8 | 1 | 5 | 5 | 2 | 6 | 2 | 0 | 1 | 1 | 5 | 2 | 3 | 6 |
| 17 | 9 | 9 | 6 | 2 | 5 | 3 | 5 | 9 | 8 | 3 | 7 | 5 | 0 | 1 | 3 | 9 | 3 | 8 | 0 | 8 |
| 18 | 9 | 9 | 9 | 6 | 1 | 2 | 9 | 3 | 4 | 6 | 5 | 6 | 4 | 6 | 5 | 8 | 2 | 7 | 4 | 0 |
| 19 | 2 | 5 | 6 | 3 | 1 | 9 | 8 | 1 | 1 | 0 | 3 | 5 | 6 | 7 | 9 | 1 | 4 | 5 | 2 | 0 |
| 20 | 5 | 1 | 1 | 9 | 8 | 1 | 2 | 1 | 1 | 6 | 9 | 8 | 1 | 8 | 1 | 9 | 9 | 1 | 2 | 0 |
| 21 | 1 | 9 | 8 | 0 | 7 | 4 | 6 | 8 | 4 | 0 | 3 | 0 | 8 | 1 | 1 | 0 | 6 | 2 | 3 | 2 |
| 22 | 9 | 7 | 0 | 9 | 6 | 3 | 8 | 9 | 9 | 7 | 0 | 6 | 5 | 4 | 3 | 6 | 5 | 0 | 3 | 2 |
| 23 | 1 | 7 | 6 | 4 | 8 | 2 | 0 | 3 | 9 | 6 | 3 | 6 | 2 | 1 | 0 | 7 | 7 | 3 | 1 | 7 |
| 24 | 6 | 2 | 5 | 8 | 2 | 0 | 7 | 8 | 6 | 4 | 6 | 6 | 8 | 9 | 2 | 0 | 6 | 9 | 0 | 4 |
| 25 | 1 | 5 | 7 | 1 | 1 | 1 | 9 | 5 | 1 | 4 | 5 | 2 | 8 | 3 | 4 | 3 | 0 | 7 | 3 | 5 |
| 26 | 1 | 4 | 6 | 6 | 5 | 6 | 0 | 1 | 9 | 4 | 0 | 5 | 2 | 7 | 6 | 4 | 3 | 6 | 8 | 8 |
| 27 | 1 | 8 | 5 | 0 | 2 | 1 | 6 | 8 | 0 | 7 | 7 | 2 | 6 | 2 | 6 | 7 | 5 | 4 | 8 | 7 |
| 28 | 7 | 8 | 7 | 4 | 6 | 5 | 4 | 3 | 7 | 9 | 3 | 9 | 2 | 7 | 9 | 5 | 4 | 2 | 3 | 1 |
| 29 | 1 | 6 | 3 | 2 | 8 | 3 | 7 | 3 | 0 | 7 | 2 | 4 | 8 | 0 | 9 | 9 | 9 | 4 | 7 | 0 |
| 30 | 2 | 8 | 9 | 0 | 8 | 1 | 6 | 8 | 1 | 7 | 3 | 1 | 3 | 0 | 9 | 7 | 2 | 5 | 7 | 9 |
| 31 | 0 | 7 | 8 | 8 | 6 | 5 | 7 | 5 | 5 | 4 | 0 | 0 | 3 | 4 | 1 | 2 | 7 | 3 | 7 | 9 |
| 32 | 8 | 4 | 0 | 1 | 4 | 5 | 1 | 9 | 1 | 1 | 2 | 1 | 5 | 3 | 2 | 8 | 5 | 5 | 7 | 5 |
| 33 | 7 | 3 | 5 | 9 | 7 | 0 | 4 | 9 | 1 | 2 | 1 | 3 | 2 | 5 | 1 | 9 | 3 | 3 | 8 | 3 |
| 34 | 4 | 7 | 2 | 6 | 7 | 6 | 9 | 9 | 2 | 7 | 8 | 7 | 5 | 5 | 5 | 2 | 4 | 4 | 3 | 4 |
| 35 | 9 | 3 | 3 | 7 | 0 | 7 | 0 | 5 | 7 | 5 | 6 | 9 | 5 | 4 | 3 | 1 | 4 | 6 | 6 | 8 |
| 36 | 0 | 2 | 4 | 9 | 7 | 8 | 1 | 6 | 3 | 8 | 7 | 8 | 0 | 5 | 6 | 7 | 2 | 7 | 5 | 0 |
| 37 | 7 | 1 | 0 | 1 | 8 | 4 | 7 | 1 | 2 | 9 | 3 | 8 | 0 | 0 | 8 | 7 | 9 | 2 | 8 | 6 |
| 38 | 9 | 7 | 9 | 4 | 4 | 5 | 3 | 1 | 9 | 3 | 4 | 5 | 0 | 6 | 3 | 5 | 9 | 6 | 9 | 8 |
| 39 | 0 | 4 | 2 | 5 | 0 | 0 | 9 | 9 | 6 | 4 | 0 | 6 | 9 | 0 | 3 | 8 | 3 | 5 | 7 | 2 |
| 40 | 0 | 7 | 1 | 2 | 3 | 6 | 1 | 7 | 9 | 3 | 9 | 5 | 4 | 6 | 8 | 4 | 8 | 8 | 0 | 6 |
| 41 | 3 | 5 | 6 | 6 | 2 | 4 | 4 | 5 | 6 | 3 | 7 | 8 | 7 | 6 | 5 | 2 | 0 | 4 | 3 | 2 |
| 42 | 6 | 6 | 8 | 5 | 5 | 2 | 9 | 7 | 9 | 3 | 3 | 1 | 6 | 9 | 5 | 9 | 7 | 1 | 1 | 2 |
| 43 | 9 | 5 | 0 | 4 | 3 | 1 | 1 | 7 | 3 | 9 | 2 | 7 | 7 | 4 | 7 | 0 | 3 | 1 | 2 | 8 |
| 44 | 5 | 1 | 7 | 8 | 9 | 4 | 7 | 2 | 9 | 2 | 8 | 9 | 9 | 8 | 0 | 6 | 3 | 7 | 2 | 1 |
| 45 | 1 | 6 | 3 | 9 | 4 | 1 | 3 | 2 | 1 | 1 | 8 | 5 | 6 | 3 | 4 | 1 | 9 | 3 | 1 | 7 |
| 46 | 4 | 4 | 8 | 6 | 4 | 0 | 3 | 8 | 3 | 8 | 3 | 5 | 9 | 5 | 9 | 4 | 8 | 3 | 9 | 4 |
| 47 | 7 | 7 | 6 | 6 | 4 | 5 | 4 | 4 | 8 | 4 | 4 | 0 | 3 | 9 | 8 | 5 | 2 | 0 | 2 | 3 |
| 48 | 2 | 5 | 6 | 6 | 3 | 7 | 0 | 6 | 5 | 6 | 9 | 0 | 1 | 9 | 5 | 2 | 6 | 9 | 1 | 2 |
| 49 | 9 | 4 | 0 | 4 | 7 | 5 | 3 | 2 | 8 | 7 | 2 | 7 | 4 | 9 | 3 | 9 | 6 | 5 | 5 | 6 |
| 50 | 7 | 3 | 1 | 5 | 6 | 6 | 5 | 0 | 3 | 5 | 3 | 7 | 2 | 8 | 6 | 2 | 4 | 1 | 8 | 7 |

Table 1 ▪ Random Numbers   705

**Table 1** Random Numbers (*Continued*)

| Row | | | | | | | | | | | | | | | | | | | | |
|---|---|---|---|---|---|---|---|---|---|---|---|---|---|---|---|---|---|---|---|---|
| 51 | 7 | 5 | 8 | 2 | 8 | 8 | 8 | 7 | 6 | 4 | 1 | 1 | 0 | 2 | 3 | 1 | 9 | 3 | 6 | 0 |
| 52 | 3 | 3 | 6 | 0 | 9 | 1 | 1 | 0 | 3 | 2 | 7 | 8 | 2 | 0 | 5 | 3 | 4 | 8 | 9 | 8 |
| 53 | 0 | 2 | 9 | 6 | 9 | 8 | 9 | 3 | 8 | 1 | 5 | 3 | 9 | 9 | 7 | 0 | 7 | 7 | 1 | 6 |
| 54 | 8 | 5 | 9 | 6 | 2 | 9 | 6 | 8 | 2 | 1 | 2 | 4 | 7 | 0 | 6 | 8 | 3 | 4 | 6 | 1 |
| 55 | 5 | 4 | 7 | 6 | 1 | 0 | 0 | 1 | 0 | 4 | 6 | 1 | 4 | 1 | 5 | 0 | 9 | 6 | 5 | 5 |
| 56 | 5 | 0 | 3 | 6 | 4 | 1 | 9 | 8 | 4 | 4 | 1 | 2 | 0 | 2 | 5 | 1 | 8 | 1 | 2 | 1 |
| 57 | 0 | 2 | 6 | 3 | 7 | 5 | 1 | 1 | 6 | 6 | 0 | 5 | 8 | 1 | 2 | 3 | 3 | 6 | 1 | 3 |
| 58 | 3 | 8 | 1 | 6 | 3 | 8 | 1 | 4 | 5 | 2 | 9 | 4 | 2 | 5 | 7 | 3 | 2 | 3 | 1 | 8 |
| 59 | 9 | 1 | 5 | 6 | 0 | 6 | 5 | 6 | 6 | 3 | 6 | 2 | 3 | 0 | 0 | 0 | 1 | 8 | 5 | 9 |
| 60 | 5 | 3 | 5 | 6 | 3 | 9 | 5 | 4 | 7 | 3 | 6 | 6 | 7 | 5 | 0 | 1 | 5 | 6 | 7 | 3 |
| 61 | 9 | 6 | 6 | 4 | 5 | 7 | 7 | 6 | 1 | 5 | 4 | 4 | 8 | 0 | 6 | 5 | 7 | 6 | 3 | 0 |
| 62 | 6 | 3 | 0 | 6 | 7 | 9 | 5 | 5 | 4 | 6 | 2 | 2 | 8 | 4 | 4 | 0 | 0 | 9 | 9 | 8 |
| 63 | 8 | 5 | 8 | 3 | 5 | 2 | 0 | 6 | 6 | 0 | 0 | 6 | 0 | 6 | 3 | 0 | 1 | 7 | 0 | 5 |
| 64 | 3 | 8 | 2 | 4 | 9 | 0 | 9 | 2 | 6 | 2 | 9 | 5 | 1 | 9 | 1 | 9 | 0 | 8 | 3 | 3 |
| 65 | 1 | 4 | 4 | 1 | 1 | 7 | 4 | 6 | 3 | 6 | 5 | 6 | 5 | 5 | 7 | 7 | 0 | 3 | 5 | 8 |
| 66 | 5 | 9 | 9 | 5 | 3 | 7 | 2 | 5 | 1 | 7 | 1 | 1 | 0 | 7 | 1 | 0 | 9 | 2 | 8 | 8 |
| 67 | 8 | 7 | 1 | 7 | 5 | 2 | 5 | 6 | 8 | 7 | 9 | 9 | 1 | 3 | 9 | 6 | 4 | 9 | 3 | 0 |
| 68 | 6 | 7 | 2 | 3 | 1 | 4 | 9 | 2 | 1 | 7 | 0 | 8 | 6 | 7 | 8 | 9 | 9 | 4 | 7 | 4 |
| 69 | 2 | 3 | 2 | 8 | 7 | 0 | 9 | 7 | 1 | 1 | 1 | 2 | 8 | 2 | 9 | 1 | 0 | 6 | 7 | 7 |
| 70 | 2 | 9 | 5 | 7 | 8 | 4 | 7 | 9 | 0 | 3 | 6 | 9 | 2 | 0 | 6 | 0 | 6 | 2 | 6 | 8 |
| 71 | 4 | 8 | 9 | 8 | 3 | 2 | 7 | 6 | 9 | 1 | 9 | 8 | 6 | 9 | 5 | 2 | 4 | 9 | 9 | 9 |
| 72 | 1 | 5 | 6 | 5 | 7 | 7 | 5 | 4 | 3 | 4 | 3 | 8 | 1 | 8 | 9 | 9 | 4 | 4 | 1 | 1 |
| 73 | 1 | 8 | 1 | 1 | 7 | 2 | 8 | 5 | 5 | 8 | 9 | 9 | 9 | 6 | 2 | 0 | 1 | 6 | 6 | 7 |
| 74 | 5 | 7 | 7 | 0 | 9 | 5 | 5 | 6 | 8 | 6 | 8 | 2 | 2 | 6 | 0 | 5 | 5 | 1 | 8 | 7 |
| 75 | 1 | 8 | 6 | 0 | 5 | 4 | 8 | 3 | 4 | 5 | 3 | 5 | 8 | 7 | 7 | 7 | 8 | 5 | 7 | 0 |
| 76 | 2 | 6 | 6 | 7 | 9 | 4 | 2 | 2 | 8 | 7 | 4 | 3 | 4 | 9 | 6 | 1 | 9 | 4 | 3 | 9 |
| 77 | 3 | 6 | 6 | 4 | 5 | 7 | 8 | 3 | 0 | 2 | 8 | 4 | 6 | 7 | 2 | 1 | 4 | 5 | 2 | 3 |
| 78 | 0 | 7 | 8 | 0 | 1 | 2 | 1 | 1 | 3 | 4 | 2 | 1 | 6 | 9 | 3 | 3 | 5 | 4 | 0 | 4 |
| 79 | 8 | 3 | 6 | 0 | 5 | 7 | 7 | 9 | 1 | 5 | 8 | 8 | 4 | 9 | 5 | 7 | 2 | 2 | 7 | 6 |
| 80 | 5 | 3 | 6 | 9 | 0 | 6 | 3 | 8 | 7 | 5 | 9 | 5 | 9 | 7 | 4 | 2 | 5 | 6 | 2 | 9 |
| 81 | 0 | 9 | 3 | 7 | 7 | 2 | 8 | 6 | 4 | 3 | 2 | 9 | 4 | 8 | 2 | 9 | 9 | 6 | 9 | 9 |
| 82 | 9 | 4 | 7 | 4 | 0 | 0 | 0 | 3 | 5 | 4 | 6 | 6 | 2 | 6 | 2 | 3 | 6 | 1 | 1 | 4 |
| 83 | 5 | 5 | 4 | 1 | 7 | 8 | 6 | 4 | 2 | 3 | 2 | 9 | 8 | 4 | 6 | 3 | 8 | 3 | 0 | 5 |
| 84 | 5 | 3 | 0 | 0 | 5 | 4 | 8 | 0 | 7 | 4 | 7 | 6 | 2 | 1 | 1 | 2 | 1 | 2 | 6 | 9 |
| 85 | 3 | 3 | 0 | 9 | 3 | 2 | 9 | 4 | 0 | 5 | 5 | 4 | 8 | 7 | 5 | 7 | 5 | 3 | 8 | 8 |
| 86 | 3 | 0 | 5 | 7 | 1 | 9 | 5 | 8 | 0 | 0 | 4 | 5 | 3 | 0 | 3 | 0 | 2 | 7 | 6 | 7 |
| 87 | 5 | 0 | 8 | 6 | 0 | 8 | 1 | 6 | 2 | 0 | 8 | 6 | 5 | 4 | 0 | 7 | 2 | 9 | 1 | 0 |
| 88 | 3 | 6 | 4 | 7 | 8 | 2 | 3 | 5 | 7 | 9 | 8 | 5 | 2 | 7 | 6 | 9 | 0 | 2 | 4 | 9 |
| 89 | 9 | 0 | 4 | 4 | 9 | 1 | 6 | 8 | 5 | 2 | 8 | 9 | 0 | 7 | 5 | 7 | 2 | 5 | 1 | 8 |
| 90 | 9 | 5 | 2 | 6 | 9 | 3 | 9 | 6 | 5 | 1 | 8 | 8 | 7 | 8 | 2 | 0 | 4 | 4 | 7 | 9 |
| 91 | 9 | 4 | 5 | 7 | 0 | 3 | 4 | 6 | 4 | 2 | 5 | 4 | 8 | 6 | 1 | 1 | 9 | 1 | 8 | 8 |
| 92 | 8 | 1 | 1 | 8 | 0 | 5 | 4 | 2 | 8 | 5 | 3 | 3 | 3 | 0 | 1 | 1 | 4 | 4 | 8 | 3 |
| 93 | 6 | 9 | 4 | 7 | 8 | 3 | 3 | 9 | 1 | 2 | 5 | 0 | 1 | 2 | 3 | 0 | 1 | 1 | 2 | 5 |
| 94 | 0 | 0 | 6 | 8 | 8 | 7 | 2 | 4 | 4 | 7 | 6 | 6 | 0 | 3 | 4 | 7 | 5 | 6 | 8 | 2 |
| 95 | 5 | 3 | 3 | 9 | 3 | 8 | 4 | 9 | 1 | 9 | 1 | 7 | 8 | 4 | 5 | 2 | 2 | 5 | 4 | 4 |
| 96 | 2 | 5 | 6 | 2 | 7 | 6 | 0 | 3 | 8 | 1 | 4 | 4 | 2 | 6 | 8 | 3 | 6 | 3 | 2 | 8 |
| 97 | 7 | 4 | 3 | 7 | 9 | 6 | 8 | 6 | 2 | 8 | 3 | 8 | 4 | 2 | 2 | 0 | 7 | 0 | 5 | 3 |
| 98 | 1 | 9 | 0 | 8 | 8 | 0 | 1 | 2 | 2 | 2 | 7 | 5 | 6 | 5 | 5 | 7 | 8 | 7 | 2 | 6 |
| 99 | 2 | 4 | 8 | 0 | 2 | 5 | 2 | 7 | 0 | 5 | 9 | 6 | 6 | 1 | 5 | 8 | 7 | 9 | 7 | 5 |
| 100 | 4 | 1 | 7 | 8 | 6 | 7 | 1 | 1 | 5 | 8 | 9 | 4 | 8 | 9 | 8 | 3 | 0 | 9 | 0 | 7 |

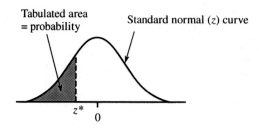

Tabulated area = probability

Standard normal (z) curve

$z^*$  0

**Table 2** Standard Normal Probabilities (Cumulative z Curve Areas)

| $z^*$ | .00 | .01 | .02 | .03 | .04 | .05 | .06 | .07 | .08 | .09 |
|---|---|---|---|---|---|---|---|---|---|---|
| −3.8 | .0001 | .0001 | .0001 | .0001 | .0001 | .0001 | .0001 | .0001 | .0001 | .0000 |
| −3.7 | .0001 | .0001 | .0001 | .0001 | .0001 | .0001 | .0001 | .0001 | .0001 | .0001 |
| −3.6 | .0002 | .0002 | .0001 | .0001 | .0001 | .0001 | .0001 | .0001 | .0001 | .0001 |
| −3.5 | .0002 | .0002 | .0002 | .0002 | .0002 | .0002 | .0002 | .0002 | .0002 | .0002 |
| −3.4 | .0003 | .0003 | .0003 | .0003 | .0003 | .0003 | .0003 | .0003 | .0003 | .0002 |
| −3.3 | .0005 | .0005 | .0005 | .0004 | .0004 | .0004 | .0004 | .0004 | .0004 | .0003 |
| −3.2 | .0007 | .0007 | .0006 | .0006 | .0006 | .0006 | .0006 | .0005 | .0005 | .0005 |
| −3.1 | .0010 | .0009 | .0009 | .0009 | .0008 | .0008 | .0008 | .0008 | .0007 | .0007 |
| −3.0 | .0013 | .0013 | .0013 | .0012 | .0012 | .0011 | .0011 | .0011 | .0010 | .0010 |
| −2.9 | .0019 | .0018 | .0018 | .0017 | .0016 | .0016 | .0015 | .0015 | .0014 | .0014 |
| −2.8 | .0026 | .0025 | .0024 | .0023 | .0023 | .0022 | .0021 | .0021 | .0020 | .0019 |
| −2.7 | .0035 | .0034 | .0033 | .0032 | .0031 | .0030 | .0029 | .0028 | .0027 | .0026 |
| −2.6 | .0047 | .0045 | .0044 | .0043 | .0041 | .0040 | .0039 | .0038 | .0037 | .0036 |
| −2.5 | .0062 | .0060 | .0059 | .0057 | .0055 | .0054 | .0052 | .0051 | .0049 | .0048 |
| −2.4 | .0082 | .0080 | .0078 | .0075 | .0073 | .0071 | .0069 | .0068 | .0066 | .0064 |
| −2.3 | .0107 | .0104 | .0102 | .0099 | .0096 | .0094 | .0091 | .0089 | .0087 | .0084 |
| −2.2 | .0139 | .0136 | .0132 | .0129 | .0125 | .0122 | .0119 | .0116 | .0113 | .0110 |
| −2.1 | .0179 | .0174 | .0170 | .0166 | .0162 | .0158 | .0154 | .0150 | .0146 | .0143 |
| −2.0 | .0228 | .0222 | .0217 | .0212 | .0207 | .0202 | .0197 | .0192 | .0188 | .0183 |
| −1.9 | .0287 | .0281 | .0274 | .0268 | .0262 | .0256 | .0250 | .0244 | .0239 | .0233 |
| −1.8 | .0359 | .0351 | .0344 | .0336 | .0329 | .0322 | .0314 | .0307 | .0301 | .0294 |
| −1.7 | .0446 | .0436 | .0427 | .0418 | .0409 | .0401 | .0392 | .0384 | .0375 | .0367 |
| −1.6 | .0548 | .0537 | .0526 | .0516 | .0505 | .0495 | .0485 | .0475 | .0465 | .0455 |
| −1.5 | .0668 | .0655 | .0643 | .0630 | .0618 | .0606 | .0594 | .0582 | .0571 | .0559 |
| −1.4 | .0808 | .0793 | .0778 | .0764 | .0749 | .0735 | .0721 | .0708 | .0694 | .0681 |
| −1.3 | .0968 | .0951 | .0934 | .0918 | .0901 | .0885 | .0869 | .0853 | .0838 | .0823 |
| −1.2 | .1151 | .1131 | .1112 | .1093 | .1075 | .1056 | .1038 | .1020 | .1003 | .0985 |
| −1.1 | .1357 | .1335 | .1314 | .1292 | .1271 | .1251 | .1230 | .1210 | .1190 | .1170 |
| −1.0 | .1587 | .1562 | .1539 | .1515 | .1492 | .1469 | .1446 | .1423 | .1401 | .1379 |
| −0.9 | .1841 | .1814 | .1788 | .1762 | .1736 | .1711 | .1685 | .1660 | .1635 | .1611 |
| −0.8 | .2119 | .2090 | .2061 | .2033 | .2005 | .1977 | .1949 | .1922 | .1894 | .1867 |
| −0.7 | .2420 | .2389 | .2358 | .2327 | .2296 | .2266 | .2236 | .2206 | .2177 | .2148 |
| −0.6 | .2743 | .2709 | .2676 | .2643 | .2611 | .2578 | .2546 | .2514 | .2483 | .2451 |
| −0.5 | .3085 | .3050 | .3015 | .2981 | .2946 | .2912 | .2877 | .2843 | .2810 | .2776 |
| −0.4 | .3446 | .3409 | .3372 | .3336 | .3300 | .3264 | .3228 | .3192 | .3156 | .3121 |
| −0.3 | .3821 | .3783 | .3745 | .3707 | .3669 | .3632 | .3594 | .3557 | .3520 | .3483 |
| −0.2 | .4207 | .4168 | .4129 | .4090 | .4052 | .4013 | .3974 | .3936 | .3897 | .3859 |
| −0.1 | .4602 | .4562 | .4522 | .4483 | .4443 | .4404 | .4364 | .4325 | .4286 | .4247 |
| −0.0 | .5000 | .4960 | .4920 | .4880 | .4840 | .4801 | .4761 | .4721 | .4681 | .4641 |

**Table 2** ▪ Standard Normal Probabilities (Cumulative z Curve Areas)   **707**

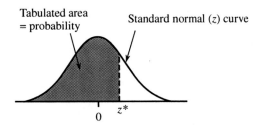

Tabulated area = probability

Standard normal (z) curve

0    z*

**Table 2** Standard Normal Probabilities (*Continued*)

| z* | .00 | .01 | .02 | .03 | .04 | .05 | .06 | .07 | .08 | .09 |
|---|---|---|---|---|---|---|---|---|---|---|
| 0.0 | .5000 | .5040 | .5080 | .5120 | .5160 | .5199 | .5239 | .5279 | .5319 | .5359 |
| 0.1 | .5398 | .5438 | .5478 | .5517 | .5557 | .5596 | .5636 | .5675 | .5714 | .5753 |
| 0.2 | .5793 | .5832 | .5871 | .5910 | .5948 | .5987 | .6026 | .6064 | .6103 | .6141 |
| 0.3 | .6179 | .6217 | .6255 | .6293 | .6331 | .6368 | .6406 | .6443 | .6480 | .6517 |
| 0.4 | .6554 | .6591 | .6628 | .6664 | .6700 | .6736 | .6772 | .6808 | .6844 | .6879 |
| 0.5 | .6915 | .6950 | .6985 | .7019 | .7054 | .7088 | .7123 | .7157 | .7190 | .7224 |
| 0.6 | .7257 | .7291 | .7324 | .7357 | .7389 | .7422 | .7454 | .7486 | .7517 | .7549 |
| 0.7 | .7580 | .7611 | .7642 | .7673 | .7704 | .7734 | .7764 | .7794 | .7823 | .7852 |
| 0.8 | .7881 | .7910 | .7939 | .7967 | .7995 | .8023 | .8051 | .8078 | .8106 | .8133 |
| 0.9 | .8159 | .8186 | .8212 | .8238 | .8264 | .8289 | .8315 | .8340 | .8365 | .8389 |
| 1.0 | .8413 | .8438 | .8461 | .8485 | .8508 | .8531 | .8554 | .8577 | .8599 | .8621 |
| 1.1 | .8643 | .8665 | .8686 | .8708 | .8729 | .8749 | .8770 | .8790 | .8810 | .8830 |
| 1.2 | .8849 | .8869 | .8888 | .8907 | .8925 | .8944 | .8962 | .8980 | .8997 | .9015 |
| 1.3 | .9032 | .9049 | .9066 | .9082 | .9099 | .9115 | .9131 | .9147 | .9162 | .9177 |
| 1.4 | .9192 | .9207 | .9222 | .9236 | .9251 | .9265 | .9279 | .9292 | .9306 | .9319 |
| 1.5 | .9332 | .9345 | .9357 | .9370 | .9382 | .9394 | .9406 | .9418 | .9429 | .9441 |
| 1.6 | .9452 | .9463 | .9474 | .9484 | .9495 | .9505 | .9515 | .9525 | .9535 | .9545 |
| 1.7 | .9554 | .9564 | .9573 | .9582 | .9591 | .9599 | .9608 | .9616 | .9625 | .9633 |
| 1.8 | .9641 | .9649 | .9656 | .9664 | .9671 | .9678 | .9686 | .9693 | .9699 | .9706 |
| 1.9 | .9713 | .9719 | .9726 | .9732 | .9738 | .9744 | .9750 | .9756 | .9761 | .9767 |
| 2.0 | .9772 | .9778 | .9783 | .9788 | .9793 | .9798 | .9803 | .9808 | .9812 | .9817 |
| 2.1 | .9821 | .9826 | .9830 | .9834 | .9838 | .9842 | .9846 | .9850 | .9854 | .9857 |
| 2.2 | .9861 | .9864 | .9868 | .9871 | .9875 | .9878 | .9881 | .9884 | .9887 | .9890 |
| 2.3 | .9893 | .9896 | .9898 | .9901 | .9904 | .9906 | .9909 | .9911 | .9913 | .9916 |
| 2.4 | .9918 | .9920 | .9922 | .9925 | .9927 | .9929 | .9931 | .9932 | .9934 | .9936 |
| 2.5 | .9938 | .9940 | .9941 | .9943 | .9945 | .9946 | .9948 | .9949 | .9951 | .9952 |
| 2.6 | .9953 | .9955 | .9956 | .9957 | .9959 | .9960 | .9961 | .9962 | .9963 | .9964 |
| 2.7 | .9965 | .9966 | .9967 | .9968 | .9969 | .9970 | .9971 | .9972 | .9973 | .9974 |
| 2.8 | .9974 | .9975 | .9976 | .9977 | .9977 | .9978 | .9979 | .9979 | .9980 | .9981 |
| 2.9 | .9981 | .9982 | .9982 | .9983 | .9984 | .9984 | .9985 | .9985 | .9986 | .9986 |
| 3.0 | .9987 | .9987 | .9987 | .9988 | .9988 | .9989 | .9989 | .9989 | .9990 | .9990 |
| 3.1 | .9990 | .9991 | .9991 | .9991 | .9992 | .9992 | .9992 | .9992 | .9993 | .9993 |
| 3.2 | .9993 | .9993 | .9994 | .9994 | .9994 | .9994 | .9994 | .9995 | .9995 | .9995 |
| 3.3 | .9995 | .9995 | .9995 | .9996 | .9996 | .9996 | .9996 | .9996 | .9996 | .9997 |
| 3.4 | .9997 | .9997 | .9997 | .9997 | .9997 | .9997 | .9997 | .9997 | .9997 | .9998 |
| 3.5 | .9998 | .9998 | .9998 | .9998 | .9998 | .9998 | .9998 | .9998 | .9998 | .9998 |
| 3.6 | .9998 | .9998 | .9999 | .9999 | .9999 | .9999 | .9999 | .9999 | .9999 | .9999 |
| 3.7 | .9999 | .9999 | .9999 | .9999 | .9999 | .9999 | .9999 | .9999 | .9999 | .9999 |
| 3.8 | .9999 | .9999 | .9999 | .9999 | .9999 | .9999 | .9999 | .9999 | .9999 | 1.0000 |

**Table 8** Upper-Tail Areas for Chi-Square Distributions

| Right-tail area | df = 1 | df = 2 | df = 3 | df = 4 | df = 5 |
|---|---|---|---|---|---|
| >0.100 | < 2.70 | < 4.60 | < 6.25 | < 7.77 | < 9.23 |
| 0.100 | 2.70 | 4.60 | 6.25 | 7.77 | 9.23 |
| 0.095 | 2.78 | 4.70 | 6.36 | 7.90 | 9.37 |
| 0.090 | 2.87 | 4.81 | 6.49 | 8.04 | 9.52 |
| 0.085 | 2.96 | 4.93 | 6.62 | 8.18 | 9.67 |
| 0.080 | 3.06 | 5.05 | 6.75 | 8.33 | 9.83 |
| 0.075 | 3.17 | 5.18 | 6.90 | 8.49 | 10.00 |
| 0.070 | 3.28 | 5.31 | 7.06 | 8.66 | 10.19 |
| 0.065 | 3.40 | 5.46 | 7.22 | 8.84 | 10.38 |
| 0.060 | 3.53 | 5.62 | 7.40 | 9.04 | 10.59 |
| 0.055 | 3.68 | 5.80 | 7.60 | 9.25 | 10.82 |
| 0.050 | 3.84 | 5.99 | 7.81 | 9.48 | 11.07 |
| 0.045 | 4.01 | 6.20 | 8.04 | 9.74 | 11.34 |
| 0.040 | 4.21 | 6.43 | 8.31 | 10.02 | 11.64 |
| 0.035 | 4.44 | 6.70 | 8.60 | 10.34 | 11.98 |
| 0.030 | 4.70 | 7.01 | 8.94 | 10.71 | 12.37 |
| 0.025 | 5.02 | 7.37 | 9.34 | 11.14 | 12.83 |
| 0.020 | 5.41 | 7.82 | 9.83 | 11.66 | 13.38 |
| 0.015 | 5.91 | 8.39 | 10.46 | 12.33 | 14.09 |
| 0.010 | 6.63 | 9.21 | 11.34 | 13.27 | 15.08 |
| 0.005 | 7.87 | 10.59 | 12.83 | 14.86 | 16.74 |
| 0.001 | 10.82 | 13.81 | 16.26 | 18.46 | 20.51 |
| <0.001 | >10.82 | >13.81 | >16.26 | >18.46 | >20.51 |
| **Right-tail area** | **df = 6** | **df = 7** | **df = 8** | **df = 9** | **df = 10** |
| >0.100 | <10.64 | <12.01 | <13.36 | <14.68 | <15.98 |
| 0.100 | 10.64 | 12.01 | 13.36 | 14.68 | 15.98 |
| 0.095 | 10.79 | 12.17 | 13.52 | 14.85 | 16.16 |
| 0.090 | 10.94 | 12.33 | 13.69 | 15.03 | 16.35 |
| 0.085 | 11.11 | 12.50 | 13.87 | 15.22 | 16.54 |
| 0.080 | 11.28 | 12.69 | 14.06 | 15.42 | 16.75 |
| 0.075 | 11.46 | 12.88 | 14.26 | 15.63 | 16.97 |
| 0.070 | 11.65 | 13.08 | 14.48 | 15.85 | 17.20 |
| 0.065 | 11.86 | 13.30 | 14.71 | 16.09 | 17.44 |
| 0.060 | 12.08 | 13.53 | 14.95 | 16.34 | 17.71 |
| 0.055 | 12.33 | 13.79 | 15.22 | 16.62 | 17.99 |
| 0.050 | 12.59 | 14.06 | 15.50 | 16.91 | 18.30 |
| 0.045 | 12.87 | 14.36 | 15.82 | 17.24 | 18.64 |
| 0.040 | 13.19 | 14.70 | 16.17 | 17.60 | 19.02 |
| 0.035 | 13.55 | 15.07 | 16.56 | 18.01 | 19.44 |
| 0.030 | 13.96 | 15.50 | 17.01 | 18.47 | 19.92 |
| 0.025 | 14.44 | 16.01 | 17.53 | 19.02 | 20.48 |
| 0.020 | 15.03 | 16.62 | 18.16 | 19.67 | 21.16 |
| 0.015 | 15.77 | 17.39 | 18.97 | 20.51 | 22.02 |
| 0.010 | 16.81 | 18.47 | 20.09 | 21.66 | 23.20 |
| 0.005 | 18.54 | 20.27 | 21.95 | 23.58 | 25.18 |
| 0.001 | 22.45 | 24.32 | 26.12 | 27.87 | 29.58 |
| <0.001 | >22.45 | >24.32 | >26.12 | >27.87 | >29.58 |

Table 8 ■ Upper-Tail Areas for Chi-Square Distributions  719

**Table 8** Upper-Tail Areas for Chi-Square Distributions (*Continued*)

| Right-tail area | df = 11 | df = 12 | df = 13 | df = 14 | df = 15 |
|---|---|---|---|---|---|
| >0.100 | <17.27 | <18.54 | <19.81 | <21.06 | <22.30 |
| 0.100 | 17.27 | 18.54 | 19.81 | 21.06 | 22.30 |
| 0.095 | 17.45 | 18.74 | 20.00 | 21.26 | 22.51 |
| 0.090 | 17.65 | 18.93 | 20.21 | 21.47 | 22.73 |
| 0.085 | 17.85 | 19.14 | 20.42 | 21.69 | 22.95 |
| 0.080 | 18.06 | 19.36 | 20.65 | 21.93 | 23.19 |
| 0.075 | 18.29 | 19.60 | 20.89 | 22.17 | 23.45 |
| 0.070 | 18.53 | 19.84 | 21.15 | 22.44 | 23.72 |
| 0.065 | 18.78 | 20.11 | 21.42 | 22.71 | 24.00 |
| 0.060 | 19.06 | 20.39 | 21.71 | 23.01 | 24.31 |
| 0.055 | 19.35 | 20.69 | 22.02 | 23.33 | 24.63 |
| 0.050 | 19.67 | 21.02 | 22.36 | 23.68 | 24.99 |
| 0.045 | 20.02 | 21.38 | 22.73 | 24.06 | 25.38 |
| 0.040 | 20.41 | 21.78 | 23.14 | 24.48 | 25.81 |
| 0.035 | 20.84 | 22.23 | 23.60 | 24.95 | 26.29 |
| 0.030 | 21.34 | 22.74 | 24.12 | 25.49 | 26.84 |
| 0.025 | 21.92 | 23.33 | 24.73 | 26.11 | 27.48 |
| 0.020 | 22.61 | 24.05 | 25.47 | 26.87 | 28.25 |
| 0.015 | 23.50 | 24.96 | 26.40 | 27.82 | 29.23 |
| 0.010 | 24.72 | 26.21 | 27.68 | 29.14 | 30.57 |
| 0.005 | 26.75 | 28.29 | 29.81 | 31.31 | 32.80 |
| 0.001 | 31.26 | 32.90 | 34.52 | 36.12 | 37.69 |
| <0.001 | >31.26 | >32.90 | >34.52 | >36.12 | >37.69 |

| Right-tail area | df = 16 | df = 17 | df = 18 | df = 19 | df = 20 |
|---|---|---|---|---|---|
| >0.100 | <23.54 | <24.77 | <25.98 | <27.20 | <28.41 |
| 0.100 | 23.54 | 24.76 | 25.98 | 27.20 | 28.41 |
| 0.095 | 23.75 | 24.98 | 26.21 | 27.43 | 28.64 |
| 0.090 | 23.97 | 25.21 | 26.44 | 27.66 | 28.88 |
| 0.085 | 24.21 | 25.45 | 26.68 | 27.91 | 29.14 |
| 0.080 | 24.45 | 25.70 | 26.94 | 28.18 | 29.40 |
| 0.075 | 24.71 | 25.97 | 27.21 | 28.45 | 29.69 |
| 0.070 | 24.99 | 26.25 | 27.50 | 28.75 | 29.99 |
| 0.065 | 25.28 | 26.55 | 27.81 | 29.06 | 30.30 |
| 0.060 | 25.59 | 26.87 | 28.13 | 29.39 | 30.64 |
| 0.055 | 25.93 | 27.21 | 28.48 | 29.75 | 31.01 |
| 0.050 | 26.29 | 27.58 | 28.86 | 30.14 | 31.41 |
| 0.045 | 26.69 | 27.99 | 29.28 | 30.56 | 31.84 |
| 0.040 | 27.13 | 28.44 | 29.74 | 31.03 | 32.32 |
| 0.035 | 27.62 | 28.94 | 30.25 | 31.56 | 32.85 |
| 0.030 | 28.19 | 29.52 | 30.84 | 32.15 | 33.46 |
| 0.025 | 28.84 | 30.19 | 31.52 | 32.85 | 34.16 |
| 0.020 | 29.63 | 30.99 | 32.34 | 33.68 | 35.01 |
| 0.015 | 30.62 | 32.01 | 33.38 | 34.74 | 36.09 |
| 0.010 | 32.00 | 33.40 | 34.80 | 36.19 | 37.56 |
| 0.005 | 34.26 | 35.71 | 37.15 | 38.58 | 39.99 |
| 0.001 | 39.25 | 40.78 | 42.31 | 43.81 | 45.31 |
| <0.001 | >39.25 | >40.78 | >42.31 | >43.81 | >45.31 |

# Answers to Selected Odd-Numbered Exercises

## Chapter 1

**1.1** Descriptive statistics is made up of those methods whose purpose is to organize and summarize the values in a data set. Inferential statistics refers to those procedures whose purpose is to allow conclusions to be drawn about a population based on information from a sample.

**1.3** A sample; the proportions were calculated from only the travelers who answered the poll.

**1.5** The population is the entire student body—15,000 students. The sample consists of the 200 students interviewed.

**1.7** The population consists of all single-family homes in Northridge. The sample consists of the 100 homes selected for inspection.

**1.9** The population consists of all 5000 bricks in the lot. The sample consists of the 100 bricks selected for inspection

**1.11 a.** categorical **b.** categorical **c.** numerical (discrete) **d.** numerical (continuous) **e.** categorical **f.** numerical (continuous)

**1.13 a.** continuous **b.** continuous **c.** continuous **d.** discrete

**1.15 a.** Gender, Brand, and Telephone Area Code. **b.** Number of previous motorcycles owned. **c.** Bar chart. **d.** Dotplot

**1.17** The most common single type of identity theft complaint is credit card fraud, with 28% of all complaints. Utility fraud and Bank fraud are the next most common at 19% and 18% respectively.

**1.21** For both sports, there are few universities where the overall graduation rate is lower than that of the scholarship athletes. At the schools where athletes do better than the overall rate, there are more schools where the basketball players do well; however, there are some schools where the basketball players graduate at a much poorer rate than overall.

**1.23 a.** Two-thirds of the beaches are rated B or above. **b.** No.

**1.27** Most business schools have acceptance rates between 15% and 40%. There are three schools that have acceptance rates of more than 40%.

**1.31.** The 20 observations are quite spread out. There is a gap that separates the three smallest and the three largest values from the rest of the data.

## Chapter 2

**2.1 a.** It is an observational study because a treatment was not imposed. **b.** No, cause-and-effect conclusions cannot be made on the basis of an observational study.

**2.3** Better educated, wealthier, and more active people tend to have better health care and look after themselves better, which may give alternative reasons for reduced risk of heart disease.

**2.5** No cause-and-effect conclusion can be made on the basis of an observational study.

**2.7 a.** The definition of affluent Americans was having a household income of over $75,000 and the sample was a simple random sample. **b.** No. This sample is not representative of all Americans.

**2.9** No, it is an observational study. Cause-and-effect conclusions cannot be made on the basis of an observational study.

**2.11** The names appear on the petition in a list ordered from first to last. Using a computer random number generator, select 30 random numbers between 1 and 500. Signatures corresponding to the 30 selected numbers constitute the random sample.

**2.13** Stratified sampling would be worthwhile if, within the resulting strata, the elements are more homogeneous than the population as a whole.
**a.** As one's class standing changes, courses may become more technical and books may become more costly. Therefore, stratifying would be worthwhile. **b.** The cost of books may be dependent on the field of study. Therefore, stratifying would be worthwhile. **c.** There is no reason to believe that the amount spent on books is related to the first letter in the last name of a student. Therefore, it is doubtful that stratifying would be worthwhile.

**2.15 a.** Cluster sampling **b.** Stratified random sampling **c.** Convenience sampling **d.** Simple random sample **e.** Systematic sampling

**2.17** Using a convenience sample may introduce selection bias. Suppose you wanted to know the average heights of students in all Stats classes, and used the students in a 10:00 class as subjects. It may be that all the basketball players (that are generally tall) are in the 10:00 class because they have a 7:00 A.M. practice.

**2.19 a.** Using a random number generator, create three-digit numbers. The three digits represent the page number, and the number of correctly defined words can be counted. Suppose we want to choose 10 pages in the book. Repeat this process until 10 page numbers are selected and count the number of words on each page. **b.** As the number of words on a page may be influenced by which topic is being discussed, it makes sense to stratify by chapter. To sample three pages in each chapter, generate a two-digit number to select a page within the chapter and repeat until three pages are chosen. Count the number of defined words on those pages and repeat for each chapter. **c.** Choose the 10th page and then every 15th page after that. **d.** Randomly choose one chapter and count the words on each page in that chapter.

**2.21** Randomization is used in selecting the households and available subjects in each family. However, it will eliminate households without a phone. It may be that the person who has recently had a birthday may be busy or too grumpy to talk to someone and someone else (who may not be of voting age) responds to the questions. Someone may lie and give responses that are not true.

**2.23** This was a small sample of people who chose to attend the workshop and were interested in dealing with the city's financial aid deficit. They are probably not representative of the population of interest.

**2.25** No, it is a volunteer sample with no random selection. There is no reason to think the sample is representative of U.S. adults. Volunteers may have had a reason to be worried about mercury contamination.

**2.27** It is possible that different subpopulations used the web site and the telephone. The different ways of responding may have attracted different types of people, and it is possible that neither group is representative of the town's residents.

**2.29** The best method to use would be a simple random sample where every different sample has an equal chance of being selected. For example, numbering every student in your school and randomly selecting a sample of them, finding them and asking them their opinion.

**2.31** The response variable is the amount of time it takes a car to exit the parking space. Extraneous factors that may affect the response variable could include: location of the parking spaces, time of day, and normal driving behaviors of individuals such as whether they have children in the car.

**2.33 a.** Select a random sample of students from the school. Choose two comparable IQ tests, Test 1 and Test 2. Randomly assign subjects to one of two groups and administer Test 1 to the first group and Test 2 to the second group. Record the IQ scores for each student. Now gather all the students in the same room and let them listen to a Mozart piano sonata. This time administer Test 2 to the first group and Test 1 to the second group. Again, record the IQ scores for each student. **b.** This design includes direct control for several extraneous variables. Two IQ tests were used to eliminate the possibility that retaking the same test may make the test easier the second time, possibly resulting in higher scores —the effect of retaking the same test may be confounded with the effects of the piano sonata. This design was chosen to eliminate the possibility that one test is more difficult than the other. All the students in the sample listened to the sonata in the same room, at the same time and under the same conditions, therefore the factor "listening conditions" can be ruled out as a confounding factor. **c.** This design has "student" as a blocking factor. Each student's IQ test score was recorded before and after listening to the Mozart sonata. This design should block out the effects of differences in IQ scores across students. **d.** By randomly selecting the sample and randomly placing students into two groups, we expect to create "equivalent" experimental groups.

**2.35 a.** Blocking. Homogeneous groups were formed by height. **b.** Direct control. The researchers only used right-handed people.

**2.37** Many other factors could have contributed to the difference in the pregnancy rate. The only way that these other factors could be ruled out as a plausible explanation for the difference between the two groups is if there was random assignment to the two experimental groups.

**2.39** Gender is a useful blocking variable if men and women of the same status tend to differ with respect to "rate of talk." Blocking on gender would make it easier to assess the effect of status on rate of talk.

**2.41** Blinding is a good strategy because people may have their own personal beliefs about the effectiveness of various treatments and their response can be influenced by their personal perception.

**2.43 a.** It is important to have comparable groups. It may be that people who have a mellow personality (and include the physical characteristics of positive attitude, lower blood pressure, and using fewer laxatives) enjoy art and so if they were allowed to choose groups they would all go and discuss works of art. The two groups should be equivalent. **b.** A control group is needed for comparison. It may be the social aspect of meeting other people that makes the physical changes so a control provides a basis for comparison that allows the researcher to determine if the discussion of art is really what is affecting the women.

**2.45** If either the dog handlers or the experimenters knew which patients had cancer, they might give physical clues (consciously or unconsciously) or simply be rooting for the dog to be successful.

**2.47 a.** No, the judges probably believed that a fancy seafood restaurant would have better chowder than Denny's and this may have influenced the rating. **b.** So that the judging is fair!

**2.49 a.** Randomly divide into two groups of 50, one group gets PH50 and the other group gets a placebo nasal spray. They are assessed before and after the treatment and any improvement in PMS symptoms measured. **b.** A placebo treatment is needed to see if any improvement is due to PH50 rather than any other influence that occurs during the time of testing. **c.** Single-blinding is strongly recommended.

**2.57 a.** It is an observational study; no treatment was imposed. **b.** If a child has attention disorder at a young age, parents who may find life difficult may be more likely to let the child watch TV so they could have a break. The watching of TV wouldn't be causing the disorder, he or she would be watching TV because of the disorder!

**2.59** If we are considering all people 12 years of age or older, there are probably more single people that are young, and more widowed people that are old. It tends to be the young who are at higher risk of being victims of violent crimes (for instance, staying out late at night). Hence, age could be a potential confounding variable.

**2.61** Any survey conducted by mail is subject to selection bias (eliminating anyone without an address) and nonresponse bias (only a few people reply).

**2.63** Consider each of the basic concepts of designing an experiment. Replication: Each of the eight actors was watched on tape by many of the primary care doctors. Direct control: The actors wore identical gowns, used identical gestures, were taped from the same position and used identical scripts. Blocking: Not used. Randomization: The article does not indicate if the 720 doctors were randomly divided into 8 groups of 90 doctors and each group randomly assigned to watch one of the actors on tape, but it is reasonable to assume this was done. This design appears to be good because it employs many of the key concepts in designing an experiment. One possible improvement would be to randomly select the 720 primary care doctors from the entire population of primary care doctors so that we can generalize our results of the study to the whole population.

**2.65 a.** Gender, age, weight, lean body mass, and capacity to lift weights were all dealt with by direct control. **b.** Yes. Knowing whether they were receiving creatine might have influenced the effort a subject put into his workout. **c.** Yes, especially if the trainer is the one taking the measurements. If the trainer knows which men are receiving creatine, it might influence the way in which he works with the subjects.

**2.67 a.** There are two treatments in this experiment—standing or squatting—and the response variable is "amount of tip." **b.** Extraneous factors include table location and how busy the restaurant is. **c.** Blocking could be used to control for these factors. For instance, one could separately evaluate the differences in tip received between squatting and standing during busy hours and during slow hours. There are several other factors that could also be used for blocking. Time of day, smoking vs. nonsmoking sections and table location are a few possibilities. **d.** There are other factors, such as economic status, that might affect response. **e.** Randomization (flipping the coin to determine which treatment is received), evens out the potential effects of other extraneous factors.

**2.69** The response variable is whether a tile is cracked or not. Since two different firings will not have exactly the same temperature, tiles made from each type of clay should be fired together. Fifty tiles of each type could be used per firing. Since temperature varies within the oven, the oven could be divided into sections (blocks) where the temperature is the same within a section, but perhaps differs between sections. Then, tiles made from each clay type should be placed within the sections. The positions of the tiles within a section should be determined in a random fashion.

## Chapter 3

**3.3** The majority of Americans did not move. Of those who moved, most stayed in the same county. The bar chart allows for easier comparison of the category frequencies.

**3.7 b.** The pass rate increased each year for San Luis Obispo High School and the State of California from 2002 to 2004 with a sharp rise in 2004. However, in San Luis Obispo County, there was a drop in the pass rate in 2003, followed by a sharp increase in 2004 when a pass in the exam was needed for graduation.

**3.9 b.** For both age groups, females are more unfit than the overall age group, and men are less unfit. However, this difference is much less marked in adolescents who on the whole are much more unfit than their older counterparts.

**3.11 a.** The proportion of Christmas shoppers who are "very likely" or "somewhat likely" to use the internet has increased from 2000 to 2002, and the proportion who are "not too likely" or "not at all likely" has decreased. However it should be noted that the vast majority of Christmas shoppers (71%) are hesitant to do their Christmas shopping on-line. **b.** The proportion of people who felt strongly about mail order catalogues ("very likely" or "not at all likely") increased over the two-year period while the proportion of those who weren't too sure decreased.

**3.13 a.** There are too many categories for this pie chart to be effective. **b.** The bar chart is much more effective than the pie chart. It is very easy to compare the hazards, even for the categories that have small percentages.

**3.15 b.** The distribution is skewed to the right with most of the states having values at the lower end of the scale. Forty out of the 50 states have fewer than 1,500,000 people who have smoked in the past month. There are some outliers at the high end of the distribution. **c.** No, it does not indicate that tobacco is necessarily a problem in these states. NY, CA, and TX are the three most heavily populated states in the United States and even if they have the same proportion of smokers as others states, they will have a higher *number* of smokers because of the greater population. **d.** No, it would be better to use the proportion of the population of each state that smoked during the past month. That way, the population of the state would not affect the result.

**3.17**

| | Calorie Content (cal/100ml) of 26 Brands of Light Beer |
|---|---|
| 1L | |
| 1H | 9 |
| 2L | 123 |
| 2H | 78899 |
| 3L | 00111223345 |
| 3H | 9 |
| 4L | 0123 |
| 4H | |

stem: tens
leaf: ones

**3.19 a.**

| Very Large Urban Areas | | Large Urban Areas |
|---|---|---|
| | 1 | 023478 |
| | 2 | 369 |
| 8 | 3 | 0033589 |
| 99 | 4 | 0366 |
| 1178 | 5 | 012355 |
| 0379 | 6 | |
| 2 | 7 | |
| | 8 | |
| 3 | 9 | |

stem: tens
leaves: ones

**b.** Not necessarily. Philadelphia is a larger urban area than Riverside, CA, but has less extra travel time. However, *overall,* taking into account all the urban areas mentioned, or if we were to calculate the average or typical value for each type of area, then we would find that *on the whole,* the larger the urban area, the greater the extra travel time.

**3.21**

| | High School Drop-Out Rates 1997–1999 by State | |
|---|---|---|
| 0f | 555 | |
| 0s | 666667777777 | stem: tens |
| 0* | 88888889999999999 | leaf: ones |
| 1. | 00011111 | |
| 1t | 22223333 | |
| 1f | | |
| 1s | 77 | |

**3.23 c.** The results for both the survey and the credit bureau show that most college student debt is less than $2000. However, the results don't agree exactly; the credit card bureau had more students with very large debt than the survey data suggested. Maybe some of the students with very large debts were reluctant to admit to the scale of their problems! **d.** Only 132 out of 1260 students replied, an 89.5% nonresponse rate. It may be that students with a large debt would be reluctant to respond, so this sample was not representative of all students.

**3.25 a.** Most men average between 0 and 200 mins a month. Far fewer average between 400 and 800 mins a month. **b.** The distribution for men and women is similar in that most women average between 0 and 200 mins as do men. Fewer women average 600 to 800 minutes than men. **c.** 0.74 **d.** 0.79 **e.** 0.1775

**3.27 a.**

| 0 | 360, 340, 960, 530, 540, 960, 450, 500, 100, 510, 240, 396 |
|---|---|
| 1 | 280, 240, 050, 000, 320, 250, 120, 850, 670, 890, 419 |
| 2 | 100, 400, 120, 250, 320, 400, 460, 700, 730, 109 |
| 3 | 060, 330, 380, 350, 870, 150, 150 |
| 4 | 390, 770 |
| 5 | 320, 700, 220, 850, 770 |

stem: thousands
leaf: hundreds, tens and ones

The stem-and-leaf display suggests that a typical or representative value is in the stem 2 row, perhaps around 2230. There are no gaps in the display. The shape of the display is not symmetric.

**3.29 a.** Negatively skewed **b.** Positively skewed **c.** Bimodal.

**3.31 b.** .06 **c.** .26

**3.33 i.** Symmetric **ii.** Positively skewed **iii.** Bimodal and approximately symmetric **iv.** Bimodal **v.** Negatively skewed.

**3.35 a.** The graft weight ratio tends to decrease as recipient body weight increases, but the relationship does not look linear.

**3.37 a.** There is a tendency for $y$ to increase as $x$ does. That is, larger values of gross efficiency tend to be associated with larger values of percentage type I fibers (a positive relationship between the variables). **b.** There are several observations that have identical $x$-values yet different $y$-values; the value of $y$ is *not* determined solely by $x$.

**3.39** There are several observations that have identical or nearly identical $x$-values yet different $y$-values. Therefore, the value of $y$ is not determined solely by x, but also by various other factors. There appears to be a general tendency for $y$ to decrease in value as $x$ increases in value. There are two data points that are far removed from the remaining data points.

**3.41 b.** There has been an increase in the ownership of computers over time since 1985. At first the increase was slow and then from 1995 ownership has been increasing at a more rapid rate.

**3.43 c.** The time-series plot gives a better trend over time as it shows a time scale, which the bar chart does not.

**3.45** In both 2001 and 2002 the box office sales dropped in Weeks 2 and 6 and in the last two weeks of the summer. The seasonal peaks occurred during Weeks 4, 9, and 13.

**3.47** For those students who have English as a first language there is very little difference between the average Verbal and Math scores. For students who speak English and another language, they do less well in both subjects, but it is more noticeable in the Verbal scores. Those students who speak a language other than English as their first language score on average about 55 points less than those who speak only English. However, their average Math scores are as high as the English only speaking students.

**3.51 b.** The time-series plots from Part (a) do agree with the statement. It is clear from the first graph that the actual expenditure has been increasing. Although the percentage of household expenditure looks volatile, in the 10 years of this study, it has varied from 14.9% to 17.2%, and is small compared with the increase in actual expenditure.

**3.53 c.** It's much easier to compare the differences using the comparative bar chart. The categories are next to each other and any difference is easy to see. Comparing the size of the slice for two pie charts is more difficult. **d.** The majority of both men and women think that men earn more money for the same work. Very few men or women think that a woman earns more. More women than men think that a man earns more or earns the same as woman.

**3.55 a.** Given the choice, most people don't care whether they work for a man or a woman. Of those that do have an opinion, most would prefer to have a male boss.

**3.59**

```
0 | 675890050
1 | 861521670631228431808 7877
2 | 56907869061971
3 | 7550001505
4 | 5678230
5 |
6 | 71              stem: tens
7 | 0               leaf: ones
```

The data values are concentrated between 0 and 40, with a few larger values. Overall, the plot appears to be skewed to the right.

**3.63 a.** For the first histogram, it appears that more frozen meals have sodium content around 800 mg. However, the second histogram suggests that sodium content is fairly uniform from 300 mg to 900 mg and then drops off above 900 mg. **b.** Using the first histogram, the proportion of observations that are less than 800 is approximately .667. Using the second histogram, the proportion of observations that are less than 800 is also approximately .667.

## Chapter 4

**4.1** Mean = 970.7, median = 738. They are different because outliers at the high end of the data set influence the mean more than the median.

**4.3 b.** Mean = 3.654%, median = 3.35% **c.** An 8% trimmed mean will drop the outlier of 10.1%; the 8% trimmed mean will be smaller than the mean.

**4.5 a.** Mean = 448.3 fatalities. **b.** Median = 446 fatalities. **c.** These 20 days had the highest number of fatalities; it is not a random sample of the 365 days of the year and cannot be used to generalize to the rest of the year.

**4.7 a.** No, we have no knowledge of the costs of any intermediate plans. **b.** The number of plans is not given in the data set. **c.** Iowa, Minnesota, Montana, Nebraska, North and South Dakota, and Wyoming. **d.** Florida. **e.** Alaska. **f.** $9.0925

**4.9** Expensive houses do not pull the median price up. Sales of very expensive houses will increase the mean price, just as the sales of inexpensive very low-priced homes will decrease the mean price. If there are more sales of either very high- or very low-priced homes, this will affect the median price.

More higher priced sales than lower priced sales, the median increases; more lower priced sales, the median price decreases.

**4.11** 32

**4.13** Median = 68; 20%, trimmed mean = 66.17

**4.15** $s^2 = 1.70$, $s = 1.3038$

**4.17** It would have a large standard deviation. Some parents would spend much more than the average and some parents would either not be able to afford to spend that much (or not be willing to) or would rather spread it over the school year.

**4.19 a.** $s = 50.058$ **b.** Smaller. There is less variability in the data for Memorial Day. **c.** There is less variability for holidays that always occur on the same days of the week. Memorial Day, Labor Day, and Thanksgiving Day have standard deviations of 18.2, 17.7, and 15.3 respectively whereas New Year's Day, July 4th and Christmas Day have standard deviations of 50.1, 47.1, and 52.4.

**4.21 a.** The sample size for Los Osos and Morro Bay are different so the average for the combined areas is $\dfrac{(606456)(114) + (511866)(123)}{(114 + 123)}$.
**b.** Because Paso Robles has the bigger range of values, it is likely to have the larger standard deviation. **c.** Because the difference in the high prices is so much greater than the difference in the low prices, it would suggest that the distribution of house prices in Paso Robles is right skewed and the mean price is higher than the median suggesting the median would be lower in Paso Robles than in Grover Beach.

**4.23** $1,961,158

**4.25** 1st quartile = 10478, 3rd quartile = 11778, interquartile range = 1300

**4.27 a.** 1st quartile = 51, 3rd quartile = 69, interquartile range = 18. **b.** The iqr for inpatient cost-to-charge ratio in Example 4.9 is 14. There is more variability in cost-to-charge ratios for outpatient services.

**4.29 a.** The mean (22.4) is greater than the median (18); the distribution is more likely to be positively skewed. **c.** The maximum (205) is more than 3 times the interquartile range ($3 \times 24 = 72$) above the upper quartile. Therefore, there is at least one extreme outlier.

**4.31 a.** Mean = 59.85 hours, median = 55.0 hours. As the mean is greater than the median, the distribution is likely to be skewed to the right.

**4.33 a.** The mean blood lead level (4.93) is higher than the median (3.6). This is due to the unusually large values in the data set.

**4.35 a.** Excited delirium: median = 0.4, Q1 = 0.1, Q3 = 2.8, iqr = 2.7 No Excited Delirium: median = 1.6, Q1 = 0.3, Q3 = 7.9, iqr = 7.6 **b.** There are two mild and two extreme outliers for the Excited Delirium sample. There are no outliers in the No Excited Delirium sample.

**4.37 a.** Approximately 68% **b.** Approximately 16%

**4.39 a.** At least 75% **b.** (2.90, 70.94) **c.** If the distribution of $NO_2$ values was normal, approximately 2.5% of the values would be less than $-9.64$ (two standard deviations below the mean). Since $NO_2$ concentration can't be negative, the distribution shape must not resemble a normal curve.

**4.41** The $z$ score is larger for the second exam, so performance was better on the second exam.

**4.43 a.** Approximately 68% **b.** Approximately 5% **c.** Approximately 13.5% **d.** Because the histogram is well approximated by a normal curve.

**4.45** The proportion is at most 0.16.

**4.47** One standard deviation below the mean is a negative number and the number of answers changed from right to wrong cannot be negative. Therefore, the distribution cannot be well described by a normal curve. From Chebyshev's Rule, the proportion who changed at least six answers from right to wrong is at most 0.106

**4.49 b. i.** 13.158  **ii.** 16.25  **iii.** 6.923  **iv.** 21  **v.** 11.842.
**4.51** The supervisors will be paid the median: $4286. The mean (more favorable to the taxpayers): $3968.67.
**4.53 a.** The mean is $1,110,766, which is larger than the median, which is $275,000. There are probably a few baseball players who earn a lot of money (in the millions of dollars) while the bulk of baseball players earn in the hundreds of thousands of dollars. The outliers have a greater influence on the mean value making the value larger than the median.
**b.** If the population was all 1995 salaries and all the salaries were used to compute the mean then the reported mean was the population mean $\mu$.
**4.55 a.** 48.364  **b.** $s^2 = 327.05$, $s = 18.08$
**4.57** $s = 180.846$, The standard deviation for the new data set is 10 times larger than the standard deviation for the original data set.
**4.59 a.** Median = 20.88, Quartile 1 = 18.09, Quartile 3 = 22.20
**b.** Interquartile range = 4.11; there are two outliers, 35.78 and 36.73.
**c.** Most of the subjects have an oxygen capacity of between 20 and 25 mL/kg/min. There are two subjects with much higher oxygen capacities of over 35 mL/kg/min.
**4.61 a.** $\bar{x} = 192.57$, median = 189  **b.** $\bar{x} = 189.71$, median = 189 (unchanged)  **c.** 191, 7.14% trimmed mean  **d.** If the largest observation is 204, new trimmed mean = 185. If the largest observation is 284, the trimmed mean is the same as in (c).
**4.63** The median line is not at the center of the box so there is a slight asymmetry in the middle half of the data. The upper whisker is slightly longer than the lower whisker. There is one extreme outlier, 511.
**4.65** The median franchise cost is about the same for each type of hotel. The variability of franchise cost differs substantially for the three types. With the exception of a couple of outliers, first-class hotels vary very little in the cost of franchises, while budget hotels vary a great deal in regard to franchise costs. Ignoring the outliers, the distribution of franchise costs for first-class hotels is quite symmetric; midrange hotels have a distribution of franchise costs that is slightly skewed to the right; while budget hotels have a distribution of franchise costs that is skewed to the left.
**4.67** Since the mean is larger than the median, this suggests that the distribution of values is positively skewed or has some outliers with very large values.
**4.69 a.** 120  **b.** 20  **c.** $-0.5$  **d.** 97.5  **e.** The value 40 is three standard deviations below the mean, so only about .5(.3%) or .15% of the scores are below 40. There would not be many scores below 40.

## Chapter 5

**5.1 a.** positive  **b.** negative  **c.** positive  **d.** no correlation  **e.** positive  **f.** positive  **g.** negative  **h.** no correlation
**5.5 a.** $r = 0.94$ The correlation is strong and positive.  **b.** Increasing sugar consumption doesn't cause or lead to higher rates of depression, it may be another reason that causes an increase in both. For instance, a high sugar consumption may indicate a need for comfort food for a reason that also causes depression.  **c.** These countries may not be representative of any other countries. It may be that only these countries have a strong positive correlation between sugar consumption and depression rate and other countries may have a different type of relationship between these factors. It is therefore not a good idea to generalize these results to other countries.
**5.7** Strong and positive.
**5.9 a.** $r = 0.335$. There is a weak positive relationship between timber sales and the amount of acres burned in forest fires.  **b.** No. Correlation does not imply a causal relationship.
**5.11 a.** There appears to be a strong, positive correlation.  **b.** $r = 0.9366$ indicates a strong positive linear relationship.  **c.** If $x$ and $y$ had

a correlation coefficient of 1, all the points would lie on a straight line, but the line would not necessarily have slope 1 and intercept 0.
**5.13** $r = 0.39$; there is a weak positive linear relationship.
**5.15** No. An $r$ value of $-0.085$ indicates, at best, a very weak relationship between support for environmental spending and degree of belief.
**5.17 a.** There appears to be a weak negative relationship.  **b.** $\hat{y} = 1082.24 - 4.691x$  **c.** Negative, consistent with description.  **d.** No, relationship is negative.
**5.19 a.** The dependent variable is the number of fruit and vegetable servings per day. The independent variable is the number of hours of TV viewed per day.  **b.** Negative, because as the number of hours of TV watched *increases*, the number of servings of fruit and vegetables *decreases*.
**5.21 b.** $r = .7863$  **c.** $\hat{y} = 714.145 + 42.521x$  **d.** 790.68  **e.** The least-squares line was calculated using values of $z$-scores of between $-0.75$ and 2.8 and therefore is only valid for values in this range.
**5.23 a.** There appears to be a positive relationship between the percentages of public school students who were at or above proficient level in mathematics in the 4th grade in 1996 and in the 8th grade in 2000. There are 2 states with slightly unusual results: CA and UT.  **b.** $\hat{y} = -3.14 + 1.52x$  **c.** The predicted value of 18 is lower than the reported value of 20.
**5.25 a.** Yes. As the carbonation depth increases, the strength of the concrete decreases.  **b.** $\hat{y} = 24.39 - 0.275x$  **c.** 17.5  **d.** The least-squares line was calculated using values of "depth" of between 8 mm and 65 mm and therefore is only valid for values in this range.
**5.27** slope = $-4000$
**5.29 a.** $\hat{y} = 59.910 + 27.462x$  **b.** 554.234  **c.** No, because the data used to obtain the least-squares equation was from steeply sloped plots, so it would not make sense to use it to predict runoff sediment from gradually sloped plots. You would need to use data from gradually sloped plots to create a least-squares regression equation to predict runoff sediment from gradually sloped plots.
**5.31 a.** The graph shows a moderately-positive linear relationship between chest capacity and vital capacity.  **c.** 0.113, 1.13  **d.** 4.9994  **e.** No—there are 2 data points whose $x$-values are 81.8 but they have different $y$-values.
**5.33 a.** $100 + 1.5$(standard deviation)  **b.** $r = 0.67$
**5.35 a.** $\hat{y} = -424.7 + 3.891x$  **b.** Both the slope and the $y$ intercept are changed by the multiplicative factor $c$.
**5.37 b.** There are 3 points with large residuals, those points with $x$-values of 40, 50, and 60.  **c.** The residuals for small $x$-values and large $x$-values are positive, while the residuals for the middle $x$-values are negative.
**5.39 a.** $\hat{y} = 94.33 - 15.388x$  **b.** There is a curved pattern in the plot, suggesting the linear model may not be appropriate.
**5.41 a.** 15.4%  **b.** No. $r^2 = 16\%$, so only 16% of the observed variation in first year college grades can be attributed to the approximate linear relationship between first year college grades and SAT II score. The least-squares line does not effectively summarize the relationship between SAT score and first year college grades.
**5.43 a.** There does appear to be a positive linear relationship between rainfall volume and runoff volume.  **b.** slope = 0.827, intercept = $-1.13$  **c.** 65.03  **d.** For small values of $x$, the residuals are relatively small in size. For the larger values of $x$, the residuals are much larger, creating a fan-shape pattern in the residual plot. This indicates that a linear regression may not be appropriate.
**5.45 a.** $\hat{y} = 914.5$, residual = $-21.5$  **b.** The typical amount that average SAT score deviates from the least squares line is 53.7.  **c.** Only about 16% of the observed variation in average SAT scores can be

attributed to the approximate linear relationship between average SAT scores and expenditure per pupil.

**5.47 a.** Yes, there is a reasonably strong linear relationship. **b.** The least-squares equation with the point deleted is $\hat{y} = 5.1151 - .0333x$. The deletion of this point does not greatly affect the equation of the line. For the full data set, the least squares line is $\hat{y} = 5.20683 - .03421x$. The deletion of this point does not have a large effect. **c.** For the full data set, $r^2 = .8829$. For the data set with the point $(143, .3)$ deleted, $r^2 = .6774$. The value of $r^2$ becomes smaller when the point $(143, 0.3)$ is deleted. The reason for this is that in the equation $r^2 = 1 - $ SSResid/SSTo, the value of SSTo is lowered by dropping the point $(143, 0.3)$ but the value of SSResid remains about the same.

**5.49 a.** $-20.8$ **b.** $r = -.755$ **c.** $11.64$

**5.51 a.** When $r = 0$, then $s_e = s_y$. The least squares line in this case is a horizontal line with intercept of $\bar{y}$. **b.** When $r$ is close to 1 in absolute value, then $s_e$ will be much smaller than $s_y$. **c.** $1.5$ **d.** $\hat{y} = 7.92 + .544x$, $s_e = 1.02$

**5.53 b.** Figure 5.31 suggests moving $x$ up or $y$ down; one reasonable choice is $y' = 1/y$. **e.** $\hat{y}' = 5.20683 - .03421x$, $\hat{y} = 1.91$

**5.55 a.** $r = -0.717$ **b.** $r = -0.835$ for the transformed data

**5.57 a.** non-linear **b.** $\hat{y} = 22.48 + 34.36x$. The curved pattern in residual plot confirms that the relationship is non-linear. **c.** The value of $r^2$ is higher and the residuals are smaller for the log transformation. **d.** $\hat{y} = 62.417 + 101.07\log(x)$ **e.** $87.0, 52.6$

**5.59 a.** The plot does show a positive relationship. **b.** The plot appears straighter, but the variability of $y$ increases as $x$ increases. **c.** The plot also looks linear, but the variability in $y$ does not appear to be increasing with $x$. **d.** The plot has a curvature in the opposite direction as the plot in part (a).

**5.61** $\ln\left(\dfrac{p}{1-p}\right) = 4.589 - 0.0659x$; $0.876$

**5.63 a.** less common **b.** $\ln\left(\dfrac{p}{1-p}\right) = 7.537 - 0.0079x$ **c.** $0.632$

**5.65 b.** $\ln\left(\dfrac{p}{1-p}\right) = -3.579 - 0.0397x$; a positive slope indicates that as the load increases, the proportion failing increases. **c.** $0.232$ **d.** $15.5$

**5.67 a.** $\hat{y} = 0.3651 + 0.9668x$ **b.** $0.8485$

**5.69** $r^2 = .6561$; 65.61% of the variability in age is explained by the linear relationship. $s_e = 13.27$; a typical prediction error is approximately 13.27.

**5.71 a.** $\hat{y} = 94.33 - 15.38x$ **b.** SSTo $= 5534.62$, SSResid $= 285.82$ **c.** 94.84% **d.** $s_e = 5.346$ **e.** $-.974$

**5.73 a.** weak linear relationship **b.** $.0121$

**5.75 a.** $\hat{y} = 13.9617 + 3.1703x$ **b.** The relationship may be better described by a curve. **c.** $34.5687$ **d.** No, relationship appears to be nonlinear and 18 is outside the range of the $x$ values in the data set.

**5.77 b.** $\hat{y} = 5.55 + 2.1975x$ **c.** $r = .5815$; moderate positive linear relationship

## Chapter 6

**6.1 a.** In the long run, 1% of all people who suffer cardiac arrest in New York City will survive. **b.** 23 or 24

**6.3** Dependent; the probability that a U.S. adult experiences pain daily is higher if the adult selected is a woman.

**6.5** They are dependent.

**6.7** They are dependent.

**6.9 a.** .7; assumed that whether Jeanie remembers any one errand is independent of whether she remembers any of the other errands. **b.** .5 **c.** .714286

**6.11 a.** The expert assumed that the positions of the two valves were independent. **b.** Larger, the actual probability is 1/12.

**6.13 a.** .81 **b.** .19, .19 **c.** .0361, .9639 **d.** .993141 **e.** .926559

**6.15** The ultrasound predicts females with a success rate of $432/562 = 0.769$ and males with a success rate of $390/438 = 0.890$, suggesting that an ultrasound has a better success rate at predicting boys.

**6.17** $60/96 = 0.625$ of current smokers view smoking as very harmful compared to $78/99 = 0.7878$ for former smokers and $86/99 = 0.8687$ for those who have never smoked. The proportion who view smoking as harmful is certainly less for current smokers.

**6.19 a.** .85 **b.** .19 **c.** .6889 **d.** .87

**6.21 a.** .3941 **b.** .1765 **c.** .0529 **d.** .3412

**6.23** The simulation results will vary from one simulation to another. The following probabilities were obtained from a computer simulation with 100,000 trials. **a.** .71293 **b.** .02201

**6.25** The simulation results will vary from one simulation to another. The approximate probability should be about .8504.

**6.27 a.** The simulation results will vary from one simulation to another. The approximate probability should be about .6504. **b.** The decrease in the probability of on-time completion for Jacob made the biggest change in the probability that the project is completed on time.

**6.29 a.** .0155 **b.** .0823 **c.** .1359 **d.** Assumption of independence is reasonable.

**6.31 a.** .40 **b.** .81 **c.** .94

**6.33 a.** .00243 **b.** .00275

## Chapter 7

**7.1 a.** Discrete. **b.** Continuous. **c.** Discrete. **d.** Discrete. **e.** Continuous.

**7.3 b.** .4

**7.5 b.** $x = 0$, because its probability is the largest. **c.** .25 **d.** .55

**7.7 a.** .82 **b.** .18 **c.** .65, .27

**7.9 a.** The distribution for Supplier 1. **b.** The distribution for Supplier 2. **c.** Supplier 1, because the bulbs generally last longer and the lifetime is less variable. **d.** About 1000.

**7.13 b.** .5, .125, .125 **c.** .375 **d.** .4375

**7.15 a.** Height $= 2$ **b.** 1/4 **c.** 7/16

**7.17 a.** .1003 **b.** .1003 **c.** .8185 **d.** .5 **e.** 1 **f.** .9390 **g.** .5910

**7.19 a.** .5398 **b.** .4602 **c.** .1469 **d.** .1469 **e.** .4577 **f.** .8944 **g.** .0730

**7.21 a.** 1.88 **b.** 2.33 **c.** $-1.75$ **d.** $-1.28$

**7.23 a.** 1.34 **b.** 0.74 **c.** 0 **d.** $-1.34$ **e.** They are negatives of one another.

**7.25 a.** .119, .6969 **b.** .0021 **c.** .7019 **d.** Weights less than 1836 g or weights greater than 5012 g. **e.** The same answer is obtained.

**7.27** The second machine.

**7.29** 94.4 sec or less.

**7.31 a.** .5, .5 **b.** .8185 **c.** Yes, the probability is about .0013. **d.** .0252 **e.** 47.4 or less words per minute.

**7.33** Because this plot appears to look like a straight line, it is reasonable to conclude that a normal distribution provides an adequate description of the steam rate distribution.

**7.35** Because the graph exhibits a curve, we cannot conclude that the variable *component lifetime* is adequately modeled by a normal distribution.

**7.37** Although the graph seems to follow a straight line for values of DDT concentration below 45 and above 45, they do not appear to be the *same* straight line. A normal distribution may not be an appropriate model for this population.

**7.39** The cube-root transformation is more symmetric.

**7.41 b.** The histogram is positively skewed. **c.** A square-root transformation will result in a more symmetric histogram.

**7.45** .0228, 0
**7.47 a.** No, only about 69.15% are shorter than 5 ft 7 in.
**b.** About 69%.
**7.49 a.** .7745   **b.** .1587   **c.** .3085   **d.** The largest 5% are those pH
readings that exceed 6.1645.
**7.51 a.** .8247   **b.** .0516   **c.** .6826   **d.** .0030   **e.** $P(x < 261) = .3783$.

## Chapter 8

**8.1** A statistic is computed from the observations in a sample, whereas
a population characteristic is a quantity that describes the whole
population.
**8.3 a.** Population characteristic   **b.** Statistic   **c.** Population characteristic   **d.** Statistic   **e.** Statistic
**8.7 c.** They are similar in that they are both symmetric about the population mean of 2.5. Also, both have largest probability at 2.5. They are
different in that the values in Part (a) cover a smaller range, 1.5 to 3.5,
than in Part (b), 1.0 to 4.0.
**8.9** Statistic #1 is the only one that is unbiased, but because it has a
large standard deviation, there is a good chance that an estimate would
be far away from the value of the population mean. For this population,
Statistic #3 may be a better choice because it is more likely to produce
an estimate that is close to the population mean.
**8.11** For $n = 36, 50, 100,$ and 400
**8.13 a.** $\mu_{\bar{x}} = 40 \; \sigma_{\bar{x}} = 0.625$, approximately normal.   **b.** 0.5762
**c.** 0.2628
**8.15 a.** $\mu_{\bar{x}} = 2, \sigma_{\bar{x}} = 0.267$   **b.** $n = 20: \mu_{\bar{x}} = 2, \sigma_{\bar{x}} = 0.179; n = 100:$
$\mu_{\bar{x}} = 2, \sigma_{\bar{x}} = 0.08$; a sample of size 100 would be most likely to result in
a value close to $\mu$.
**8.17 a.** 0.8185, 0.0013   **b.** 0.9772, 0
**8.19** 0.0026
**8.21** Approximately 0
**8.23 a.** 0.65, 0.1508   **b.** 0.65, 0.1067   **c.** 0.65, 0.0871   **d.** 0.65,
0.0675   **e.** 0.65, 0.0477   **f.** 0.65, 0.0337
**8.25 a.** $\mu_p = 0.07, \sigma_p = 0.0255$   **b.** No, because $n\pi < 10$.   **c.** If
$n = 200, \mu_p$ does not change, but $\sigma_p$ becomes 0.01804   **d.** Yes, $n\pi$
and $n(1 - \pi)$ are now both $>10$   **e.** 0.0485
**8.27 a.** $\mu_p = 0.005, \sigma_p = 0.007$   **b.** Since $n\pi < 10$, the sampling distribution of $p$ cannot be assumed to be approximated by a normal curve.
**c.** $n \geq 2000$
**8.29 a.** $\pi = 0.5: \mu_p = 0.5, \sigma_p = 0.0333, \pi = 0.6: \mu_p = 0.6, \sigma_p =$
$0.0327$; in both cases, the sampling distribution of $p$ is approximately
normal.   **b.** $\pi = 0.5: P(p \geq 0.6) = 0.0013, \pi = 0.6: P(p \geq 0.6) = 0.5$
**c.** The probability for $\pi = 0.5$ would decrease and the probability for
$\pi = 0.6$ would stay the same.
**8.31 a.** 0.9744   **b.** Approximately 0
**8.33 a.** Approximately normal with a mean of 50 lbs and a standard
deviation of 0.1 lb   **b.** 0.9876   **c.** 0.5
**8.35 a.** 0.8185   **b.** 0.9992
**8.37** 0.0786

## Chapter 9

**9.1** Statistic II because it is unbiased and it has a smaller variability than
the other two.
**9.3** 0.2769
**9.5** 0.70
**9.7 a.** 1.957   **b.** 0.15945   **c.** 0.3993, the statistic used is not an unbiased estimator.
**9.9 a.** $s = 1.886$   **b.** sample median $= 11.35$   **c.** One possibility
is a trimmed mean. An 8.3% trimmed mean $= 11.73$.   **d.** $11.967 +$
$(1.28)(1.886) = 14.31$

**9.11 a.** 95% confidence level   **b.** $n = 100$
**9.13 a.** Yes   **b.** No   **c.** No   **d.** No   **e.** Yes   **f.** Yes   **g.** Yes
**h.** No
**9.15 a.** (0.38, 0.46); we can be 99% confident that the true proportion of
adult Americans who made plans in May 2005 based on an incorrect
weather report is between .38 and .46.   **b.** No, weather reports may be
more or less reliable during other months.
**9.17 a.** (0.6598, 0.7402)   **b.** Wider
**9.19 a.** (0.2225, 0.2975)   **b.** The confidence level is lower and the estimated standard error is smaller.
**9.21** Bound on error $= 0.0238$
**9.23 a.** (0.2441, 0.4159)   **b.** (0.1307, 0.2513)   **c.** Increased confidence level in Part (a), increased sample proportion in Part (a).
**9.25** (0.2169, 0.4755); must assume that it is reasonable to regard this
sample as representative of young adults with pierced tongues.
**9.27** With $p = .25$ and $n = 1002$, the bound on error is
$$1.96\sqrt{\frac{(.25)(.75)}{1002}} \approx .03.$$
**9.29** 385
**9.31 a.** 2.12   **b.** 1.80   **c.** 2.81   **d.** 1.71   **e.** 1.78   **f.** 2.26
**9.33** (49.4, 50.6) is based on the larger sample size because the interval
is narrower.
**9.35** A 95% confidence interval is (262.045, 350.135). Other confidence
levels are possible.
**9.37** (26.72. 30.28); with a confidence level of 90%, we estimate the
mean daily commute time for working residents of Calgary to be between 26.72 min and 30.28 min.
**9.39 a.** (179.03, 186.97)   **b.** (185.44, 194.56)   **c.** The new FAA recommendations are above the upper bounds for both summer and winter.
**9.41 a.** (52.07, 56.33)   **b.** If we took many samples using this sampling
method and obtained confidence intervals from each of the samples, 90%
of them would capture the true mean airborne time for Flight 448.
**c.** 10:57 A.M.
**9.43** (0.874, 0.978)
**9.45** (5.77, 28.23)
**9.47** No. The sample size is small and there are two outliers in the data
set, indicating that the assumption of a normal population distribution is
not reasonable.
**9.49** 385
**9.51** 0.4596
**9.53** (0.586, 0.714) Yes, because the lower bound is greater than 0.5.
**9.55 a.** (20.558, 30.682)   **b.** (15.875, 20.325)   **c.** The sample size is
much larger.   **d.** Yes, the lower end of the confidence interval is greater
than 20.
**9.57** 385
**9.59** 166
**9.61 a.** (14.21, 16.99)   **b.** CBS: (10.51, 13.29), FOX: (10.31, 13.09),
NBC: (9.61, 12.39)   **c.** Yes
**9.63** (7.56, 11.84)
**9.65** 246
**9.67** (9.976, 11.824)
**9.69** 20.004
**9.71** (5.704, 6.696)
**9.73** (17.9, 25.9)

## Chapter 10

**10.1** $\bar{x}$ is a statistic and hypotheses are always expressed in terms of a
population characteristic.
**10.3** The burden of proof is placed on the contractor to show that the
mean weld strength is greater than 100 lb/in$^2$.

**10.5** Failing to reject the null hypothesis is not the same as proving it to be true or even being able to claim strong support in favor of the null hypothesis.

**10.7** $H_0: \pi = 0.5$ versus $H_a: \pi > 0.5$

**10.9** $H_0: \pi = 0.5$ versus $H_a: \pi > 0.5$

**10.11** $H_0: \mu = 40$ versus $H_a: \mu \neq 40$

**10.13 a.** A Type I error is concluding the symptoms are due to disease when they are really due to child abuse. A Type II error is concluding the symptoms are due to child abuse when they are really due to disease. **b.** Based on the doctor's quote, a Type I error is more serious.

**10.15 a.** Reject $H_0$  **b.** Type I error

**10.17 a.** A Type I error is returning to the supplier a shipment that is not of inferior quality. A Type II error is accepting a shipment of inferior quality.  **b.** The calculator manufacturer would consider a Type II error more serious, since it would end up producing defective calculators. **c.** The supplier would consider a Type I error more serious because it would lose the profits from perfectly good printed circuits.

**10.19 a.** We would probably not complain if the defective rate was below 10%; we would want to determine whether the defective rate is greater than is claimed by the manufacturer.  **b.** A Type I error is concluding that the defect rate exceeds 10%, when in fact, it isn't. This would lead to unjustified charges of false advertising. A Type II error is concluding that there isn't enough evidence to conclude that the defective rate exceeds 10% when, in fact, it is. This would allow the manufacturer to continue making an incorrect claim.

**10.21 a.** Failed to reject $H_0$  **b.** Type II error  **c.** Since the null hypothesis is initially assumed to be true, and is rejected only if there is strong evidence against it, if we fail to reject the null hypothesis, we have not "proven" it to be true. We can say only that there is not strong evidence against it.

**10.23 a.** A $P$-value of 0.0003 indicates that these test results are very unlikely to occur if $H_0$ is true. The more plausible explanation for the occurrence of these results is that $H_0$ is false.  **b.** A $P$-value of 0.35 indicates that these results are quite likely to occur (consistent with) if $H_0$ is true. The data do not cast reasonable doubt on the validity of $H_0$.

**10.25 a.** Fail to reject  **b.** Fail to reject  **c.** Fail to reject  **d.** Reject  **e.** Fail to reject  **f.** Fail to reject

**10.27 a.** Not appropriate  **b.** Not appropriate  **c.** Appropriate  **d.** Not appropriate

**10.29** $z = -4.43$, $P$-value $\approx 0$, reject $H_0$

**10.31** $z = 3.93$, $P$-value $\approx 0$, reject $H_0$

**10.33** $z = 0.79$, $P$-value $= 0.2148$, fail to reject $H_0$

**10.35 a.** $z = -1.90$, $P$-value $= 0.0287$, reject $H_0$  **b.** $z = -0.6$, $P$-value $= 0.2743$, fail to reject $H_0$  **c.** The denominator of the test statistic is different because the sample sizes are different. With a small sample the difference between the sample proportion of 0.47 and the hypothesized proportion of 0.5 could plausibly be attributed to chance, whereas when the sample size is larger this difference is no longer likely to be attributable to chance.

**10.37** $z = 7.54$, $P$-value $\approx 0$, reject $H_0$

**10.39** $z = -11.7$, $P$-value $\approx 1$, fail to reject $H_0$

**10.41** $z = 7.75$, $P$-value $\approx 0$, reject $H_0$

**10.43** $z = 1.90$, $P$-value $= 0.058$, fail to reject $H_0$ (at $\alpha = 0.01$ and at $\alpha = 0.05$)

**10.45 a.** 0.0358  **b.** 0.0802  **c.** 0.562  **d.** 0.1498  **e.** 0

**10.47 a.** 0.040  **b.** 0.003  **c.** 0.019  **d.** 0  **e.** 0.13  **f.** 0.13  **g.** 0

**10.49 a.** Reject $H_0$  **b.** Reject $H_0$  **c.** Fail to reject $H_0$

**10.51 a.** Fail to reject $H_0$  **b.** Fail to reject $H_0$  **c.** Fail to reject $H_0$  **d.** $H_0$ would be rejected for any $\alpha > 0.002$

**10.53** $t = 14.8$, $P$-value $\approx 0$, reject $H_0$; to generalize, we would need to assume that the sample could be considered as representative of the population of interest.

**10.55** With large samples, it is possible to be convinced that the observed difference is not attributable to chance and still have a relatively small difference from a practical point of view.

**10.57 a.** There is a lot of variability in online time.  **b.** $t = 9.16$, $P$-value $\approx 0$, reject $H_0$

**10.59** The authors are saying that the positive effects of music on pain intensity found in the study are statistically significant, but not practically significant from a clinical point of view.

**10.61** $t = 1.0$, $P$-value $= 0.187$, fail to reject $H_0$

**10.63 a.** Since the boxplot is nearly symmetric with no outliers and the normal probability plot is reasonably straight, the $t$ test is appropriate.  **b.** The sample median is slightly less than 245 and because of the near symmetry and variability, a mean of 240 is plausible.  **c.** $t = 1.21$, $P$-value $\approx 0.256$, fail to reject $H_0$

**10.65 a.** When the significance level is held fixed, increasing the sample size will increase the power of the test.  **b.** When the sample size is held fixed, increasing the significance level will increase the power of the test.

**10.67 a.** 0.1003  **b.** 0.2358  **c.** It would be smaller.  **d.** 0.7642, 1

**10.69 a.** $t = 0.47$, $P$-value $\approx 0.317$, fail to reject $H_0$.  **b.** $\beta \approx 0.75$  **c.** Power $\approx 0.25$

**10.71 a.** $\beta \approx 0.06$  **b.** $\beta \approx 0.06$  **c.** $\beta \approx 0.21$  **d.** $\beta \approx 0$  **e.** $\beta \approx 0.06$  **f.** $\beta \approx 0.01$  **g.** Answers will vary.

**10.73** $z = 1.08$, $P$-value $= 0.1401$, fail to reject $H_0$

**10.75** $z = 7.56$, $P$-value $\approx 0$, reject $H_0$

**10.77** $z = -1.93$, $P$-value $= 0.0268$, reject $H_0$

**10.79** $z = 0.7491$, $P$-value $= 0.2269$, fail to reject $H_0$

**10.81** $t = 4.84$, $P$-value $\approx 0$, reject $H_0$

**10.83** $t = 13.51$, $P$-value $\approx 0$, reject $H_0$

**10.85** $z = 2.50$, $P$-value $= 0.0124$, at $\alpha = 0.05$: reject $H_0$, but fail to reject $H_0$ at $\alpha = 0.01$

**10.87** $t = 3.86$, $P$-value $\approx 0$, reject $H_0$

**10.89 a.** If the distribution were normal, the Empirical Rule implies that about 16% of the values would be less than the value that is one standard deviation below the mean. Since the standard deviation is larger than the mean, this value is negative. Caffeine consumption can't be negative, so it is not plausible that the distribution is normal. However, since the sample size is large ($n = 47$), the $t$ test can still be used.  **b.** $t = 0.44$, $P$-value $\approx 0.346$, fail to reject $H_0$

**10.91** $t = -1.16$, $P$-value $= 0.15$, at $\alpha = 0.01$: fail to reject $H_0$

**10.93** $t = 5.68$, $P$-value $\approx 0$, reject $H_0$

**10.95** $\alpha = 0$, $0.1 < \beta < 0.3$

## Chapter 11

**11.1** Approximately normal with mean 5 and standard deviation 0.529

**11.3 a.** Assumptions are that the population distributions are approximately normal and that the samples are independently selected and can be regarded as random samples.  **b.** $t = 2.24$, df $= 33$, $P$-value $\approx 0.032$, reject $H_0$, the conclusion is consistent with the paper.

**11.5** $t = 1.06$, df $= 497$, $P$-value $\approx 0.2876$, fail to reject $H_0$

**11.7 a.** $H_0: \mu_1 = \mu_2$ vs. $H_a: \mu_1 < \mu_2$, where $\mu_1$ is the mean payment for all claims not involving errors and $\mu_2$ is the mean payment for all claims involving errors.  **b.** With sample sizes so large (515 and 889) the df will be large and the bottom row of the $t$ table can be used. With a $P$-value of 0.004 and a lower tail test, the value of the test statistic must have been between 2.58 and 3.09. $t = 2.65$ is the best answer.

**11.9 a.** $(-69, -19)$ **b.** $t = 2.76$, df $= 6$, $P$-value $\approx 0.016$, reject $H_0$
**11.11 a.** $t = 10.4$, df $= 82$, $P$-value $\approx 0$, reject $H_0$ **b.** $t = 16.3$, df $= 62$, $P$-value $\approx 0$, reject $H_0$ **c.** $t = -4.69$, df $= 85$, $P$-value $\approx 0$, reject $H_0$ **d.** Although it appears that the male monkeys spent time playing with the "boy" toys and the female monkeys spent more time playing with the "girl" toys, there was a difference in the "neutral" toy as well. Any difference in the time spent playing with these toys may have nothing to do with the gender choices—male monkeys may like a certain color better, or shiny surfaces, or some other underlying factor. This is an observational study and as such, causation cannot be shown. **e.** One of the conditions of a two-sample $t$ test is that the two samples are independent. In this example, if the mean percentage of the time spent playing with the police car increased, the mean percentage of the time spent playing with the doll would have to decrease. Therefore, one affects the other, they are not independent, and this violates one of the conditions of the test.
**11.13** $t = 1.23$, df $= 214$, $P$-value $\approx 0.110$, fail to reject $H_0$
**11.15 a.** $t = -6.56$, df $= 201$, $P$-value $\approx 0$, reject $H_0$ **b.** $t = -6.25$, df $= 201$, $P$-value $\approx 0$, reject $H_0$ **c.** $t = 0.07$, df $= 201$, $P$-value $\approx 0.92$, fail to reject $H_0$
**11.17** $(0.643, 1.357)$ Because the interval does not include zero, there is evidence that the mean score for males is higher than the mean score for females.
**11.19 a.** $t = 2.93$, df $= 54$, $P$-value $\approx 0.006$, reject $H_0$ **b.** $t = 0.15$, df $= 68$, $P$-value $\approx 0.842$, fail to reject $H_0$ **c.** $(0.242, 1.458)$
**11.21** $t = 113.17$, df $= 45$, $P$-value $\approx 0$, reject $H_0$
**11.23** $t = 3.30$, df $= 98$, $P$-value $\approx 0.001$, reject $H_0$
**11.25** $t = 2.97$, df $= 10$, $P$-value $\approx 0.007$, reject $H_0$
**11.27** $t = 2.94$, df $= 26$, $P$-value $\approx 0.003$, reject $H_0$
**11.29 a.** If possible, treat each patient with both drugs, with one drug used on one eye and the other drug used on the other eye. Determine which eye will receive the new drug at random. If this treatment method is not possible, then request that the ophthalmologist pair patients according to their eye pressure so that the two people in a pair have approximately equal eye pressure. Then select one patient in each pair at random to receive the new drug, and treat the other patient in each pair with the standard treatment. **b.** Both procedures in Part (a) would result in paired data. **c.** Randomly assign subjects to one of the two treatment groups. This experiment is probably not as informative as a paired experiment with the same number of subjects.
**11.31** $t = 4.46$, df $= 8$, $P$-value $\approx 0$, reject $H_0$
**11.33** $t = 2.46$, df $= 9$, $P$-value $\approx 0.017$, reject $H_0$
**11.35 a.** $(2.032, 6.10)$ **b.** $(-0.54, 1.005)$ **c.** Yes, the confidence interval from Part (a) (for pitchers) lies entirely above the confidence interval from Part (b) (for position players).
**11.37 a.** $t = 4.32$, df $= 23$, $P$-value $\approx 0$, reject $H_0$ **c.** A mean difference of 8.82 is more unusual when there is no difference and the standard deviation of the difference distribution is small.
**11.39** $t = 8.13$, df $= 5$, $P$-value $\approx 0$, reject $H_0$
**11.41** It is not necessary to use an inference procedure since complete information on all 50 states is available. Inference is necessary only when a sample is selected from some larger population.
**11.43 a.** $(6.702, 20.548)$ **b.** $(2.071, 13.929)$ **c.** Because the two intervals overlap, it is possible that the mean change is the same for men and women.
**11.45** $z = 0.77$, $P$-value $= 0.4412$, fail to reject $H_0$
**11.47** $(.0184, .0816)$, 0 is not included in the interval indicating that the proportion of Americans age 12 and older who own an MP3 player was significantly higher in 2006 than in 2005.

**11.49** $z = -0.71$, $P$-value $= 0.4778$, fail to reject $H_0$
**11.51 a.** $(-0.401, -0.225)$ **b.** The sample consisted only of volunteers.
**11.53** $z = 3.86$, $P$-value $\approx 0$, reject $H_0$
**11.55** $(.357, .495)$
**11.57 a.** $z = 9.17$, $P$-value $= 0$, reject $H_0$ **b.** No, this was an observational study.
**11.59** $H_0: \pi_1 - \pi_2 = 0$ vs. $H_a: \pi_1 - \pi_2 \neq 0$, fail to reject
**11.61 a.** $t = 11.95$, df $= 18$, $P$-value $\approx 0$, reject $H_0$ **b.** $t = -68.8$, df $= 10$, $P$-value $\approx 0$, reject $H_0$ **c.** $t = 0.698$, df $= 17$, $P$-value $\approx 0.247$, fail to reject $H_0$
**11.63** $t = -4.94$, df $= 57$, $P$-value $\approx 0$, reject $H_0$
**11.65 a.** $(-0.529, 0.329)$ No, because the interval includes 0.
**11.67** $t = 3.1$, df $= 113$, $P$-value $\approx 0.001$, reject $H_0$
**11.69 a.** This would be the case if alcohol consumption varies quite a bit from week to week for the individuals in the samples. **b.** $(-0.738, 1.498)$ **c.** $t = 0.764$, df $= 849$, $P$-value $= 0.445$, fail to reject $H_0$
**11.71** $z = 8.07$, $P$-value $\approx 0$, reject $H_0$
**11.73** $z = -4.12$, $P$-value $\approx 0$, reject $H_0$
**11.75** $z = -1.84$, $P$-value $= 0.066$, fail to reject $H_0$
**11.77** $(-0.2053, 0.0777)$
**11.79** $z = 6.83$, $P$-value $\approx 0$, reject $H_0$
**11.81** $t = 2.43$, df $= 32$, $P$-value $\approx 0.0105$, fail to reject $H_0$
**11.83** $t = 2.94$, df $= 21$, $P$-value $\approx 0.0039$, reject $H_0$
**11.85** $t = 3.88$, df $= 163$, $P$-value $\approx 0$, reject $H_0$
**11.87** $t = 0.504$, df $= 288$, $P$-value $\approx 0.6150$, fail to reject $H_0$
**11.89** $z = 5.59$, $P$-value $\approx 0$, reject $H_0$

## Chapter 12

**12.1 a.** $0.020 < P$-value $< 0.025$, fail to reject $H_0$ **b.** $0.040 < P$-value $< 0.045$, fail to reject $H_0$ **c.** $0.035 < P$-value $< 0.040$, fail to reject $H_0$ **d.** $P$-value $< 0.001$, reject $H_0$ **e.** $P$-value $> 0.10$, fail to reject $H_0$
**12.3 a.** $X^2 = 19.0$, $P$-value $< 0.001$, reject $H_0$ **b.** If $n = 40$, the chi-squared test should not be used because the expected cell count for one of the categories (nut type 4) would be less than 5
**12.5 a.** $X^2 = 21.81$, $P$-value $< 0.001$, reject $H_0$ **b.** If 50% of all the smokers in this population start smoking between the ages of 16 to 20 and if all five years in this age range are equally likely, there should be about 10% starting to smoke for each of the ages 16, 17, 18, 19, 20. This is equivalent to 20% of all the smokers starting between the ages of 16 and 17 and 30% of all the smokers starting between the ages of 18 and 20.
**12.7 a.** $X^2 = 82.2$, $P$-value $< 0.001$, reject $H_0$ **b.** The proportion for each month would reflect the number of days in the month out of the 366 days in 2004. April, June, September, and November have 30 days $(30/366 = .082)$, February has 29 $(29/366 = .079)$ and the rest have 31 $(31/366 = .085)$.
**12.9** $X^2 = 11.242$, $0.010 < P$-value $< 0.015$, fail to reject $H_0$
**12.11** $X^2 = 0.931$, $P$-value $> 0.100$, fail to reject $H_0$
**12.13** $X^2 = 1.47$, $P$-value $> 0.100$, fail to reject $H_0$
**12.15 a.** 10 **b.** 12 **c.** 15
**12.17** $X^2 = 5.204$, $P$-value $> 0.100$, fail to reject $H_0$
**12.19 a.** $X^2 = 34.544$, $P$-value $< 0.001$, reject $H_0$ **b.** Menopausal women who are in the large HMO
**12.21** $X^2 = 95.921$, $P$-value $< 0.001$, reject $H_0$
**12.23** $X^2 = 339.994$, $P$-value $< 0.001$, reject $H_0$

**12.25** $X^2 = 12.091$, $0.005 < P\text{-value} < 0.010$, reject $H_0$

**12.27** $X^2 = 68.953$, $P\text{-value} < 0.001$, reject $H_0$

**12.29 a.** $X^2 = 6.852$, $P\text{-value} > 0.100$, fail to reject $H_0$ **b.** Yes, because there is no evidence of an association between gender and workaholism type.

**12.31** One cell has an expected count of less than five. The chi-squared approximation is probably not reasonable.

**12.33** $X^2 = 1.978$, $P\text{-value} > 0.10$, fail to reject $H_0$

**12.35** $X^2 = 9.84$, $0.005 < P\text{-value} < 0.010$, reject $H_0$

**12.37** $X^2 = 303.09$, $P\text{-value} < 0.001$, reject $H_0$

**12.39 a.** The proportions falling into each category appear to be dissimilar. For instance, only 17.62% of the subjects in the "never smoked" category consumed one drink a day, whereas 34.97% of those in the "currently smokes" category consume one drink per day. Similar discrepancies are seen for other categories as well. **b.** $X^2 = 980.068$, $P\text{-value} < 0.001$, reject $H_0$ **c.** The results are consistent with our observations in Part (a).

**12.41** $X^2 = 10.97$, $P\text{-value} < 0.001$, reject $H_0$

**12.43** $X^2 = 22.855$, $P\text{-value} < 0.0001$, reject $H_0$

**12.45 a.** homogeneity **b.** $X^2 = 28.51$, $P\text{-value} < 0.001$, reject $H_0$

**12.47** $X^2 = 5.1$, $P\text{-value} > 0.100$, fail to reject $H_0$

## Chapter 13

**13.1 a.** $y = -5.0 + 0.017x$ **c.** 30.7 **d.** 0.017 **e.** 1.7 **f.** No, the model should not be used to predict outside the range of the data.

**13.3 a.** 3.6, 4.3 **b.** 0.121 **c.** 0.5, 0.1587

**13.5 a.** 47, 4700 **b.** 0.3156, 0.0643

**13.7 a.** $r^2 = 0.6228$ **b.** $s_e = 1.5923$ **c.** $b = 3.4307$ **d.** 3.4426

**13.9 a.** $r^2 = 0.883$ **b.** $s_e = 13.682$, df = 14

**13.11 a.** There seems to be a general tendency for $y$ to increase at a constant rate as $x$ increases. However, there is also quite a bit of variability in the $y$ values. **b.** $\hat{y} = -0.002274 + 1.246712x$. When $x = 0.09$, the predicted value is 0.1099 **c.** $r^2 = 0.436$. This means that 43.6% of the total variability in market share can be explained by the linear relationship with advertising share. **d.** $s_e = 0.0263$, df = 8

**13.13 a.** $\sigma_b = 0.253$ **b.** $\sigma_b = 0.179$, no **c.** It would require four observations at each $x$ value.

**13.15 a.** $s_e = 9.7486$, $s_b = 0.1537$ **b.** (2.17, 2.83) **c.** Yes, the interval is relatively narrow.

**13.17 a.** $a = 592.1$, $b = 97.26$ **b.** $\hat{y} = 786.62$. Residual = −29.62. **c.** (87.76, 106.76)

**13.19 a.** $t = 2.8302$, $P\text{-value} = 0.008$, reject $H_0$, and conclude that the model is useful. **b.** (4.294, 25.706) Based on this interval, the estimated change in mean average SAT score associated with an increase of $1000 in expenditures per child is between 4.294 and 25.706.

**13.21 a.** $\hat{y} = -96.6711 + 1.595x$ **b.** $t = 27.17$, $P\text{-value} \approx 0$, reject $H_0$, and conclude that the model is useful. **c.** The mean response time for individuals with closed-head injuries is 1.48 times as great as for those with no head injury.

**13.23 a.** $t = 6.53$, $P\text{-value} \approx 0$, reject $H_0$, and conclude that the model is useful. **b.** $t = 1.56$, $P\text{-value} = 0.079$, fail to reject $H_0$.

**13.25** $t = -17.57$, $P\text{-value} \approx 0$, reject $H_0$.

**13.27** The standardized residual plot does not exhibit any unusual features.

**13.29 b.** The plot is reasonably straight. The assumption of normality is plausible. **c.** There are two residuals that are unusually large. **d.** There is a pattern in the residual plot; negative residuals are for the small $x$ values and the positive residuals are for the large $x$ values.

**13.31 a.** There are several large residuals and potentially influential observations. **b.** The residuals associated with the potentially influential observations are all negative. Without these three, there appears to be a

positive trend to the standardized residual plot. The plot suggests that the simple linear regression model might not be appropriate. **c.** There does not appear to be any pattern in the plot that would suggest that it is unreasonable to assume that the variance of $y$ is the same at each $x$ value.

**13.33** The residuals are positive in 1963 and 1964, then they are negative from 1965 through 1972. This pattern in the residual plot casts doubt on the appropriateness of the simple linear regression model.

**13.35** If the request is for a confidence interval for $\beta$ the wording would likely be "estimate the *change* in the average $y$ value associated with a one unit increase in the $x$ variable." If the request is for a confidence interval for $\alpha + \beta x^*$ the wording would likely be "estimate the *average y* value when the value of the $x$ variable is $x^*$."

**13.37** (−0.459, 0.798)

**13.39 a.** (6.4722, 6.6300) **b.** (6.4779, 6.6973) **c.** Yes, because $x^* = 60$ is farther from $\bar{x}$.

**13.41 a.** $\hat{y} = -133.02 + 5.919x$ **b.** $s_b = 1.127$ **c.** $t = 5.25$, $P\text{-value} \approx 0$, reject $H_0$ **d.** 251.715. **e.** Shouldn't use regression equation to predict for $x = 105$ because it is outside the range of the data.

**13.43 a.** $\hat{y} = 2.78551 + 0.04462x$ **b.** $t = 5.25$, $P\text{-value} \approx 0$, reject $H_0$, and conclude that the model is useful **c.** (3.671, 4.577) **d.** Since 4.1 is in the interval, it is plausible that a box that has been on a shelf 30 days will not be acceptable.

**13.45 a.** $\hat{y} = 30.019 + 0.1109x$ **b.** (38.354, 43.864) **c.** (30.311, 51.907) **d.** The interval of Part (b) is for the mean blood level of all people who work where the air lead level is 100. The interval of Part (c) is for a single randomly selected individual who works where the air lead level is 100.

**13.47 a.** Prediction interval for $x = 35$ is (1.9519, 3.0931). Prediction interval for $x = 45$ is (1.3879, 2.5271). **b.** The simultaneous prediction level would be at least 97%.

**13.49** $r$ is the sample correlation coefficient and measures the strength of the linear relationship in the sample. $r$ is an estimate of $\rho$, the population correlation coefficient.

**13.51** $t = 2.07$, $P\text{-value} \approx 0.036$, reject $H_0$.

**13.53 a.** $t = -6.175$, $P\text{-value} \approx 0$, reject $H_0$. **b.** No, $r^2 = 0.0676$

**13.55** $r = 0.574$, $t = 1.85$, $P\text{-value} \approx 0.1$, fail to reject $H_0$

**13.57** $t = 2.2$, $P\text{-value} = 0.028$, reject $H_0$. The result of the test is significant, indicating that we are convinced that $\rho \neq 0$ (largely because of the very large sample size). However $r$ is quite close to 0, indicating a very weak linear relationship.

**13.59 a.** Yes, $t = -3.40$ and for either a one- or two-tailed test $P\text{-value}$ is less than 0.05. **c.** Probably not. $r^2 = (-0.18)^2 = 0.0324$, so only about 3.24% of the observed variability in sense of humor can be explained by the linear regression model

**13.61 a.** $t = -3.95$, $P\text{-value} = 0.003$, reject $H_0$ and conclude that the linear model is useful **b.** A 95% confidence interval is (−3.669, −0.998). Other confidence levels are possible. **c.** A 95% prediction interval is (60.276, 70.646). Other confidence levels are possible. **d.** Because 11 is farther from $\bar{x}$.

**13.63 a.** $t = -6.09$, $P\text{-value} \approx 0$, reject $H_0$, and conclude that there is a linear relationship. **b.** A 95% confidence interval is (2.346, 3.844). Other confidence levels are possible. **c.** The predicted trail length when soil hardness is 10 is −2.58. Since trail length cannot be negative, the predicted value makes no sense.

**13.65 a.** $H_0: \beta = -0.5$, $H_a: \beta \neq -0.5$, $t = 0.49$, $P\text{-value} \approx 0.624$, fail to reject $H_0$, the data do not contradict the researchers' prior belief. **b.** A 95% confidence interval is (47.083, 54.099). Other confidence levels are possible.

**13.67** $H_0: \beta = \beta'$, $H_a: \beta \neq \beta'$, $t = -1.03$, $P\text{-value} \approx 0.322$, fail to reject $H_0$

**13.69** When the point is included in the computations, the slope will be negative and much more extreme (farther from 0) than if the point is excluded from the computations.

**13.71** Since the $P$-value of 0.0076 is smaller than most reasonable levels of significance, the percentage raise does appear to be linearly related to productivity.

**13.73** Even though the $P$-value is small and $r^2 = 0.65$, the variability about the least-squares line appears to increase as soil depth increases. If this is so, a residual plot would be "funnel shape," opening up toward the right. One of the conditions for valid application of the procedures described in this chapter is that the variability of the $y$'s be constant. It appears that this requirement may not be true in this instance.

**13.75 a.** When $r = 0$, then $s_e \approx s_y$. The least squares line in this case is a horizontal line with intercept of $\bar{y}$.   **b.** When $r$ is close to 1 in absolute value, then $s_e$ will be much smaller than $s_y$.

## Chapter 14

**14.1** A deterministic model does not have the random deviation component $e$, while a probabilistic model does contain such a component.

**14.3** $y = \beta_0 + \beta_1 x_1 + \beta_2 x_2 + e$. An interaction term is not included in the model because it is given that $x_1$ and $x_2$ make independent contributions.

**14.5 a.** 103.11   **b.** 96.87   **c.** $\beta_1 = -6.6$; 6.6 is the expected *decrease* in yield associated with a one-unit increase in mean temperature when the mean percentage of sunshine remains fixed. $\beta_2 = -4.5$; 4.5 is the expected *decrease* in yield associated with a one-unit increase in mean percentage of sunshine when mean temperature remains fixed.

**14.7 b.** The mean chlorine content is higher for $x = 10$ than for $x = 8$.   **c.** When the degree of delignification increases from 8 to 9 the mean chlorine content increases by 7. Mean chlorine content decreases by 1 when degree of delignification increases from 9 to 10.

**14.9 c.** The parallel lines in each graph are attributable to the lack of interaction between the two independent variables.   **d.** Because there is an interaction term, the lines are not parallel.

**14.11 a.** $y = \alpha + \beta_1 x_1 + \beta_2 x_2 + \beta_3 x_3 + e$
**b.** $y = \alpha + \beta_1 x_1 + \beta_2 x_2 + \beta_3 x_3 + \beta_4 x_1^2 + \beta_5 x_2^2 + \beta_6 x_3^2 + e$
**c.** $y = \alpha + \beta_1 x_1 + \beta_2 x_2 + \beta_3 x_3 + \beta_4 x_1 x_2 + e$, $y = \alpha + \beta_1 x_1 + \beta_2 x_2 + \beta_3 x_3 + \beta_4 x_1 x_3 + e$, $y = \alpha + \beta_1 x_1 + \beta_2 x_2 + \beta_3 x_3 + \beta_4 x_2 x_3 + e$
**d.** $y = \alpha + \beta_1 x_1 + \beta_2 x_2 + \beta_3 x_3 + \beta_4 x_1^2 + \beta_5 x_2^2 + \beta_6 x_3^2 + \beta_7 x_1 x_2 + \beta_8 x_1 x_3 + \beta_9 x_2 x_3 + e$

**14.13 a.** Three dummy variables would be needed to incorporate a non-numerical variable with four categories. For example, could define $x_3 = 1$ if the car is a sub-compact and 0 otherwise, $x_4 = 1$ if the car is a compact and 0 otherwise, and $x_5 = 1$ if the car is a midsize and 0 otherwise. The model equation is then $y = \alpha + \beta_1 x_1 + \beta_2 x_2 + \beta_3 x_3 + \beta_4 x_4 + \beta_5 x_5 + e$.   **b.** For the variables defined in Part (a), $x_6 = x_1 x_3$, $x_7 = x_1 x_4$, and $x_8 = x_1 x_5$ are the additional predictors needed to incorporate interaction between age and size class.

**14.15 a.** $b_1 = -2.18$ is the estimated change in mean fish intake associated with a one-unit increase in water temperature when the value of the other predictor variables are fixed. $b_4 = 2.32$ is the estimated change (increase) in mean fish intake associated with a one-unit increase in speed when the values of the other predictor variables are fixed.
**b.** $R^2 = 0.40$   **c.** $s_e = 10.305$   **d.** Adjusted $R^2 = 0.2857$; Adjusted $R^2$ is smaller than $R^2$.

**14.17 a.** $P$-value $> 0.10$   **b.** $0.001 < P$-value $< 0.01$   **c.** $0.01 < P$-value $< 0.05$   **d.** $P$-value $< 0.001$   **e.** $0.01 < P$-value $< 0.05$

**14.19** $F = 34.286$, $P$-value $< 0.001$, reject $H_0$, and conclude that the model is useful.

**14.21 a.** $\hat{y} = 86.85 - 0.12297 x_1 + 5.090 x_2 - 0.07092 x_3 + 0.001538 x_4$
**b.** $F = 64.4$, $P$-value $< 0.001$, reject $H_0$, and conclude that the model is useful.   **c.** $R^2 = 0.908$. This means that 90.8% of the variation in the observed tar content values has been explained by the fitted model. $s_e = 4.784$. This means that the typical distance of an observation from the corresponding mean value is 4.784.

**14.23 a.** $\hat{y} = -511 + 3.06$ length $- 1.11$ age   **b.** $F = 10.21$, $0.001 < P$-value $< 0.01$, reject $H_0$, and conclude that the model is useful.

**14.25 a.** $\hat{y} = -859 + 23.7$ minwidth $+ 226$ maxwidth $+ 225$ elongation   **b.** Adjusted $R^2$ takes into account the number of predictors used in the model whereas $R^2$ does not do so.   **c.** $F = 16.03$, $P$-value $< 0.001$, reject $H_0$, and conclude that the model is useful.

**14.27 a.** SSResid = 390.4347, SSTo = 1618.2093, SSRegr = 1227.774
**b.** $R^2 = 0.759$. This means that 75.9% of the variation in the observed shear strength values has been explained by the fitted model.   **c.** $F = 5.039$, $0.01 < P$-value $< 0.05$, reject $H_0$, and conclude that the model is useful.

**14.29** $F = 96.64$, $P$-value $< 0.001$, reject $H_0$, and conclude that the model is useful.

**14.33** $\hat{y} = 35.8 - 0.68 x_1 + 1.28 x_2$, $F = 18.95$, $P$-value $< 0.001$, reject $H_0$, and conclude that the model is useful.

## Chapter 15

**15.1 a.** $0.001 < P$-value $< 0.01$   **b.** $P$-value $> 0.10$   **c.** $P$-value $= 0.01$   **d.** $P$-value $< 0.001$   **e.** $0.05 < P$-value $< 0.10$   **f.** $0.01 < P$-value $< 0.05$ (using $df_1 = 4$ and $df_2 = 60$)

**15.3 a.** $H_0: \mu_1 = \mu_2 = \mu_3 = \mu_4$, $H_a$: At least two of the four $\mu_i$'s are different.   **b.** $0.01 < P$-value $< 0.05$, fail to reject $H_0$   **c.** $0.01 < P$-value $< 0.05$, fail to reject $H_0$

**15.5** $F = 25.09$, $P$-value $< 0.001$, reject $H_0$

**15.7 a.** 1996 and 1997 boxplots are similar, but the 1998 boxplot values are higher. The boxplot for 1998 also has a longer tail on the upper end than the other two boxplots.   **b.** $F = 6.83$, $0.01 < P$-value $< 0.05$, reject $H_0$

**15.9** $F = 1.71$, $P$-value $> 0.10$, fail to reject $H_0$

**15.11** $F = 2.62$, $0.05 < P$-value $< 0.10$, fail to reject $H_0$

**15.13** $F = 1.895$, $.05 < P$-value $< 0.10$, fail to reject $H_0$

**15.15**

| Source of variation | Degrees of freedom | Sum of squares | Mean square | F |
|---|---|---|---|---|
| Treatments | 3 | 75081.72 | 25027.24 | 1.70 |
| Error | 16 | 235419.04 | 14713.69 | |
| Total | 19 | 310500.76 | | |

$F = 1.70$, $P$-value $> 0.10$, fail to reject $H_0$

**15.17**

| Source of variation | Degrees of freedom | Sum of squares | Mean square | F |
|---|---|---|---|---|
| Treatments | 3 | 29.304 | 9.768 | 2.56 |
| Error | 418 | 1595.088 | 3.816 | |
| Total | 421 | 1624.392 | | |

$F = 2.56$, $0.05 < P$-value $< 0.10$, fail to reject $H_0$

**15.19** $F = 6.97$, $0.001 < P$-value $< 0.01$, reject $H_0$

**15.21 a.** See solutions manual for detailed computations.   **b.** $F = 2.142$, $P$-value $> 0.10$, fail to reject $H_0$

**15.23** Since the intervals for $\mu_1 - \mu_2$ and $\mu_1 - \mu_3$ do not contain zero, $\mu_1$ and $\mu_2$ are judged to be different and $\mu_1$ and $\mu_3$ are judged to be different. Since the interval for $\mu_2 - \mu_3$ contains zero, $\mu_2$ and $\mu_3$ are not judged to be different. Hence, statement (iii) is the correct choice.

**15.25** $\mu_1 - \mu_2$: $(-1.81, 3.91)$, $\mu_1 - \mu_3$: $(1.39, 7.11)$, $\mu_1 - \mu_4$: $(4.14, 9.86)$, $\mu_2 - \mu_3$: $(0.34, 6.06)$, $\mu_2 - \mu_4$: $(3.09, 8.81)$, $\mu_3 - \mu_4$: $(-0.11, 5.61)$; $\mu_1$ differs from $\mu_3$, $\mu_1$ differs from $\mu_4$, $\mu_2$ differs from $\mu_3$, and $\mu_2$ differs from $\mu_4$.

| Method | 4 | 3 | 2 | 1 |
|--------|------|-------|-------|-------|
| $\bar{x}$ | 9.30 | 12.05 | 15.25 | 16.30 |

**15.27** $\mu_1 - \mu_2$: $(-0.1465, 0.2665)$, $\mu_1 - \mu_3$: $(-0.3190, 0.1090)$, $\mu_1 - \mu_4$: $(-0.2277, 0.1677)$, $\mu_2 - \mu_3$: $(-0.3890, 0.0490)$, $\mu_2 - \mu_4$: $(-0.2877, 0.1077)$, $\mu_3 - \mu_4$: $(-1.308, 2.908)$. No differences are detected.

**15.29**

| Group | Simultaneous | Sequential | Control |
|-------|--------------|------------|---------|
| Mean | $\bar{x}_3$ | $\bar{x}_2$ | $\bar{x}_1$ |

**15.31** The mean water loss when exposed to 4 hours fumigation is different from all other means. The mean water loss when exposed to 2 hours fumigation is different from that for levels 16 and 0, but not 8. The mean water losses for duration 16, 0, and 8 hours are not different from one another.

**15.33** $\mu_1 - \mu_2$: $(0.24, 2.22)$, $\mu_1 - \mu_3$: $(0.36, 2.44)$, $\mu_2 - \mu_3$: $(-0.87, 1.21)$; $\mu_1$ differs from $\mu_2$ and $\mu_3$, but $\mu_2$ and $\mu_3$ do not differ.

# Index

Italicized hyphenated entries (*14-*, *15-*, *16-*) pertain to sections of the book found at www.cengage.com/statistics/peck

**737**

Italicized hyphenated entries (*14-*, *15-*, *16-*) pertain to sections of the book found at www.cengage.com/statistics/peck